Photon '97

Photon '97

Incorporating the XIth International Workshop on
Gamma–Gamma Collisions

Egmond aan Zee, The Netherlands   10–15 May, 1997

Editors

Adriaan Buijs
University Utrecht

Frits C. Erné
NIKHEF Amsterdam

World Scientific
Singapore • New Jersey • London • Hong Kong

Published by

World Scientific Publishing Co. Pte. Ltd.
P O Box 128, Farrer Road, Singapore 912805
USA office: Suite 1B, 1060 Main Street, River Edge, NJ 07661
UK office: 57 Shelton Street, Covent Garden, London WC2H 9HE

Library of Congress Cataloging-in-Publication Data
Photon '97 (1997 : Netherlands)
    Photon '97 : incorporating the XIth International Workshop on
Gamma-Gamma Collisions : Egmond aan Zee, The Netherlands, 10–15 May,
1997 / editors Adriaan Buijs, Frits C. Erné.
        p.   cm.
    ISBN 9810232446
    1. Photon-photon interactions -- Congresses.   2. Photons -
- Multiplicity -- Congresses.   3. Inclusive processes (Nuclear
physics) -- Congresses.   4. Exclusive reactions (Nuclear physics) -
- Congresses.   I. Buijs, Adriaan.   II. Erné, Frits C.
III. International Workshop on Gamma-Gamma Collisions (11th : 1997 :
Netherlands)   IV. Title.
QC794.8.P4P476   1997
539.7'217--dc21   97-52725
                                                              CIP

British Library Cataloguing-in-Publication Data
A catalogue record for this book is available from the British Library.

This book is printed on acid-free paper.

Printed in Singapore by Uto-Print

John Storrow 1943-1996

John Storrow, a well-known and much loved figure in British particle physics and beyond, died on September 5th. He had been ill for some time, but appeared to be making a successful recovery from an operation to remove a tumour when he died suddenly of a pulmonary embolism.

John Storrow made many significant contributions to particle physics phenomenology. He started his research in Cambridge, submitting his Ph.D. thesis on "Photons in S-matrix theory" in 1968. This was followed by two years in the CERN theory division, working mainly on applications of duality and the Veneziano model to strange particle physics. Subsequently he moved to Daresbury and then, in 1974, to the University of Manchester, where he spent the rest of his career. His irrepressible sense of humour and generosity of spirit made him a very effective teacher at all levels and he was justly proud of his successful supervision of no less than fifteen graduate students, two of whom (Jeff Forshaw and Lionel Gordon) attended this conference. For many years, he worked on Regge pole phenomenology, where his contributions to our understanding of pion photoproduction and baryon exchange processes were particularly important. More recently, he played a leading part in the revival of interest in the structure of the photon and its role in interpreting data from HERA. He worked on next-to-leading order photon parton density parameterisations and prompt photon production, as well as minijet production. He was an enthusiastic advocate of two photon physics at LEP, and was eagerly anticipating the realisation of his hopes at LEP2.

Those people who knew John have much to treasure. The warmth of his humanity will remain with us all.

J. Forshaw

PREFACE

The PHOTON'97 conference, the eleventh in a series of photon-photon workshops which started with the emergence of high-energy electron-positron colliders, was held from May 10 to 15 in Egmond aan Zee. The Dutch interest in this physics dates back to NIKHEF's participation in the TPC/2γ experiment at SLAC and has continued in the L3 experiment at LEP. Two years ago, at the Sheffield conference, part of the HERA electron-proton collider community joined forces, as they studied QCD phenomena at low and moderate photon virtualities as well. It was therefore only natural that PHOTON'97 was organised by NIKHEF's ZEUS and L3 colleagues. Our special thanks go to Joop Konijn, our treasurer, and to Fransje Backerra and Marijke Oskam who guaranteed smooth operation. We have fond memories of the fine hotel, the walks along the beach, the excursions to the Rijksmuseum and the Keukenhof and the excellent diner in Ouderkerk aan de Amstel. The conference was sponsored by the Netherlands Foundation for Fundamental Research FOM, by the Netherlands Institute for Nuclear and High Energy Physics NIKHEF, by the Netherlands Royal Academy of Sciences KNAW, by the Foundation for Conferences and Summer Schools about Nuclear Physics, and by the Foundation Physica.

The physics programme of the conference was quite rich. Hadronic particle production showed that the photon behaves partly like a hadron and partly like a gauge boson. The photon structure function has fascinated physicists since the late seventies. One reason was that it shows anomalies which are absent in the structure functions of hadrons. Furthermore, as shown first by Witten, it seems to be calculable at sufficiently large Q^2. Confidence in this last proposition has varied with time. Certainly a perennial problem has been the lack of sufficient and accurate data. For the first time an adequate accelerator, excellent detectors and interested experimenters and theorists have become available with the LEP2 programme. As a result, the present workshop showed considerable progress in this domain and also pointed to a number of hurdles that still have to be taken.

The physics of photon-induced hard processes has become similar to that of purely hadronic interactions, but the dynamics is more complex. There is a wealth of data on jet production, single particle production, open heavy flavour and quarkonium production to compare with, both from HERA and from LEP2.

Diffraction phenomena are being investigated in detail at HERA; all present indications at HERA point to a dominant gluonic content of the Pomeron. Diffraction is also expected to occur in photon-photon scattering at low Q^2, but no clear observations of it have been reported yet.

The progress in the design of linear photon colliders parallels that of e^+e^- colliders. It is good to keep an eye on the special benefits and possibilities of scattering very high energy photons on photons and electrons. Its most outstanding objective at high energy is Higgs Boson formation in the s-channel.

July 1997

F.C. Erné

A. Buijs

The International Advisory Committee

C. Berger	Aachen	S. Brodsky	SLAC
D. Bauer	U.C. Santa Barbara	F. Combley	Sheffield
A. Courau	Orsay	V. Fadin	Novosibirsk
J. Field	Genève	K. Gaemers	Amsterdam
S. Iwata	KEK	U. Karshon	Weizmann
P. Kessler	Collège de France	D. Miller	Univ. Coll., London
T. Nozaki	KEK	H. Paar	U.C. San Diego
G. Pancheri	Frascati	B. Richter	SLAC
G. Schuler	CERN	K. Strauch	Harvard
P. Zerwas	DESY		

The Local Organising Committee

Frits Erné	NIKHEF/Utrecht, chairman
Fransje Backerra	NIKHEF, secretary
Adriaan Buijs	Utrecht
Jos Engelen	Amsterdam
Joop Konijn	NIKHEF, treasurer
Henk Tiecke	NIKHEF

CONTENTS

Session A

Photon Structure

THE PARTON STRUCTURE OF REAL PHOTONS

ANDREAS VOGT

Institut für Theoretische Physik, Universität Würzburg,
Am Hubland, D-97074 Würzburg, Germany

The QCD treatment of the photon structure is recalled. Emphasis is given to the recently derived momentum sum rule, and to the proper choice of the factorization scheme and/or the boundary conditions for the evolution equtions beyond the leading order. Parametrizations of the photon's parton content are examined and compared. The small-x behaviour of the photon structure is briefly discussed

1 Introduction

Deep–inelastic electron–photon scattering has been the classical process for investigating the hadronic structure of the photon[1]. This process is kinematically analogous to the usual lepton–nucleon scattering. It has quite early received special interest, since the structure function $F_2^\gamma(x, Q^2)$ can be completely calculated in perturbation theory[2,3] at large Bjorken-x and large resolution Q^2. At scales accessible at present or in the near future, however, these results are unfortunately not applicable. Hence the photon structure functions have to be analyzed in terms of non–perturbative initial distributions for the QCD evolution equations[4], very much like the nucleon case.

Experimentally F_2^γ has been determined, albeit with rather limited accuracy, via $e^+e^- \rightarrow e^+e^- + hadrons$ at all electron–positron colliders since PEP and PETRA. The longitudinal structure function F_L^γ has been unaccessible so far, and will presumably remain so in the foreseeable future[5,6]. On the other hand, the past month have witnessed a substantial amount of new results on F_2^γ from LEP, and many more can be expected from forthcoming LEP2 runs. If systematic problems in extractions of F_2^γ from final–state modeling[6] can be overcome, these results will be able to challenge seriously the present, model-driven theoretical understanding of the photon structure.

In this talk a brief survey is given of the present theoretical and phenomenological status of this subject. In Section 2 we recall the evolution equations for the photon's parton distributions, including the recently derived momentum sum rule. The factorization scheme ambiguities are more relevant here as in the usual hadronic case, this issue is discussed in Section 3. Some of the most relevant parametrizations of the quark and gluon densities of the photon are discussed in Section 4 with respect to their assumption and limitations. Finally Section 5 is devoted to the small-x behaviour of the photon structure functions. For other aspects the reader is referred to refs.[1].

2 The evolution of the photon's parton densities

The photon is a genuine elementary particle, unlike the hadrons. Hence it can directly take part in hard scattering processes, in addition to its quark and gluon distributions arising from quantum fluctuations, $q^\gamma(x, Q^2)$ and $g^\gamma(x, Q^2)$. Denoting the corresponding photon distribution in the photon by $\Gamma^\gamma(x, Q^2)$, the evolution equations for these parton densities are generally given by

$$\frac{dq_i^\gamma}{d\ln Q^2} = \frac{\alpha}{2\pi}\overline{P}_{q_i\gamma} \otimes \Gamma^\gamma + \frac{\alpha_s}{2\pi}\left\{2\sum_{k=1}^f \overline{P}_{q_iq_k} \otimes q_k^\gamma + \overline{P}_{q_ig} \otimes g^\gamma\right\}$$

$$\frac{dg^\gamma}{d\ln Q^2} = \frac{\alpha}{2\pi}\overline{P}_{g\gamma} \otimes \Gamma^\gamma + \frac{\alpha_s}{2\pi}\left\{2\sum_{k=1}^f \overline{P}_{gq_k} \otimes q_k^\gamma + \overline{P}_{gg} \otimes g^\gamma\right\} \quad (1)$$

$$\frac{d\Gamma^\gamma}{d\ln Q^2} = \frac{\alpha}{2\pi}\overline{P}_{\gamma\gamma} \otimes \Gamma^\gamma + \frac{\alpha}{2\pi}\left\{2\sum_{k=1}^f \overline{P}_{\gamma q_k} \otimes q_k^\gamma + \overline{P}_{\gamma g} \otimes g^\gamma\right\}.$$

Here $\alpha \simeq 1/137$ is the electromagnetic coupling constant, and $\alpha_s \equiv \alpha_s(Q^2)$ denotes the running QCD coupling. $\otimes$ represents the Mellin convolution, and f stands for the number of active (massless) quark flavours. The antiquark distributions do not occur separately in Eq. (1), as $\bar{q}_i^\gamma(x, Q^2) = q_i^\gamma(x, Q^2)$ due to charge conjugation invariance. The generalized splitting functions read

$$\overline{P}_{ij}(x, \alpha, \alpha_s) = \sum_{l,m=0} \frac{\alpha^l\alpha_s^m}{(2\pi)^{l+m}}\overline{P}_{ij}^{(l,m)}(x), \quad (2)$$

with $\overline{P}_{q_iq_k}$ being the average of the quark–quark and antiquark–quark splitting functions. The parton densities are subject to the energy–momentum sum rule

$$\int_0^1 dx\, x\left[\Sigma^\gamma(x, Q^2) + g^\gamma(x, Q^2) + \Gamma^\gamma(x, Q^2)\right] = 1, \quad (3)$$

where Σ represents the singlet quark distribution, $\Sigma^\gamma = 2\sum_{i=1}^f q_i^\gamma$.

Usually calculations involving the photon's parton structure are restricted to first order in $\alpha \ll 1$. In this approximation all $l \neq 0$ terms in Eq. (2) can be neglected, since q_i^γ and g^γ are already of order α. This reduces the functions $\overline{P}_{ij}$ to the usual QCD quantities $P_{ij}(x, \alpha_s)$, with $P_{\gamma q_i}$ and $P_{\gamma g}$ dropping out completely. Moreover one has $P_{\gamma\gamma} \propto \delta(1-x)$ to all orders in α_s, as real photon radiations from photons starts at order α^2 only. Thus the last line of Eq. (1) can be integrated immediately, at leading order (LO), $m = 0$, resulting in

$$\Gamma_{\rm LO}^\gamma(x, Q^2) = \delta(1-x)\left[1 - \frac{\alpha}{\pi}\left(\sum_q e_q^2 \ln\frac{Q^2}{Q_0^2} + c_1\right)\right]. \quad (4)$$

Here e_q stands for the quark charges, Q_0^2 is some reference scale for the evolution, and the constant c_1 will be discussed below. Only the $O(1)$ part of
Γ^γ affects the quark and gluon densities at order α, as well as any observable
involving hadronic final states like F_2^γ, leading to the evolution equations [7]

$$\frac{dq_i^\gamma}{d\ln Q^2} = \frac{\alpha}{2\pi} P_{q_i\gamma} + \frac{\alpha_s}{2\pi}\left\{2\sum_{k=1}^{f} P_{q_i q_k} \otimes q_k^\gamma + P_{q_i g} \otimes g^\gamma\right\}$$

$$\frac{dg^\gamma}{d\ln Q^2} = \frac{\alpha}{2\pi} P_{g\gamma} + \frac{\alpha_s}{2\pi}\left\{2\sum_{k=1}^{f} P_{gq_k} \otimes q_k^\gamma + P_{gg} \otimes g^\gamma\right\}. \tag{5}$$

The splitting functions $P_{ij}(x, \alpha_s)$ are presently known to next–to–leading order
(NLO) in α_s, $m = 1$, see refs. [8,9,10].

The momentum sum rule (3) holds order by order in α, thus Eq. (4) implies

$$\int_0^1 dx\, x\left[\Sigma_{\rm LO}^\gamma(x, Q^2) + g_{\rm LO}^\gamma(x, Q^2)\right] = \frac{\alpha}{\pi}\left(\sum_q e_q^2 \ln\frac{Q^2}{Q_0^2} + c_1\right). \tag{6}$$

The photon's quark and gluon densities are therefore not related by a hadron–
type sum rule. Instead their momentum fractions rise logarithmically with Q^2
as long as the lowest–order approximation in α is justified. Hence, on the level
of Eq. (5) alone, an important constraint on the parton densities is missing.
That deficit can be removed by inferring c_1 from elsewhere, as recently done
in refs. [11,12] by connecting Eq. (4) to the cross section $\sigma(e^+e^- \to hadrons)$ via
a dispersion relation in the photon virtuality. This procedure yields [11]

$$\left(\frac{c_1}{\pi}\right)_{\rm LO} = \sum_{V=\rho,\omega,\phi} \frac{4\pi}{f_V^2} \simeq 0.55 \quad \text{at} \quad Q_0^2 \simeq (0.6\,\text{GeV})^2. \tag{7}$$

An error of about 20% can be assigned to this value, arising from the uncer-
tainties of f_ρ^2 (leptonic ρ width vs. $\gamma p \to \rho^0 p$) and of the scale Q_0^2 where the
connection of c_1 to the vector–meson decay constants holds. The numerical
results of refs. [11,12] agree well within this margin.

The general solution of the inhomogeneous evolution equations (5) reads

$$\vec{q}^\gamma = \begin{pmatrix} \Sigma^\gamma \\ g^\gamma \end{pmatrix} = \vec{q}_{\rm PL}^\gamma + \vec{q}_{\rm had}^\gamma, \tag{8}$$

where only the flavour singlet part has been indicated. The solution of the
homogeneous ('hadronic') equation, $\vec{q}_{\rm had}^\gamma(x, Q^2)$, contains the perturbatively
uncalculable boundary conditions $\vec{q}^\gamma(x, Q_0^2)$. The inhomogeneous ('pointlike')
part, on the other hand, is completely calculable once Q_0^2 has been specified.

At next–to–leading order these solutions can be written as [10,13]

$$\vec{q}_{\text{had}}^{\gamma} = \left(\left[\frac{\alpha_s}{\alpha_0} \right]^{\hat{d}} + \frac{\alpha_s}{2\pi} \left\{ \hat{U} \otimes \left[\frac{\alpha_s}{\alpha_0} \right]^{\hat{d}} - \left[\frac{\alpha_s}{\alpha_0} \right]^{\hat{d}} \otimes \hat{U} \right\} \right) \otimes \vec{q}^{\,\gamma}(Q_0^2) \qquad (9)$$

and

$$\vec{q}_{\text{PL}}^{\gamma} = \left\{ \frac{2\pi}{\alpha_s} + \hat{U} \right\} \otimes \left\{ 1 - \left[\frac{\alpha_s}{\alpha_0} \right]^{1+\hat{d}} \right\} \otimes \frac{1}{1+\hat{d}} \otimes \vec{a} + \left\{ 1 - \left[\frac{\alpha_s}{\alpha_0} \right]^{\hat{d}} \right\} \otimes \frac{1}{\hat{d}} \otimes \vec{b} \qquad (10)$$

with $\alpha_0 = \alpha_s(Q_0^2)$. $\vec{a}$, $\vec{b}$, $\hat{d}$ and $\hat{U}$ stand for known combinations of the splitting functions and the QCD β–function. The LO evolution is obtained from Eqs. (9) and (10) by putting $\hat{U} = 0$ and $\vec{b} = 0$. A convenient way to evaluate these expressions is by transformation to Mellin moments, which reduces the convolutions to simple products. The x–dependent distributions are then calculated by a numerical Mellin inversion of the final result (8).

3   Boundary conditions and factorization schemes

The structure function F_2^{γ} is, at first order in the electromagnetic coupling α,

$$F_2^{\gamma} = \sum_{q=u,d,s} 2x\, e_q^2 \left\{ q^{\gamma} + \frac{\alpha_s}{2\pi} (C_{2,q} \otimes q^{\gamma} + C_{2,g} \otimes g^{\gamma}) + \frac{\alpha}{2\pi} e_q^2 C_{2,\gamma} \right\}. \qquad (11)$$

Only the contribution of the light flavours has been written out here. The reader is referred to refs. [14,15] for the heavy quark part $F_{2,h}^{\gamma}$. At LO in α_s, just the first term in Eq. (11) is taken into account since $q^{\gamma} \sim 1/\alpha_s$, see Eq. (10). At NLO the usual hadronic one–loop coefficient functions $C_{2,q}(x)$ and $C_{2,g}(x)$ enter, together with the direct–photon contribution $C_{2,\gamma}$ given by [3]

$$C_{2,\gamma}^{\overline{\text{MS}}}(x) = 3 \left([x^2 + (1-x^2)] \ln \frac{1-x}{x} - 1 + 8x(1-x) \right). \qquad (12)$$

This term causes difficulties in this standard factorization scheme, as it leads to a large LO/NLO difference for the inhomogeneous part $F_{2,\text{PL}}^{\gamma}$. In particular it is strongly negative at large x, see Fig. 1. Thus $F_{2,\text{PL}}^{\gamma}$ turns positive over the full x-range, for $Q_0^2 = 1 \text{ GeV}^2$, only at $Q^2 \simeq 20 \text{ GeV}^2$. This unphysical behaviour has to be overcome in the complete F_2^{γ} by the $\overline{\text{MS}}$ initial distributions, which are therefore forced to be very different from their LO counterparts.

These problems are circumvented by adopting the DIS_{γ} scheme introduced in refs. [10,16]. Here $C_{2,\gamma}$ is absorbed into the quark distributions according to

$$q_{\text{DIS}_{\gamma}}^{\gamma} = q_{\overline{\text{MS}}}^{\gamma} + \frac{\alpha}{2\pi} e_q^2 C_{2,\gamma}^{\overline{\text{MS}}}, \quad C_{2,\gamma}^{\text{DIS}_{\gamma}} = 0. \qquad (13)$$

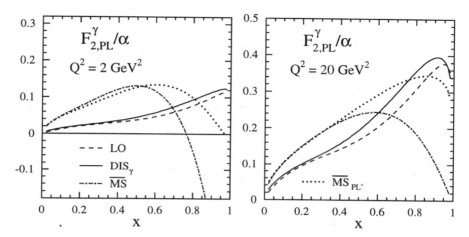

Figure 1: The pointlike structure function $F_{2,\,\mathrm{PL}}^{\gamma}$ in LO and in NLO for the $\overline{\mathrm{MS}}$ and DIS_{γ} schemes. $Q_0^2 = 1$ GeV^2, three active flavours and $\Lambda_{\mathrm{LO}} = \Lambda_{\mathrm{NLO}} = 0.2$ GeV have been used.

The coefficient functions $C_{2,q}$ and $C_{2,g}$ in Eq. (11), as well as the definition of the gluon density remain unchanged, in contrast to the hadronic DIS scheme[17]. Therefore F_2^{γ} assumes the usual hadronic $\overline{\mathrm{MS}}$ form without a direct term in DIS_{γ}, resulting in a good LO/NLO stability of $F_{2,\,\mathrm{PL}}^{\gamma}$ as illustrated in Fig. 1. Consequently physically motivated boundary conditions for the quark and gluon densities can be employed in this scheme also beyond leading order. An additional advantage of the DIS_{γ} scheme is that the leading $\overline{\mathrm{MS}}$ terms for $x \to 0$ cancel in the transformed NLO photon–parton splitting functions[18]

$$
P_{q\gamma}^{(1)} \sim \left\{ \begin{array}{l} \ln^2 x + \ldots \\ 2\ln x + \ldots \end{array} \right. , \quad P_{g\gamma}^{(1)} \sim \left\{ \begin{array}{ll} 1/x + \ldots & \overline{\mathrm{MS}} \\ -3\ln x + \ldots & \mathrm{DIS}_{\gamma} \end{array} \right. . \tag{14}
$$

In fact, this cancellation of the leading small-x term of $P_{g\gamma}^{\overline{\mathrm{MS}}}$ does not only take place at NLO, but persists to all orders in α_s[19].

An equivalent $\overline{\mathrm{MS}}$ formulation of the above solution to the $C_{2,\gamma}$ problem has been pursued in refs[20,21]. It can be written as a modification of the pointlike part $(\overline{\mathrm{PL}})$ in Eq. (8) by an additional 'technical' NLO input density,

$$
q_{\overline{\mathrm{PL}}}^{\gamma}(x, Q_0^2) = -\frac{\alpha}{2\pi} e_q^2 \, C_{2,\gamma}^{\overline{\mathrm{MS}}}(x) \,, \quad g_{\overline{\mathrm{PL}}}^{\gamma}(x, Q_0^2) = 0 \,. \tag{15}
$$

This leads to $F_{2,\overline{\mathrm{PL}}}^{\gamma}(x, Q_0^2) = 0$ and thus allows for similar 'physical' initial distributions on top of Eq. (15). The resulting quark distributions, however,

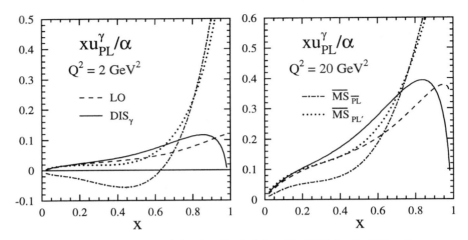

Figure 2: The pointlike up–quark density u^γ_{PL} in LO and in NLO for the DIS$_\gamma$ scheme, compared to the physically equivalent $\overline{\mathrm{MS}}$ distribution ($\overline{\mathrm{PL}}$) with the input (15). The parameters Q_0^2, f and Λ are as in Fig. 1. Also shown is the result for the PL$'$ boundary condition (16).

exhibit a rather unphysical shape. As displayed in Fig. 2, they are suppressed (strongly enhanced) at medium (large) values of x, respectively, with respect to the pointlike LO and DIS$_\gamma$ results. In a fully consistent NLO calculation, this $\overline{\mathrm{MS}}$ procedure is nevertheless strictly equivalent to the DIS$_\gamma$ treatment. On the other hand, as soon as not all terms beyond NLO are carefully omitted, the $\overline{\mathrm{MS}}$ treatment turns out to be unstable at large x, see refs. [22,23].

Due to the non–universality of the coefficient function $C_{2,\gamma}$, a special role is assigned to F_2^γ in the redefinitions (13,15) of the quark densities, similar to the hadronic DIS scheme. An alternative process–independent approach was worked out in ref. [24]. A universal technical $\overline{\mathrm{MS}}$ input has been inferred from a detailed analysis of the Feynman diagrams for $\gamma^*\gamma \to \gamma^*\gamma$, which leads to

$$q^\gamma_{\mathrm{PL}'}(x, Q_0^2) = -\frac{\alpha}{2\pi} e_q^2\, C_\gamma'(x)\,, \quad g^\gamma_{\mathrm{PL}'}(x, Q_0^2) = 0 \qquad (16)$$

with

$$C_\gamma'(x) = 3\Big(\big[x^2 + (1 - x^2)\big]\ln(1 - x) + 2x(1 - x)\Big)\,. \qquad (17)$$

The resulting modified pointlike structure function $F^\gamma_{2,\,\mathrm{PL}'}$, also shown in Fig. 1, remains negative at large x due to the uncompensated -1 in Eq. (12) only close to the reference scale Q_0^2. At medium to small x, $F^\gamma_{2,\,\mathrm{PL}'}$ is similar to the pointlike $\overline{\mathrm{MS}}$ results, i.e., larger than its LO and DIS$_\gamma = \overline{\mathrm{PL}}$ counterparts. The corresponding up–quark distributions are also illustrated in Fig. 2.

4   Parametrizations of photonic parton distributions

In order to specify the photon's parton densities, the perturbatively uncalculable initial distributions, $q_i^\gamma(x, Q_0^2)$ and $g^\gamma(x, Q_0^2)$, have to be fixed at some scale Q_0^2. Only one combination of quark densities (dominated by u^γ) is presently well constrained, however, by F_2^γ data at $0.01 \lesssim x \lesssim 0.8$ from PETRA [25,26,27], PEP [28], TRISTAN [29,30], and LEP [31,32,33]. The complete present data, including new results presented at this conference, is shown in Fig. 3 together with the NLO parametrizations of refs. [16,24]. The gluon distribution is not tightly constricted either: there is sound evidence for $g^\gamma \neq 0$, and a very large and hard g^γ has been ruled out by jet production results [34,35,36].

Due to these limitations, current parametrizations invoke theoretical estimates and model assumptions, in particular from vector meson dominance (VMD). For safely high reference scales, $Q_0^2 \gtrsim 2$ GeV^2, however, purely hadron–like initial distributions are known to be insufficient. An additional hard quark component has to be supplemented there in order to meet the F_2^γ data at larger Q^2. In view of this situation two approaches have been used. First one can keep $Q_0 \geq 1$ GeV, fit the quark densities to F_2^γ data, and estimate the gluon input. This method has been adopted in refs. [37,38] and, more recently, in refs. [11,21,39,40]. The second option is to retain a pure VMD ansatz,

$$(q_i^\gamma, g^\gamma)(x, Q_0^2) = \frac{4\pi\alpha}{f_\rho^2}(q_i^\rho, g^\rho)(x, Q_0^2) + \dots, \qquad (18)$$

together with assumptions on the experimentally unknown ρ distributions, and to start the evolution at a very low scale $Q_0 \simeq 0.5 \dots 0.7$ GeV [11,16,24,41]. Note that this boundary condition complies with the momentum sum rule (7) if the ω and ϕ contributions are appropriately added.

In the following, the three available NLO parametrizations [16,21,24] are briefly compared, together with the recent LO sets of ref. [11]. For all these distributions $\Lambda_{\mathrm{LO},\overline{\mathrm{MS}}} = 200$ MeV have been employed at $f = 4$.

The resulting u–quark densities are displayed in Fig. 4. Considering the LO results first, one notices that the parametrizations form two groups in the well–measured intermediate x-range, $0.2 \lesssim x \lesssim 0.7$. The lower one consists of the two low–Q_0 sets, GRV [16] and SAS 1D [11], which start the evolution at $Q_0^2 = 0.25$ GeV^2 and 0.36 GeV^2, respectively. The reference scales for the higher SAS 2D ^{a}, and GS (96) [21] distributions read $Q_0^2 = 4$ GeV^2 and 3 GeV^2. This difference has been driven at least partly by first LEP data [32,42], see ref. [43], which were considerably higher than previous results around $x = 0.2$. A more consistent picture is now emerging from the new LEP data in this range.

---

^{a}The additional SaS 1M and SaS 2M sets in ref. [11] are theoretically inconsistent, as the leading–order evolution is combined with the scheme–dependent coefficient function $C_{2,\gamma}$.

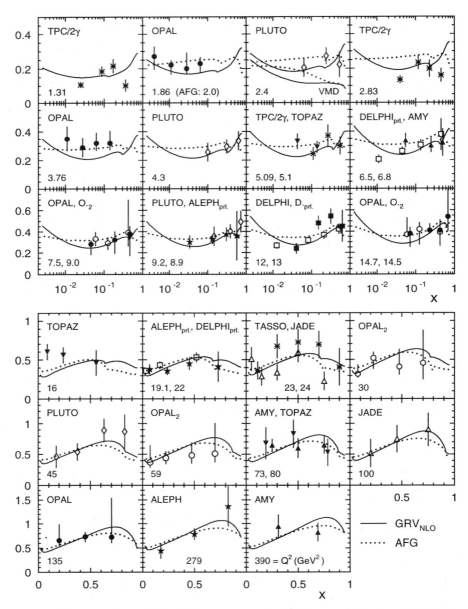

Figure 3: The presently available F_2^γ data compared to NLO parametrizations of refs. [16,24]. The hadron–like VMD components of the latter are separately displayed at $Q^2 = 2.4$ GeV^2.

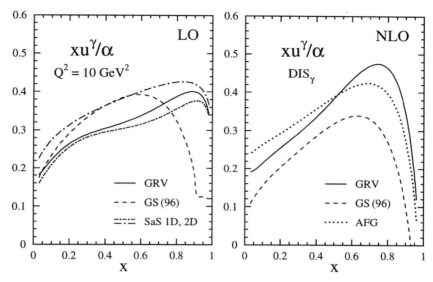

Figure 4: Parametrizations of the up–quark distribution at LO [11,16,21] and NLO [16,21,24]. NLO results in $\overline{\text{MS}}$ have been transformed to the DIS_γ scheme according to Eq. (13).

The second striking feature in Fig. 4 is the large–x behaviour of the GS parametrization. Unlike SaS 2D, where a simple hard term $\propto x$ is employed, GS choose the massive Born expressions for $\gamma^*\gamma \rightarrow q\bar{q}$ at Q_0^2 on top of the hadronic VMD input. All power–law contributions $O(\,[m_q^2/Q^2]^n\,)$, $n \geq 1$, are retained, resulting in a threshold at $x \simeq 0.9$ for typical constituent quark masses. Such a procedure, however, may be considered as inadequate for the construction of leading–twist parton densities.

Let us now turn to the NLO distributions. The results of GRV [16] and AFG [24] are both based on the VMD ansatz (18), imposed at $Q_0^2 = 0.3$ GeV^2 and 0.5 GeV^2, respectively. The differences between these two parametrizations at $x \gtrsim 0.1$ can be understood in terms of the non–hadronic NLO boundary conditions discussed in Sec. 3, cf. Fig. 1. At lower x, the deviations are dominated by the differing assumptions [44,45] on the experimentally virtually unconstrained pion sea – both groups estimate the unknown ρ distributions by their pionic counterparts. The third NLO set, GS (96), is technically flawed: it should at Q_0^2, by construction, lead to the same F_2^γ results as the LO fit. However, u^γ turns out to be sizeably too small over the full x–range. Hence this parametrization is unfortunately not usable in its present form [b].

---

[b] This discussion also applies to the previous NLO parametrization[20] of the same group.

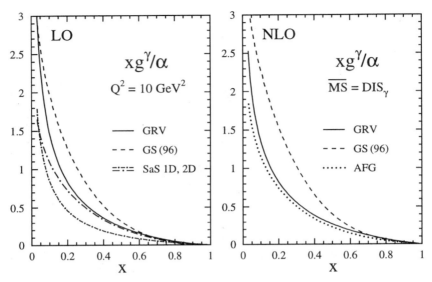

Figure 5: Parametrizations of the photon's gluon density at LO [11,16,21] and NLO [16,21,24].

Before considering the gluon density, it is appropriate to comment on the quark–flavour decomposition and the momentum sum rule. Both SaS 1D and AFG perform a coherent addition of the three light vector–mesons at their respective input scales, with slightly differing assumptions on SU(3) breaking and the value of f_ρ. That leads to a suppression of the d–valence density by a factor of four with respect to the ρ–meson's u–valence component. This approach is able to describe the F_2^γ data without any further adjustment, hence the momentum sum rule (7) is met in both cases. On the other hand, GRV use just a ρ distribution, with a prefactor adjusted to the data. Although a factor of 1.6 perfectly mimics the F_2 of the (SU(3) symmetric) coherent superposition, too much momentum is spent due to the $u_v = d_v$ symmetry. Thus Eq. (6) is violated, e.g., by about +40% in LO at $Q^2 = 4$ GeV^2. Finally the high–Q_0 fits, SaS 2D and GS, do not impose the momentum sum rule at all.

The gluon distributions of these parametrizations are finally presented in Fig. 5. The pion distributions of AFG [44] and GRV [45] both describe the direct–photon production data in πp collisions [46], that is why these photonic gluons are so similar except at very x. For the GS parametrization, the gluon densities have been constrained by a LO comparison to TRISTAN jet production data [34,35], which seem to prefer a relatively large gluon distributions. The shapes of the SaS gluon densities are fixed by theoretical estimates, no direct or indirect experimental constraint has been imposed here.

5 Photon structure at small x

The region of very small parton momenta, $10^{-5} \lesssim x \lesssim 10^{-2}$, has attracted considerable interest in the proton case since the advent of HERA. The quark and gluon distributions show a marked rise at small-x [47,48], in good agreement with perturbative predictions for a low input scale $Q_0 \simeq 600$ MeV [49]. The corresponding NLO evolution of the photon structure is shown in Fig. 6.

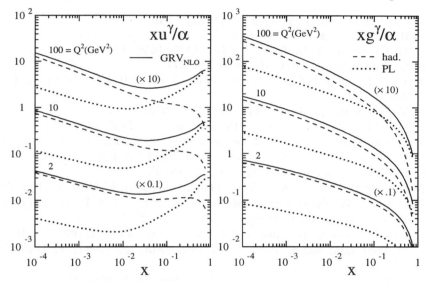

Figure 6: The NLO small-x evolution of the photon's quark and gluon distributions as predicted in ref [16]. The hadronic (VMD) and pointlike contributions are shown separately.

The parton distributions of the photon behave very differently in the limits of large and small x. In the former case, the perturbative part (10) dominates, especially for the quark distributions. On the other hand, this calculable contribution amounts at most to about 20% at very small-x, at scales accessible in the foreseeable future, in LO as well as in NLO. One may therefore expect, by VMD arguments for the hadronic component (9), a very similar rise as observed in the proton case. It will be very interesting to see whether this expectation is borne out by future F_2^{γ} measurement.

Let me finally mention that there is an even more intriguing, if exotic, possibility here: the calculable pointlike contribution could be drastically enhanced by large logarithmic small-x terms in the perturbation series [19]. If this component could be projected out, for example, by final-state observables, it would provide a rather unique small-x QCD laboratory.

14

Acknowledgment

This work has been supported by the German Federal Ministy for Research and Technology (BMBF) under contract No. 05 7WZ91P (0).

References

1. Ch. Berger and W. Wagner, *Phys. Rep.* **146**, 1 (1987);
   H. Abramowicz *et al*, *Int. J. Mod. Phys.* **A8**, 1005 (1993);
   M. Drees and R. Godbole, *J. Phys.* **G21**, 1559 (1995).
2. E. Witten, *Nucl. Phys.* **B120**, 189 (1977).
3. W.A. Bardeen and A.J. Buras, *Phys. Rev.* **D20** 166, (1979), E: **D21** 2041, (1980).
4. M. Glück and E. Reya, *Phys. Rev.* **D28**, 2749 (1983);
   M. Glück, K. Grassie and E. Reya, *Phys. Rev.* **D30**, 1447 (1984).
5. P. Aurenche *et al*, in: *Proceedings of the LEP2 Physics Workshop*, eds. G. Altarelli, T. Sjöstrand and F. Zwirner (CERN 1996), p. 291.
6. D.J. Miller, hep-ex/9708002, these proceedings.
7. R.J. De Witt *et al*, *Phys. Rev.* **D19**, 2046 (1979), E: **D20**, 1751 (1979).
8. G. Curci, W. Furmanski and R. Petronzio, *Nucl. Phys.* **B175**, 27 (1980);
   W. Furmanski and R. Petronzio, *Phys. Lett.* **B97**, 437 (1980);
   E.G. Floratos, C. Kounnas and R. Lacaze, *Nucl. Phys.* **B192**, 417 (1981).
9. M. Fontannaz and E. Pilon, *Phys. Rev.* **D45**, 382 (1992), E: **D46**, 484 (1992).
10. M. Glück, E. Reya and A. Vogt, *Phys. Rev.* **D45**, 3986 (1992).
11. T. Sjöstrand and G.A. Schuler, *Z. Phys.* **C68**, 607 (1995);
    G.A. Schuler in: *Proceedings of Photon '95*, eds. D.J. Miller, S.L. Cartwright and V. Khoze (World Scientific, Singapore, 1995).
12. L.L. Frankfurt and E.G. Gurvich, hep-ph/9505406; *J. Phys.* **G22**, 903 (1996).
13. W. Furmanski and R. Petronzio, *Z. Phys.* **C11**, 293 (1982).
14. E. Laenen, S. Riemersma, J. Smith and W.L. van Neerven, *Phys. Rev.* **D49**, 5753 (1994).
15. E. Laenen and S. Riemersma, in: *Proceedings of Photon '95*, eds. D.J. Miller, S.L. Cartwright and V. Khoze (World Scientific,Singapore, 1995); *Phys. Lett.* **B376**, 169 (1996).
16. M. Glück, E. Reya and A. Vogt, *Phys. Rev.* **D46**, 1973, (1992).
17. G. Altarelli, R.K. Ellis and G. Martinelli, *Nucl. Phys.* **B157**, 461 (1979).
18. M. Glück, E. Reya and A. Vogt, *Phys. Rev.* **D48**, 116 (1993).
19. J. Blümlein and A. Vogt, DESY 96-096, August 1997.

20. L.E. Gordon and J.K. Storrow, *Z. Phys.* **C56**, 307 (1992).
21. L.E. Gordon and J.K. Storrow, *Nucl. Phys.* **B489**, 405 (1997).
22. M. Glück, E. Reya and A. Vogt, *Phys. Lett.* **B285**, 285 (1992).
23. A. Vogt in: *Proceedings of the Workshop on Two-Photon Physics at LEP and HERA*, eds. G. Jarlskog and L. Jönsson (Lund Univ., 1994), p. 141.
24. P. Aurenche, M. Fontannaz and J.P. Guillet, *Z. Phys.* **C64**, 621 (1994).
25. PLUTO Coll., Ch. Berger *et al*, *Phys. Lett.* **B142**, 111, (1984); *Nucl. Phys.* **B281**, 365 (1987).
26. JADE Coll., W. Bartel *et al*, *Z. Phys.* **C24**, 231 (1984).
27. TASSO Coll., M. Althoff *et al*, *Z. Phys.* **C31**, 527 (1986).
28. TPC/2γ Coll., H. Aihara *et al*, *Phys. Rev. Lett.* **58**, 97 (1987); *Z. Phys.* **C34**, 1 (1987).
29. AMY Coll., S.K. Sahu *et al*, *Phys. Lett.* **B346**, 208 (1995); T. Kojima *et al*, *Phys. Lett.* **B400**, 395 (1997).
30. TOPAZ Coll., K. Muramatsu *et al*, *Phys. Lett.* **B332**, 477 (1994).
31. OPAL Coll., K. Ackerstaff *et al*, *Z. Phys.* **C74**, 33 (1997); CERN-PPE/97-087, CERN-PPE/97-104, July 1997; R. Nisius, these proceedings; J. Bechtluft, these proceedings.
32. DEPLHI Coll., P. Abreu *et al*, *Z. Phys.***C69**, 223 (1996); I. Tyapkin, these proceedings; F. Kapusta *et al*, HEP'97, contribution 416.
33. ALEPH Coll., A. Finch *et al*, these proceedings; HEP'97, contribution 607.
34. TOPAZ Coll., H. Hayashij et al., *Phys. Lett.* **B314**, 149 (1993).
35. AMY Coll., B.J. Kim et al., *Phys. Lett.* **B325**, 248 (1994).
36. H1 Coll., T. Ahmed et al., *Nucl. Phys.* **B445**, 195 (1995).
37. M. Drees and K. Grassie, *Z. Phys.* **C28**, 451 (1985).
38. H. Abramowicz, K. Charchula and A. Levy, *Phys. Lett.* **B269**, 458 (1991)
39. K. Hagiwara, M. Tanaka, I. Watanabe, and T. Izubuchi, *Phys. Rev.* **D51**, 3197 (1995).
40. H. Abramowicz, E. Gurvich, and A. Levy, TAUP 2438-97, July 1997.
41. P. Aurenche et al., *Z. Phys.* **C56**, 589 (1992).
42. OPAL Coll., R. Akers *et al*, *Z. Phys.* **C61**, 199 (1994).
43. T. Sjöstrand, J.K. Storrow, and A. Vogt, *J. Phys.* **G22**, 893 (1996).
44. P. Aurenche *et al*, *Phys. Lett.* **B233**, 517 (1989).
45. M. Glück, E. Reya and A. Vogt, *Z. Phys.* **C53**, 651 (1992).
46. WA70 Coll., M. Bonesini et al., *Z. Phys.* **C37**, 535 (1988).
47. H1 Coll., S. Aid *et al*, *Nucl. Phys.* **B470**, 3 (1996).
48. ZEUS Coll., M. Derrick *et al*, *Z. Phys.* **C72**, 399 (1996).
49. M. Glück, E. Reya and A. Vogt, *Z. Phys.* **C53**, 127 (1992); **C67**, 433 (1995).

MEASUREMENT OF QED PHOTON STRUCTURE FUNCTIONS USING AZIMUTHAL CORRELATIONS

MATHIEU DOUCET

for the OPAL Collaboration

Lab. de Physique Nucléaire, Université de Montréal,
Montréal (Québec) H3C 3J7, Canada

We have studied [1] azimuthal correlations in singly-tagged $e^+e^- \to e^+e^-\mu^+\mu^-$ events at an average Q^2 of 5.2 GeV^2. The data were taken with the OPAL detector at LEP at e^+e^- centre-of-mass energies close to the Z^0 mass, with an integrated luminosity of approximately 100 pb^{-1}. The azimuthal correlations are used to extract the ratio F_B^γ/F_2^γ of the QED structure functions $F_B^\gamma(x,Q^2)$ and $F_2^\gamma(x,Q^2)$ of the photon. The measurement of F_B^γ/F_2^γ is found to be significantly different from zero and to be consistent with the QED prediction.

1 Introduction

The study of the structure of the photon provides an excellent way to test the theories of QED and QCD. Information about the underlying physics of this structure can be obtained by the measurement of structure functions. At e^+e^- colliders, these can be extracted by studying the two-photon process $e^+e^- \to e^+e^-\gamma\gamma \to e^+e^- X$. In particular, the structure of the real photon can be investigated by considering events in which one of the final electrons [a] – the tag – is detected, while the other is scattered at too low an angle to be captured and is lost in the beampipe. In such a process, the photon emitted by the lost electron – the target photon – is considered to be quasi-real and directed along the axis of the colliding beams. The cross-section for such events is related to the $e\gamma$ cross-section by the Weizsäcker-Williams approximation [2] for the flux of quasi-real photons. The $e\gamma$ cross-section is itself given by [3]

$$\frac{d\sigma(e\gamma \to eX)}{dx dQ^2} = \frac{2\pi\alpha^2}{xQ^4} \left[\left(1 + (1-y)^2\right) F_2^\gamma(x,Q^2) - y^2 F_L^\gamma(x,Q^2) \right]. \quad (1)$$

The functions F_2^γ and F_L^γ are the structure functions and α is the QED coupling constant. The kinematics are defined by the Bjorken variable x, the dimensionless variable $y \simeq 1 - \frac{E_{tag}}{E_{beam}} \cos^2 \frac{\theta_{tag}}{2}$ and the squared four-momentum Q^2 of the virtual photon emitted by the tagged electron.

Several efforts have already been made by the OPAL Collaboration to carry out such measurements. Notably, extractions of the structure function F_2^γ have

---

[a]Positrons are also referred to as electrons.

been performed for both hadronic[4] and leptonic[5] processes. Unfortunately, the structure function F_L^γ is very difficult to measure at LEP[6] because of its small contribution and because it is weighted by the factor y. As an alternative, it has been pointed out [7-12] that there are azimuthal correlations in the final state of two-photon collisions which are sensitive to additional structure functions. The main variable to study these is the azimuthal angle χ. In terms of muonic two-photon events (and similarly for hadronic events), this angle is defined in the $\gamma^*\gamma$ centre-of-mass frame as the angle between the planes formed by the $\gamma^*\gamma$ axis and the directions of the μ^- and e_{tag}^-, respectively (for e^- tags) or the angle between the planes formed by the $\gamma^*\gamma$ axis and the directions of the μ^+ and e_{tag}^+, respectively (for e^+ tags). We also define $\eta = \cos\theta^*$, where θ^* is the angle between the $\mu^-(\mu^+)$ and the photon axis in the $\gamma^*\gamma$ centre-of-mass. Figure 1a depicts the angles of the system. The differential cross-section can be written as

$$\frac{d\sigma(e\gamma \to e\mu^+\mu^-)}{dx\,dy\,d\eta\,d\chi/4\pi} = \frac{2\pi\alpha^2}{Q^2}\left(\frac{1+(1-y)^2}{xy}\right) \times \left[(2x\tilde{F}_T^\gamma + \epsilon(y)\tilde{F}_L^\gamma) - \rho(y)\tilde{F}_A^\gamma\cos\chi + \frac{1}{2}\epsilon(y)\tilde{F}_B^\gamma\cos 2\chi\right], \qquad (2)$$

where $\tilde{F}_T^\gamma$, $\tilde{F}_A^\gamma$, $\tilde{F}_B^\gamma$ and $\tilde{F}_L^\gamma$ are differential structure functions. The functions $\epsilon(y)$ and $\rho(y)$ are approximately equal to unity for small y. The dependence of the QED cross-section on the azimuthal angle χ is explicit in equation 2 and the QED differential structure functions do not depend on χ. The conventional structure functions F_i^γ can be recovered by integration over η and χ.

The structure functions F_i^γ are combinations of transition amplitudes for specific helicity states of the photons. The longitudinal structure function F_L^γ has been shown to be equal to the structure function F_B^γ, in leading order and for massless muons. It is not known if this identity is still valid for higher orders. Although they are equal, they are related to different helicity states of the photons. The structure function F_B^γ is related to the interference term between two transverse helicity states, while F_L^γ is related to the longitudinal polarization of the virtual photon.

In this paper, the result of the extraction of F_B^γ for muonic two-photon events, $e^+e^- \to e^+e^-\mu^+\mu^-$, is presented. The structure function F_A^γ was not studied in this analysis. Its contribution is zero when integrated over η (see for example in [12] that $\tilde{F}_A^\gamma$ is antisymmetric in η). The data sample consists of all the OPAL data taken at centre-of-mass energies on and near the mass of the Z^0 since the upgrade of the forward detectors, amounting to approximately 100 pb^{-1}. The results presented in this text are the subject of a paper [1].

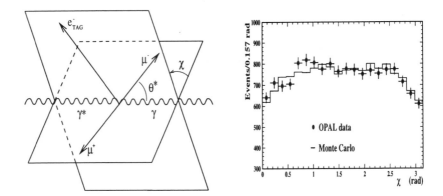

Figure 1: (a) Illustration of the azimuthal angle. (b) Azimuthal angle distribution before correction, for the whole x range.

2 Event selection

Events with one tagged electron having an energy greater than half the energy of the beam and two charged tracks, of which at least one was identified as a muon [1], were selected. The selected angular range of the tagged electron is $0.026 < \sin\theta_{\text{tag}} < 0.120$. It corresponds to a range in Q^2 of $0.85 < Q^2 < 31$ GeV^2. Muons having a momentum greater than 1 GeV/c were selected. A total of 14878 events passed the selection. The Vermaseren Monte Carlo generator [13] was used for the simulation.

3 Azimuthal angle distribution

The azimuthal angle χ is measured in the $\gamma^*\gamma$ centre-of-mass system. The latter is found using the combined momentum of the muons. The azimuthal angle is well measured. The resolution, of about 20 mrad, is nearly constant over the whole χ range. Figure 1b shows the measured azimuthal angle distribution for the whole x range. This distribution does not exhibit directly the $\cos 2\chi$ dependence predicted by QED. This is due to the acceptance of the detector, mainly for the muons lost in the forward region, in the polar angle range between the acceptance limit of the central detector and the beam axis. A bin-by-bin correction in χ, for every range of x, was applied to the data distributions. Once the azimuthal angle distributions were corrected, they were fitted to the following function:

$$F(\chi) = A(1 + B\cos 2\chi), \tag{3}$$

where A is a normalization factor and B gives the ratio of F_B^γ to F_2^γ. Figure 2a shows the corrected azimuthal angle distribution for the whole x range, fitted to equation 3.

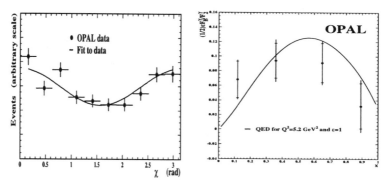

Figure 2: (a) Fitted azimuthal angle distribution for whole x range, after correction. (b) F_B^γ/F_2^γ obtained from the azimuthal angle distributions corrected for the effects of the detector. The points are the data and the solid line is the QED prediction.

4   Background and systematic errors

Various sources of backgrounds were considered. The principal source of contamination is expected to be muonic decays of tau pairs. The KORALZ generator [14] was used to estimate the contribution of $e^+e^- \to Z^0 \to \tau^+\tau^-$ events, the Vermaseren generator [13] was used to estimate the background from $e^+e^- \to e^+e^-\tau^+\tau^-$ events and the HERWIG generator [15] was used to estimate the background from hadronic two-photon events. The background from $\gamma^*\gamma \to \pi^+\pi^-$ was also considered and was estimated to be negligible [16].

The background, being very small (about 2.7%), was not subtracted from the signal, but was included in the systematic error. Because of the role of the Monte Carlo in providing the correction to obtain the shape of the azimuthal angle distribution, several tests were made to establish the reliability of the procedure. The systematic uncertainty was found to be around 20%.

5   Results and conclusions

The value of $\frac{1}{2}\epsilon F_B^\gamma/F_2^\gamma$ for each x range is shown in figure 2b and compared to the QED prediction for $Q^2 = 5.2$ GeV^2 and $\epsilon = 1$. The measured value of $\frac{1}{2}\epsilon F_B^\gamma/F_2^\gamma$ over the whole x range is $0.076 \pm 0.013 \pm 0.015$, close to the QED prediction of 0.083. The variation with x is consistent with QED (χ^2/dof =

0.94). It is also consistent with a constant F_B^γ/F_2^γ ($\chi^2/\text{dof} = 0.74$), but the measured values are significantly different from zero ($\chi^2/\text{dof} = 6.7$).

In summary, azimuthal correlations can supplement the direct measurement of structure functions from total cross-sections. We have made the first measurement of the size of the ratio of the structure functions F_B^γ and F_2^γ for muonic two-photon events, based on azimuthal correlations in data from the OPAL experiment at LEP. This structure function F_B^γ is identical to the structure function F_L^γ in leading order for massless muons. This identity enables us to infer information about the structure of the photon that we would have obtained had we measured F_L^γ, although these two structure functions come from different helicity states of the photons. A first attempt to measure the variation of F_B^γ/F_2^γ with the scaling variable x has also been obtained, although the sensitivity on this dependence is limited.

References

1. OPAL Collaboration, K. Ackerstaff et al., *Zeit. f. Phys.* **C74**, 49 (1997).
2. C. F. von Weizsäcker, *Zeit. f. Phys.* **88**, 612 (1934);
   E. J. Williams, *Phys. Rev.* **45**, 729 (1934).
3. V. M. Budnev et al., *Phys. Rep.* **15**, 181 (1974).
4. OPAL Collaboration, R. Akers et al., *Zeit. f. Phys.* **C61**, 199 (1994).
5. OPAL Collaboration, R. Akers et al., *Zeit. f. Phys.* **C60**, 593 (1993).
6. D. J. Miller, Proc. ECFA workshop on LEP200, eds. A. Böhm and W. Hoogland, CERN 87-08, 202 (1987).
7. C. Peterson, P. M. Zerwas and T. F. Walsh, *Nucl. Phys.* **B229**, 301 (1983).
8. CELLO Collaboration, H.-J. Behrend et al., *Zeit. f. Phys.* **C43**, 1 (1989).
9. J. H. Field, Proc. Photon '95, Sheffield, eds. D. J. Miller, S. L. Cartwright and V. Khoze, World Scientific, Singapore, 490 (1995).
10. N. Arteaga et al., Proc. Photon '95, Sheffield, eds. D. J. Miller, S. L. Cartwright and V. Khoze, World Scientific, Singapore, 281 (1995).
11. N. Arteaga et al., *Phys. Rev.* **D52**, 4920 (1995); **D53**, 2854 (1996).
12. P. Aurenche et al., Physics at LEP2, eds. G. Altarelli, T. Sjöstrand and F. Zwirner, CERN 96-01, 301 (1996).
13. J. A. M. Vermaseren, *Nucl. Phys.* **B229**, 347 (1983).
14. S. Jadach, B. F. L. Ward and Z. Was, *Comp. Phys. Comm.* **79**, 503 (1994).
15. G. Marchesini et al., *Comp. Phys. Comm.* **67**, 465 (1992).
16. S. J. Brodsky, T. Kinoshita and H. Terazawa, *Phys. Rev.* **D4**, 1532 (1971).

MUONIC STRUCTURE FUNCTIONS OF THE PHOTON

C.A. BREW, S. CARTWRIGHT, M. LEHTO

Department of Physics, University of Sheffield, Sheffield.
S3 7RH, United Kingdom

We studied muon pair production in single tagged $\gamma\gamma$ events in the ALEPH detector at LEP. The F_2 structure function is extracted for $< Q^2 > = 2.7$ and 14.6 GeV^2. Then azimuthal asymmetries are used to measure the other structure functions F_A and F_B.

1 Introduction

The QED process $e^+ e^- \rightarrow e^+ e^- \mu^+ \mu^-$ was studied in the single tag mode. In this region only the multiperipheral diagram gives a significant contribution. This gives direct access to $O(\alpha^4)$ QED reactions, which in principle should be fully calculable.

The differential cross section for $e\gamma$ scattering can be written as:

$$\frac{d^2\sigma}{dx dQ^2} = \frac{4\pi\alpha^2}{Q^4} \left\{ (1-y)F_2(x, Q^2) + xy^2 F_1(x, Q^2) \right\},\tag{1}$$

where Q^2 is the momentum transfer squared of the photon, $F_{1,2}$ are the QED structure functions, x is the kinematic variable defined as $x = Q^2/(W^2 + Q^2)$, where W^2 is the invariant mass squared of the muon pair, and y is defined as $y = 1 - E_{Tag}/E_{Beam} \cos^2(\theta_{Tag}/2)$. In the kinematic region occupied by our events y is generally small, which in turn means that the contribution to the cross section from F_1 can be neglected. F_2 is a function of x and Q^2.

By measuring the distribution of the final state particles, other structure functions can be measured [1,2,3]. Defining χ as the angle between the plane containing the photons and the muons and the plane containing the photons and the tag, and z as $z = \frac{1}{2}(1 - cos\theta)$ where θ is the angle between the photons and the muons, in the $\gamma\gamma$ center of mass frame, the differential cross section can be written (taking y to be small) [4]:

$$\frac{d\sigma}{dx dy dz d\chi/4\pi} = \frac{2\pi\alpha^2}{Q^2} \left(\frac{1 + (1-y)^2}{xy} \right) F_2 \left\{ 1 + \frac{F_A}{F_2} \cos\chi + \frac{1}{2} \frac{F_B}{F_2} \cos 2\chi \right\}.\tag{2}$$

2   The ALEPH Detector

Full details of the ALEPH detector can be found elsewhere [5]. In this analysis the Time Projection Chamber (TPC) is used to measure charge track position and momentum. The scattered electron is tagged mainly with the small angle calorimeters, the Silicon Calorimeter (SiCAL) and the Luminosity Calorimeter (LCAL), with a few in the Electromagnetic Calorimeter (ECAL). Muon identification is done with the Hadron Calorimeter (HCAL) and the Muon Chambers. Triggering is based mainly on the Muon Chambers and the Inner Tracking Chamber.

3   Event Selection and Backgrounds

The event selection is based upon detecting the tag and the muon pair.

- There must be two or three charged tracks with momenta greater than 0.4GeV, with polar angle θ above 318 mrad, four or more hits in the TPC and a minimum distance from the interaction point less than 2.0 cm transverse to the beam axis and 5.0 cm parallel to it.

- There must a cluster in one of the electromagnetic calorimeters with energy greater than 40% of the beam energy. The cluster is required to be away from gaps at the edges of the detectors so the polar angle is restricted to be between 26 and 55 mrad (SiCAL) or above 60 mrad (LCAL and ECAL). If this cluster has a polar angle above 318 mrad the cluster must have an associated charged track.

- At least one of the remaining charged tracks must be identified as a muon. Muon identification is based on Muon Chamber hits, HCAL shower shape information and the fraction of the charged track's energy deposited in the ECAL and HCAL. If only one particle is identified as a muon, the other track is required to have the opposite charge and to have deposited less than 30% of its energy in the ECAL.

Additional cuts were made on the event as a whole to lower the background from annihilation events. These were:

- The total energy of the event is less than 75.0 GeV.

- The total longitudinal momentum of the event is greater than 15.0 GeV.

- The total neutral energy recorded in the detector, excluding the tag, is less than 5.0 GeV. This cut also operated as an antitag veto on the "unseen" electron.

Since the position of the tag electron is known with much greater accuracy than its energy, we used the following equation to recalculate the energy (ignoring the lepton masses):

$$E_{Tag} = \frac{P_\mu \cos\theta_\mu + (2E_{Beam} - E_\mu)\cos\theta_{Anti-Tag}}{\cos\theta_{Anti-Tag} - \cos\theta_{Tag}}, \quad (3)$$

where P_μ is the momentum of the muon system, E_μ is its energy and θ_μ its polar angle. $\theta_{Anti-Tag}$ is the polar angle of the unseen electron assumed to be either 0 or π depending on the direction of the tag. According to the Monte Carlo this reduces the error on E_{Tag} from 3.5 GeV to 0.5 GeV.

Four sources of background were considered: $\gamma\gamma \rightarrow \tau^+\tau^-$, $\gamma\gamma \rightarrow$ hadrons, $e^+e^- \rightarrow \mu^+\mu^-\gamma(\gamma)$ and $e^+e^- \rightarrow \tau^+\tau^-(\gamma)$. The background from annihilation events was found to be negligible. The major background was $\gamma\gamma \rightarrow \tau^+\tau^-$ with a little from $\gamma\gamma \rightarrow$ hadrons: these were modelled with Monte Carlo and subtracted from the data.

After all cuts 4967 events were selected from 42 pb^{-1} with an estimated background of 149 events.

4 Results

The QED structure function F_2 was extracted from the data as follows.

1. $e^+e^- \rightarrow e^+e^-\mu^+\mu^-$ single tag events were generated with an integrated luminosity of 574.7 pb^{-1}, using Vermaseren [6], and passed through the full detector simulation and the analysis cuts.

2. The data were corrected for detector effects and the $\gamma\gamma$ luminosity function by dividing the measured x distribution of the data by that of the fully simulated selected Monte Carlo.

3. This distribution was then weighted by the factor $F_2(x, Q^2)/\alpha$ used to generate the Monte Carlo, to obtain a distribution for F_2 which can be compared directly with QED predictions.

Fig. 1a shows the values of F_2 for events tagged in the SiCAL ($0.6 < Q^2 < 6.3\,\text{GeV}^2$, $\langle Q^2 \rangle = 2.8\ \text{GeV}^2$). Fig. 1b shows the F_2 values for events with the tag in the LCAL ($3.0 < Q^2 < 60.0\,\text{GeV}^2$, $\langle Q^2 \rangle = 14.6\,\text{GeV}^2$). The points show the measured data corrected for the estimated backgrounds from $\gamma\gamma \rightarrow \tau^+\tau^-$ and $\gamma\gamma \rightarrow q\bar{q}$, with the curves being the QED prediction [7]. The errors shown are statistical only.

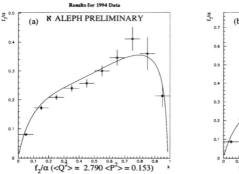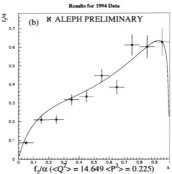

Figure 1: The measured values of the structure function F_2 for tags in SiCAL (a) and LCAL (b). The solid lines are the QED expectations.

In order to measure F_A and F_B one needs to boost the event into the $\gamma\gamma$ center of mass frame ($\equiv \mu\mu$ C.O.M. frame).

The azimuthal angle distribution of the data does not show the $\cos\chi$ and $\cos 2\chi$ dependence predicted by QED (eq. 2). This is due to muons being lost below the inner edge of the tracking chambers. The acceptance in χ is asymmetric due to the transverse component of the boost given to the event, so a bin by bin correction of the data is done in χ for all ranges of x. The correction factor was calculated by dividing the χ distribution of the selected Monte Carlo events into the generator level χ distribution of the Monte Carlo sample from which the events were selected.

Once the χ distributions had been recovered, they were fitted with the following function:

$$F(\chi) = N(1 + A\cos\chi + B\cos 2\chi), \qquad (4)$$

where N is a normalisation factor, $A = F_A/F_2$ and $B = \frac{1}{2}F_B/F_2$.

x range	$F_A \pm$ Stat $\pm$ Syst	$F_B \pm$ Stat $\pm$ Syst
0.0-0.2	$0.2021 \pm 0.0506 \pm 0.0179$	$0.0452 \pm 0.0486 \pm 0.0180$
0.2-0.4	$0.2426 \pm 0.0528 \pm 0.0182$	$0.1588 \pm 0.0474 \pm 0.0196$
0.4-0.6	$0.0588 \pm 0.0618 \pm 0.0205$	$0.1202 \pm 0.0575 \pm 0.0261$
0.6-0.8	$-0.1602 \pm 0.0816 \pm 0.0426$	$0.2111 \pm 0.0696 \pm 0.0492$
0.8-1.0	$-0.1927 \pm 0.0938 \pm 0.0831$	$0.2208 \pm 0.0767 \pm 0.0554$

Table 1: Measured values of the structure functions F_A and F_B with their statistical and systematic errors.

The values of F_A/F_2 and $\frac{1}{2}F_B/F_2$ are given in Table 1 and plotted in Figure 2, with their statistical and systematic errors.

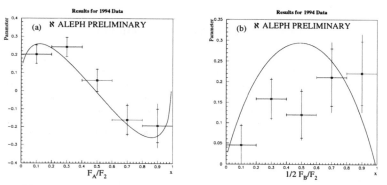

Figure 2: The measured values of the structure functions F_A (a) and F_B (b). The solid lines are the QED expectations[4].

5 Conclusion

We have measured the QED photon structure functions F_2, F_A and F_B with 42 pb^{-1} of data taken at an e^+e^- center of mass energy of 91.2 GeV with the ALEPH detector at LEP. The F_2 and F_A structure functions agree very well with the QED prediction of their variation with x; the agreement between measured F_B and the QED prediction is less good though they are not wholly out of agreement. We believe this discrepancy to be a simple statistical fluctuation and are presently extending the analysis to include the full ALEPH data sample. Our results are in braor agreement with other LEP experiments[8,9,10].

References

1. C.Peterson, F.M.Zerwas, T.F.Walsh, *Nucl. Phys.* B **229**, 301 (1983).
2. CELLO Collab., H.J.Behrend *et al.*, *Z. Phys.* C **43**, 1 (1989).
3. N.Arteaga, P.Kessler *et al.*, proceedings of Photon '95, Sheffield U.K. World Scientific, Singapore 281 (1995).
4. M.Seymour, private communications.
5. ALEPH Collaboration, *Nucl. Instrum. Methods* A **360**, 481 (1995).
6. J.A.M.Vermaseren, Proceedings of the IV International Workshop on Gamma Gamma Interactions, Amiens (1980).
7. C.T.Hill and G.G.Ross, *Nucl. Phys.* B **148**, 373 (1979).
8. OPAL Collab., K.Ackerstaff *et al.*, *Z. Phys.* C **74**, 49 (1997).
9. OPAL Collab., R.Akers *et al.*, *Z. Phys.* C **60**, 593 (1993).
10. E.Leonardi, proceedings of Photon '95, Sheffield U.K. World Scientific, Singapore 268 (1995).

STUDY OF THE PHOTON STRUCTURE FUNCTION F_2^γ AT LEP1 AND LEP2.

I. TYAPKIN, DELPHI COLLABORATION

The photon structure function F_2^γ is studied in the Q^2 range from 3 to 150 $(\text{GeV}/c^2)^2$. The data correspond to an integrated luminosity of 70 pb^{-1}, collected by the DELPHI detector during the 1994-1995 LEP runs at centre-of-mass energies around the Z^0 mass, and the 15 pb^{-1} during 1996 LEP run at at centre-of-mass energies from 161 GeV to 172 GeV. Experimental distributions, including variables from a jet analysis, and the energy flow distributions, are compared with Monte Carlo predictions. The data are found to be in good agreement with model predictions. The photon structure function estimation is reconstructed in 6 Q^2 bins. The Q^2 evolution of the photon structure function has been estimated.

1 Introduction

Recent photon structure function measurements have been done at LEP [1] in the reaction $e^+e^- \to e^+e^-X$, where X is a multihadronic system and one of the scattered leptons is observed at a large scattering angle (tagging condition) while the other, remaining at a small angle, is undetected (anti-tagging condition). This reaction can be described as a deep inelastic $e\gamma$ scattering (DIS), where γ is almost a real photon. The study of photon structure function is heavily based on the procedure where F_2^γ is reconstructed from $x_{visible}$, the so-called unfolding procedure, which strongly depends on the models used in it. Most previous studies were done with generators based on two models, the one that is QPM-like, describing a perturbative part, and the other, which is VDM-like, for the hadron-like part. It is shown by the DELPHI collaboration that an added resolved photon contribution (RPC) significantly improves agreement with experimental data, essentially a description of the final state topology of the hadronic system, which is very important for interpretation of the results. The present study extended to the wider Q^2 region.

2 Model

The TWOGAM event generator is based on an exact decomposition of the matrix element of the process. The total cross-section is described by the sum of three parts: point-like (QPM), resolved photon contribution (RPC) and soft hadronic (VDM). The QPM and VDM models can be used at any Q^2. The RPC can be partially extended to the high Q^2 region by their $\gamma q(g)$ component. For the point-like part exact differential cross sections are used.

The quark masses are taken to be 0.3 GeV/c^2 for u and d quarks, 0. 5 GeV/c^2 for s and 1.6 GeV/c^2 for c quarks. The produced $q\bar{q}$ pair is fragmented as a LUND string by JETSET 7.3 [2]. For the single or double resolved perturbative part the lowest order cross-sections are used. Only the transverse-transverse part of the luminosity function is used in this case. There is no initial or final state parton showering. Strings are formed following the colour flow of the sub-processes and are fragmented according to the LUND model by JETSET. The remnant of a quark is an antiquark (and vice versa), and the remnant of a gluon is a $q\bar{q}$ pair. TWOGAM treats exactly the kinematics of the scattered electron and positron, and uses exact (unfactorised) expressions for the two-photon luminosity functions. All the parameters in the TWOGAM generators was fixed in 1993 and no tuning was performed up to now.

3 Event selection

The tagged particle was detected by the DELPHI luminometer STIC. The main criteria used to select two-photon events with tagging are:

1. Etag > 0.5*Ebeam (0.25 for LEP2);
2. No additional clusters with energy exceeding 0.3*Ebeam;
3. Ntrk > 2 ;
4. W > 3 GeV ;
5. Longitudinal and transverse momentum balance.

Jets were reconstructed by the LUCLUS algorithm with d_{join}=1.6 GeV. None of the conclusions drawn below is sensitive to the variation of d_{join} across a fairly wide region. All calorimeters (including forward luminometer) are used in this analysis to reconstruct invariant mass. The main source of background was $\gamma\gamma \to \tau\tau$ interactions and their contribution was estimated from a simulation as 0.8 pb (0.13 pb LEP2). The Z^0 hadronic decays contributed 0.2 pb (negligible for LEP2) to the background. Contamination from other background sources was found to be much lower. After subtracting this background the visible cross-section of the investigated process was estimated as being 30.4 pb (39.3 pb for LEP2). The trigger efficiency was studied and found to be of the order of $98 \pm 1\%$.

4 Comparison of experimental and simulated data

A great many of the observables were studied, with special attention to those that are not strongly correlated with x_{true}. Most such observables are defined by the hadronic final state topology. All variables were found to be in good agreement with TWOGAM prediction. Some of them are presented in Fig.1

28

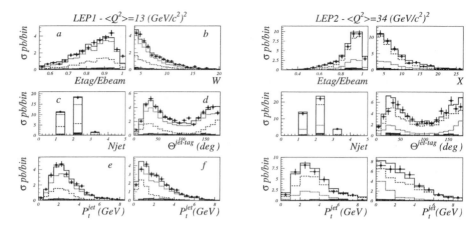

Figure 1: Comparison between data and Monte Carlo prediction for a sample with $< Q^2 >=13$ (GeV/c^2)^2 and $< Q^2 >=34$ (GeV/c^2)^2. a) Energy of tagged particle, b) Invariant mass, c) Number of jets; d) Jet angle with respect to the tagged particle; e) Transverse momentum of reconstructed jets for jets in the same hemisphere as the tagged particle; f) Transverse momentum of reconstructed jets for jets in the opposite hemisphere to the tagged particle. Points are data and lines show the Monte Carlo predictions. QPM+GVDM+RPC - solid line, GVDM+QPM - dotted line, GVDM - dashed line, hatched area is the background estimate.

for the LEP1 and LEP2 data. The events from a 3 jet domain, mostly described by the RPC, were selected and many of distributions studied. All of them were found to be in good agreement with the model. Event energy flow, which strongly depends on the event topology, was studied and found to be in reasonable agreement with the TWOGAM prediction (Fig.2).

5 Photon structure function

As TWOGAM describes data well, it can be used to estimate F_2^γ. First of all both (LEP1 and LEP2) samples were separated in to two statistically equivalent ones by Q^2. This yields three Q^2 bins for both LEP1 and LEP2 samples. The x distributions for these samples are shown in the Fig.3. Even from these plots it can be concluded that F_2^γ unfolding results should be very close to the structure function used in the TWOGAM. There is some indication of deviations of TWOGAM predictions for the data in the high Q^2 region. Unfolding is performed by the Blobel program. Some examples of the unfolding results are shown on the Fig.4 and confirm the conclusions drawn on the basis of Fig.3. Systematics included in the total error on the plot consist of the cut varia-

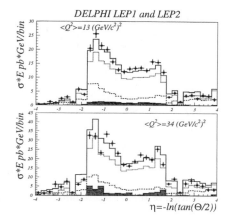

Figure 2: Event energy flow normalized over the visible cross-section. Rapidity is measured from the detection of tagged particles, i.e. a tagged particle is always in the range from -4.0 to -2.5 units of rapidity. Notations as in Fig.1.

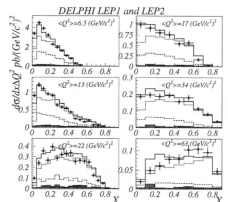

Figure 3: Distributions of x visible for 3 Q^2 bins for LEP1 and LEP2 measurements. Notations as in Fig.1.

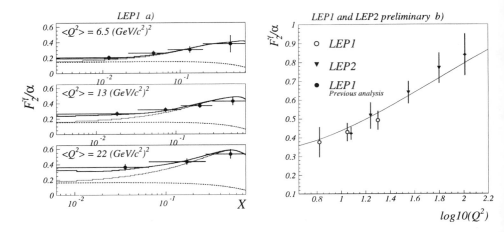

Figure 4: a) Unfolding results for the LEP1. b)Q^2-evolution of the structure function for the x-region between 0.3 and 0.8.

tion effect, uncertainty from virtuality suppression in RPC, and background uncertainty. Fig.4b shows the average value extracted from the data of F_2^γ for $0.3 < x < 0.8$ as a function of Q^2 for the DELPHI measurements.

6 Conclusions

The model, including RPC was tested in the wider Q^2 region. It is demonstrated that TWOGAM describes data quite well up to Q^2 close to $100(GeV/c^2)^2$ without any tuning. The main advantage of this generator is that it describes observables that are not very closely correlated with x_{true} and are determined by the event topology. All this means that F_2^γ can be estimated with small extra systematics, determined by the description of the event shape.

References

1. DELPHI Coll., Warsaw, pa02-021; OPAL Coll. Warsaw, pa03-007.
2. T. Sjöstrand, Comp. Phys. Comm. **82** (1994) 74;

MEASUREMENT OF THE PHOTON STRUCTURE FUNCTION F_2^γ AT LOW x IN INELASTIC ELECTRON-PHOTON SCATTERING AT LEP1

JÖRG BECHTLUFT

FOR THE OPAL COLLABORATION

III. Phys. Inst., RWTH-Aachen, Sommerfeldstr. 28

52056 Aachen, Germany

Inelastic electron-photon scattering has been studied using data taken by the OPAL detector at LEP1 energies to explore the photon structure function in a Q^2 range of 1.5 to 6 GeV^2, reaching lower x values than ever before. To probe this particular kinematic region events have been selected with a beam particle scattered into one of the OPAL luminosity calorimeters at scattering angles between 27 and 55 mrad. A measurement of the photon structure function $F_2^\gamma(x, Q^2)$ at $\langle Q^2 \rangle = 1.86$ and 3.76 GeV^2 is presented in five x bins from 0.0025 to 0.2.

1 Introduction

Experimentally very little is known about $F_2^\gamma(x, Q^2)$ at low x. Only TASSO [1] and TPC/2γ [2] have published measurements down to x values below 0.05, a region where theoretical predictions differ significantly. This region has attracted even more attention since the HERA experiments detected the rise of F_2^p [3]. At LEP energies, kinematic regions become accessible where x is small and, at the same time, Q^2 is large enough so that perturbative QCD calculations are expected to be more reliable. $F_2^\gamma(x, Q^2)$ was measured using "singly tagged" two photon events, where only one scattered beam particle is seen in the detector, see Ref. [4] for details.

2 Selection and data sample

Singly tagged events were selected by demanding a cluster in the luminosity calorimeter in the angular range 27-55 mrad with an energy in the range $0.775 - 1.2E_{\text{beam}}$, and no cluster with more than $0.25E_{\text{beam}}$ in the opposite hemisphere. More than two charged tracks were required, excluding the tag. The measured invariant mass W_{vis} of the hadronic system had to be in the range $2.5 - 40$ GeV. Both, the component of transverse momentum parallel to the tag plane and the component perpendicular to the tag plane were required to be less than 3 GeV. The tag plane is defined as the plane containing the momentum vectors of the incoming beam electron and the tagged electron.

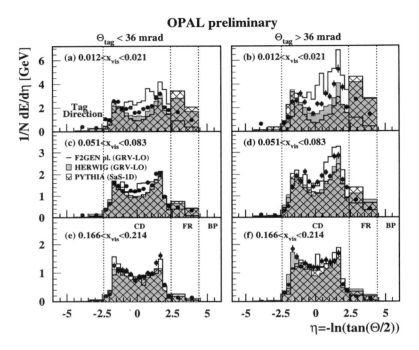

Figure 1: The measured hadronic energy flow as a function of pseudorapidity η for the data (full circles, errors statistical only) and various Monte Carlo samples. Three bins in x_{vis} and two bins in θ_{tag} are shown.

With these requirements 7112 events, with $\langle Q^2 \rangle = 2.8$ GeV^2, were selected for an integrated luminosity of 70.8 pb^{-1}. The trigger efficiency is $98 \pm 2\%$. The only relevant background comes from leptonic two-photon events. It was estimated to be 2.5% using the VERMASEREN[5] Monte Carlo generator.

3 Modelling of the $\gamma^\star\gamma$ fragmentation

The two-photon signal events were simulated with the generators HERWIG 5.18d PYTHIA 5.722 and F2GEN[6], where F2GEN includes two final state models, "pointlike" and "peripheral", to describe the hard and soft limit of the process $\gamma^\star\gamma \rightarrow$ hadrons (see Ref.[4] for details).

Significant differences of the hadronic final state have been reported[4], both between the data and the Monte Carlo models and between the different Monte Carlo models. In the present analysis comparable differences were found, especially in the hadronic energy flow (Figure 1). For $x_{\text{vis}} > 0.05$ the differences are small, at low x_{vis} they increase. The peripheral final state model of F2GEN behaves similarly to that of PYTHIA and is not shown.

An analysis of the systematic error originating from the final state modelling was performed in an almost identical way to that in Ref. [4], with the generator F2GEN used in a different way. A mixture of the two final state models available in F2GEN was used to improve the description of the data in the lowest x_{vis} bin. This mixture was obtained by a fit to the hadronic energy flow of the data in this x_{vis} bin (81% peripheral and 19% pointlike events).

4   The determination of F_2^{γ}

F_2^{γ} was unfolded from the x_{vis} distribution of the data in two Q^2 ranges $Q^2 < 2.5$ GeV^2 and $Q^2 > 2.5$ GeV^2 using the method of regularised unfolding [7]. In order to resolve very low x values the unfolding was performed on a logarithmic x scale. The x binning was chosen to keep correlations low between the unfolded F_2^{γ} values in the different x bins.

The ability of the unfolding to recover the underlying F_2^{γ} of the data was tested by unfolding the known structure function of Monte Carlo samples instead of data. A Monte Carlo sample, the "mock data", took the role of the data events. These events were then unfolded with another Monte Carlo sample. The unfolded F_2^{γ} recovers the F_2^{γ} of the mock data sample with systematic deviations of the same order of magnitude as the systematic errors obtained for the result given below.

The central values and statistical errors of the measured F_2^{γ} were determined by a "reference" unfolding [4] based on a HERWIG sample of 11658 selected events, generated using the GRV-LO [8] parametrisation of F_2^{γ}. The unfolded F_2^{γ} for the data is shown in Figure 2 together with the F_2^{γ} calculated from the GRV-LO and the SaS-1D [9] leading order parton density parametrisations and the higher order GRV-HO [8] parametrisation. In addition mesurements from PLUTO [10] and TPC/2γ [2] for similar Q^2 values are shown for comparison. The results agree within the errors with the lowest value published by PLUTO. Compared to the TPC/2γ measurement our results tend to be higher. The results are consistent with the other OPAL measurements [11]. The TASSO measurement [1] corresponds to higher Q^2 values and is not shown.

The estimation of the systematic error included four components. The unfolding was performed using the HERWIG generator and the SaS-1D F_2^{γ} in order to study the uncertainty due to the structure functions assumed in

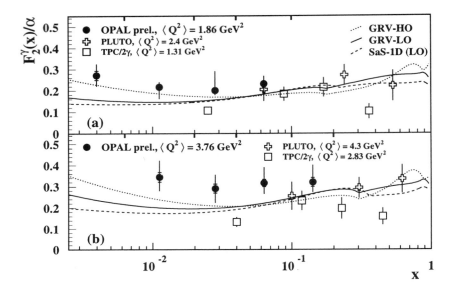

Figure 2: The full circles show our result for $F_2^\gamma(x)$ at $\langle Q^2 \rangle = 1.86\,\mathrm{GeV}^2$ (a) and $\langle Q^2 \rangle = 3.76\,\mathrm{GeV}^2$ (b). The points are placed in the middle of the bin. The total error and the statistical contribution are shown. The tick marks at the top show the bin limits in x. The curves indicate predictions for F_2^γ at the corresponding Q^2. The open symbols show results from other experiments at similar Q^2, only the total errors are indicated. The points are placed at the center of the bins on a linear x scale.

the Monte Carlo samples. The selection requirements were varied to take into account possible deviations in the description of cut distributions. A varied set of quality criteria for calorimeter clusters and tracks was used to determine systematic errors resulting from imperfections in the simulation of the detector acceptance for tracks and calorimeter clusters. The unfolding was performed using PYTHIA and the SaS-1D F_2^γ, or using F2GEN and the GRV-LO F_2^γ in order to study the effect of a different modelling of the hadronic final state in the different Monte Carlo programs.

For each of the four components, the maximum deviations, above and below, of the unfolding results from the result of the reference unfolding were taken as systematic errors. The total systematic error is the quadratic sum of these four contributions.

The F_2^γ values presented here were not corrected for the effect of a non-zero virtuality P^2 of the quasi-real photon.

5 Summary and conclusions

The photon structure function $F_2^\gamma(x, Q^2)$ was measured as a function of x in two bins of Q^2 with $\langle Q^2 \rangle = 1.86$ GeV^2 and $\langle Q^2 \rangle = 3.76$ GeV^2. Low x values down to 0.0025 were reached, lower than measured previously [2,1,10]. Our result is consistent with a flat $F_2^\gamma(x)$ in both Q^2 ranges within the errors, although it is not in contradiction with a small rise. The unfolding result is consistent in shape with the GRV-LO and SaS-1D parameterisations for the corresponding Q^2 values. The measured $F_2^\gamma(x, Q^2)$ is significantly higher than the GRV-LO and SaS-1D predictions, but in acceptable agreement with the GRV-HO prediction, especially in the lower Q^2 bin.

The systematic errors dominate the total errors. They could be significantly reduced by an improved modelling of the hadronic final state.

References

1. TASSO Collaboration, M. Althoff *et al.*, Z. Phys. **C31** (1986) 527.
2. TPC/2γ Collaboration, H. Aihara *et al.*, Phys. Rev. Lett. **58** (1987) 97;
   TPC/2γ Collaboration, H. Aihara *et al.*, Z. Phys. **C34** (1987) 1;
   The Durham/RAL Databases γγ → hadrons, AIHARA86
   (http://durpdg.dur.ac.uk/scripts/reaclist.csh/5957).
3. H1 Collaboration, S.Aid *et al.*, Nucl. Phys. **B470** (1996) 3;
   ZEUS Collaboration, M. Derrick *et al.*, Z. Phys. **C69** (1996) 607.
4. OPAL Collaboration, K. Ackerstaff *et al.*, Z. Phys. **C74** (1997) 33.
5. J. A. M. Vermaseren *et al.*, Phys. Rev. **D19** (1979) 137.
6. J. J. Ward, PhD Thesis, University College London UCL (1996), unpub.
7. V. Blobel, DESY-84-118, 1984;
   V. Blobel, Proceedings of the 1984 CERN School of Computing, Aiguablava, Spain, 9–22 September 1984, CERN 85-09.
8. M. Glück, E. Reya and A. Vogt, Phys. Rev. **D46** (1992) 1973;
   M. Glück, E. Reya and A. Vogt, Phys. Rev. **D45** (1992) 3986.
9. G. A. Schuler and T. Sjöstrand, Z. Phys. **C68** (1995) 607.
10. PLUTO Collaboration, C. Berger *et al.*, Phys. Lett. **B107** (1981) 168;
    PLUTO Collaboration, C. Berger *et al.*, Phys. Lett. **B142** (1984) 111.
11. OPAL Collaboration, R. Nisius, this proceedings.

MEASUREMENT OF THE PHOTON STRUCTURE FUNCTION

A. FINCH

(on behalf of the ALEPH collaboration)

School of Physics and Chemistry, University of Lancaster,
Lancaster, LA1 4YB, United Kingdom.

The photon structure function F_2^γ has been measured at LEP I with data collected in the ALEPH detector. The data are analyzed in two Q^2 ranges, 6 to 12 and 12 to 45 GeV^2/c^2 and compared to the sum of QPM and VDM and the HERWIG program. The data are adequately described by both, provided that the latter uses the GRV parameterisation. The discrepancy between data and models reported by OPAL is confirmed. F_2^γ is extracted from the data.

1 Event selection

This paper describes a measurement of the photon structure function F_2^γ at LEP in the Q^2 range 6 to 44 (GeV/c)^2 and x between 0.002 and 0.9. The analysis presented here is described in detail in Ref.1. The data were selected from the 119 pb^{-1} collected with the ALEPH detector between 1991 and 1994. The ALEPH detector has been described in detail elsewhere[2,3]. The analysis uses charged tracks, and neutral calorimeter energy as defined by the ALEPH energy flow package[4]. A tagged electron is specified to be a cluster in the small angle luminosity calorimeter (LCAL) with energy $E_{tag} \geq 30$ GeV and angle 60 mrad $< \theta_{\text{tag}} < 150$ mrad. All remaining energy flow objects are summed to form the hadronic final state.

The following selections were applied to events. The event must contain a tagged electron. In the half of the detector opposite the tagged electron there must be neither an identified electron with $|\cos(\theta)| < 0.8$ nor a cluster in the luminosity calorimeters with energy greater than 15 GeV. The invariant mass of the observed final state hadrons (W_{vis}) must be greater than 2.5 GeV/c^2 and the total energy in the hadronic final state must be less than 50 GeV. The event must contain at least three charged tracks. NLMB, the Normalised Longitudinal Momentum Balance must be greater than 0.5. where $NLMB = (p_z(total).p_z(tag))/(E_{beam}.|p_z(tag)|)$. No energy deposit must be observed in the hadron calorimeter with an angle to the tag less than 11.5 degrees. The difference in azimuthal angle between the momentum vector of the hadronic final state and the tag must be at least 2 radians. A vertex must be reconstructed within 2.5 cm of the interaction point along the beam direction. After all the cuts a sample of 1968 events remained. All data has been corrected for the measured trigger efficiency which is generally close to 100%.

Table 1: Background Events Passing Event Selection Cuts

Source	Events	Fraction
$Z \rightarrow q\bar{q}$	4.6 ± 1.7	$0.23 \pm 0.08\%$
$Z \rightarrow \tau^+\tau^-$	0.13 ± 0.13	$0.006 \pm 0.006\%$
Beam-gas	3.75 ± 0.97	$0.18 \pm 0.5\%$
Bhabha	< 1	0.05%
Off-Mom. Coinc.	13.7 ± 4.1	$0.68 \pm 0.20\%$
$\gamma\gamma \rightarrow \tau^+\tau^-$	152.2 ± 5.2	$7.7 \pm 0.3\%$

The final sample contained small residual backgrounds as shown in Table 1. The size of the background from $Z \rightarrow q\bar{q}$, $Z \rightarrow \tau^+\tau^-$ and Bhabha events has been calculated using Monte Carlo, the others have been calculated from the data. The background from $\gamma\gamma \rightarrow \tau^+\tau^-$ events is subtracted in the final result.

2 Simulation and comparison with data

In this analysis two independent models were used for simulation of the data. The first model, QPM+VDM, consists of a sum of VDM and QPM components, as used in our untagged analysis [5]. A fit of the models to the data was performed in which the normalisation of the constant VDM component (A) was a free parameter, with the $1/W$ term (B) fixed at either 300 or 1000 nb GeV/c^2. Figure 1 shows a number of distributions which indicate the extent to which the data are described by the models.

The second model is the HERWIG program [7] which was used with three different structure function parameterisations as input. The parameterisations chosen were those of Gordon and Storrow (GS)[8], Glück, Reya and Vogt (GRV) [9] and set I of Abramowicz, Charcula and Levy (LAC1)[10]. All other parameters were kept at their default values. Figure 1 contains a number of distributions which show that the data are well described by the model using GRV but less well described by LAC1 and GS. As differences arising from the different input structure functions are cancelled out during the unfolding procedure, these samples can still be used to extract a measurement.

The distributions of a large number of variables were used to determine whether either the QPM+VDM model or the HERWIG model (with GRV parameters) provides a better description of the data. It was found that they both describe the data equally well with a typical χ^2 of around 4.0/d.o.f.

38

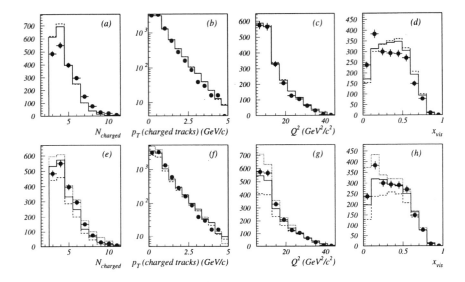

Figure 1: Comparison of models to the data. The data are shown by the points with error bars. In (a-d) the histograms are the sum of the QPM,VDM, and $\tau^+\tau^-$ models. B = 300 (solid line), or 1000 (dashed line) nb (GeV/c^2). In (e-h) the histograms are for HERWIG+ $\tau^+\tau^-$ with GRV (solid line), GS (dashed line), or LAC1 (dotted line) input.

2.1 Rapidity and Azimuthal distribution

In Ref.12, and also reported at this conference by J. Lauber, the OPAL collaboration has shown that the models they used do not describe their tagged $\gamma^*\gamma$ data when considered in terms of the pseudorapidity η and and the azimuthal separation ϕ_{sep}. Fig. 2 shows these distributions for the ALEPH data compared to the Monte Carlo events. The same trend is seen in these data, namely that when compared to all models the data have a less pronounced peak at $\phi_{\rm sep} = \pi$ and tend towards larger values of η.

3 Unfolded Results

Two unfolding programs[13,14] were used to extract the final result. The first of these programs, was the R.U.N. program of Blobel[13], the second [14], (SVD), is based on the same mathematical principles as the Blobel program but is implemented differently. Combined with each of the five models this provided

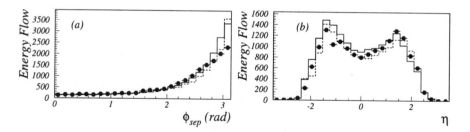

Figure 2: Energy flow as a function of (a) ϕ_{sep} , (b) η. The points are the data. Solid line: QPM+VDM dashed line: HERWIG with GRV .

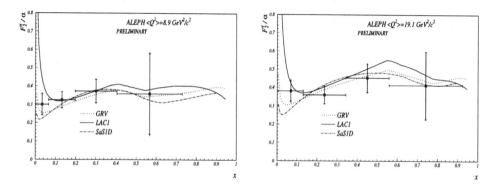

Figure 3: F_2^γ as a function of x compared to various theoretical predictions[9,10,11].

a total of ten results. The final result was obtained by taking the mean of the results. The scatter of the results was used to estimate the systematic errors due to the model uncertainty and the unfolding procedure. Systematic errors from the accuracy of the detector modelling, the unknown contribution from F_L^γ, and the trigger efficiency correction are taken into account by an additional 3% contribution to the systematic error.

Figure 3 shows the unfolded results for F_2^γ. The error bars show the total errors, with the size of the statistical errors indicated by the short horizontal lines. To allow comparison of results from a number of experiments $< F_2^\gamma(x, Q^2) >$ has been calculated averaged over the conventional range $0.3 < x < 0.8$. In the low Q^2 bin the result is $0.36 \pm 0.16(stat) \pm 0.06(sys)$, while in the high Q^2 bin the result is $0.44 \pm 0.08(stat) \pm 0.02(sys)$.

4 Conclusions

A sample of tagged two photon events has been studied using ALEPH LEP I data. The data have been compared to a number of models and are found to be equally well described by both a model based on an incoherent sum of QPM and VDM components, and the HERWIG[7] model with the GRV[9] structure function used as an input. Use of the GS and LAC1 parameterisations are clearly disfavoured by the data. The data show a discrepancy from the models when energy flow is plotted as a function of rapidity and azimuthal separation.

The data have been used to extract a measurement of F_2^γ in two Q^2 bins, $6 < Q^2/(\text{GeV}/c)^2 < 12$ and $12 < Q^2/(\text{GeV}/c)^2 < 44$, using two unfolding programs[13,14]. The measurement is consistent with the three parameterisations presented.

References

1. RAL-TH-97-005, A Measurement of the Photon Structure Function $F_2^\gamma(x, Q^2)$, Using the ALEPH Detector. Gordon R. Crawford University of Lancaster. PhD thesis, December 1996
2. ALEPH collab., D. Decamp et al., *Nucl. Instr. Meth.* **A 294** (1990) 121.
3. ALEPH collab., D. Buskulic et al., *Nucl. Instr. Meth.* **A360** (1995) 481.
4. ALEPH collab., D. Decamp et al., *Phys. Lett.* **B246** (1990) 306.
5. ALEPH collab., D. Buskulic et al., *Phys. Lett.* **B313** (1993) 509.
6. J.A.M. Vermaseren, in Proc. of the IV Intern. Workshop on Gamma Gamma Interactions, eds. G. Cochard and P. Kessler (1980); Long program write up by J.A.M. Vermaseren (unpubl.).
7. G. Marchesini, et al., *Computer Phys. Commun.* **67** (1992) 465.
8. L.E. Gordon and J.K. Storrow, *Z. Phys.* **C56** (1992) 307.
9. M. Glück, E. Reya and A. Vogt, *Phys. Rev.* **D45** (1992) 3986.
10. H. Abramowicz, K. Charchula and A. Levy, *Phys. Lett.* **B269** (1991) 458.
11. G.A. Schuler and T. Sjöstrand, *Z. Phys.* **C68** (1995) 607.
12. OPAL Collab., K. Ackerstaff et al., *Z. Phys.* **C74** (1997) 33.
13. V. Blobel in Proceedings of the CERN School of Computing, Aiguablava, Spain (1984), CERN 85-09.
14. A. Hoecker, V. Kartvelishvili, *Nucl. Instr. Meth.* **A372** (1996) 469.

THE PHOTON STRUCTURE AT MEDIUM x AND Q^2 IN DEEP INELASTIC eγ SCATTERING AT $\sqrt{s_{ee}} = 91-172$ GeV

RICHARD NISIUS, for the OPAL Collaboration

CERN, PPE Division, CH-1211 Geneve 23, Switzerland

New measurements are presented for the photon structure function $F_2^\gamma(x, Q^2)$ at four values of Q^2 between 9 and 59 GeV^2 based on data taken with the OPAL detector at e$^+$e$^-$ centre-of-mass energies of $161-172$ GeV, with a total integrated luminosity of 18.1 pb^{-1}. The evolution of F_2^γ with Q^2 in bins of x is determined, in the Q^2 range from 1.86 to 135 GeV^2, using data taken at centre-of-mass energies of $91-172$ GeV. The slope $\alpha^{-1} \mathrm{d} F_2^\gamma / \mathrm{d} \ln Q^2$ in the range $0.1 < x < 0.6$ is measured to be $0.10 \pm 0.02^{+0.05}_{-0.02}$.

1 Introduction

The measurement of the photon structure function F_2^γ and in particular of its evolution with the momentum transfer squared, Q^2, is a classic test of perturbative QCD [1]. The large range of Q^2 values accessible at the e$^+$e$^-$ collider LEP makes it an ideal place to study this evolution.

The results presented in this paper are based on data taken by the OPAL detector at e$^+$e$^-$ centre-of-mass energies $\sqrt{s_{ee}}$ around the mass of the Z^0 (denoted by $\sqrt{s_{ee}} = 91$ GeV) [2,3] and on new measurements of F_2^γ in the Q^2 range from 6 to 100 GeV^2, using data recorded in 1996 for $\sqrt{s_{ee}} = 161 - 172$ GeV. This measurement is an extension of the analysis of F_2^γ detailed in [2] using basically the same methods to analyse the singly-tagged two-photon events.

In the singly-tagged region the process e$^+$e$^-$ $\rightarrow$ e$^+$e$^-$ + hadrons can be regarded as deep inelastic scattering of an e$^\pm$ on a quasi-real photon. The cross-section for this process is expressed as

$$\frac{d^2 \sigma_{e\gamma \to eX}}{dx dQ^2} = \frac{2\pi\alpha^2}{x \, Q^4} \left[\left(1 + (1-y)^2 \right) F_2^\gamma(x, Q^2) - y^2 F_L^\gamma(x, Q^2) \right]. \tag{1}$$

Q^2 is the absolute value of the four momentum squared of the virtual photon, x and y are the usual dimensionless variables of deep inelastic scattering and α is the fine structure constant. In the region studied here ($y \ll 1$) the contribution of the term proportional to $F_L^\gamma(x, Q^2)$ is small and neglected.

Because the energy of the quasi-real photon is not known, x has to be derived from the hadronic final state. This leads to a dependence of F_2^γ on the modelling of the hadronic final states by the Monte Carlo generators.

2 Data Selection and Background Contribution

The measurement of $F_2^\gamma(x, Q^2)$ involves the determination of x and Q^2 which are obtained from the four-vectors of the tagged electron and the hadronic final state using $Q^2 = 2\,E_b\,E_{\text{tag}}\,(1 - \cos\theta_{\text{tag}})$ and $x = \frac{Q^2}{Q^2 + W^2 + P^2}$. Here E_{tag} and θ_{tag} are the energy and polar angle of the observed electron, E_b is the beam energy and W is the invariant mass of the hadronic system. P^2 is much smaller than Q^2 and W^2 and it is neglected in the calculation.

The events are divided into two samples depending on the detector components in which the scattered electron is observed, the SW sample and the FD sample. The SW (FD) samples require a large energy deposit $E_{\text{tag}} \geq 0.775(0.60)\,E_b$ in the ranges $33 \leq \theta_{\text{tag}} \leq 55$ $(60 \leq \theta_{\text{tag}} \leq 120)$ mrad of polar angle, and a hadronic system with at least three tracks and a visible hadronic mass in the range $2.5 \leq W_{\text{vis}} \leq 40$ GeV. To ensure the scattering on a quasi-real photon, an antitag requirement $E_{\text{at}} \leq 0.08\,E_b$ is applied in the hemisphere opposite to the tagged electron. With these cuts 879 and 414 events, with average squared momentum transfers $\langle Q^2 \rangle$ of approximately 11 GeV^2 and 41 GeV^2 are selected in the SW and FD samples. The accessible x ranges for the two samples are $0.004 < x < 0.76$ and $0.012 < x < 0.94$. The trigger efficiency is evaluated from the data to be above 95% for the SW sample and essentially 100% for the FD sample.

The dominant background source is $\gamma^\star\gamma \rightarrow$ leptons. These processes were simulated with the Vermaseren program. The background contribution from $\gamma^\star\gamma \rightarrow \tau^+\tau^-$ events is 36.0 ± 1.8 (29.0 ± 2.2) and the $\gamma^\star\gamma \rightarrow e^+e^-$ process contributes 16.8 ± 1.2 (9.1 ± 0.9) events to the SW (FD) samples.

3 Modelling of the Hadronic Final State

The data are compared to the HERWIG [4] and PYTHIA [5] Monte Carlo models and to the more specialised F2GEN generator [6]. The data are described reasonably well by the models for global hadronic variables such as the visible hadronic mass, the visible neutral energy, and the charged multiplicity, but there are serious discrepancies in the hadronic energy flow especially at $x_{\text{vis}} \leq 0.1$, between the data and any of the models at all rapidities [2,7].

4 The Determination of F_2^γ

F_2^γ is determined as a function of x from the x_{vis} distribution using the method of regularised unfolding [8], Fig. 1. The figures also show F_2^γ evaluated at the

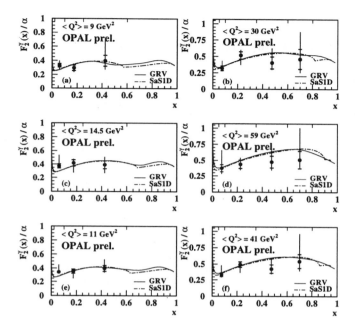

Figure 1: The measurement of F_2^γ as a function of x in bins of Q^2.

corresponding values of $\langle Q^2 \rangle$ for the GRV [9] and the SaS1D [10] parton density parametrisation, in each case including the expected contribution from massive charm quarks. The value of F_2^γ/α is given at the centre of the x bin. The bin sizes are indicated by the vertical lines at the top of the figure. The error bars show both the statistical error alone and the full error, given by the quadratic sum of statistical and systematic errors. The F_2^γ values presented here are not corrected for the fact that P^2 is not strictly equal to zero, because this correction is uncertain as it depends strongly on the model chosen [11,2].

The estimation of the systematic error includes three parts: the variation of the compositions of signal and background events in the sample, the use of different F_2^γ structure functions assumed in the Monte Carlo samples, and the different modelling of the formation of the hadronic final state. The systematic error assigned to the result, which is taken as the maximum deviation of any unfolding result from the central values, is dominated by the model uncertainties. The results on F_2^γ as a function of x are well described by the GRV and SaS1D predictions in all Q^2 ranges.

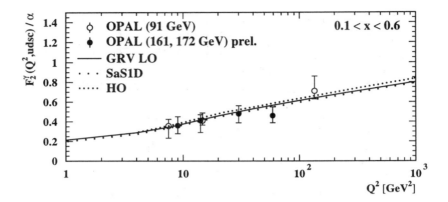

Figure 2: The evolution of F_2^γ as a function of Q^2 for $0.1 < x < 0.6$.

Figure 2 shows the measurement of $F_2^\gamma(Q^2)/\alpha$ as a function of Q^2 in the region $0.1 < x < 0.6$ together with the results obtained in [2]. The results of the two analyses at very different centre-of-mass energies, which use different detector components to measure the deep inelastic scattered electron for similar Q^2 values, are consistent. A clear increase of F_2^γ/α with Q^2 is observed in the data, in agreement with the QCD predictions. The data are compared to the LO GRV and the SaS1D parametrisations, and to a higher order (HO) prediction based on the HO GRV parametrisations for light quarks and on the charm contribution calculated in [12], as described in more detail in [2].

A fit to the OPAL data in the Q^2 range $7.5-135$ GeV^2 using a linear function of the form $a + b \ln(Q^2/\text{GeV}^2)$, where a and b are parameters which do not depend on x, yields:

$$F_2^\gamma(Q^2)/\alpha = (0.16 \pm 0.05^{+0.17}_{-0.16}) + (0.10 \pm 0.02^{+0.05}_{-0.02}) \ln Q^2/\text{GeV}^2 \,,$$

where the first error is statistical and the second systematic.

The measurement is consistent with results obtained by other experiments [13,14], Fig. 3a. The data are usually compared without referring to the different x ranges studied by the experiments. Based on the GRV parametrisation it is shown that the predictions for $Q^2 > 100$ GeV^2 are significantly different for the various x ranges.

QCD predicts a positive scaling violation of F_2^γ which varies in size as a function of x. To study this variation in $\alpha^{-1} dF_2^\gamma/d\ln Q^2$, the data in the Q^2 range $1.86-135$ GeV^2 are analysed using the same x ranges for all data. Fig. 3b shows the measurement in comparison to the HO calculation. The

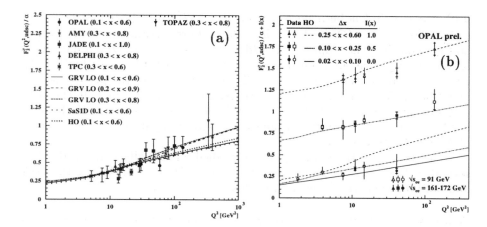

Figure 3: The evolution of F_2^γ with Q^2 in several bins in x compared to other measurements and theoretical predictions.

changes in slope of the predictions for Q^2 below 15 GeV^2 is caused by the charm threshold. The results from [2,3] are only rebinned in x but not reanalysed. They consistently extend the measurement into the region of low x and low Q^2. For fixed Q^2 and varying x the data in general lie closer together than the prediction, and the agreement between the prediction and the data is best for the range $0.10 < x < 0.25$. In order to experimentally observe the variation of $\alpha^{-1}\mathrm{d}F_2^\gamma/\mathrm{d}\ln Q^2$ with x more data and a reduced systematic error are needed.

5   Summary and Conclusion

Data from the OPAL experiment at LEP have been used to study the hadronic structure of the photon. A slightly better agreement between the predictions for the hadronic energy flow of the various models and the data in the region $0.1 < x_{\mathrm{vis}} < 0.6$ is found for the data taken at $\sqrt{s_{ee}} = 161 - 172$ GeV, than for the data collected at $\sqrt{s_{ee}} = 91$ GeV. For $x_{\mathrm{vis}} < 0.1$ significant differences [2] persist, as the data prefer a more pointlike angular distribution of the final state hadrons than assumed in either HERWIG or PYTHIA, and for $x_{\mathrm{vis}} > 0.6$ the statistical precision is insufficient to draw firm conclusions.

Using the data at $\sqrt{s_{ee}} = 161 - 172$ GeV the photon structure function $F_2^\gamma(x, Q^2)$ has been unfolded as a function of x in four Q^2 intervals, with mean momentum transfers $\langle Q^2 \rangle = 9, 14.5, 30$ and 59 GeV^2. Using data at $\sqrt{s_{ee}} = 91 - 172$ GeV the evolution of F_2^γ with Q^2 in the range

0.10 < x < 0.60 has been measured to be $F_2^\gamma(Q^2)/\alpha = (0.16 \pm 0.05^{+0.17}_{-0.16}) + (0.10 \pm 0.02^{+0.05}_{-0.02}) \ln(Q^2/\text{GeV}^2)$, where the first error is statistical and the second systematic. The slope $\alpha^{-1}\mathrm{d}F_2^\gamma/\mathrm{d}\ln Q^2$, based on the OPAL data alone is significantly different from zero and consistent with the logarithmic evolution of F_2^γ with Q^2 expected from QCD. The variation of the positive scaling violation of F_2^γ with varying x was studied in three ranges in x, $0.02 - 0.10$, $0.10 - 0.25$ and $0.25 - 0.60$. The QCD prediction is in agreement with the data, but the accuracy of the data is insufficient to show a significantly different slope of F_2^γ for the ranges in x studied.

The data, over the x and Q^2 range studied, are equally well described by several of the available parton density parametrisations, including the GRV and SaS1D parametrisations used in this analysis.

Acknowledgement: I wish to thank the organisers of this conference for the fruitful atmosphere they created throughout the meeting.

References

1. E. Witten, *Nucl. Phys.* B **120**, 189 (1977).
2. OPAL Collab., K. Ackerstaff et al., *Z. Phys.* C **74**, 33 (1997).
3. OPAL Collab., J. Bechtluft these proceedings.
4. G. Marchesini *et al.*, *Comp. Phys. Comm.* **67**, 465 (1992); CERN 96-01, Physics at LEP2, (1996) Vol. 2, p. 213.
5. T. Sjöstrand, *Comp. Phys. Comm.* **82**, 74 (1994); CERN 96-01 Physics at LEP2, (1996) Vol. 2, p. 218.
6. A. Buijs *et al.*, *Comp. Phys. Comm.* **79**, 523 (1994).
7. J. A. Lauber *et al.*, these proceedings.
8. V. Blobel, DESY-84-118, 1984; CERN 85-09.
9. M. Glück, E. Reya and A. Vogt, *Phys. Rev.* D **46**, 1973 (1992); M. Glück, E. Reya and A. Vogt, *Phys. Rev.* D **45**, 3986 (1992).
10. G. A. Schuler and T. Sjöstrand, *Z. Phys.* C **68**, 607 (1995).
11. M. Glück, E. Reya and M. Stratmann *Phys. Rev.* D **51**, 3220 (1995); G. A. Schuler and T. Sjöstrand, *Phys. Lett.* B **376**, 193 (1996).
12. E. Laenen *et al.*, *Phys. Rev.* D **49**, 5753 (1994).
13. Ch. Berger and W. Wagner, *Phys. Rep.* **146**, 1 (1987).
14. TPC/2γ Collab., H. Aihara *et al.*, *Z. Phys.* C **34**, 1 (1987); TPC/2γ Collab., H. Aihara *et al.*, *Phys. Rev. Lett.* **58**, 97 (1987); DELPHI Collab., P. Abreu *et al.*, *Z. Phys.* C **69**, 223 (1996); JADE Collab., W. Bartel *et al.*, *Z. Phys.* C **24**, 231 (1984); TOPAZ Collab., K. Muramatsu *et al.*, *Phys. Lett.* B **332**, 477 (1994).

DETECTOR KEDR TAGGING SYSTEM FOR TWO–PHOTON PHYSICS

B.O. BAIBUSINOV, A.E. BONDAR, G.Ya. KEZERASHVILI, A.M. MILOV,
N.Yu. MUCHNOJ, Ya.A. POGORELOV T.A. PURLATZ, <u>L.V. ROMANOV</u>, V.N.
ZHILICH

Budker Institute of Nuclear Physics, Lavrentyeva st. 11 Novosibirsk 630090, Russia

A special system to tag scattered e^+e^- from $\gamma\gamma$–processes is described. The system
is intended for the experiments at the VEPP–4m storage ring. This system has a
high double-tag efficiency and good resolution on the $\gamma\gamma$ invariant mass.

1 Introduction

This Tagging System (TS) [1] to study $\gamma\gamma$ interactions, is a part of detector
KEDR [2] at the VEPP–4m collider. The e^+e^- after scattering will be called
below Scattered Electrons (SE). The detection of both SE's ("double-tag" experiment) determines the parameters of the $\gamma\gamma$–system. This method is complementary to the commonly used "no-tag" and "single–tag" approaches. But
as the SE angles are of order $1/\gamma$, to attain the high detection efficiency for
SE emitted from the interaction point at zero angle is necessary.

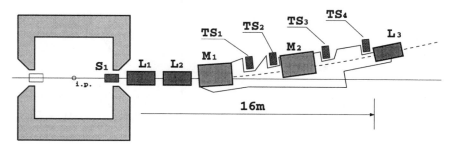

Figure 1: VEPP–4m experimental region with KEDR Tagging System. L_1, L_2 are
quadrupoles, M_1, M_2 are bending magnets

The main problems to investigate with the help of the TS are:

- Study of the total cross section $\gamma\gamma \rightarrow hadrons$ at low Q^2

- Study of C–even resonances

47

- Search for exotic states

- Study of the cross section $\gamma\gamma \to \pi^+\pi^-$ close to the threshold

The basic idea of the system is to use accelerator quadrupole lenses together with bending magnets as a focusing spectrometer. (Fig. 1). The SE coming out from the interaction point passes through the main detector magnet with longitudinal magnetic field, compensating solenoid, quadrupole lenses L_1 and L_2 and bending magnets M_1 and M_2. Then SE is detected by one of four detection blocks(DB) $TS_1 - TS_4$. The whole set-up is symmetrical relatively interaction point.

Due to the focusing properties of the quadrupoles there is some distance from the interaction point where the transverse coordinate of the SE will be independent of its initial angle. This point is optimal for SE energy measurement, because the crucial limitation on the angle resolution would be multiple scattering at the tagging system entrance. Naturally, this distance depends on SE energy, so we use 4 separate DB for different energy range.

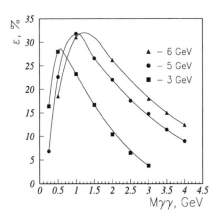
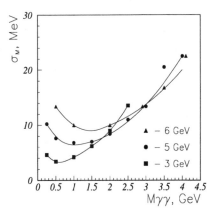

Figure 2: Double–tag detection efficiency   Figure 3: Invariant mass resolution

2   The Design of the Tagging System

The most important contributions in the energy resolution of SE at the our TS are the following:

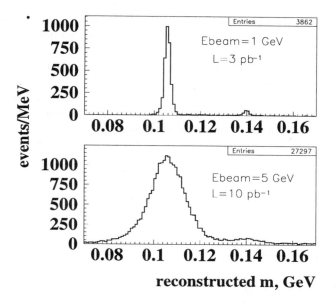

Figure 4: Reconstructed charged particles masses

- The angular spread in the beam

- The beam energy spread

- The transverse beam size in the interaction point.

Luckily for VEPP–4m the initial energy and the position of the particle at the interaction point are correlated and the errors in the measured energy of SE due to the beam energy spread and due to the beam size compensate each other. The level of this compensation depends on the SE energy.

The double–tag detection efficiency for different beam energies is presented in Fig. 2. The resolution in the reconstructed invariant mass of the $\gamma\gamma$ system for different beam energies is given in Fig. 3. It is much better than other tagging systems had. That resolution is close to the natural width of C–even resonances (e.g. $\eta_c(2980)$ with the total width of about 10 MeV), so the ratio of the effect to the nonresonant background will be increased.

Also, one can use the TS to mesure cross section $\gamma\gamma \to \pi^+\pi^-$. One can combine the momenta of charged particles measured with drift chamber and

SE energies to calculate these particles masses and thus to separate muons from $\gamma\gamma \to \mu^+\mu^-$ and the pions. The possibilities of this separation are illustrated in Fig. 4. For the event generation the program of F.A.Berends[3] was used. The interesting feature is that for the low beam energy the effect of the radiation corrections is not so important as for the high energy.

As DB we use hodoscopes of drift tubes (DT's). Each TS includes one hodoscope designed as an independent module which contains six detecting planes. The plane is made of two rows of stainless steel drift tubes with 6 mm in diameter and 90 μ wall thickness. The total number of tubes in the TS is 1440.

3 Calibration System and Test Results

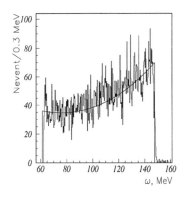

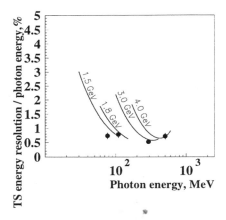

Figure 5: The Compton spectrum of SE lost energies

Figure 6: Energy resolution of TS_4

The absolute energy calibration of the TS at the level 10^{-3} is nessesary. For that we use the backward Compton scattering of laser photons on e^-e^+ beams. The maximum lost energy of e^- is: $\omega = 4\gamma^2\omega_0 / (1 + 4\gamma\omega_0/m_e)$, where γ is a relativistic factor for initial electrons ω_0 is the energy of the laser photon and m_e is electron mass. The natural width of this edge is very small in our situation. Therefore, the measured width of this edge gives the energy resolution of the TS. It allows the absolute calibration of the TS with an accuracy not worse than 10^{-3}. This technics was earlier used in our Institute for other goals (see, for example, [4]).

In order to test the TS performance, the measurements were done with 2.34 eV laser photons at the different beam energies. The typical Compton spectrum is shown in the Fig. 5. The TS energy resolution obtained from the Compton spectra edges is shown in the Fig. 6. The points are the experiment, the lines are the results of Monte–Carlo calculations.

In April 1997 the TS and the first stage of the KEDR were installed at the VEPP–4m. That stage includes all important detector components with the exception of the liquid kripton barrel calorimeter and aerogel cherenkov counters. and, together with the TS itself, will provide reliable trigger to select two-photon events. Now the VEPP–4m luminosity is close to expected at this stage for energy range from 1.5 to 5.3 GeV. Though the VEPP–4m primary was intended for Υ-physics, it is difficult for it to compete with the CESR and future B-fabrics, but for beam energies 1–3.5 GeV it is possible to collect the integrated luminosity which will be comparable with other experiments. So now different experiment shedules are discussed, and meanwhile the general tuning in order to begin the data-taking in June 1997 (most probable in J/Ψ region) is in progress.

4 Conclusions

The described Tagging System for $\gamma\gamma$- physics is a part of the multipurpose detector KEDR and e^+e^- collider VEPP–4m at Novosibirsk. Use of some accelerator magnetic structure elements allows to obtain high double tagging efficiency and resolution in e^+ and e^- energies. The "double–tag" method giving the two–photon mass without reconstruction by its decay products has serious advantages and is complementary to the commonly used "no–tag" and "single–tag" approaches. It is expected to be especially useful for measurements of the two–photon width of resonances and the total cross section of two gammas into hadrons.

The TS design is finished, and now different tests and tuning for data-taking together with first stage of the KEDR are in progress.

The measured energy resolution does not contradict to the expected one.

References

1. V.M. Aulchenko et al.,*Nucl. Instrum. Methods* A **355**, 261 (1995)
2. V.V. Anashin et al., Proceed. of the International Symposium on Coordinate detectors, Dubna (1987)
3. F.A.Berends et al., *Nucl. Phys.* B **253**, 421 (1985)
4. G.Ya. Kezerashvili et al.,*Nucl. Instrum. Methods* A **328**, 506 (1993)

TUNING MC MODELS TO FIT DIS eγ SCATTERING EVENTS

J.A. LAUBER[1], L. LÖNNBLAD[2], M.H. SEYMOUR[3]

1) University College London, Gower Street, London WC1E 6BT, England
2) Nordita, Blegdamsvej 17, DK-2100 København, Denmark
3) Rutherford Appleton Laboratory, Chilton, Didcot OX11 0QX, England

Monte Carlo models of DIS eγ scattering must describe hard emissions as well as the soft and collinear limits. Comparison with the observed experimental hadronic energy flow has shown that various models underestimate the high-p_T contribution, in particular at low x. We have attempted to tune the HERWIG, PYTHIA and ARIADNE models to improve the agreement with the data, and to understand the physical implications of the changes required. Unless the physics of these processes is understood it will not be possible to unfold the photon structure functions F_2^γ from the e^+e^- data without large model dependent systematic errors.

1 The Problem

The measurement of F_2^γ in deep inelastic $e\gamma$ scattering, where only one of the electrons is "tagged" in the detector and the other one escapes unseen, involves the determination of the $\gamma^*\gamma$ invariant mass W from the hadronic final state. Because of the non-uniform detection efficiency and incomplete angular coverage the correlation between W_{vis} and W critically depends on the modelling of the hadronic final state. It has been shown [1] that there exist serious discrepancies in the description of this hadronic final state. Fig. 1 shows the transverse energy out of the plane, defined by the tag and the beam. For $x_{\mathrm{vis}} > 0.1$ all of the generators are adequate, but for $x_{\mathrm{vis}} < 0.1$ they are mutually inconsistent, and in disagreement

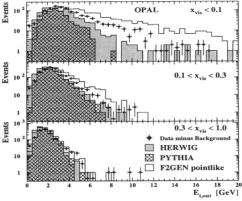

Figure 1: Transverse energy out of the tag plane.

with the data. At high $E_{\mathrm{t,out}}$ the data show a clear excess over HERWIG [2] and PYTHIA [3], while the pointlike F2GEN [4] sample exceeds the data. Similar discrepancies are observed in the hadronic energy flow per event [1] where both HERWIG and PYTHIA overestimate the energy in the forward region ($|\eta| > 2.5$) and underestimate the energy in the central region of the detector.

2 The Tools

To study the contributions of the various partons, the PYTHIA/ ARIADNE [5] energy flow in the lab frame as a function of pseudorapidity is plotted in Figure 2 for the quark that couples to the off-shell probe photon γ^*, denoted the probe quark, and for the quark that couples to the quasi-real target photon γ, denoted the target quark. The total energy flow of all partons after gluon radiation is also shown. The direction of the tagged electron is always at negative η. It is apparent

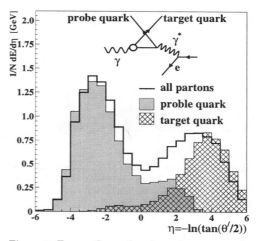

Figure 2: Energy flows of probe and target quarks.

that the hump at negative η stems mostly from the probe quark which is scattered in the hemisphere of the tag, while the hump at positive η originates mostly from the target quark in the opposite hemisphere of the struck photon.

From comparisons of the hadronic energy flow of the data with the various models, it became apparent that the energy flow of the probe quark needs to be shifted to lower η, corresponding to an increased transverse energy. This can be achieved in several ways:

Anomalous events carry more transverse momentum than hadronic events. Figure 3a) shows the partonic energy flow after gluon radiation. Increasing the fraction of anomalous to hadronic or VMD type events would have the desired effect, but the parton density functions (PDF) used (in this case SaS1D [6] in PYTHIA and GRV [7] in HERWIG) does not readily allow changing this ratio.

Another way to increase the transverse energy is to allow for more gluon radiation. This can be achieved by augmenting the inverse transverse size of the remnant, μ, in the ARIADNE colour dipole model, shown in Figure 3b). μ is set proportional to the intrinsic k_T of the struck quark on an event-by-event basis. For VMD events, k_T is gaussian with a width of 0.5 GeV. For anomalous events k_T follows a power law. But even a generous increase of the μ parameter ($\mu = 10$) has a relatively small effect on the partonic energy flow.

Increasing the intrinsic transverse momentum k_T of the struck photon is another way of directly influencing the angular distribution of the hadronic final state. Figure 3c) shows the energy flow for PYTHIA events with default settings and enhanced k_T. This appears to be the most promising method.

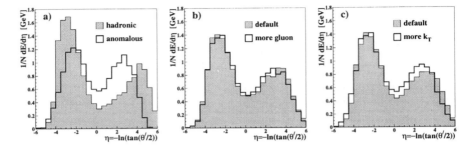

Figure 3: Different methods of increasing the energy flow in the central detector region using the PYTHIA/ARIADNE Monte Carlo generators.

3   The Fix

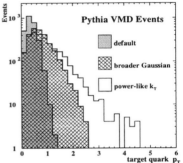

Figure 4: Transverse momentum of the target quark in PYTHIA/ARIADNE.

In PYTHIA the PDF determines whether an event is generated as a VMD or an anomalous event. The intrinsic k_T of the quasi-real photon can be controlled with parameters[3]. Just increasing the width of the gaussian distribution does not produce events that populate the region of high $E_{t,out}$ at low x observed in the data (Fig. 1). A similar deficiency had been observed in the resolved photoproduction data at Zeus[9], which lead to the introduction of a power-like k_T-distribution of the form $dk_T^2/(k_T^2 + k_0^2)$, improving the distributions of the photon remnant. k_0 is a constant, for which 0.66 GeV was used. The PYTHIA parameters only allow adjusting the k_T for VMD type events, figure 4, but not for anomalous evens. To change the intrinsic k_T of anomalous events a gaussian smearing is added in quadrature[8].

Figure 5 show the $E_{t,out}$ and figure 7 the hadronic energy flows on detector level of PYTHIA with default parameter settings and with the $dk_T^2/(k_T^2 + k_0^2)$ distribution for VMD plus a gaussian smearing of the anomalous events, compared to the OPAL data taken in 1993–1995 at $\sqrt{s_{ee}} = 91$ GeV. In addition the ARIADNE distributions with enhanced gluon radiation are shown. While the $E_{t,out}$ spectrum has been improved, it still falls short of the data in the tail of the distribution. The hadronic energy flow generated by the enhanced PYTHIA recreates the peak on the remnant side (positive η) seen in the data at low x_{vis}, at the expense of a somewhat worse fit on the tag side.

The 2-jet rates, listed in Table 1, found with the cone algorithm, requiring

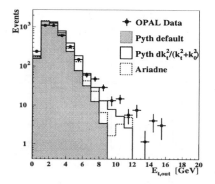

Figure 5: PYTHIA: Transverse energy out of the tag plane.

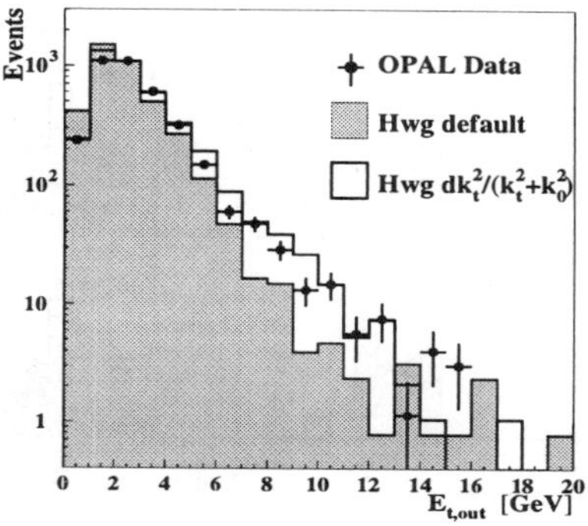

Figure 6: HERWIG: Transverse energy out of the tag plane.

	0 jet	1 jet	2jet
Data	30.7%	63.8%	5.4%
PYTHIA	32.8%	65.5%	1.7%
$dk_T^2/(k_T^2+k_0^2)$	36.5%	60.6%	2.9%

Table 1: Jet rates for PYTHIA

	0 jet	1 jet	2jet
Data	30.7%	63.8%	5.4%
HERWIG	34.0%	63.6%	2.4%
$dk_T^2/(k_T^2+k_0^2)$	31.0%	63.0%	5.9%

Table 2: Jet rates for HERWIG

a minimum $E_{T,jet} > 3$ GeV in the pseudorapidity range of $|\eta_{jet}| < 2$ are almost doubled over the default version of PYTHIA, but are still substantially lower than the data [10].

HERWIG separates events dynamically into hadronic and anomalous type. A similar $dk_T^2/(k_T^2 + k_0^2)$ distribution of the intrinsic transverse momentum of the photon can be added by hand. The results of this are shown in figures 6 and 8. Both the $E_{t,out}$ and the energy flows are greatly improved with the inclusion of the power-like k_T distribution, with the exception of the peak in the energy flow at low x_{vis} – high Q^2, which still falls short of the data.

The cone algorithm 2-jet rate, listed in Table 2, is more than doubled over the default version of HERWIG and is in agreement with the data.

4   Conclusion

The power-like distribution of the intrinsic transverse momentum of the struck photon of the form $dk_T^2/(k_T^2 + k_0^2)$ greatly improves the hadronic final state distributions of both PYTHIA and HERWIG. This improved description of the data should reduce the model-dependent systematic errors in the unfolded result of the photon structure function F_2^γ. More fine-tuning is required.

56

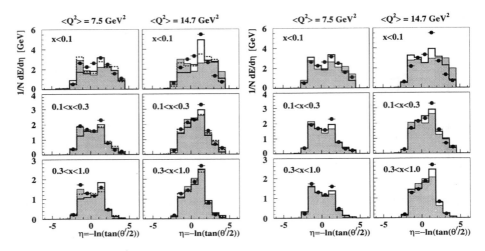

Figure 7: PYTHIA: Hadronic energy flow as function of x and Q^2. The symbols are the same as in Fig. 5

Figure 8: HERWIG: Hadronic energy flow as function of x and Q^2. The symbols are the same as in Fig. 6

It should be stressed, though, that this is just an *ad hoc* solution which does not explain the origin of the discrepancies. It appears that the photon displays a more pointlike behaviour at low x than predicted. F_2^γ and the $\gamma^*\gamma$ fragmentation are not orthogonal. Changing the latter will affect the measurement of the former. A thorough enquiry is urgently needed.

References

1. OPAL Collaboration, K. Ackerstaff et al., *Z. Phys.* C**74** (1997) 33.
2. G. Marchesini, B. R. Webber, G. Abbiendi, I. G. Knowles, M. H. Seymour and L. Stanco, *Comp. Phys. Comm.* **67** (1992) 465.
3. T. Sjöstrand, *Comp. Phys. Comm.* **82** (1994) 74; PYTHIA 5.7 and JETSET 7.4, Physics and Manual, CERN-TH/93-7112 (1993).
4. A. Buijs, *et al.*, *Comp. Phys. Comm.* **79** (1994) 523.
5. L. Lönnblad, *Comp. Phys. Comm.* **71** (1992) 15.
6. G. A. Schuler and T. Sjöstrand, *Z. Phys.* C**68** (1995) 607.
7. M. Glück, E. Reya and A. Vogt, *Phys. Rev.* D**46** (1992) 1973.
8. T. Sjöstrand, *Private communications*.
9. ZEUS Collaboration, *Phys. Lett.* B**354** (1995) 163.
10. OPAL Collaboration, A.M. Rooke, *these proceedings*.

MODEL-INDEPENDENT QED CORRECTIONS TO PHOTON STRUCTURE-FUNCTION MEASUREMENTS

ERIC LAENEN

Institute for Theoretical Physics, State University of New York at Stony Brook,
Stony Brook, NY 11794, USA

GERHARD A. SCHULER[a]

CERN TH-Division, CH-1211, Geneva 23, Switzerland

We present the first calculation of QED radiative corrections to deep-inelastic electron–photon scattering in terms of those variables that are reconstructed in measurements of the photon structure function in electron–positron collisions. In order to cover the low-Q^2 region, we do not invoke the QCD-improved parton model but rather express our results in terms of the photon structure functions. Both analytical and numerical results are given.

QED radiative corrections distort the usual kinematics of deep-inelastic scattering (DIS) and hence have to be taken into account for precise structure-function measurements. In the case of the proton structure function, the Born kinematics (corresponding to non-radiative events) of charged lepton–nucleon scattering is fully constrained by two measurable variables. The arguments of $F_2(x, Q^2)$, Bjorken-x and the squared momentum transfer Q^2, can directly be determined from either the scattered lepton or the hadronic system. Alternatively, the kinematics can be fixed by two "mixed" variables such as the polar angles of the scattered lepton and the hadronic system. Photon radiation affects different variables differently but, in general, several variables can be reconstructed experimentally and hence one has experimental cross checks on the size of radiative corrections [1].

The situation is more complicated for measurements of the photon structure function in electron–positron collisions. At given e^+e^- c.m. energy $\sqrt{s} = 2E_b$ (E_b is the beam energy), three variables are needed in order to specify the Born kinematics since the target-photon energy is not known. (Actually, for precision measurements also the effects of the non-zero target mass P^2 have to be considered.) Moreover, there is just one way to experimentally reconstruct three independent variables.

The angle θ and energy E of the tagged electron give the leptonic DIS

---

[a]Heisenberg Fellow.

variables y_l and Q_l^2 as follows:

$$y_l = 1 - \frac{E}{E_b} \cos^2 \frac{\theta}{2} , \qquad Q_l^2 = 4\, E\, E_b \, \sin^2 \frac{\theta}{2} . \tag{1}$$

A measurement of the hadronic mass W_h (which involves an unfolding of W_h from the visible hadronic energy W_{vis}) yields the "mixed" Bjorken-x variable

$$x_m = \frac{Q_l^2}{Q_l^2 + W_h^2} . \tag{2}$$

In general, neither x_m nor Q_l coincide with the actual arguments x_h and Q_h of the photon structure function $F_2(x_h, Q_h^2)$, see e.g. (12) or Fig. 1 below. Consider DIS of electrons on (quasi-real) photons in the presence of an additional photon:

$$e(l) + \gamma(p) \rightarrow e(l') + \gamma(k) + X(p_X) , \tag{3}$$

and define leptonic and hadronic DIS variables:

$$
\begin{array}{rclrcl}
q_l & = & l - l' & q_h & = & p_X - p = q_l - k \\
W_l^2 & = & (p + q_l)^2 & W_h^2 & = & (p + q_h)^2 = p_X^2 \\
Q_l^2 & = & -q_l^2 & Q_h^2 & = & -q_h^2 \\
x_l & = & Q_l^2/2p \cdot q_l & x_h & = & Q_h^2/2p \cdot q_h \\
y_l & = & p \cdot q_l/p \cdot l & y_h & = & p \cdot q_h/p \cdot l
\end{array}
\tag{4}
$$

Obviously, leptonic and hadronic variables do not coincide ($Q_h^2 \neq Q_l^2$, etc.); they agree only for nonradiative events, i.e. if $k = 0$.

In this paper we present the $O(\alpha)$ correction to DIS in terms of the experimentally relevant variables x_m, Q_l^2, and y_l:

$$\frac{\mathrm{d}^3\sigma}{\mathrm{d}x_m\,\mathrm{d}y_l\,\mathrm{d}Q_l^2} = g^{\mathrm{B}}(x_m, y_l, Q_l^2, s) + g^{\mathrm{corr}}(x_m, y_l, Q_l^2, s) . \tag{5}$$

Since the accessible Q values are far below the weak scale, we can safely neglect weak corrections apart from the running of the electromagnetic coupling $\alpha(Q^2)$. For the case of charged lepton–nucleon scattering it is known [2] that QED corrections are very well approximated by calculations in the leading-log approximation (LLA), that is the QED corrections are dominated by photon radiation off the tagged-lepton line. For the case of electron–photon scattering, there might in principle be additional corrections to the untagged electron line, but they are small.

The target photon $\gamma(p)$ is part of the flux of equivalent photons around the non-tagged lepton. To leading order in α, this flux has a momentum density given by the Weizsäcker-Williams expression $f_{\gamma/e}(z)$, where z is the longitudinal momentum fraction of the target photon with respect to its parent lepton:

$$f_{\gamma/e}(z) = \frac{\alpha}{2\pi} \left\{ \frac{Y_+(z)}{z} \ln \frac{P^2_{max}}{P^2_{min}} - 2m_e^2 z \left(\frac{1}{P^2_{min}} - \frac{1}{P^2_{max}} \right) \right\} . \tag{6}$$

Here we have defined $Y_+(z) = 1 + (1-z)^2$, $P^2_{min} = (z^2 m_e^2)/(1-z)$, $P^2_{max} = (1-z)(E_b \theta_{max})^2$, and θ_{max} is the anti-tag[b] angle. In the following we put $P^2 \equiv -p^2 = 0$ and neglect electron masses everywhere except in (6). Moreover we substitute P^2_{max} by $P^2_{max} + P^2_{min}$ so that we can easily extend the z range to 1. The Born cross section of (5) is given by

$$g^B(x, y, Q^2, s) = \frac{2\pi\alpha^2 \, Y_+(y)}{x^2 y^2 s Q^2} f_{\gamma/e} \left(\frac{Q^2}{xys} \right) F_2(x, Q^2) \left\{ 1 + R(x, Q^2, y) \right\} , \tag{7}$$

where

$$R(x, Q^2, y) = \frac{-y^2}{1 + (1-y)^2} \frac{F_L(x, Q^2)}{F_2(x, Q^2)} , \tag{8}$$

and $F_{2,L}$ are the photon structure functions (we have dropped the superscript γ).

In the LLA, photon radiation from the tagged lepton line can (in a gauge-invariant way) be subdivided into photon bremsstrahlung from the initial electron line, the final electron line, and the Compton process. For the cross section relevant for experimental analyses, which is differential in x_m, Q^2_l, and y_l, there is no contribution from final-state radiation as the calorimeter measurement combines the electron with the nearby photon(s).

The initial state radiation correction to the triple differential cross section in eq. (5) can be written as the following convolution

$$g^{ISR}(x_m, y_l, Q^2_l, s) = \int_0^1 dx_1 \, D_{e/e}(x_1, Q^2_l)$$

$$\left[\Theta \left(x_1 - x_1^0 \right) \frac{\hat{x}_m^2}{x_m^2 x_1} g^B(\hat{x}_m, \hat{y}_l, \hat{Q}^2_l, \hat{s}) - g^B(x_m, y_l, Q^2_l, s) \right] \tag{9}$$

where

$$x_1^0 \equiv \frac{x_m (1 - y_l) s + (1 - x_m) Q^2_l}{x_m (s - Q^2_l)} , \tag{10}$$

---

[b]i.e. all events in which the parent lepton scatters at an angle larger than θ_{max} are rejected.

Table 1: Corrections in per cents due to initial-state radiation (parameters see text).

Q_l^2/GeV^2									
$10^4\,c$									3.3
10^4								-11.6	-2.1
$10^3\,c$							-14.6	-7.3	-1.9
10^3						-15.6	-8.4	-4.8	-1.1
$10^2\,c$					-15.9	-8.6	-5.3	-3.4	-0.6
10^2				-16.0	-8.7	-5.3	-3.8	-2.6	-0.3
$10^1\,c$			-16.1	-8.9	-5.4	-3.6	-2.9	-2.0	-0.4
10		-17.3	-8.5	-3.7	-0.3	2.0	3.6	5.2	6.5
$c/10^{-4}$	$c\,10^{-4}$	10^{-3}	$c\,10^{-3}$	10^{-2}	$c\,10^{-2}$	10^{-1}	$c\,10^{-1}$	1	
				x_m	$(c=\sqrt{10}\approx 3.16)$				

and $D_{e/e}(x,Q^2)$ is the structure function for the initial-state electron evaluated at the scale given by the squared momentum transfer $Q^2 = Q_l^2$:

$$D_{e/e}(x,Q^2) = \frac{\alpha}{2\pi}\ln\left(\frac{Q^2}{m_e^2}\right)\frac{1+x^2}{1-x}\ . \tag{11}$$

It represents the probability of finding, inside a parent electron, an electron with longitudinal momentum fraction x. The Born cross section is written in terms of the reduced ("hatted") variables, $g^{\mathrm{B}}(\hat{x}_m, \hat{y}_l, \hat{Q}_l^2, \hat{s})$. The scaling behavior of the relevant variables is

$$\hat{Q}_l^2 = x_1 Q_l^2 = Q_h^2\ , \qquad \hat{y}_l = 1 - (1-y_l)/x_1 = \frac{y_h}{x_1}\ , \qquad \hat{s} = x_1 s\ ,$$

$$\hat{x}_m = x_h = \frac{\hat{Q}_l^2}{\hat{Q}_l^2 + W_h^2} = \frac{x_m x_1}{x_1 + (1-x_1)(1-x_m)}\ . \tag{12}$$

We find the following result for the Compton contribution to the total cross section

$$\sigma[ee \to eeX] = \frac{y_l\,dy_l}{1-y_l}\,\frac{dx_m}{x_m(1-x_m)}\,\frac{dQ_l^2}{Q_l^4}\,\frac{dz}{z}\,\frac{dQ_h^2}{Q_h^2}\,\frac{(1-x_m)\,Q_l^2}{(1-x_m)\,Q_l^2 + x_m\,Q_h^2}\,\Sigma\ , \tag{13}$$

where

$$\Sigma(x_h, x_l, y_l, Q_h^2, Q_l^2, z) = \alpha^3\, Y_+(y_l)\, z f_{\gamma/e}(z)$$

$$\left\{\left[1 + \left(1-\frac{x_l}{x_h}\right)^2\right] F_2(x_h, Q_h^2) - \left(\frac{x_l}{x_h}\right)^2 F_L(x_h, Q_h^2)\right\}\ . \tag{14}$$

Table 2: Corrections in per **mille** due to the Compton process (parameters see text).

Q_l^2/GeV^2									
$10^4 c$									15.4
10^4								0.07	1.2
$10^3 c$							0.07	0.3	1.0
10^3						0.1	0.4	0.5	1.1
$10^2 c$					0.2	0.7	0.9	0.8	1.1
10^2				0.2	0.9	1.4	1.3	1.0	1.1
$10^1 c$			0.3	1.1	1.7	2.0	1.7	1.1	1.1
10		0.5	1.9	3.3	4.4	4.7	3.8	2.6	2.1
$c/10^{-4}$	$c\,10^{-4}$	10^{-3}	$c\,10^{-3}$	10^{-2}	$c\,10^{-2}$	10^{-1}	$c\,10^{-1}$	1	
			x_m	$(c = \sqrt{10} \approx 3.16)$					

Note that Σ is a very smooth function, hardly dependent on its arguments. Only at very low Q_h^2, gauge invariance forces F_2 (and hence Σ) to vanish linearly with $Q_h^2 \to 0$. The fall-off at $x_h \to 1$ may be very slow due to the pointlike contribution to F_2^γ (in contrast to F_2^p).

The argument x_h of F_2 is here related to the integration variables via

$$x_h = \frac{x_m\,Q_h^2}{(1 - x_m)\,Q_l^2 + x_m\,Q_h^2} \,, \tag{15}$$

and the integration limits read

$$\frac{1 - x_m}{x_m}\,Q_l^2\,\frac{Q_l^2}{y_l\,z\,s - Q_l^2} \;<\; Q_h^2 < y_l\,z\,s - \frac{1 - x_m}{x_m}\,Q_l^2$$
$$\text{Max}\left\{\frac{W_{\min}^2 + Q_l^2}{y_l\,s},\,\frac{Q_l^2}{y_l\,x_m\,s}\right\} \;<\; z < 1 \,. \tag{16}$$

In tables 1 and 2 we present the size of the radiative corrections for (logarithmically distributed) bins ranging from 10^{-4} up to 1 in x_m and $3.2\,\text{GeV}^2$ up to $3.2 \times 10^4\,\text{GeV}^2$ in Q_l^2. For example, the bin in the lower left corner corresponds to $10^{-4} < x_m < 3.2 \times 10^{-4}$ and $3.2 < Q_l^2 < 10\,\text{GeV}^2$. The numbers are for a typical LEP kinematics, namely $2\,E_b = \sqrt{s} = 175\,\text{GeV}$, $W_h > 2\,\text{GeV}$, anti-tag angle $\theta_{\max} = 30\,\text{mrad}$, minimum tagging angle $\theta_{\text{tag}} = 30\,\text{mrad}$, minimum tagging energy $E_{\text{tag}} = 0.5\,E_b$, and we have used the SaS 1D distribution functions of the photon [4]. While the corrections from the Compton process are small, the correction from initial-state radiation are sizeable and cannot be neglected.

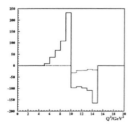 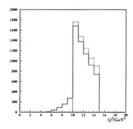 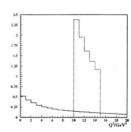

Figure 1: Q^2 distributions of numbers of events (for an integrated luminosity of 500 pb^{-1}) for initial-state radiation (left), the sum of Born and initial-state radiation (middle) and Compton (right) events; Q_h^2 distributions as solid lines, Q_l^2 ones as dashed lines (parameters see text). The Q_l^2 range was restricted to $10 < Q_l^2 < 15\,\mathrm{GeV}^2$.

As an example of the distortion of the Born (non-radiative) kinematics we show in Fig. 1 the distributions in Q_l^2 and Q_h^2 for the same kinematical situation: the scale entering the structure function (Q_h) does differ substantially from the one (Q_l) measured from the scattered electron. A Fortran program ("RADEG") that computes the corresponding correction factors either for fixed x, y, Q^2 or for user-defined bins in these variables, with integration inside the bin, is available from the authors.

References

1. H. Spiesberger et al., in *Proc. of the Workshop on Physics at HERA* (Hamburg, Germany, 1991), eds. W. Buchmüller and G. Ingelman, p. 798.
2. M. Consoli and M. Greco, *Nucl. Phys.* B **186**, 519 (1981);
   W. Beenakker, F. Berends and W. van Neerven, in *Proc. of the Workshop on Radiative Corrections for* e$^+$e$^-$ *Collisions* (Schloß Ringberg, Tegernsee, Germany, 1989), ed. J. Kühn, p. 3;
   J. Blümlein, *Z. Phys.* C **47**, 89 (1990);
   G. Montagna. O. Nicrosini and L. Trentadue, *Nucl. Phys.* B **357**, 390 (1991);
   J. Kripfganz, H. Möhring and H. Spiesberger, *Z. Phys.* C **49**, 501 (1991);
   A. Akhundov, D. Bardin, L. Kalinovskaya and T. Riemann, Fortsch. Phys. **44**, 373 (1996).
3. E. Laenen and G.A. Schuler, *Phys. Lett.* B **B374**, 217 (1996).
4. G.A. Schuler and T. Sjöstrand, *Z. Phys.* C **68**, 607 (1995).

QUASI-REAL COMPTON SCATTERING AT DAΦNE FOR A CONTINUOUS CALIBRATION OF THE KLOE DETECTOR

A. COURAU

Laboratoire de l'Accélérateur Linéaire, IN2P3-CNRS et Université de Paris-Sud,
F-91405 Orsay Cedex, France

G. PANCHERI

INFN, Laboratori Nazionali di Frascati, P.O. Box 13, I00044 Frascati, Italy

Quasi-real Compton scattering, previously used in e^+ e^- and e p collisions for luminosity measurements and detector calibration at PEP and HERA, is discussed for the energy range available at the construenda ϕ-factory DAΦNE. We show that the very high rate expected at DAΦNE makes this process particularly convenient for a continuous calibration of the KLOE detector over the full angular range, directly from the data.

The use of overconstrainted quasi-real Compton $e\gamma$ events at ee and ep colliders[1,2] was suggested in 1985 as means to perform luminosity measurement, detector calibration and search for excited electrons. This method was indeed successfully used for e^*-searches at PEP[3], PETRA[4], Tristan[5], LEP1[6] and HERA[7], as well as for calibration and luminosity measurements at PEP and HERA[8]. In this note, we apply it to the calibration of the detector KLOE[9], which will study CP violation in the kaon system at the ϕ-factory DAΦNE , under completion at Frascati. The high rates should also allow for the control of the efficiency of the tracker and its rate of photon conversion[10].

Like "Bremsstrahlung" and "radiative Bhabha scattering at finite angle", the Compton process considered here is just a specific configuration of the reaction $ee \rightarrow ee\gamma$. Looking at both the diagrams with a photon and elec-

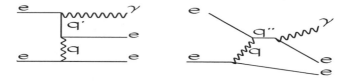

Figure 1: Feynman diagrams of $ee \rightarrow ee\gamma$ with photon exchange

tron exchange which contribute to this reaction[a], one notices that the corresponding amplitude contains two propagators $(dq^2/q^2)(dq'^2/(q'^2 - me^2))$ resp

---

[a]Note that $e^+e^- \rightarrow e^+e^-\gamma$ also implies additional annihilation grahs.

64

$(dq^2/q^2)(dq''^2/(q''^2 - me^2))$. Clearly then, the dominant contribution to the cross-section stems from configurations where both $q^2, q'^2(q''^2)$ stay close to zero with the electrons and the photon going practically straightforward.It leads to a very large cross section but with nothing detected within the central detector. The observation of particles at finite angle requires one of the two q^2 to be not close to zero. In this case, the cross-section will be dominated by the other q^2 being close to zero, and two different kinematical configurations giving rise to still relatively significant counting rates, will be observed:
1) $q'^2(q''^2) \to 0$ with $q^2 >> q'^2, (q''^2)$; this is the so called "Radiative Bhabha scattering at finite angle" with both electrons detected at finite angle and the radiated photon emitted along the incident (outgoing) electron.
2) $q^2 \to 0$ with $q'^2(q''^2) >> q^2$; this is what we call "Quasi-real Compton" with an electron and a photon detected in the central region, the other electron being scattered at zero degree.

It is the second of these configurations which we shall consider here. For simplicity, we shall neglect here the beam-crossing angle of DAΦNE and shall consider the e^+e^- system at rest to be the Laboratory frame. As q^2 tends to zero, we can consider this process as a Compton scattering, in which a quasi-real photon generated by one beam undergoes a head-on collision with an electron from the other beam. There are then only three independent parameters $W/2$, $\vartheta^\star$ and $\varphi^\star$ (energy, polar and azimuthal angles of the outgoing electron in the $e\gamma$ frame), while there are 6 quantities measured in the Lab $(E', \Theta, \Phi)_{e,\gamma}$. The full kinematics of such events can then be obtained from the measurement of the angles alone, which leads to 3 constraints over $\Delta\Phi$, E'_1, E'_2.

The result is that Compton events can be selected by looking at events with 2 and only 2 electromagnetic clusters (only one of which is associated with a track of well defined charge $e^\pm$), being coplanar $\Delta\Phi = \pi$, with $| \Sigma\vec{p_t} | \sim 0$ and $E_{vis} = E'_1 + E'_2 > E_0$, with remaining kinematical constraints

$$E'_1(\Theta_1, \Theta_2) = \frac{2E_0 \sin\Theta_2}{\sin\Theta_1 + \sin\Theta_2 - \sin(\Theta_1 + \Theta_2)}$$

$$E'_2(\Theta_1, \Theta_2) = \frac{2E_0 \sin\Theta_1}{\sin\Theta_1 + \sin\Theta_2 - \sin(\Theta_1 + \Theta_2)}$$

Therefore, the measurement of both angles can be used to perform the energy calibration of the electromagnetic calorimeter, to determine its experimental resolution and to test the linearity of the response according to the energy and the nature of the particle (e or γ).
Let us note that we do not need to identify the particles (e or γ) nor to use track informations in the selection (only one track of definite charge). Now looking at the observed tracks, it is also possible to check the value of the magnetic

field and, from the comparison of events with respectively 0 track,1 track and 2 tracks, to determine the efficiency of the tracker and its rate of photon conversion. All these results can be obtained by (fitting only) the data itself. They include the experimental effects and do not need a priori any Monte-carlo simulation.

Such analyses were successfully performed for the H1 detector [8], and should be likewise very relevant at DAΦNE. since, as shown below, the number of Compton events per second expected within KLOE at DAΦNE will be of the same order as the total number of events obtained in one year at H1

The exact differential cross section and various approximations for $Q^2 << W^2$ can be found in ref [10]. It results that , for ee colliders with an angular acceptance in the Lab given by $| \cos \Theta_{e,\gamma} | < \cos \Theta_0$, one gets

$$\sigma \propto 2f(\Theta_0)(\ln \frac{E_0}{m_e})/s$$

This implies that for a given detector (with a given angular acceptance) the cross-section at DAΦNE is 6000 times larger that at LEP100 and, taking into account the difference between luminosities one expects:

$$(N_{evts/sec})_{DA\Phi NE} \sim (N_{evts/day})_{LEP1}.$$

At HERA, where the electron scatters with a photon generated by the proton beam, the cross-section loses the factor 2, relative to the e^+e^- case, and it is generally smaller because of the mass of the proton and its non point-like nature [2]. Moreover, the machine luminosity is smaller than the one designed at DAΦNE but the angular acceptance is larger. Taking all those facts into account one gets:

$$(N_{evts/sec})_{DA\Phi NE} \sim (N_{evts/year})_{HERA}$$

The cross section expected for this process at the nominal energy of DAΦNE, is shown in Fig. 2a as a function of the angular acceptance. One notices that for KLOE, with $| \cos \Theta | \leq 0.985$, this cross-section is of the order of 1 μbarn and, for a luminosity of $5 \times 10^{32}cm^{-2}sec^{-1}$, this leads to a rate of 500 evts/sec (i.e.10^3 clusters/sec). Obviously, the particles tend to be peaked at small angles. However, as shown in Fig. 2b , the rate of clusters remains significant at any angle.

Regarding the errors on the energy, they essentially arise from the experimental resolutions and not from the theoretical tails of the overdominant contribution of quasi-real photons. The experimental resolution, ΔE can be obtained by fitting the experimental distribution of $(E(\Theta_i \Theta_j) - E_{i,measured})$ and

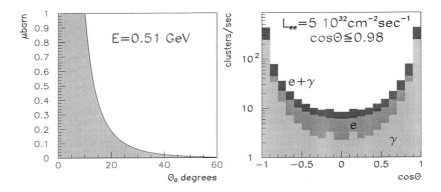

Figure 2: cross section versus the acceptance and Angular configurations of the clusters

the calibration factor K could be determined by minimizing $\chi^2 = \Sigma(E(\Theta_i\Theta_j) - KE_{i,measured})^2/\Delta E$. Extrapolating from the HERA experience[8], the expected accuracy should be better than one per mille.

Initial State Radiation (ISR) from the colliding Compton electron represents the most important effect on the calibration method just discussed, as it affects not only the total cross section but also the kinematical relations between energy and angles of the outgoing particles. The contribution from ISR can be taken into account using the so-called peaking approximation. This procedure is justified by the fact that the radiated photon and the scattered one are emitted at different angles so that interference terms are suppressed. Actually we introduce an energy loss of the initial electron according to a probability law given by the semi-classical formula[11]:

$$dP(k) = \beta \; k^{\beta-1}(1 - k + k^2/2)dk$$

$$with \quad \beta = \frac{2\alpha}{\pi}\ln(\frac{2E_0}{m_e} - \frac{1}{2})$$

where k is the fraction of incident electron energy carried off by the radiated photon. Let us note that the hard-photon tail of the radiated spectrum has a low emission probability, but on the other hand it leads to smaller values of W, and then to an increase of the Compton cross section. Actually, it is possible to eliminate (to a large extent) the hard photon tail by imposing a lower limit on the visible energy. However it remains a correction to the energy calibration which is not negligible with respect to the expected accuracy but is a priori known and can be experimentaly controled from the tail of the visible energy.

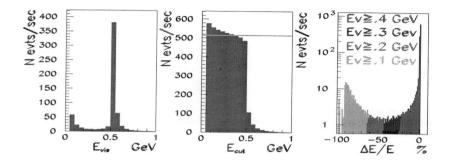

Figure 3: counting rates versus E_{vis}, cut on E_{vis} and error on Energy calibration

In conclusion, we have outlined the main characteristics of a calibration method for the KLOE detector at DAΦNE through the measurement of final state electron and photon produced in quasi-real Compton scattering. The method proposed will allow to check quantitatively the detector response in a continuous way in space and time.

The authors acknowledge the support of the European Economic Commission, HCMP Contract # CT920026.

References

1. A. Courau and P. Kessler, Phys.Rev. D33, 2021, (1986).
2. A. Courau and P. Kessler, Phys.Rev. D33, 2028, (1986); ib. D46, 117, (1992) and references therein.
3. Delco collaboration, Phys.lett. B177, 109 (1986).
4. Cello collaboration, Phys. Lett. B168, 420 (1986).
5. Venus collaboration, Phys. Lett. B213, 400 (1988).
6. Aleph collaboration, Phys. lett. B336, 501 (1990);
   Delphi collaboration, Zeit.fur.Phys C53, 41 (1992).
7. H1 collaboration, Phys.lett. B340, 205 (1994).
8. H1 collaboration,Z.Phys. C66, 529 (1995)
   S. Kermiche, Phd. thesis,University Paris-sud,LAL94-14(1994).
9. KLOE Collaboration, "The KLOE Detector Technical Proposal", LNF-93/002, January 1993.
10. A.Courau and G.Pancheri, Phys.Lett. B396, 287 (1997).
11. E.Etim,G.Pancheri and B.Toushek,Nuovo cimento B51, 276 (1967).

THE PHOTON SPECTRUM IN QUARKONIA DECAYS

F. HAUTMANN

Institute of Theoretical Science, University of Oregon
Eugene, OR 97403

I discuss recent theoretical results for inclusive decays of quarkonia into a photon plus hadrons, and summarize the status of perturbative calculations.

Radiative decays of heavy quark bound states have been investigated in the framework of perturbative QCD and have been used to measure the QCD coupling at scales of the order of the heavy quark mass (for recent studies see Refs. [1-3], and references therein). Away from the boundaries of the phase space, the inclusive spectra are expected to be well described by first or second order perturbation theory. Near the phase space boundaries, effects associated with non-perturbative contributions and with high orders in perturbation theory are expected to become important. In this paper I focus on two of these effects. First, I describe the role of the fragmentation of gluons and light quarks into a photon. This is relevant to the shape of the inclusive photon spectrum at small z, where $z = 2 E_\gamma/M$ is the energy fraction carried by the photon, with M being the quarkonium mass. Second, I consider the opposite end of the spectrum, $z \to 1$. I discuss the resummation of soft gluons in this region and its physical implications.

Consider the decay of a $^3S_1$ quarkonium state into a prompt photon plus hadrons:

$$X_{Q\bar{Q}} \to \gamma + \text{hadrons} \qquad . \tag{1}$$

It was pointed out in Ref. [4] that this reaction receives contributions at leading logarithmic order (LO) both when the photon is coupled to highly virtual processes ("direct term") and also when the photon is produced by collinear emission from light quarks ("fragmentation term"). As a consequence of the factorization theorem for collinear mass singularities, the decay width $d\Gamma/dz$ has the structure

$$\frac{d\Gamma}{dz}(z, M) = C_\gamma\left(z, \alpha_s(M)\right) + \sum_{a = q, \bar{q}, g} \int_z^1 \frac{dx}{x} C_a\left(x, \alpha_s(M)\right) D_{a\gamma}\left(\frac{z}{x}, M\right) \quad . \tag{2}$$

The first term in the right hand side denotes the direct contribution, while the second term denotes the fragmentation contribution. The functions C_A, with $A = \gamma, q, \bar{q}, g$, are short-distance coefficient functions, calculable as power

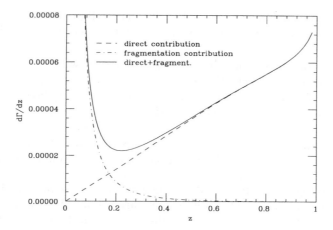

Figure 1: The photon spectrum in Υ decay to leading order (LO). The solid curve is the full LO result. The dashed curve is the contribution from the direct term, while the dot-dashed curve is the contribution from the fragmentation term. We use units $4\pi\,\psi_0^2/M^2 = 1$, with ψ_0 being the bound state wave function at the origin, and $\alpha_s = 0.2$.

series expansions in α_s:

$$C_A = C_A^{(0)} + \alpha_s\, C_A^{(1)} + \cdots \;. \tag{3}$$

The functions $D_{a\gamma}$ are the fragmentation functions for $a \to \gamma + X$, satisfying evolution equations of Altarelli-Parisi type. Through these functions, the process is sensitive to long-distance physics. In general, both the C's and D's depend on a factorization scale μ. The separation between direct and fragmentation components depends on the choice of this scale. For simplicity, in Eq. (2) the factorization scale μ and the renormalization scale that appears in the running coupling have been set equal to M.

The direct term to LO, $C_\gamma^{(0)}$, stemming from the decay $X_{Q\bar Q} \to \gamma gg$, was calculated in Ref. [5]. It is shown by the dashed curve in Fig. 1 for the case of $\Upsilon(1S)$. The fragmentation terms to LO, $C_a^{(0)} \otimes D_{a\gamma}$, were calculated in Ref. [4]. To this order, the fragmentation contribution comes entirely from the gluon channel ($a = g$), as coefficients in the quark channels ($a = q, \bar q$) vanish. This contribution is shown by the dot-dashed curve in Fig. 1, where we use the set of fragmentation functions given in Ref. [6]. The solid curve in Fig. 1 is given by the sum of the direct and fragmentation terms, and provides the full LO result.

We see that the fragmentation component is suppressed with respect to the direct component if z is sufficiently large. As z decreases, fragmentation becomes important. In particular, to this order in perturbation theory one finds the behavior in $1/z$ for $z \to 0$ characteristic of the soft bremsstrahlung spectrum.

Fig. 1 suggests that, if one wishes to analyze the inclusive photon data in Υ decay by using theoretical formulas based on direct production only, one should restrict oneself to the region above some minimum value $z_{\min}$. However, the question of how big this value should be is also influenced by the size of the next-to-leading terms. I will comment on this below. Alternatively, and more interestingly, Fig. 1 suggests that, if the experimental errors on the measurement of the spectrum at relatively low z were reduced with respect to their present very large values[3], one could use this process to perform a test of the full QCD prediction, and to learn about gluon fragmentation into photons.

The theory has not been fully developed to the next-to-leading order (NLO) yet. The NLO coefficients $C_A^{(1)}$ are not known at present. Only the result of a calculation for the integral $\int_0^1 dz\, C_\gamma^{(1)}(z)$ is available[7]. Besides, there have been studies of $C_\gamma(z)$ based on modeling[8,9] certain classes of higher order corrections. A calculation of $C_\gamma^{(1)}(z)$ is in progress[10]. The full calculation of the coefficients $C_A^{(1)}$ would be important. It could be combined with the results of the next-to-leading evolution of fragmentation functions[11] to give a consistent NLO treatment of radiative Υ decays. In particular, note that in NLO quark fragmentation starts to contribute. Quark fragmentation functions are much harder than gluon fragmentation functions. As a result, the value of the cut $z_{\min}$ introduced above might be pushed significantly to the right with respect to the value that can be read from Fig. 1.

The second aspect that I discuss in this paper concerns the region near the endpoint $z = 1$ of the spectrum. This region is influenced by non-perturbative QCD effects. The shape of the spectrum is expected to become very sensitive to hadronization corrections as $z \to 1$. A way of dealing with such effects was proposed in the Monte Carlo study of Ref. [8]. This calculation uses a parton-shower description for the gluon radiation in higher orders, and an independent-fragmentation model for hadronization. A different approach may be found in Refs. [2,12], based on parametrizing non-perturbative contributions in terms of an effective gluon mass[13].

Further sensitivity to nonperturbative parameters may enter through higher

Fock states in the quarkonium. The role of these states has been studied recently [14]. Away from $z = 1$, the color-singlet Fock state dominates the decay, as color-octet contributions are suppressed by powers of the relative velocity v of the quark pair in the non-relativistic expansion. Near $z = 1$, however, this power counting may be overcome due to the form of the short-distance coefficient associated with the color-octet component. This coefficient formally starts with a δ-function distribution in lowest order. The analysis of the hadronic smearing in Ref. [14] indicates that color-octet terms may become important within a range $\Delta z \sim v^2$ from the endpoint.

A crucial issue for the understanding of the endpoint spectrum is the behavior of high-order terms in perturbation theory as $z \to 1$. It is known that potentially large contributions in $\ln(1 - z)$ may appear to all orders in α_s, associated with the unbalance between real and virtual emission of soft gluons near the phase space boundary. The problem then arises of summing these logarithmically enhanced terms. In particular, it is important to see whether this summation gives rise to a Sudakov damping factor of the form $\sim \exp\left(-\alpha_s \ln^2(1 - z)\right)$ in the decay width.

This question is addressed in a perturbative analysis now in progress [15]. This analysis shows that, in the color-singlet channel, the logarithms of $(1 - z)$ cancel at each order in α_s. As a consequence, no Sudakov factor arises. In contrast, the color-octet channel does have a Sudakov suppression.

The reason for this behavior lies in the properties of coherence of color radiation. Qualitatively, the cancellation mechanism can be understood from an illustration at one-loop level. Consider the amplitude for the Born process in the singlet case, $\Upsilon(P) \to \gamma(k) + g(k_1) + g(k_2)$, and consider the emission of an additional soft gluon from this amplitude. In the leading infrared approximation, the decay width has the factorized structure

$$\frac{d\Gamma}{dz} \sim \mathbf{J}^2 \left(\frac{d\Gamma}{dz}\right)_{\text{Born}} d\Phi \quad , \tag{4}$$

where $\mathbf{J}$ is the eikonal current for soft gluon emission, and $d\Phi$ is the associated phase space. The standard power counting in terms of the soft gluon energy ω gives

$$d\Phi \sim \omega \, d\omega \, d\Omega \quad , \quad \mathbf{J}^2 \sim \frac{1}{\omega^2} \frac{k_1 \cdot k_2}{f(z; \text{angles})} \quad , \tag{5}$$

where $d\Omega$ is the angular phase space, and f is a function of z and the angles as $\omega \to 0$. Up to the first order in ω the gluon correlation is

$$k_1 \cdot k_2 \sim M^2 \left[(1 - z) + \frac{\omega}{M} g(z; \text{angles})\right] \quad . \tag{6}$$

That is, as $z \to 1$ the photon recoils against two almost-collinear hard gluons. In this configuration, the logarithmic integration $d\omega / \omega$ in Eq. (5) is canceled. One can show that this mechanism generalizes to all orders in α_s.

An interesting spin-off of this analysis is that the coherence scale for the QCD radiation associated with the decay is not the heavy quarkonium mass M^2 but rather the final-state invariant mass $(k_1 + k_2)^2$. Correspondingly, destructive interference occurs outside a cone with opening $\theta^2 \propto 1 - z$. We note that, in contrast, the assumptions underlying the Monte Carlo model of Ref. [8] amount to fixing the coherence scale to be M^2, and $\theta^2 \sim 1$. This model therefore does not take account of the gluon radiation in higher orders correctly. It would be of interest to see how a Monte Carlo model in which coherence is correctly implemented compares with the inclusive photon data.

Acknowledgments

I thank the organizers for arranging such an enjoyable conference. The results presented in this paper have been obtained in collaboration with S. Catani and M. Mangano. This work is supported in part by the US Department of Energy grant DE-FG03-96ER40969.

References

1. M. Kobel, in *Perturbative QCD and Hadronic Interactions*, Proc. 27th Rencontres de Moriond, ed. J. Tran Thanh Van (Editions Frontieres, Gif-sur-Yvette, 1992), p. 145.
2. J.H. Field, Nucl. Phys. **B**, Proc. Suppl. **54 A**, 247 (1997).
3. CLEO Collaboration, B. Nemati et al., Phys. Rev. D **55**, 5273 (1997).
4. S. Catani and F. Hautmann, Nucl. Phys. **B**, Proc. Suppl. **39 BC**, 359 (1995).
5. S.J. Brodsky, T.A. DeGrand, R.R. Horgan and D.G. Coyne, Phys. Lett. B **73**, 203 (1978); K. Koller and T. Walsh, Nucl. Phys. **B140**, 449 (1978).
6. J.F. Owens, Rev. Mod. Phys. **59**, 465 (1987).
7. P.B. Mackenzie and G.P. Lepage, in *Perturbative QCD*, Proc. Tallahassee Conf., eds. D.W. Duke and J.F. Owens (AIP, New York, 1981), p. 176.
8. R.D. Field, Phys. Lett. B **133**, 248 (1983).
9. D.M. Photiadis, Phys. Lett. B **164**, 160 (1985).
10. M. Krämer, private communication.
11. P. Aurenche, P. Chiappetta, M. Fontannaz, J.P. Guillet and E. Pilon, Nucl. Phys. **B399**, 34 (1993); M. Glück, E. Reya and A. Vogt, Phys. Rev.

D **48**, 116 (1993); L. Bourhis, M. Fontannaz and J.P. Guillet, preprint LPTHE-Orsay-96-103, e-print archive hep-ph/9704447.

12. M. Consoli and J.H. Field, Phys. Rev. D **49**, 1293 (1994); preprint UGVA-DPNC 1994/12-164.

13. G. Parisi and R. Petronzio, Phys. Lett. B **94**, 51 (1980).

14. I.Z. Rothstein and M.B. Wise, Phys. Lett. B **402**, 346 (1997).

15. S. Catani, F. Hautmann and M. Mangano, in progress.

STUDY OF MULTIHADRON PRODUCTION IN TWO-PHOTON COLLISIONS AT LEP1 AND LEP2

N. ZIMIN

Joint Instutute for Nuclear Research,
ul. Joliot-Curie 6, 141980 Dubna, Russian Federation

DELPHI Collaboration

Results of an experimental study of the reaction $e^+e^- \rightarrow e^+e^- + hadrons$ are presented. The data were obtained by the DELPHI detector at LEP1 and LEP2. Together with Monte Carlo predictions they illustrate the evolution of the two-photon process under no-tag conditions. Double-tag events with both scattered e^+ and e^- measured by the DELPHI VSAT detector were observed for the first time at LEP1. The total $\gamma\gamma$ hadronic cross-section is estimated for the $\gamma\gamma$ centre of mass energy up to 35 GeV.

1 Introduction

Multihadron production in $\gamma\gamma$ reaction has been studied in many previous experiments, more recently at KEK [1] and LEP [2,3]. According to those studies a correct leading order description of the experimental data has to combine three components: a soft interaction term described by the generalized Vector meson Dominance Model (VDM), a perturbative term described by the Quark Parton Model (QPM) with a direct quark exchange, and a term for the hard scattering of the partonic constituents of the photon, the so-called Resolved Photon Contribution (QCD-RPC). All these models were realized in the TWOGAM generator which describes DELPHI data reasonably well for both the no-tag and single tag cases. The QPM and VDM events are generated with the same parameters as in previous DELPHI analyses [3]. The QCD-RPC was treated using leading order QCD factorization: a hard scattering subprocess gives the dominant scale p_T^2, taken also as the factorization scale. Since such subprocesses are considered as perturbative, a single free parameter, p_T^{min}, the transverse momentum of the outgoing partons has to be specified and used in order to separate the RPC from the non-perturbative contribution. These values of p_T^{min} were found for parton density functions from the requirement to reproduce the visible experimental two-photon cross-section at Z^0 peak. The Gordon-Storrow (GS2 with $p_t^{min}(GS2) = 1.88 \pm 0.020 \, GeV/c$) and Glück-Reya-Vogt (GRV with $p_t^{min}(GRV) = 1.58 \pm 0.018 \, GeV/c$,) parameterizations of the parton density functions have been shown to reproduce data better and were chosen for simulation. Errors come from statistical errors in the experimental data and those of the simulated samples. The generated events were processed by the full detector simulation program and then subjected to the same selection procedure as the experimental data. A description of the DEL-PHI detector together with basic criteria used to select $\gamma\gamma$ hadronic events can be found in ref. [3,4].

2 No tag visible cross-section behaviour

The experimental data analyzed were collected during 1995 and 1996 LEP runs. They correspond to integrated luminosities of 29.4 pb^{-1}, 5.8 pb^{-1} and 7.9 pb^{-1} for centre-of-mass energies of $\simeq$ 91, $\simeq$ 135 and $\simeq$ 172 GeV, respectively. The configuration of the DELPHI detector was quite stable during that period providing an opportunity to look at the evolution of the $\gamma\gamma$ process at different energies. In order to select hadronic two-photon events at least 4 charged particles in the event with an energy below 20 GeV are required together with invariant mass of the hadronic system in the range 4-30 GeV/c^2 and total transverse momentum of the events below 3 GeV/c. Those criteria suppress the Z^0 decay background at peak, the background from $\tau\tau$ pairs and beam-gas interactions and remove the $\gamma\gamma$ resonance energy region. To validate trigger conditions a total energy of the charged particles greater than 3 GeV was also required together with a momentum of the most energetic particle that was greater than 1 GeV/c. In order to use a neutral component of the hadronic system and hence to provide better rejection of the background and increase the sensitivity to the parton distribution function behaviour, all calorimetric information was included in the analysis The visible cross-section (Fig.1) for

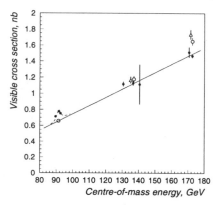

Figure 1: Visible cross-section of the process $e^+e^- \rightarrow e^+e^- + hadrons$ for no-tag events. Points are experimental results, white circles - simulation with GS2 parton density function, white triangle - the same with GRV parameterization. Also shown is the result of the fit by the combination of Cahn's formula and a linear term (dashed line). The solid line shows the linear term alone expressed as $\sigma_{\gamma\gamma} = \sigma_{\gamma\gamma}^Z + d\sigma/dE \times (E_{cms} - 91.25)$, where $\sigma_{\gamma\gamma}^Z = 658.6\pm7.6$ pb, $d\sigma/dE = 10.3\pm0.2$ pb/GeV and E_{cms} is the centre-of-mass energy in GeV.

the events meeting the selection criteria was calculated for each LEP energy point. A simulation was used to check the visible $\gamma\gamma$ cross-section due to Z^0

background. A visible Z^0 background corresponds to $\sigma_Z^{MC} = 92.9 \pm 5.7$ pb (averaged over points around the peak) and only 2.5 ± 0.5 pb at $\simeq 135$ GeV. The cross-section of the beam-gas background was estimated to be below 1 pb for all samples using events originated far from the interaction point. The remaining background contribution was found to be negligible. After bin-by-bin subtraction of the background the visible $\gamma\gamma$ cross-section at the Z^0 peak was found to be $\sigma_{\gamma\gamma}^{exp} = 658.6 \pm 7.6$ pb, which is in agreement with our previous studies[3]. The experimental values are well fitted by the combination of a linear term and Cahn's formula[5], describing the shape of the Z^0 peak. An indication that there is an excess of Monte Carlo predictions is seen for higher energies. The errors of the simulated points come from the uncertainty of p_t^{min} determinations and statistical errors of the simulated samples. Systematic errors relevant for comparing different parton density parameterizations are highly correlated and move the points in the same direction. Different experimental distributions were produced and compared with a simulation shown in Fig.2. It can be seen that the Monte Carlo predicts perfect agreement at $\simeq 91$ GeV

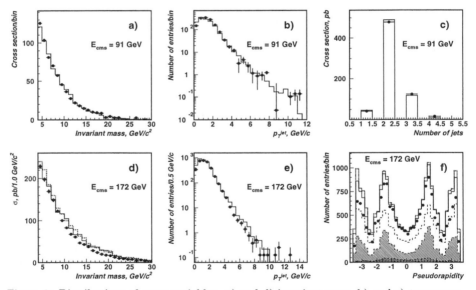

Figure 2: Distributions of event variables. a) and d) invariant mass, b) and e) transverse momentum of jets c) number of reconstructed jets, f) energy flow. Points are data, solid and dotted lines are the full VDM + QPM+RPC predictions with GS2 and GRV parton density functions correspondingly while dashed line is QCD-RPC contribution for GS2, hatched histogram is VDM part, double hatched - QPM part.

and slightly exceeds data at $\simeq 172$ GeV. The increasing activity in the forward direction comes mainly from the QCD-RPC processes (Fig.2f) and is more pronounced for the GRV parton density parameterization. Estimation of errors affecting the level of agreement of the simulated and experimental samples is much more complicated. It was found that the main disagreement comes from the events with a low energy of charged particles and a low fraction of transverse energy, where detector effects (tracking and trigger efficiencies, calorimeter thresholds) are very important and hard to simulate. These effects are still being studied.

3 Double tagged events

Full statistics collected at LEP1 with corresponding integrated luminosity of 101 pb^{-1} are used in the analysis. Four electromagnetic luminometers, the so-called Very Small Angle Taggers (VSAT) [6], are used for energy and angle reconstruction for both scattered e^+ and e^- that was measured. They are placed symmetrically $\simeq$7.7 m downstream of the DELPHI interaction point behind the superconducting quadrupoles at $\simeq$ 60 mm from the beam line covering polar angles θ between 4-15 mrad. Despite the low angles measured the visible cross-section for double tag events is small due to the acceptance of modules (3 cm in X and 5 cm in Y-directions). Moreover, the reconstruction of θ and ϕ angles is quite sensitive to LEP beam parameters, many run-time corrections should be defined and then applied (incident angles of beams for each fill, beam spot position for each run). After all corrections are applied the energy resolution was found to be $\simeq$ 7%, accuracy of angle reconstruction σ_θ = 0.6 mrad and $\sigma_\phi = 9°$. Due to a high cross-section of Bhabha scattering for diagonal modules, it is important to have sufficient rejection of background, to avoid random coincidence mainly with the no-tag events measured by DELPHI. Specific cuts were applied to do so: the difference in X and Y coordinates measured for both scattered leptons $\leq$ 2 $\times$ σ of the corresponding narrow distributions found for Bhabha events (due to their specific kinematics) for each fill, the energy measured in each module $\leq 0.7 \times Ebeam$. Together with the requirement for total event energy measured $\leq$ 115 GeV, 99% of bhabha events are rejected with only 1% for double tagged events. Outer modules are also populated by off-momentum electrons located narrowly around the horizontal plane. This fact can be used for the relative alignment of those modules and thus, with the use of collinearity of Bhabha events, for the relative alignment of internal modules as well. To eliminate possible background from leptonic $\gamma\gamma$ production for the hadronic part of event $3 \leq N_{Charged} \leq 15$, energy of the charged particles below 12 GeV and total energy of the hadronic system below 20 GeV are required. The procedure described above is used for full simulation of double tagged events. Only GS2 parameterization is used for the QCD-RPC part. The VSAT part of the events was treated by specific programs used for luminosity studies. Only 43 events met all selection criteria. Different distributions obtained for such events are shown in Fig.3. Reasonable agreement is shown between data and simulation predictions both

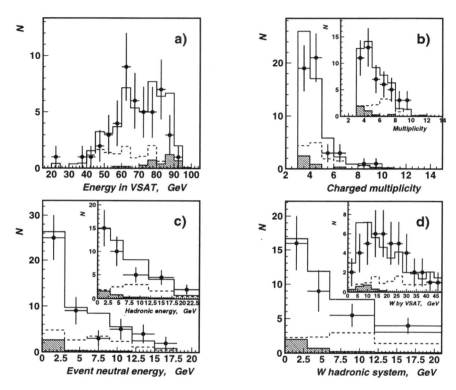

Figure 3: Double tag events. a) energy of scattered e^+ and e^-, b) event multiplicity, c) energy of hadronic system, d) invariant mass reconstructed. Points are data, solid lines are the full VDM+QPM+RPC predictions, dotted lines are the QPM+RPC and hatched histogram -QPM part.

for the VSAT measurements (Fig.3a) and hadronic component of events shown in Fig.3b-3d. There is an indication that an unfolding procedure should be adopted for better reconstruction of invariant mass from the scattered leptons measured by VSAT (upper part of Fig. 3d) but it is of greatest importance for the lower range. It is clear that due to the very low Q^2 range covered the main contribution comes from the VDM while the QCD-RPC has $\simeq 22\%$ and the QPM only 5%. Taking these fractions into account it becomes possible to estimate a total effective $\gamma\gamma$ hadronic cross-section from those components implemented in the TWOGAM generator. For points combined in the range

Table 1: Effective total $\gamma\gamma$ hadronic cross-section

$\sqrt{s}$ GeV	$No\ of\ events$	$Total\ \sigma_{Tot}^{\gamma\gamma}\ \ nb$
25	16	356 ± 90
35	10	325 ± 105

of $\gamma\gamma$ invariant mass 20-30 GeV and 30-48 GeV results are shown in Table 1, with only statistical errors presented.

4   Conclusions

We have studied hadronic events produced in two-photon collisions at centre-of-mass energies $\sqrt{s} \simeq 91$, 135 and 172 GeV. The visible cross-section of the process $e^+e^- \rightarrow e^+e^- + hadrons$ with the anti-tag condition as a function of e^+e^- centre-of-mass energy is well described by the linear function. Different experimental distributions can be reproduced by the simulation with reasonable accuracy and can be used to evaluate the role of the two-photon process as a background for some physics analyses. At higher energies a certain indication of the increased simulated activity is observed in the forward direction due to QCD-RPC processes which is higher for the GRV parton density parameterization. Preliminary results have been obtained for double tagged events at LEP1 energies. Reasonable agreement with Monte Carlo predictions was shown for such events with very low measured Q^2. The effective total $\gamma\gamma$ cross-section is estimated for $\gamma\gamma$ centre-of-mass energy up to 35 GeV. The forthcoming higher energy LEP runs will contribute to a better understanding of two-photon phenomena.

1. AMY Coll., R. Tanaka et al., *Phys. Lett.* **B277** (1992) 215;
   TOPAZ Coll., R. Enomoto et al., KEK-93-107, KEK-93-215.
2. ALEPH Coll., D. Buskulic et al., *Phys. Lett.* **B313** (1993) 509;
   OPAL Coll., R. Akers et al., *Z. Phys. C* **61** (1994) 119;
   L3 Coll., O. Adriani et al., *Phys. Lett.* **B318** (1993) 575.
3. DELPHI Coll., P. Abreu et al., *Z. Phys. C* **62** (1994) 357.
4. DELPHI Coll., P. Abreu et al., *Nucl. Instr. Meth.* **A378** (1996) 57.
5. R.N. Cahn, *Phys. Rev.* **D36** (1987) 2666.
6. DELPHI Coll., P. Abreu et al., *Phys. Lett.* **B342** (1995) 402.

CROSS SECTION FOR HADRON PRODUCTION IN TWO PHOTON EVENTS AT LEP

W.L. VAN ROSSUM

Utrecht University, Princetonplein 4,
3508 TA, Utrecht, The Netherlands

Here the measurement of the total cross section for hadron production will be discussed. The data has been taken at LEP using the L3 detector at $\sqrt{s}$ equals 91 GeV, 130-136 GeV and 161 GeV. The total cross section is given as a function of the true mass, which is obtained from the measured mass using different unfolding technics. The results show a nice agreement between the two-photon cross sections at the different values for $\sqrt{s}$. The two-photon cross section is consistent with a rise at larger masses as expected from universal Regge behaviour of total hadronic cross sections.

1 Physics motivation

At LEP the values for $\sqrt{s}$ are higher than previous accelerators have achieved. The events which have large two-photon masses can be used to measure the two-photon cross section in a region which has not been available before. The cross section is expected to rise in this mass region.

The background at $\sqrt{s} = 91$ GeV is very large due to the Z^0 pole in the annihilation channel. At the higher energies, 130-136 GeV and 161 GeV, the background from annihilation and W-pair production is small. The selection of the data taken at 91 GeV is thus different from the one for the higher energies. The two samples (low-energy sample taken at 91 GeV and high-energy sample at 130-136 GeV and at 161 GeV) will be treated separately in the following sections.

2 Event selection

The selection criteria for the high-energy data will be discussed first.

In order to select hadron events, at least three charged particles have to be seen in the detector. This is done by selecting at least three good tracks.

In order to reduce the background, the energy reconstructed in the hadron calorimeter should be lower than 20 GeV, and the energy in the electromagnetic calorimeter should be lower than 30 GeV. There is also a minimum on the energy in the electromagnetic calorimeter of 0.5 GeV. This is to remove beam-wall and beam-gas events.

The tagged events are anti-selected when the energy in the forward luminosity monitor is higher than 30 GeV. The minimum angle of this subdetector is 27 mrad for data taken around 133 GeV and 33 mrad at 161 GeV.

Finally the visible mass, calculated with the use of all the clusters seen in the detector, must be larger than 5 GeV.

For data taken at 91 GeV there is a large background coming from annihilation events. A large reduction of this background is obtained by requiring that the hadron system is moving along the beam pipe with respect to the detector system. Events with an absolute value of the longitudinal energy imbalance normalised to the total visible energy larger than 0.4 are selected.

When an (annihilation) event is badly reconstructed, the longitudinal energy is affected by this, but also the transverse energy. Events with a large transverse energy imbalance are considered badly reconstructed events, and are anti-selected when this imbalance is larger than 4 GeV.

The hadronic events are selected by two cuts. Again the number of good tracks should be larger than three. An extra cut is the requirement that the hadron energy should be higher than 1. GeV.

Here, also the energy in the luminosity monitor should be lower than 30 GeV in order to select untagged data and the visible mass should be larger than 5 GeV.

For both samples the data is compared with two different MC samples. The first one has been generated with a dedicated two-photon generator, called PHOJET [1]. The second generator, PYTHIA [2], is a general purpose generator which describes the interaction between two photons. The production of these photons by the initial state electron and positron, described by the luminosity function $\mathcal{L}_{\gamma\gamma}$, had to be implemented. This was done by using the Equivalent-Photon Approximation.

In figure 1 the visible mass for the 161 GeV data is shown. The mass distribution is compared to the two MC samples. There is a nice agreement between both data and the MC samples, and between the two MC samples.

3 Unfolding

The visible mass of an event is different from the true mass because particles are lost down the beam pipe and hadronic particles are not reconstructed well in the forward region because there are only electromagnetic calorimeters in this region. This means that the visible-mass distribution must be unfolded to give the true-mass distribution. The unfolding is done differently for the two data sets.

The high-energy sample is unfolded using Bayes' theorem:

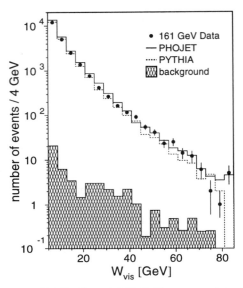

Figure 1: The visible mass distribution at 161 GeV, compared to the two MC samples generated by PHOJET (solid line) and PYTHIA (dashed line).

$$N^{\mathrm{unf}}(W_{\gamma\gamma}) = \sum_{W_{\mathrm{vis}}} [\frac{A(W_{\mathrm{vis}}, W_{\gamma\gamma}) N^{\mathrm{gen}}(W_{\gamma\gamma})}{\sum_{W'_{\gamma\gamma}} A(W_{\mathrm{vis}}, W'_{\gamma\gamma}) N^{\mathrm{gen}}(W'_{\gamma\gamma})}] N^{\mathrm{meas}}(W_{\mathrm{vis}}) \qquad (1)$$

Here, $A(W_{\mathrm{vis}}, W_{\gamma\gamma})$ is the probability that an event, generated in the true-mass bin $W_{\gamma\gamma}$, is measured in the visible-mass bin W_{vis} and $N^{\mathrm{gen}}(W_{\gamma\gamma})$ is the generated number of events in the true-mass bin $W_{\gamma\gamma}$ (this is thus model dependent). The part between the square brackets is then the likelihood that an event measured in the visible-mass bin W_{vis} originated from the true-mass bin $W_{\gamma\gamma}$. The measured visible-mass distribution , N^{meas}, is then unfolded to the true-mass distribution, N^{unf}, by using equation 1.

For the low-energy sample it was concluded that due to the resolution of the detector only four different mass bins can be used. The sample is unfolded by using the inverse matrix of A:

$$N^{\mathrm{unf}}(W_{\gamma\gamma}) = \sum_{W_{\mathrm{vis}}} [A(W_{\mathrm{vis}}, W_{\gamma\gamma})]^{-1} N^{\mathrm{meas}}(W_{\mathrm{vis}}) \qquad (2)$$

4 Results

From the unfolded mass distributions the two-photon cross sections can be calculated as a function of the true mass. This is done in the following way:

$$\sigma_{\gamma\gamma}(W_{\gamma\gamma}) = \frac{N^{\mathrm{unf}}(W_{\gamma\gamma})}{\epsilon(W_{\gamma\gamma})\mathcal{L}_{e^+e^-}\mathcal{L}'_{\gamma\gamma}} \tag{3}$$

Here, $\epsilon(W_{\gamma\gamma})$ is the selection efficiency for the selected events and $\mathcal{L}_{e^+e^-}$ is the total integrated e^+e^- luminosity. The two-photon cross section, $\sigma_{\gamma\gamma}$ is not only a function of the mass but also depends on the separate masses of the two virtual photons, Q_i^2. For low-Q^2 data this cross section can be approximated as follows:

$$\sigma_{\gamma\gamma}^{ab}(W_{\gamma\gamma}, Q_1^2, Q_2^2) \approx \sigma_{\gamma\gamma}(W_{\gamma\gamma})F^a(Q_1^2)F^b(Q_2^2) \tag{4}$$

Here, a and b denote the two different states of the virtual photon: $a, b = T$ or S. The two form factors, $F(Q_1^2)$ and $F(Q_2^2)$, give the behaviour of the cross section as function of the virtual mass of the two photons. The modified luminosity function $\mathcal{L}'_{\gamma\gamma}$ can be calculated as follows:

$$\mathcal{L}'_{\gamma\gamma} = \int \sum_{a,b=T,S} \mathcal{L}_{\gamma\gamma}^{ab} F^a(Q_1^2)F^b(Q_2^2)d\Gamma \tag{5}$$

Here, $\mathcal{L}_{\gamma\gamma}^{ab}$ are the true luminosity functions, the integration over that part of phase space, $\int d\Gamma$, which contributes to the true mass bin is calculated numerically using a program of Schuler[3].

The results for the cross section are shown in figure 2. The error bars for the L3 results are total errors. These errors consist out of a statistical and a systematical part. The statistical parts are the diagonal elements coming from the error matrix as given by the unfolding procedures. The systematical error is obtained by changing the selection criteria, by comparing the results obtained by PYTHIA with the ones obtained by PHOJET and by using different form factors for calculating $\mathcal{L}'_{\gamma\gamma}$.

The high-energy data can be fitted by a Donnachie-Landshoff fit[5]. The exponents describing the mass behaviour are taken to be universal and can be obtained from other experiments. The fit gives (with $\chi^2/dof = 3/8$):

$$\sigma_{\gamma\gamma}(s) = (173 \pm 7)s^{0.079} + (519 \pm 125)s^{-0.47} \text{ nb} \tag{6}$$

Here, $s = W_{\gamma\gamma}^2$ is given in GeV^2. The errors used to obtain χ^2 are total errors but without the overall scaling uncertainty of the result, which is about 8 %.

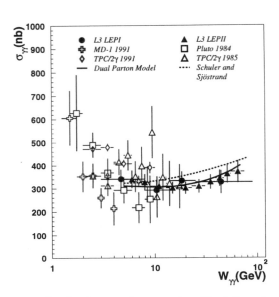

Figure 2: The cross section for the two data samples. The full markers are the L3 results, the open markers are previous results. The full line gives the Dual Parton Model, which is inside PHOJET. The dashed line is a parametrisation obtained by Schuler and Sjöstrand[4].

5   Conclusions

At L3 the total cross section for hadron production has been measured for different values of $\sqrt{s}$ of 91 GeV, between 130-136 GeV and of 161 GeV. The two-photon masses obtained are larger than those of previous experiments, and their range is increased up to 80 GeV. The results for the two different data samples agree nicely, see figure 2, within the overall errors of 10 to 15 %.

Both MC samples describe the distributions reasonable. But still the largest systematical error comes from the difference between the results obtained with PYTHIA or PHOJET.

And finally, as can be seen from the result of the fit, the data is consistent with a rise of the two-photon cross section at larger masses as expected from universal Regge behaviour of total hadronic cross sections.

References

1. R. Engel and J. Ranft, Phys. Rev **D 54**, 4246 (1996).
2. T. Sjöstrand, Comput. Phys. Commun. **82**, 74 (1994).

3. G.A. Schuler, CERN-TH/96-297 , (1996).
4. G.A. Schuler and T. Sjöstrand, Z. Phys. **C 73**, 677 (1997).
5. A.Donnachie and P.V. Landshoff, Phys. Lett. **296**, 227 (1992).

SCALE INFLUENCE ON THE ENERGY DEPENDENCE OF PHOTON-PROTON CROSS SECTIONS AND F_2 AT LOW Q^2

N.Z. GOGITIDZE

DESY, Notkestr. 85, D-22603 Hamburg, Germany
and LPI RAS, 117924 Moscow, Russia

New results of a measurement of the proton structure function $F_2(x, Q^2)$ and the total virtual photon-proton cross section are presented for momentum transfer squared Q^2 between 0.35 GeV^2 and 0.35 GeV^2 and for Bjorken-x values down to $6 \cdot 10^{-6}$ using data collected by the HERA experiment H1. The results are compared to phenomenological models at low Q^2. The slope of the W dependence of the cross sections is studied as function of the scale Q^2. In a second study, the scale dependence of the evolution of photoproduction cross sections with the photon-proton centre of mass energy W is studied using low $Q^2 < 0.01$ GeV^2 e^+p interactions. The charged particle with the largest transverse momentum in the photon fragmentation region is used to define the hard scale of the interactions. The slope of the W dependence of the cross section is observed to increase steeply with increasing transverse momentum. The result is compared to measurements of the Q^2 evolution of the W dependence of the virtual photon-proton cross section, as obtained in the first study presented here. Interpretations in terms of QCD and in terms of Regge phenomenology are discussed.

1 Introduction

The energy dependence of the real photon-proton cross section is consistently described at high energies by the power law $\sigma_{\gamma p}^{tot} \propto (W^2)^\lambda$, where W is the γp centre of mass energy and the power $\lambda \approx 0.08$ [1,2]. The value $\lambda \approx 0.08$ is found to be universal for all photon or hadron interactions with protons [3]. In contrast, the virtual photon-proton cross section, which at large W is related to the structure function F_2 via $\sigma_{\gamma^* p}^{tot} \approx 4\pi^2 \alpha/Q^2 \cdot F_2(W^2, Q^2)$, is found to rise fast with increasing W^2 for Q^2 values larger than a few GeV^2 [4,5]. Here Q^2 is the virtuality of the photon and α the fine structure constant. In the HERA regime fits of the form $\sigma_{\gamma^* p}^{tot} \propto (W^2)^\lambda$ lead to values of λ which rise from 0.2 to 0.4 in the Q^2 range from 1.5 to 10^3 GeV^2 [4].

The change of the slope parameter λ with increasing Q^2 is associated with a transition from the non-perturbative 'soft' to the perturbative 'hard' regime [6,7]. Indeed, in the domain where Q^2 is larger than a few GeV^2 and perturbative QCD (pQCD) can be safely applied, it predicts an increase of λ with Q^2. In the domain of 'soft' interaction phenomenology the change of λ can be interpreted in Reggeon Field Theory as a reduction of screening corrections with increasing Q^2 [8]. Reggeon Field Theory and perturbative QCD are two complementary approaches which successfully describe physics processes in different regimes. But the transition region between these soft and hard regimes is not yet well understood.

Here, in order to bring more understanding of this transition region, we select a certain process, define a scale which allows the transition region to be probed and study the energy behaviour of the corresponding cross sections.

Whereas in deep inelastic scattering (DIS) the hardness of the interaction (scale) can be characterized by the momentum transfer squared Q^2, it is the large p_t of the final state hadrons which indicates a hard scattering process in photoproduction ($Q^2 \approx 0$). For the interaction with the proton a high value of Q^2 may indeed play a similar role as production of high p_t particles in the photon fragmentation region.

The results presented in the following have recently been published[9].

2   HERA Kinematics and the H1 Detector

At the collider HERA 27.5 GeV positrons and 820 GeV protons collide, producing e^+p interactions at a centre of mass energy $\sqrt{s} = 300$ GeV in a wide range of Q^2, from the regime of quasi real photoproduction ($Q^2 \approx 0$) to DIS at large Q^2. The hadronic final state can be detected in the same experiment for both kinds of interactions. Therefore, HERA provides an ideal testing ground to study the transition from soft to hard physics by comparing real and virtual photon-proton collisions.

The H1 detector[10] covers almost 4π of the solid angle and consists, viewed outwards from the interaction point, of tracking detectors, calorimeters and muon detectors. During the winter shutdown 1994/1995 a new calorimeter and a new tracking chamber with increased acceptance for small scattering angles were installed in the backward (electron beam direction) region. In the analyses presented here data come both from the data-taking period with nominal interaction vertex, and from a short period with the interaction vertex shifted downstream by 70 cm. This shift increases the acceptance for electrons scattered through small angles. As a result, the kinematic range in DIS was extended in Q^2 and x down to $Q^2 \sim 0.3$ GeV^2 and $x \sim 6 \cdot 10^{-6}$. x is the Bjorken scaling variable, which is related to W by $W^2 = Q^2/x$.

3   A Measurement of the Proton Structure Function $F_2(x, Q^2)$ at Low x and Q^2

The measured ep cross section in the HERA kinematic range can be expressed either in terms of proton structure functions or the virtual photon-proton cross section as follows

$$\frac{d^2\sigma_{ep}}{dx\,dQ^2} = \frac{2\pi\alpha^2}{Q^4 x}(2 - 2y + \frac{y^2}{1+R})F_2(x, Q^2)$$
$$= \Gamma[\sigma_T(x, Q^2) + \epsilon(y)\sigma_L(x, Q^2)] \equiv \Gamma\sigma_{\gamma^* p}^{eff}(x, y, Q^2). \tag{1}$$

Here σ_L and σ_T are the cross sections for the transverse and longitudinally po-

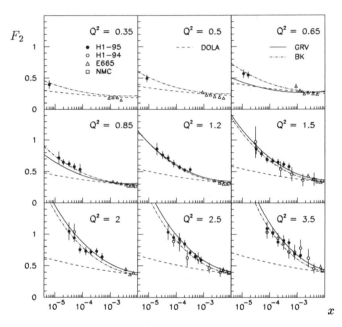

Figure 1: Measurements of the proton structure function $F_2(x, Q^2)$ at low Q^2 from H1 and from fixed target experiments, compared to different model predictions specified in the text.

larized virtual photons, Γ is a flux factor and ϵ is the ratio of the longitudinal to the transverse flux. R is the ratio $F_L/(F_2 - F_L)$ where F_L is the longitudinal structure function. To extract the structure function F_2 from these measurements of the ep cross section, an assumption has to be made for the longitudinal structure function F_L since it is not yet measured in this kinematic region. The Badelek - Kwiecinski model[11] is applied for calculating R^a. This model is based on the photon-gluon fusion process and has the proper

---

[a]Note that this is an arbitrary choice of R. As long as R is specified together with the extracted F_2, another choice of R can easily be applied for a new derivation of F_2 from the measured σ_{ep}.

limit for $Q^2 \to 0$ where F_L should vanish $\propto Q^4$. In our kinematic range R has values between 0.1 and 0.3, and the effect on the F_2 measurements is rather small. In Fig.1 the F_2 data are shown as function of x in 9 different Q^2 bins. The data are compared with previous H1 measurements [12] and with the fixed target measurements [13,14]. In the overlapping Q^2 bins the new results are in good agreement with the previous measurements. The total error has been reduced by a factor 2 to 3. F_2 is seen to rise steeply with decreasing x for $Q^2 \geq 2$ GeV^2, while for smaller Q^2 values this rise is less steep. The data also show a smooth continuous transition towards the low x region.

The data are compared (see Fig.1) with several model predictions for F_2 at low x. The model of Donnachie and Landshoff (DOLA) [15] assumes a pomeron intercept of $1 + \lambda \sim 1.08$ for the energy dependence of the cross section, independent of the virtuality of the photon. The model gives a prediction of F_2 which is too low for $Q^2 \geq 0.85$ GeV^2, but which approaches the data for the lowest Q^2 values. The DOLA prediction can also be interpreted as the contribution of soft pomeron exchange to the cross section at non-zero Q^2. Contrary to this Regge inspired model, the model of Glück, Reya and Vogt

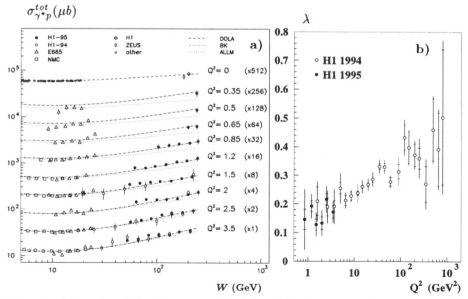

Figure 2: a) The virtual photon-proton cross section $\sigma^{tot}_{\gamma^* p}$ as function of W in different Q^2 bins. The curves represent Donnachie and Landshoff (dashed line), Badelek and Kwiecinski (dashed-dotted line) and Abramowicz et al. (dotted line) parametrizations. b) The slope λ of the W^2 dependence of the proton structure function F_2, as function of Q^2.

(GRV) [16] is defined completely within the parton picture. It is assumed that all parton distributions at very low $Q_0^2 = 0.34$ GeV^2 have a valence-like shape, i.e. vanish for $x \to 0$. Assuming further that F_2 evolves towards large Q^2 values via parton radiation, given by the leading twist QCD evolution equations, GRV predict that the structure function F_2 should rise with decreasing x, even for low values of $Q^2 \sim 1$ GeV^2. The GRV distributions describe the data well for $Q^2 \geq 1$ GeV^2, but fail for $Q^2 < 1$ GeV^2. At low Q^2 values the QCD evolution covers too small a Q^2 range, and the parton distributions become dominated by the valence behaviour at the starting scale Q_0^2. The model of Badelek and Kwiecinski (BK) [17] combines the concepts of Vector Meson Dominance (VMD) with dynamical parton models such as the GRV model. It has per force a smooth transition from pQCD to the real photon limit, which coincides with the region measured here. The BK model predicts F_2 well for all Q^2 bins.

The total virtual photon-proton cross section is here defined as

$$\sigma_{\gamma^* p}^{tot} = \sigma_T(x, Q^2) + \sigma_L(x, Q^2) \simeq \frac{4\pi^2 \alpha}{Q^2} F_2(x, Q^2). \qquad (2)$$

With this definition $\sigma_{\gamma^* p}^{tot}$ depends only on Q^2 and x (or W) and the results of different experiments may easily be compared. The W dependence of $\sigma_{\gamma^* p}^{tot}$ is shown in Fig.2a in different Q^2 bins. The data are compared with low energy measurements and with photoproduction data. It is observed that $\sigma_{\gamma^* p}^{tot}$ rises faster with increasing W when Q^2 increases. To quantify this observation fits of the F_2 data in the form $F_2 \propto x^{-\lambda}$ ($\sim W^{2\lambda}$) were made in the Q^2 bins. The results of these fits are shown in Fig.2b, where λ is presented as function of Q^2 together with previous H1 measurements. The data confirm the trend already observed in the previous measurements. When $Q^2 \to 0$, data tend towards the 'soft' pomeron limit. The new data show that the transition towards this limit is smooth and continuous. Thus, in this study the intrinsically 'hard' DIS process is used, and the scale Q^2 was followed towards lower values into the transition region.

4 Scale Influence on the Energy Dependence of Photon - Proton Cross Sections

Another way to study the transition region is to use high p_t charged particles as a measure of a typical scale in photoproduction processes, a scale which can be varied in a similar way as the scale Q^2 in DIS.

In total about two million photoproduction events were selected in the scaled energy range $0.25 < y = 1 - E_{e'}/E_e < 0.70$, where E_e and $E_{e'}$ are the initial and scattered positron energies respectively. The corresponding energy range is $150 < W_{\gamma p} < 250$ GeV. The W dependence of the cross section is then measured in different bins of maximum p_t ($p_{t,max}$) of the charged particles.

Good detector acceptance and high resolution of p_t measurements, together with large statistics of photoproduction events, allow a continuous coverage of both soft and hard scattering domains. The acceptance and resolution requirements limit the charged particles to the pseudo-rapidity range $1.1 < \eta^* < 3.1$. $\eta^* = -\ln(\tan(\theta^*/2))$ is measured with respect to the γ direction in the γp centre of mass system, where θ^* is the polar angle.

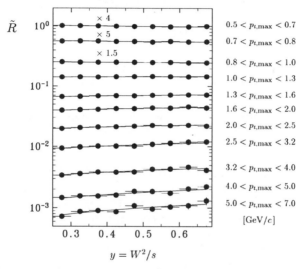

Figure 3: Energy dependence of the ratio $\tilde{R}$ in different bins of $p_{t,max}$. The curves represent fits $\tilde{R} = W^{2 \cdot \lambda}$

In Fig.3 the energy dependence of the ratio of the partial γp cross section to the total γp cross section (which is equal to the ratio $\tilde{R}$ of observed numbers of events) is shown for different $p_{t,max}$ bins. The higher the $p_{t,max}$ values, the steeper is the rise of the ratio with increasing $W_{\gamma p}$.

To quantify this observation fits of the data were made (similar to the ones made in our first study) in the form $\sigma_{\gamma p}(W, p_{t,max}^2) \propto W^{2\lambda(p_{t,max}^2)}$, with the scale defined by the maximum p_t charged particles in the photon fragmentation region. The results of these fits are shown in Fig.4, where the slope λ is given as function of $4p_{t,max}^2$. A strong increase of λ is observed with increasing $p_{t,max}$, as well as a smooth transition from lower to higher values of $p_{t,max}$, so that the data are well fitted by a straight line. Is this rise an effect of phase space

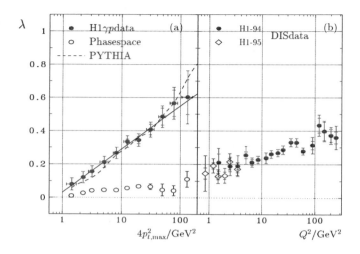

Figure 4: Slope λ of the W^2 dependence dependence of the photoproduction and DIS cross sections as function of $4p_t^2$ and Q^2 respectively.

increase with increasing of $p_{t,max}$? Comparison with a longitudinal phase space model (Fig.4) shows that the phase space effects play only a minor role.

In Fig.4 the date are also compared with the PYTHIA model predictions[18]. The model is based on the Monte Carlo version which includes both pQCD for the hard scattering process and a Regge inspired soft interaction component. Seing that PYTHIA reproduces the trend of the data well it is interesting to understand the reason for this agreement. A study of the different ingredients of the model shows that the main part of the rise can be explained by the integration of the leading order matrix elements over the available phase space. The effects of using different proton and photon structure functions are small. Parton showers, simulating next to leading order effects as well as multiple parton-parton scattering, also give only a small effect. Therefore, the change of the slope λ is not associated with the growth of the gluon density in the proton at small x, contrary to the naive expectation.

5   Conclusions

In summary, a clear similarity is seen in the evolutions of the W dependence of γp and $\gamma^* p$ cross sections with increasing scales ($4p_{t,max}^2$ and Q^2 respectively). Another interesting observation is that the transition from soft to hard regimes is smooth in both cases. This similarity can be qualitatively understood both in terms of pQCD and in terms of a Regge approach. In pQDC the effect of more steeply rising cross sections with increasing hard scale can be readily explained by leading order partonic scattering contributions [19], while in Reggeon Field Theory it is a consequence of the reduction of unitarity corrections to one-pomeron exchange.

Acknowledgments

It is a pleasure for me to thank all my colleagues in H1 for useful discussions and help in preparing the report. I would like to thank the organizers for hospitality and for creating a pleasant and inspiring conference atmosphere.

References

1. H1 Collab., S.Aid et al., *Z. Phys.* C **69**, 27 (1995).
2. ZEUS Collab., M.Derrick et al., *Z. Phys.* C **63**, 391 (1994).
3. A.Donnachie and P.V.Landshoff, *Phys. Lett.* B **296**, 227 (1992); H.Cheng, J.K.Walker and T.T.Wu, *Phys. Lett.* B **44**, 97 (1973).
4. H1 Collab., I.Abt et al., *Nucl. Phys.* B **407**, 515 (1993); H1 Collab., T.Ahmed et al., *Nucl. Phys.* B **439**, 471 (1995); H1 Collab., S.Aid et al., *Nucl. Phys.* B **470**, 3 (1996).
5. ZEUS Collab., M.Derrick et al., *Phys. Lett.* B **316**, 412 (1993); ZEUS Collab., M.Derrick et al., *Z. Phys.* C **65**, 379 (1995); ZEUS Collab., M.Derrick et al., *Z. Phys.* C **69**, 607 (1996).
6. J.Bartels, DIS and QCD, Eds. J.-P.Laporte and Y.Sirois, (1995) 105.
7. A.Levy, TAUP 2349-96 (1996).
8. A.Capella et al., *Phys. Lett.* B **337**, 358 (1994).
9. H1 Collab., S.Aid et al., DESY-97-042 (1997); H1 Collab., S.Aid et al., *Phys. Lett.* B **392**, 234 (1997).
10. H1 Collab., I.Abt et al., *Nucl. Instrum. Methods* A **386**, 310 (1997).
11. B.Badelek, J.Kwiecinski and A.Stasto, Durham DTP /96/16 (1996).
12. H1 Collab., S.Aid et al., *Nucl. Phys.* B **470**, 3 (1996).
13. E665 Collab., M.R.Adams et al., *Phys. Rev.* D **54**, 3006 (1996).
14. NMC Collab., M.Arneodo et al., *Phys. Lett.* B **364**, 107 (1995).
15. A.Donnachie and P.V.Landshoff, *Z. Phys.* C **61**, 139 (1994).
16. M.Glück, E.Reya and A.Vogt, *Z. Phys.* C **67**, 433 (1995).
17. B.Badelek and J.Kwiecinski, *Phys. Lett.* B **295**, 263 (1992).
18. T.Sjöstrand, CERN-TH-6488 (1992).
19. D.Cline, F.Halzen and J.Luthe, *Phys. Rev. Lett.* **31**, 493 (1973); W.Buchmüller and D.Haidt, DESY-96-061 (1996).

PHOTON-PHOTON TOTAL INELASTIC CROSS-SECTION

A. CORSETTI

Physics Department, Northeastern University, Boston, USA

R. M. GODBOLE

Center for Theoretical Studies, Indian Institute of Science, Bangalore, India

G. PANCHERI

INFN - Laboratori Nazionali di Frascati, Frascati, Italy

We discuss predictions for the total inelastic $\gamma\gamma$ cross section and their model dependence on the input parameters. We compare results from a simple extension of the Regge Pomeron exchange model as well as predictions from the eikonalized mini-jet model with recent LEP data.

It is by now established that all total cross sections, including photoproduction, rise as the c.m. energy of the colliding particles increases. So far a successful description of total cross-sections is obtained in the Regge/Pomeron exchange model [1], in which a Regge pole and a Pomeron are exchanged and total cross-sections are seen to first decrease and subsequently rise according to the expression

$$\sigma_{ab}^{tot} = Y_{ab}s^{-\eta} + X_{ab}s^{\epsilon}$$

where ϵ and η are related to the intercept at zero of the leading Regge trajectory and of the Pomeron; respectively $\eta \approx 0.5$ and $\epsilon \approx 0.08$. This parametrization applies successfully [1] to photoproduction, as shown in Fig. 1, and to the lower energy data on $\gamma\gamma$ [2]. Assuming the hypothesis of factorization at the poles, one can make a prediction for $\gamma\gamma$ total inelastic cross-section, using

$$Y_{ab}^2 = Y_{aa}Y_{bb} \qquad X_{ab}^2 = X_{aa}X_{bb}$$

and extracting the coefficients X and Y from those for the fit to photo-production and hadron-hadron data. In particular, using for η and ϵ the average values from the Particle Data Group compilation [3] and averaging among the pp and $\bar{p}p$ coefficients, one can have a first check of the factorization hypothesis. Noticing that the coefficient Y from photoproduction data has a large error and that prediction from the Regge/Pomeron exchange model refer to total cross-sections rather than the inelastic ones, these predictions can be enlarged into a band as shown in Fig.2.

An alternative model for the rise of all total cross-sections, relies on hard parton-parton scattering. It was suggested [4] that hard collisions between elementary constituents of the colliding hadrons, the partons, could be responsible for this rise which starts around $\sqrt{s} \geq 10 \div 20 \ GeV$. This suggestion has subsequently evolved into mini-jet models [5], whose eikonal formulation satisfies unitarity while embodying the concepts of rising total cross-sections with rising jet cross-sections. For processes involving photons, the model has to incorporate [6] the hadronisation probability P_γ^{had} for the photon to fluctuate itself into a hadronic state. The eikonalised mini–jet cross-section is then

$$\sigma_{ab}^{inel} = P_{ab}^{had} \int d^2\vec{b}[1 - e^{n(b,s)}] \tag{1}$$

with the average number of collisions at a given impact parameter $\vec{b}$ given by

$$n(b,s) = A_{ab}(b)(\sigma_{ab}^{soft} + \frac{1}{P_{ab}^{had}}\sigma_{ab}^{jet}) \tag{2}$$

In eqs.(1, 2), P_{ab}^{had} is the probability that the colliding particles a, b are both in a hadronic state, $A_{ab}(b)$ describes the transverse overlap of the partons in the two projectiles normalised to 1, σ_{ab}^{soft} is the non-perturbative part of the cross-section from which the factor of P_{ab}^{had} has already been factored out and σ_{ab}^{jet} is the hard part of the cross–section. The basic statement of the mini-jet model for total cross-sections is that the rise in σ_{ab}^{jet} drives the rise of σ_{ab}^{inel} with energy. Letting

$$P_{\gamma p}^{had} = P_\gamma^{had} \quad and \quad P_{\gamma\gamma}^{had} \approx (P_\gamma^{had})^2 \tag{3}$$

one can extrapolate the model from photoproduction to photon-photon collisions. The issue of total $\gamma\gamma$ cross-sections assumes an additional significance in view of the large potential backgrounds that Beamstrahlung photons could cause at future Linear Colliders [7]. Because the hadronic structure of the photon involves both a perturbative and nonperturbative part, it has been proposed [2,8] to use a sum of eikonalized functions instead of eq.(1) in processes involving photons.

The predictions of the eikonalised mini-jet model for photon induced processes thus depend on 1) the assumption of one or more eikonals 2) the hard jet cross-section $\sigma_{jet} = \int_{p_{tmin}} \frac{d^2\hat{\sigma}}{dp_t^2} dp_t^2$ which in turn depends on the minimum p_t above which one can expect perturbative QCD to hold viz. p_{tmin} and the parton densities in the colliding particles a and b, 3) the soft cross–section

σ_{ab}^{soft} 4) the overlap function $A_{ab}(b)$, defined as

$$A(b) = \frac{1}{(2\pi)^2} \int d^2\vec{q}\,\mathcal{F}_1(q)\mathcal{F}_2(q)e^{i\vec{q}\cdot\vec{b}} \tag{4}$$

where $\mathcal{F}$ is the Fourier transform of the b-distribution of partons in the colliding particles and 5) last, but not the least, P_{ab}^{had}.

In this note we shall restrict ourselves to a single eikonal. The hard jet cross-sections are calculated in LO perturbative QCD and use photonic parton densities GRV [9] calculated to the leading order. We determine $\sigma_{\gamma\gamma}^{soft}$ from $\sigma_{\gamma p}^{soft}$ which in turn is determined by a fit to the photoproduction data. ¿From inspection of the photoproduction data, one can assume that σ_{soft} should contain both a constant and an energy decreasing term. Following the suggestion[8]

$$\sigma_{\gamma p}^{soft} = \sigma^0 + \frac{A}{\sqrt{s}} + \frac{B}{s} \tag{5}$$

we then calculate values for σ^0, A and B from a best fit [10] to the low energy photoproduction data, starting with the Quark Parton Model ansatz $\sigma_{\gamma p}^0 \approx \frac{2}{3}\sigma_{pp}^0$. For $\gamma\gamma$ collisions, we repeat the QPM suggestion and propose

$$\sigma_{\gamma\gamma}^{soft} = \frac{2}{3}\sigma_{\gamma p}^{soft}, \ i.e. \ \sigma_{\gamma\gamma}^0 = 20.8mb, A_{\gamma\gamma} = 6.7 \ mb \ GeV^{3/2}, B_{\gamma\gamma} = 25.3 \ mb \ GeV \tag{6}$$

Whereas the effect of the uncertainties in the above three quantities on the predictions of the inelastic photoproduction and $\gamma\gamma$ cross-sections has been studied in literature to a fair extent [2,8,11] the effect of the other two has not been much discussed. In the original use of the eikonal model, the overlap function $A_{ab}(b)$ of eq.(4) is obtained using for $\mathcal{F}$ the electromagnetic form factors. For protons this is given by the dipole expression

$$\mathcal{F}_{prot}(q) = [\frac{\nu^2}{q^2 + \nu^2}]^2 \tag{7}$$

with $\nu^2 = 0.71 \ GeV^2$. For photons a number of authors [8,12],

on the basis of Vector Meson Dominance, have assumed the same functional form as for pion, i.e. the pole expression

$$\mathcal{F}_{pion}(q) = \frac{k_0^2}{q^2 + k_0^2} \quad with \quad k_0 = 0.735 \ GeV. \tag{8}$$

There also exists another possibility, i.e. that the b-space distribution of partons is the Fourier transform of their intrinsic transverse momentum distributions [13]. While for the proton this would correspond to use a Gaussian distribution instead of the dipole expression, eq.(7), for the photon one can argue that the intrinsic transverse momentum ansatz [14] would imply the use of a different value of the parameter k_o[15] in the pole expression for the form factor. By varying k_o one can then explore both the intrinsic transverse distribution case and the form factor cum VMD hypothesis. Notice that the region most important to this calculation is for large values of the parameter b, where the overlap function changes trend, and is larger for smaller k_o values.

Let us now look at P_γ^{had}. This is clearly expected to be $\mathcal{O}(\alpha_{em})$. Based on Vector Meson Dominance one expects,

$$P_\gamma^{had} = P_{VMD} = \sum_{V=\rho,\omega,\phi} \frac{4\pi\alpha}{f_V^2} = \frac{1}{250} \tag{9}$$

Although in principle, P_γ^{had} is not a constant, for simplicity, we adopt here a fixed value[12] of $1/204$, which includes a non-VMD contribution of $\approx 20\%$. Notice that a fixed value of P_{had} can be absorbed into a redefinition of the parameter k_o through a simple change of variables [16].

Having thus established the range of variability of the quantities involved in the calculation of total inelastic photonic cross sections, we can proceed to compare the predictions of the eikonalized minijet model with data. We use GRV (LO) densities and show the mini-jet result in Fig.1, using the form factor model for A(b), i.e. eq.(4) with $k_o = 0.735~GeV$. In the figures, we have not added the direct contribution, which will slightly increase the cross-section in the 10 GeV region. We observe that it is possible to include the high energy points using GRV densities and $p_{tmin} = 2~GeV$, but the low energy region would be better described by a smaller p_{tmin}. This is the region where the rise, according to some authors, notably within the framework of the Dual Parton Model, is attributed to the so-called *soft Pomeron*.

We now apply the same criteria and parameter set used in γp collisions to the case of photon-photon collisions, i.e. $P_{h/\gamma} = 1/204$, $p_{tmin} = 2~GeV$ and A(b) from eq.(4). A comparison with $\gamma\gamma$ data shows that although the value $k_o = 0.735$, corresponding to the pion-factor, is compatible with the low energy data up to 10 GeV [17] within the limits established by the large errors involved, at higher energies [18] the best fit is obtained using a slightly larger value, i.e. $k_0 = 1~GeV$, and this is the one used in Fig.2. For comparison, we have also added mini-jet model predictions with SAS1 photon densities [19]and predictions (Pomeron/SaS) based on a Pomeron/Regge type parametrization[2].

References

1. A. Donnachie and P.V. Landshoff, Phys. Lett. B296 (1992) 227.

98

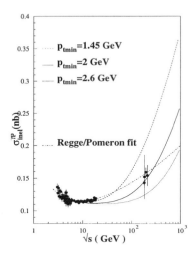
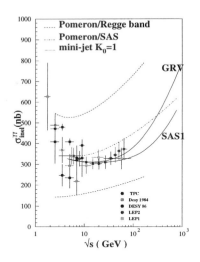

(a) Fig.1: Total inelastic photon-proton cross-section

(b) Fig.2: Total inelastic photon-photon cross-section.

2. G. Schuler and T. Sjöstrand, Phys. Lett. **B 300** (1993) 169, Nucl. Phys. **B 407** (1993) 539, CERN-TH/95-62.

3. Particle Data Group, Physical Review D54 (1996) 191.

4. D.Cline, F.Halzen and J. Luthe, Phys. Rev. Lett. **31** (1973) 491.

5. A. Capella and J. Tran Thanh Van, Z. Phys. **C23** (1984)168, T.Gaisser and F.Halzen, Phys. Rev. Lett. **54** (1985) 1754, G.Pancheri and Y.N.Srivastava, Phys. Letters **B182** (1985), P. l'Heureux, B. Margolis and P. Valin, Phys. Rev. **D 32** (1985) 1681, L. Durand and H. Pi, Phys. Rev. Lett. **58** (1987) 58.

6. J.C. Collins and G.A. Ladinsky, Phys. Rev. **D 43** (1991) 2847.

7. M. Drees and R.M. Godbole, Phys. Rev. Lett. **67** (1991) 1189, P. Chen, T.L. Barklow and M. E. Peskin, Phys. Rev. **D 49** (1994) 3209.

8. K. Honjo, L. Durand, R. Gandhi, H. Pi and I. Sarcevic, Phys. Rev. **D 48** (1993) 1048.

9. M. Glück, E. Reya and A. Vogt, Phys. Rev. **D 46** (1992) 1973.

10. A. Corsetti, September 1994 Laurea Thesis, University of Rome La Sapienza.

11. J.R. Foreshaw and J.K. Storrow, Phys. Lett. **B 278** (1992) 193; Phys. Rev. **D46** (1992) 3279.

12. R.S. Fletcher , T.K. Gaisser and F.Halzen, Phys. Rev. **D 45** (1992) 377;

erratum Phys. Rev. **D 45** (1992) 3279.

13. A. Corsetti, Grau, G. Pancheri and Y.N. Srivastava, **PLB 382** (1996) 282.

14. J. Field, E. Pietarinen and K. Kajantie, Nucl. Phys. **B 171** (1980) 377; M. Drees, *Proceedings of 23rd International Symposium on Multiparticle Dynamics*, Aspen, Colo., Sep. 1993. Eds. M.M. Block and A.R. White.

15. M. Derrick et al., ZEUS collaboration, PLB 354 (1995) 163.

16. M. Drees, Univ. Wisconsin report **MAD/PH-95-867**,*Proceedings of the 4th workshop on TRISTAN physics at High Luminosities*, KEK, Tsukuba, Japan, Nov. 1994; M. Drees and R. Godbole, J. Phys. G 21 (1995) 1559.

17. A. Corsetti, R. Godbole and G. Pancheri, in Proceedings of the Workshop on e^+e^- Collisions at TeV Energies, Annecy, Gran Sasso, Hamburg, DESY 96-123D, June 1996, page. 495.

18. W. van Rossum, these propceedings.

19. G. Shuler and T. Sjostrand, Zeit Phys. C68 (1995) 607: Phys., Lett. B376 (1996) 193.

BFKL SCATTERING AT LEPII AND A NEXT e^+e^- COLLIDER

S.J. BRODSKY

Stanford Linear Accelerator Center, Stanford University
Stanford, CA 94309

F. HAUTMANN, D.E. SOPER

Institute of Theoretical Science, University of Oregon
Eugene, OR 97403

We discuss virtual photon scattering in the region dominated by BFKL exchange, and report results for the cross sections at present and future e^+e^- colliders.

The BFKL equation describes scattering processes in QCD in the limit of large energies and fixed (sufficiently large) momentum transfers. The study that we present in this paper analyzes the prospects for using photon-photon collisions as a probe of QCD dynamics in this region. The quantity we focus on is the total cross section for scattering two photons sufficiently far off shell at large center-of-mass energies, $\gamma^*(Q_A^2) + \gamma^*(Q_B^2) \to$ hadrons, $s \gg Q_A^2, Q_B^2 \gg \Lambda_{QCD}^2$. This process can be observed at high-energy and high-luminosity e^+e^- colliders as well as e^-e^- or $\mu^{\pm}\mu^-$ colliders, where the photons are produced from the lepton beams by bremsstrahlung. The $\gamma^*\gamma^*$ cross section can be measured in collisions in which both the outgoing leptons are tagged.

The basic motivation for this study is that compared to tests of BFKL dynamics in deeply inelastic lepton-hadron scattering (see, for instance, the review in Ref. [1]) the off-shell photon cross section presents some theoretical advantages, essentially because it does not involve a non-perturbative target. The photons act as color dipoles with small transverse size, so that the QCD interactions can be treated in a fully perturbative framework.

The structure of $\gamma^*\gamma^*$ high-energy scattering is shown schematically in Fig. 1. We work in a frame in which the photons q_A, q_B have zero transverse momenta and are boosted along the positive and negative light-cone directions. In the leading logarithm approximation, the process can be described as the interaction of two $q\bar{q}$ pairs scattering off each other via multiple gluon exchange. The $q\bar{q}$ pairs are in a color-singlet state and interact through their color dipole moments. The gluonic function $\mathcal{F}$ is obtained from the solution to the BFKL equation [2].

The analysis of the transverse-distance scales involved in the scattering illustrates a few distinctive features of this process. The mean transverse size of each $q\bar{q}$ dipole is given, in the first approximation, by the reciprocal of the

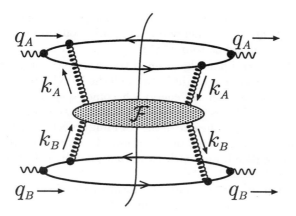

Figure 1: The virtual photon cross section in the high energy limit.

corresponding photon virtuality:

$$< R_{\perp A} > \sim 1/Q_A \quad , \quad < R_{\perp B} > \sim 1/Q_B \quad . \tag{1}$$

However, fluctuations can bring in much larger transverse sizes. Large-size fluctuations occur as a result of the configurations in which one quark of the pair carries small transverse momentum and a small fraction of the photon longitudinal momentum (the so-called aligned-jet configurations[3]). For example, for the momentum p_A of the quark created by photon A:

$$\mathbf{p}_{\perp A} \ll Q_A \quad , \quad z_A \equiv p_A^+/q_A^+ \ll 1 \quad . \tag{2}$$

The actual size up to which the $q\bar{q}$ pair can fluctuate is controlled by the scale of the system that it scatters off. Therefore, in $\gamma^*\gamma^*$ scattering the fluctuations in the transverse size of each pair are suppressed by the off-shellness of the photon creating the other pair. If *both* photons are sufficiently far off shell, the transverse separation in each $q\bar{q}$ dipole stays small[4]. This can be contrasted with the case of deeply inelastic ep scattering (or $e\gamma$, where γ is a (quasi-)real photon). In this case, the $q\bar{q}$ pair produced by the virtual photon can fluctuate up to sizes of the order of a hadronic scale, that is, $1/\Lambda_{QCD}$. This results in the deeply inelastic cross section being determined by an interplay of short and long distances.

In principle, the $q\bar{q}$ dipoles in the $\gamma^*\gamma^*$ process could still fluctuate to bigger sizes in correspondence of configurations in which the jet alignment occurs twice, once for each photon. However, such configurations cost an extra overall power of $1/Q^2$ in the cross section (terms proportional to $1/(Q_A^2 Q_B^2)$ rather than $1/(Q_A Q_B))$ [5]. Therefore, they only contribute at the level of sub-leading power corrections to $\sigma(\gamma^* \gamma^*)$.

Even though the $q\bar{q}$ dipoles have small transverse size, sensitivity to large transverse distances may be brought in through the BFKL function $\mathcal{F}$. This indeed is expected to occur when the energy s becomes very large. As s increases, the typical impact parameters dominating the cross section for BFKL exchange grow to be much larger than the size of the colliding objects[6]. One can interpret this as providing an upper bound on the range of values of $(\alpha_s(Q^2) \ln(s/Q^2))$ in which the simple BFKL approach to virtual photon scattering is expected to give reliable predictions [4].

The calculation of $\sigma(\gamma^* \gamma^*)$ and the form of the result are discussed in detail in Refs. [7,4]. We recall here the main features:

i) for large virtualities, $\sigma(\gamma^* \gamma^*)$ scales like $1/Q^2$, where $Q^2 \sim \max\{Q_A^2, Q_B^2\}$. This is characteristic of the perturbative QCD prediction. Models based on Regge factorization (which work well in the soft-interaction regime dominating $\gamma\gamma$ scattering near the mass shell) would predict a higher power in $1/Q$.

ii) $\sigma(\gamma^* \gamma^*)$ is affected by logarithmic corrections in the energy s to all orders in α_s. As a result of the BFKL summation of these contributions, the cross section rises like a power in s, $\sigma \propto s^\lambda$. The Born approximation to this result (that is, the $\mathcal{O}(\alpha_s^2)$ contribution, corresponding to single gluon exchange in the graph of Fig. 1) gives a constant cross section, $\sigma_{Born} \propto s^0$. This behavior in s can be compared with lower-order calculations which do not include the corrections associated to (single or multiple) gluon exchange. Such calculations would give cross sections that fall off like $1/s$ at large s.

These features are reflected at the level of the $e^+ e^-$ scattering process. The $e^+ e^-$ cross section is obtained by folding $\sigma(\gamma^* \gamma^*)$ with the flux of photons from each lepton. In Figs. 2 and 3, we integrate this cross section with a lower cut on the photon virtualities (in order that the coupling α_s be small, and that the process be dominated by the perturbative contribution) and a lower cut on the photon-photon c.m.s. energy (in order that the high energy approximation be valid). We plot the result as a function of the lower bound $Q^2_{\min}$, illustrating the expected dependence of the photon-photon cross section on the photon virtualities. Fig. 2 is for the energy of a future $e^+ e^-$ collider. Fig. 3 refers to the LEP collider operating at $\sqrt{s} = 200$ GeV. Details on our choice of cuts may be found in Ref. [4].

From Figs. 2 and 3, for a value of the cut $Q_{\min} = 2$ GeV we find $\sigma \simeq 1.5\,\mathrm{pb}$ at LEP200 energies, and $\sigma \simeq 12\,\mathrm{pb}$ at the energy of a future collider. These cross sections would give rise to about 750 events at LEP200 for a value of the luminosity $L = 500\,\mathrm{pb}^{-1}$, and about 6×10^5 events at $\sqrt{s} = 500$ GeV for

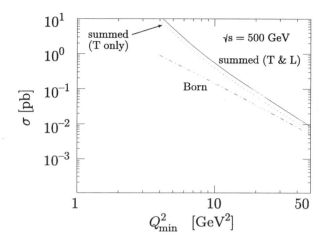

Figure 2: The Q^2_{min} dependence of the e^+e^- integrated rate for $\sqrt{s} = 500$ GeV. The choice of the cuts and of the scales in the leading logarithm result is as in Ref.[4]. The dot-dashed and solid lines correspond to the result of using, respectively, the Born and the BFKL-summed expressions for the photon-photon cross section. The dotted curve shows the contribution to the summed result coming from transversely polarized photons.

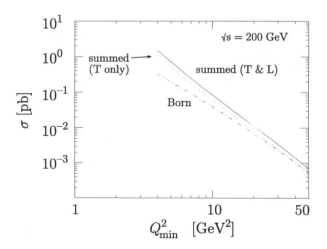

Figure 3: Same as in Fig. 2 for $\sqrt{s} = 200$ GeV.

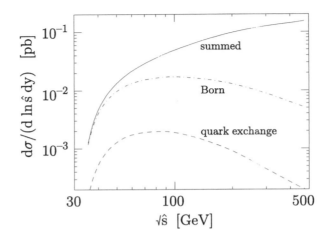

Figure 4: The cross section $d\sigma/(d\ln\hat{s}\,dy)$ at $y = 0$ for $\sqrt{s} = 500$ GeV. We take $Q^2_{\min} = 10$ GeV^2. The solid curve is the summed BFKL result. The dot-dashed curve is the Born result. The dashed curve shows the (purely electromagnetic) contribution arising from the scattering of (transversely polarized) photons via quark exchange.

$L = 50\,\mathrm{fb}^{-1}$. The above value of $Q_{\min}$ would imply detecting leptons scattered through angles down to about 20 mrad at LEP200, and about 8 mrad at a future 500 GeV collider. If instead we take, for instance, $Q_{\min} = 6$ GeV, the minimum angle at a 500 GeV collider is 24 mrad. Then the cross section is about 2×10^{-2} pb, corresponding to about 10^3 events.

The dependence on the photon-photon c.m. energy $\sqrt{\hat{s}}$ can be best studied by fixing $Q_{\min}$ and looking at the cross section $d\sigma/(d\ln\hat{s}\,dy)$ (here y is the photon-photon rapidity). In Fig. 4 we plot this cross section at $y = 0$. While at the lowest end of the range in $\sqrt{\hat{s}}$ the curves are strongly dependent on the choice of the cuts, for increasing $\sqrt{\hat{s}}$ the plotted distribution is rather directly related to the behavior of $\sigma(\gamma^*\gamma^*)$ discussed earlier. In particular, as $\sqrt{\hat{s}}$ increases to about 100 GeV we see the Born result flatten out and the summed BFKL result rise, while the contribution from quark exchange is comparatively suppressed. The damping towards the higher end of the range in $\sqrt{\hat{s}}$ affects all curves and is due to the influence of the photon flux factors.

Fig. 4 is for $\sqrt{s} = 500$ GeV. The corresponding curves at LEP200 energies are qualitatively similar. The main difference is that at $\sqrt{s} = 200$ GeV there is less available range for $\sqrt{\hat{s}}$.

We see from the results presented above that at a future e^+e^- collider it should be possible to probe the effects of pomeron exchange in a range of Q^2 where summed perturbation theory applies. One should be able to investigate this region in detail by varying Q_A, Q_B and $\hat{s}$ independently. At LEP200 such studies appear to be more problematic mainly because of limitations in luminosity. Even with a modest luminosity, however, one can access the region of relatively low Q^2 if one can get down to small enough angles. This would allow one to examine experimentally the transition between soft and hard scattering.

Acknowledgments

We thank F. Erné and the organizing committee for arranging such an enjoyable conference. This work is supported in part by the United States Department of Energy grants DE-AC03-76SF00515 and DE-FG03-96ER40969.

References

1. H. Abramowicz, plenary talk at ICHEP96 (Warsaw, July 1996), in Proceedings of the XXVIII International Conference on High Energy Physics, eds. Z. Ajduk and A.K. Wroblewski, World Scientific, p.53.
2. L.N. Lipatov, Sov. J. Nucl. Phys. **23**, 338 (1976); E.A. Kuraev, L.N. Lipatov and V.S. Fadin, Sov. Phys. JETP **45**, 199 (1977) ; I. Balitskii and L.N. Lipatov, Sov. J. Nucl. Phys. **28**, 822 (1978).
3. J.D. Bjorken and J. Kogut, Phys. Rev. D **8**, 1341 (1973).
4. S.J. Brodsky, F. Hautmann and D.E. Soper, preprint OITS-629/97, SLAC-PUB-7480, e-print archive hep-ph/9706427.
5. J.D. Bjorken, preprint SLAC-PUB-7341, presented at Snowmass 1996 Summer Study on New Directions for High Energy Physics, e-print archive hep-ph/9610516.
6. A.H. Mueller, Nucl. Phys. **B437**, 107 (1995).
7. S.J. Brodsky, F. Hautmann and D.E. Soper, Phys. Rev. Lett. **78**, 803 (1997); F. Hautmann, talk at ICHEP96 (Warsaw, July 1996), preprint OITS 613/96, in Proceedings of the XXVIII International Conference on High Energy Physics, eds. Z. Ajduk and A.K. Wroblewski, World Scientific, p.705.

Session B

Inclusive Processes

INCLUSIVE HARD PROCESSES IN PHOTON INDUCED REACTIONS

P. AURENCHE

Laboratoire de Physique Théorique ENSLAPP, B.P. 110,
(URA 1436 du CNRS associée à l'Université de Savoie et l'ENS-Lyon)
F-74941 Annecy-le-Vieux Cedex, France

In the following some aspects of inclusive hard processes in photon induced reactions are reviewed. After a discussion on the properties of hard processes, the
phenomenology of jet production and of charmonium production is presented in
the context of the next-to-leading logarithm approximation of QCD

1   Introduction

Over the last few years the physics of hard processes in photon-induced reactions (*e.g.* photo-production at HERA and photon-photon collisions at TRIS-
TAN and LEP) has almost reached the status of sophistication of hard processes in purely hadronic reactions. The experimental results are becoming
more and more accurate and many observables measured in hadronic reactions
are now being accessible in photon-induced reactions while the corresponding theoretical calculations have been performed at the next-to-leading order
(NLO) of perturbative QCD. Since PHOTON'95[1] an enormous progress has
been made in this respect so that one should be able to start quantitative
phenomenology. The main points that deserve special attention now are: 1)
matching the calculated observables with the experimental ones; 2) matching
the appropriate non-perturbative input to the conventions used in the NLO
calculations.

It is well known that the physics of photon-induced processes is more
complex than that of pure hadronic reactions. This arises from the fact that
the photon acts either as a *parton* which couples directly to the hard scattering
and contributes to *direct* processes, or as a *composite* object (a bag of partons)
the constituents of which couple to the hard scattering via the photon structure
functions: this leads to *resolved* processes. Furthermore, as discussed in ref.[2]
the photon structure function contains two pieces:

$$F_{i/\gamma}(x,Q) = F_{i/\gamma}^{\text{had}}(x,Q) + F_{i/\gamma}^{\text{anom}}(x,Q), \qquad i = \text{quark, gluon} \qquad (1)$$

where the first term on the right hand-side is similar to the hadronic structure function while the second term increases logarithmically with Q^2 and is
asymptotically calculable in perturbation theory.

In the following, in a theoretical introduction, the structure of a "typical" cross section will be derived stressing the features distinguishing the *direct* processes from the *resolved* ones. Two topics are selected for further discussion: the production of jets and single particle on the one hand and the production of hidden charm for which HERA offers the possibility to test models of J/Ψ production at the Tevatron.

2 Photon induced reactions: theory

We consider photon-photon collisions as an example. The lowest order diagram is shown in fig. 1a. To apply the perturbative approach a large scale is needed which is provided by the transverse momentum of the produced jet or the mass of the heavy quark. Considering jet production, the Born approximation

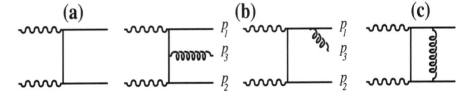

Figure 1: *Feynman diagrams for $\gamma\gamma$ scattering. (a): Born approximation; (b) real corrections; (c) virtual corrections.*

is valid for large values of $p_T/\sqrt{s}$ where unfortunately the cross section is very small since it behaves as $d\sigma^{jet}/d\vec{p}_T \sim \alpha^2/p_T^4$. To obtain reliable predictions at lower p_T values it is necessary to consider diagrams with an extra gluon emission, leading in principle, to $\mathcal{O}(\alpha_s)$ corrections to the cross section (fig. 1b,c). When integrating over the phase-space of final state partons to reconstruct *e.g.* the single inclusive jet cross section, one encounters "dangerous" regions where the virtualities of some fermion propagators may vanish and the corresponding matrix elements are not defined. This happens, for example, when the final state parton of momentum p_1 is collinear to the initial photon of momentum k_a $(s_{a_1} = (k_a - p_1)^2 \to 0)$ or the emitted gluon is collinear to a final state quark $(s_{13} = (p_1 + p_3)^2 \to 0)$. Considering the s_{a_1} singular region, the process can be pictured as in fig. 2a where the initial photon fragments into a collinear $q\bar{q}$ pair followed by the hard 2 body $\to$ 2 body scattering of the q or $\bar{q}$, the other parton flying off down the beam pipe. The photon fragmentation is a soft process (the relevant scale s_{a_1} is small) which takes place on a long time scale before the short-distance process scatters the partons at large transverse

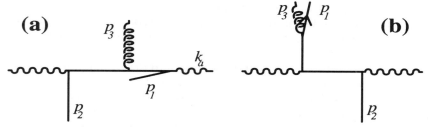

Figure 2: *Diagrammatic representation of the collinear singularities.*

momenta. The cross section can be written as

$$\frac{d\sigma^{\gamma\gamma}}{d\vec{p}_T d\eta} = \int dz P_{q/\gamma}(z) \ln\left(\frac{M^2}{\lambda^2}\right) \frac{d\sigma^{\gamma q}}{d\vec{p}_T d\eta} + \frac{\alpha_s}{2\pi} K^D(p_T, M), \qquad (2)$$

where λ is a cut-off introduced to regularise the collinear singularity, and $M \sim \mathcal{O}(p_T)$ is an arbitrary scale introduced to separate the contribution from the collinear region, generating the "large" $\ln(M^2/\lambda^2)$ piece, from the hard region (rouhgly $s_{a_1} > M^2$) leading to the term K^D containing only finite terms such as $\ln(p_T/M^2)$. The above expression is rigourously independent of the scale M. In fact, at this level of approximation the scale M is not necessary but it is introduced for later use. The integration variable in eq. 2 is simply the fraction of the photon momentum carried by the interacting q or $\bar{q}$. Using the factorisation theorem, we can substitute to the "large logarithm" term $P_{q/\gamma}(z) \ln(M^2/\lambda^2)$ the photon structure function $F_{q/\gamma}(z, M)$, measured in $\gamma^*\gamma$ collisions, which satisfies evolution equations of type:

$$\frac{dF_{i/\gamma}(M)}{d\ln M^2} = P_{i\gamma} + \sum_{j=q,g} P_{ij} \otimes F_{j/\gamma}(M), \qquad i, j = q, g \qquad (3)$$

where the symbol $\otimes$ denotes a convolution over the longitudinal variable and the P_{ij} are the usual splitting functions. After replacing $P_{q/\gamma} \ln(M^2/\lambda^2)$ by $F_{q/\gamma}(M)$ in eq. (2) the compensation in the M dependence on the right-hand side is only approximate as the evolution equation effectively resums large higher order corrections (of type $[\alpha_s(M) \ln(M/\Lambda_{QCD})]^n$) in $F_{q/\gamma}(M)$ whereas no such resummation is performed in K^D. The cross section can be written

$$\frac{d\sigma^{\gamma\gamma}}{d\vec{p}_T d\eta} = \left(\frac{d\sigma^{\gamma\gamma}}{d\vec{p}_T d\eta}^{(0)} + \frac{\alpha_s}{2\pi} K^D(p_T, M)\right) + \int dz F_{q/\gamma}(z, M) \frac{d\sigma^{\gamma q}}{d\vec{p}_T d\eta} \qquad (4)$$

where the K^D term is a correction to the Born cross section $d\sigma^{\gamma\gamma(0)}$ and contributes to the *direct* cross section evaluated in the NLO approximation. The last term in the equation is the *resolved* process. Since in the latter case only

part of the energy of the photon contributes to the large p_T process, the rest being carried by the longitudinal fragment, the *resolved* term is qualitatively (*i.e.* in the LO approximation) distinguished from the *direct* one by:
- a softer p_T spectrum;
- a jet system boosted in the direction opposite to that of the resolved photon: *e.g.* a backward moving resolved photon produces forward going jets;
- some hadronic activity in the direction of the resolved photon.
In the NLO approximation the *direct* and *resolved* components are *not separatly observable* since they depend on the arbitrary renormalisation scale M. However, using the properties above it is possible to define observables related to these two components (see below).

Until now we have discussed features related to the initial state singularities. The final state singularities (of type $s_{13} \to 0$) also lead to 2 body $\to$ 2 body hard scattering with the singular behaviour associated to the fragmentation process exactly as in purely hadronic processes (fig. 2b). The cross section is made finite by adding the virtual diagrams and properly defining the jets, merging the two almost collinear partons into one jet, or by convoluting with a fragmentation function and using the factorisation theorem to build the scaling violations in the fragmentation function.

One could continue the perturbative analysis and consider the emission of more partons: this will lead to *double resolved* processes where each photon interacts via its structure function. Finally, the $\gamma\gamma$ cross section for inclusive jet production takes the form:

$$\frac{d\sigma^{\gamma\gamma}}{d\vec{p}_T d\eta} = \frac{d\sigma^D}{d\vec{p}_T d\eta} + \frac{d\sigma^{SR}}{d\vec{p}_T d\eta} + \frac{d\sigma^{DR}}{d\vec{p}_T d\eta} \tag{5}$$

with the *direct, single resolved* and *double resolved* pieces given in the NLO approximation by an expansion of type:

$$\frac{d\sigma^D}{d\vec{p}_T d\eta}(R) = \frac{d\sigma^{\gamma\gamma}}{d\vec{p}_T d\eta}^{(0)} + \frac{\alpha_s}{2\pi} K^D(R; p_T, M), \tag{6}$$

and similarly for the other terms. The variable R specifies the jet cone size. The factorisation scale variation associated to the inhomogeneous term $P_{i\gamma}$ in eq. (3) is compensated between the D, SR and DR pieces while the variation associated to the homogeneous terms P_{ij} compensates within each of these pieces between the lowest order and the correction terms. Thus only eq. (5) is expected to be stable under variation of scale M but not its individual components.
For hadron production an extra convolution of the above expresssions with the

relevant fragmentation function is needed. For photo-production processes one of the $F_{i/\gamma}(x, M)$ should be replaced by the hadronic structure function. In an obvious notation, the cross section takes the simpler form:

$$\frac{d\sigma^{\gamma p}}{d\vec{p}_T d\eta} = \frac{d\sigma^D}{d\vec{p}_T d\eta} + \frac{d\sigma^R}{d\vec{p}_T d\eta}. \tag{7}$$

3 Phenomenology of jet production

One of the aims of studies of hard processes in γ induced reactions is the NLO determination of the photon structure function[3]. To achieve this it is very useful to isolate in an experimental way the *resolved* component of the cross section. In a *direct* process, all the photon energy is given to jets at large p_T so that by momentum conservation one has for a 2-jet event (the photon is assumed to move towards negative rapidity):

$$x_\gamma = \frac{E_{T_1} e^{-\eta_1} + E_{T_2} e^{-\eta_2}}{2E_\gamma} = 1 \tag{8}$$

Higher order correction are not expected to change this relation drastically. In contrast, for a *resolved* event $x_\gamma < 1$ since part of the photon energy disappears in the beam pipe (fig. 2a) (in ref.[4] a modified definition of x_γ is proposed). At HERA, the experimental groups choose the value $x_\gamma = .75$ as a cut-off so that above this value the events are produced mostly by the *direct* process while below they are mainly *resolved*. The integrated di-jet cross sections for HERA,

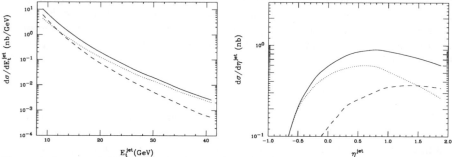

Figure 3: *Integrated di-jet cross section in the domains $0 < x_\gamma < 1$ (solid line), $x_\gamma < .75$ (dashed line), $x_\gamma > .75$ (dotted line). From ref.* [5].

shown in fig. 3, nicely illustrate, in the NLO approximation[5] the different characteristics of the two components. In the first figure the direct component shows a faster decrease with E_T, while in the second one the resolved

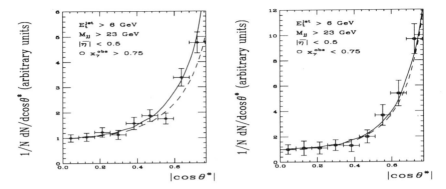

Figure 4: *Dijet angular distribution as measured by ZEUS[6] normalized to one at* $\cos\theta^* = 0$ *compared with LO (dash lines) and NLO result (solid lines), from ref.[5].*

cross section is seen to contribute mainly forward jets. In fig. 4 a very good agreement is seen, between the NLO theory[5] and experiment[6], in the shape of the di-jet angular distribution (the angle is measured in the di-jet rest frame): as expected the *resolved* component has a steeper angular dependence due to the importance of gluon exchange diagrams while for the *direct* term only quark exchange is allowed. In the next figure, we compare theoretical predictions of two independent groups[5, 7] with ZEUS data for the di-jet cross section[8] $d\sigma/d\bar\eta$, integrated over the phase space $E_{T_1}, E_{T_2} \geq E_0$ and $|\eta_1 - \eta_2| < .5$, with $\bar\eta = (\eta_1 + \eta_2)/2$. The first point to notice is the disagreement between the two sets of theoretical predictions: this arises because the groups do not calculate the same observable due to instabilities in the perturbatively calculated quantity. This is related to the fact that the boundary condition $E_{T_1} = E_{T_2} = E_0$ is an infrared singular point. Typically, in the NLO approximation one needs to consider the production of 3 partons in the final state: it can be separated into two classes:

$$\sigma^{2\to3} = \sigma^{2\to3}(y_c) + \sigma_R^{2\to2}(y_c) \tag{9}$$

with the parameter y_c such that the first term on the right hand side contains events generated with "dangerous" invariant masses [*i.e.* leading to soft and collinear singularities in the matrix element] $s_{ij} > y_c s_{ab}$, while $\sigma_R^{2\to2}(y_c)$ contains events which look like 2-body hard scattering as discussed above. This part contains all divergences and y_c is chosen small enough ($y_c = 10^{-5}$ to 10^{-2}) so that approximations can be used to extract divergences analytically. Upon adding the virtual corrections which are also of type 2 body $\to$ 2 body scattering all divergences cancel and the theoretical cross section is:

$$\sigma = \sigma^{2\to3}(y_c) + \sigma^{2\to2}(y_c) \tag{10}$$

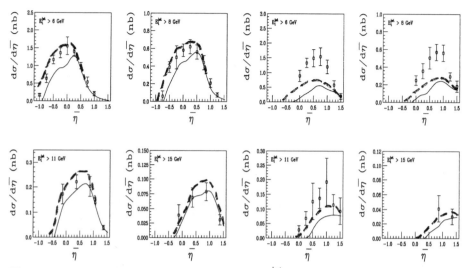

Figure 5: *Dijet cross section vs. $\overline{\eta}$ integrated over $E_T^{\text{jet}} > E_0$ for $E_0 = 6, 8, 11, 15 \, \text{GeV}$; the four figs. on the left are as for $x_\gamma > 0.75$; those on the right are for $x_\gamma < 0.75$. The data are from [8]. Thin lines from ref.[5]; thick dashed lines from ref.[7].*

each piece being regular, the first one beeing calculated numerically and the second one semi-analytically. By histogramming one reconstructs any observable but it should be checked that the result is independent of y_c. It turns out that for the dijet observable of fig. 5, the condition $E_{T_1}, E_{T_2} > E_0$ introduces constraints on the phase space which spoil the y_c compensation between the terms in the above equation. Harris and Owens[5] (who use a more elaborate method than the one described above) observe that the remaining dependence on y_c is much less than the experimental error bars and present results with some value of y_c while Klasen and Kramer[7] modify the boundary condition to $E_{T_1} > E_0$, allowing for a smaller E_{T_2} if the third unobserved jet has transverse energy less than $E_{T_3} < 1$ GeV. This is sufficient to remove the y_c dependence but the result is rather sensitive to the latter energy cut. As seen in the figure this slight modification of the boundary condition considerably affects the predictions[9]. If one considers that the calculation of ref.[5] is closer to the experimental observable there remains a drastic disagreement between the data and the theoretical predictions specially concerning the *resolved* cross section. Disagreement between theory[5,10,11] and experiment[12] is also seen when comparing the rapidity distribution of single inclusive jet production as displayed in fig. 6: this is particularly marked at low E_T and large pseudo-rapidities, *i.e.* where the resolved component plays a dominant role. This leads us to the important question of whether or not the theoretical predictions are able to match the experimental observables. Two questions can be raised:

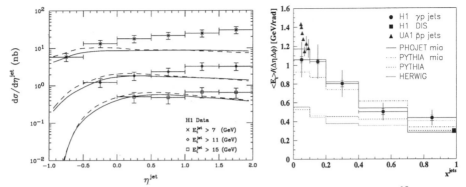

Figure 6: *Comparison of the single jet inclusive cross section measured by $H1^{12}$ compared with NLO predictions[5] using 2 different sets of photon structure functions. Transverse energy of the underlying event at HERA as measured by $H1^{12}$.*

- is it possible to match theoretical jets, made up of partons, with experimental jets reconstructed, via various algorithms, from energy deposited in calorimeter cells?

- how does one take into account the transverse energy of the *underlying event*, *i.e.* the energy generated by the interaction of the *spectator* partons?

The first point was studied many years ago in connection to jet production at the Tevatron[13] and was recently re-analysed in detail for HERA by Kramer and collaborators[14]: the idea is to introduce an extra parameter R_{sep} controlling the width of the jets which is adjusted to fit the data: a better description of the data by the NLO calculations is indeed achieved at the expense, however, of the predictive power of the theory.

Concerning the second point the problem can be qualitatively understood in the following way. At HERA, in events with *direct* photo-production of jets the transverse energy of the *underlying event* is produced by string-like effects: typically a transverse energy of $300 - 400$ MeV per unit of rapidity is expected. On the contrary, in resolved photo-production, the remnants of the photon can undergo soft or semi-hard interactions with those of the proton[15] generating transverse energies in the GeV range: the larger the energy of the photon remnant (*i.e.* the smaller x_γ is) the larger is the underlying transverse energy: this is illustrated in fig. 6 from $H1^{12}$ which shows the E_T outside the jets as a function of x_γ. Such an effect is of course present in purely hadronic reactions but is relatively less important because the much higher E_T values of jets probed in hadronic colliders. On the other hand, jets in $\gamma\gamma$ reactions should be less affected except at very low E_T values ($E_T < 5$ GeV at LEP1) where the *double-resolved* process is dominant. Good agreement of TRISTAN[16, 17] and LEP[18] data with the NLO predictions[19] has been obtained for inclusive two-jet production.

A discussion about the determination of the gluon density in the photon using jet cross sections is given, in the LO approximation, in ref.[3].

A way to avoid problems related to jet definition or to underlying transverse energy is to consider single hadron production. Good agreement is indeed found in photo-production between the NLO predictions[20] and HERA data[21].

4 Charmonium production

There has been new developments concerning the production of hidden heavy flavor at the Tevatron where the usual model predictions, based on the color singlet model, for prompt Ψ production fall an order of magnitude below the experimental results. The interest of HERA lies in the fact, that many of the new parameters introduced in the model can be tested independently. We consider here only the non-diffractive mechanism, corresponding to a Ψ inelasticity factor of $z = p.k_\Psi/p.k_\gamma < .9$. In the factorisation approach of ref.[22] the cross section for the production of a heavy quark bound state H is

$$d\sigma(\gamma p \to HX) = \sum_{[\mathbf{n}]} d\hat{\sigma}(\gamma p \to Q\overline{Q}[\mathbf{n}]X) < \mathcal{O}^H[\mathbf{n}] >, \tag{11}$$

where $d\hat{\sigma}$ is the cross section for producing a heavy $Q\overline{Q}$ sytem in state $[\mathbf{n}]$ defined by its color $[\mathbf{1,8}]$, its spin $[0,1]$ and orbital angular momentum. This term is calculable perturbatively, the large scale beeing provided by the heavy quark mass or eventually by the transverse momentum of the system. The factor $< \mathcal{O}^H[\mathbf{n}] >$ describes the non-perturbative transition from the state with quantum numbers $[\mathbf{n}]$ to quarkonium H. Typically $< \mathcal{O}^\Psi[^3S_1,\mathbf{1}] >= 1.16$ GeV^3 (from Ψ leptonic decay) while the $\mathbf{8}$ matrix elements $< \mathcal{O}^\Psi[^3S_1,\mathbf{8}] >\sim$ $< \mathcal{O}^\Psi[^3S_0,\mathbf{8}] >\sim< \mathcal{O}^\Psi[^3P_J,\mathbf{8}] > /m_c^2 \sim 10^{-2}$ GeV^3 as determined from fits to the Tevatron data[23]. The colour $\mathbf{8}$ values are consistent with non-relativistic QCD which predicts their suppression by powers of the velocity of the heavy quark in the bound state[24]. Although the $\mathbf{8}$ matrix elements are small it may happen that the perturbative cross section $d\hat{\sigma}([\mathbf{8}])$ is large so that a non negligible contribution occurs. In the colour $\mathbf{1}$ model the $\mathbf{8}$ matrix elements are assumed to vanish. Many processes contribute to the cross section $d\hat{\sigma}(Q\overline{Q}[\mathbf{n}])$: it is convenient to distinguish fusion processes which are important at small p_T, but are suppressed by a factor m_Q^2/p_T^2, from fragmentation processes where the $Q\overline{Q}$ state is found in the decay of a Q or gluon jet produced at large transverse momentum. Furthermore, both processes come in the *direct* variety if the photon couples to the hard sub-scattering, or the *resolved* one if the photon structure function is involved. These mechanisms have different z and p_T dependences so that varying the kinematical conditions they could be separated.

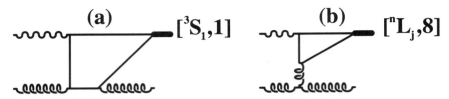

Figure 7: *Some Feynman diagrams for charmonium production. (a): colour singlet production;(b) diagram contributing only to colour octet production.*

Consider first direct fusion processes which should be a good approximation of cross sections at small transverse momentum ($p_T \leq m_Q$) or integrated over p_T. The basic colour singlet diagram is shown in fig. 7a: the heavy $Q\bar{Q}$ pair is produced by photon-gluon fusion and an extra gluon is necessarily emitted so that a $Q\bar{Q}$ state in a **1** component can be projected out. NLO corrections to this process have also been calculated[25]. A similar diagram contributes also to the production of a colour **8** state together with the diagram of fig. 7b: because of the gluon exchange this diagram will be enhanced near the kinematical region $z \sim 1$. The comparison of the theory[26] with HERA[27, 28] data is shown in fig. 8 where one sees the excellent agreement between data and the colour **1** NLO predictions while the **8** component seems to yield much too large a contribution at large z values. To claim quantitative disagreement is premature as the non-perturbative **8** matrix elements may have been overestimated in the Tevatron analysis; furthermore, doubts have been raised about the validity of the factorisation approach (velocity expansion) in the large z region[30].

The resolved fusion diagrams are easily obtained by substituting to the

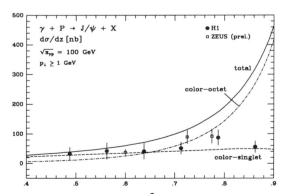

Figure 8: *Fusion contribution to charmonium production at HERA.*

photon a gluon, fragment of the photon: obviously this process dominates at small z where it is further found that the **8** contribution overwhelms the **1** one by more than one order of magnitude: thus the region at small p_T, small z

or equivalently large rapidity since $z \sim e^{-y_{\text{lab}}}$, should be able to probe the **8** matrix elements.

At large p_T, on the other hand, the production of charmonium in the fragments of a jet should be considered[31, 32]. In the factorisation approach, the fragmentation funtion of parton i into H takes the form:

$$D_i^H(z, M) = \sum_{[\mathbf{n}]} d_{i \to c\bar{c}[\mathbf{n}]}(z, M) < \mathcal{O}^H[\mathbf{n}] >, \qquad i = c, g \tag{12}$$

where the functions d_i are perturbatively calculated (all scales involved are large) and the same non-perturbative matrix elements as above appear. A detailed study at the NLO order[32], including both direct and resolved processes, has recently been performed where it is found an overwhelming dominance of the colour **8** channels at HERA for large y_{lab} and p_T, the more so the larger the γp invariant mass.

The exclusive channel $\gamma p \to \Psi \gamma$ has also been proposed[33] as a test of the model as it is obviously dominated at large z by the **8** component (see fig. 7a with the final state gluon changed into a photon).

Thus HERA appears a promising place to support or invalidate the colour **8** model if detailed measurements of specific channels can be done over a wide rapidity range for $J\Psi$ production.

Acknowledgements

I am grateful to M. Erdmann for discussions and very helpful advice in the preparation of this talk. I also thank L. Bourhis, I. Butterworth, M. Cacciari, J. Forshaw, J.Ph. Guillet, B.W. Harris, U. Karshon, B. Kniehl, M. Mangano, J.F. Owens and E. Pilon. Support by the EEC program "Human Capital and Mobility", Network "Physics at High Energy Colliders", contract CHRX-CT93-0357 (DG 12 COMA), is greatefully acknowledged.

References

1. Proceedings of PHOTON'95, D.J. Miller, S.L. Cartwright, V. Khoze *eds.*, World Scientific, Singapore, 1995.
2. A. Vogt, these proceedings.
3. M. Erdmann, 'The Partonic Structure of the Photon', Springer Tracts in Modern Physics 138, Heidelberg, Springer (1997).
4. L. Bourhis, these proceedings; proceedings of the 1995-1996 Workshop for Future Physics at HERA, ed. G. Ingelman.

5. B.W. Harris and J.F. Owens, Florida State University preprint FSU-HEP-970411, hep-ph/9704234.

6. ZEUS collab., M. Derrick et al., Phys. Lett. B **384**, 401 (1996).

7. M. Klasen and G. Kramer, hep-ph/9611450, preprint DESY 96-246.

8. ZEUS collab., M. Derrick et al., 28th International Conference on High Energy Physics, Warsaw, 1997.

9. I thank B.W. Harris and J.F. Owens for a discussion on the differences between the calculations of ref.[5] and ref.[7].

10. P. Aurenche, M. Fontannaz, J.Ph. Guillet, Phys. Lett. B **338**, 98 (1994).

11. D. Bödeker, G. Kramer, S.G. Salesh, Z. Phys. C **63**, 471 (1994).

12. H1 collab, S. Aid et al., Z. Phys. C **70**, 17 (1996).

13. S.D Ellis, Z. Kunszt, D.E. Soper, Phys. Rev. Lett. **69**, 3615 (1992).

14. J.M. Butterworth et al., hep-ph/9608481;
    M. Klasen and G. Kramer, hep-ph/9701247, preprint DESY-97-002.

15. R. Engel, Z. Phys. C **66**, 203 (1995);
    R. Engel, J. Ranft, Phys. Rev. D **52**, 1459 (1995), D **54**, 4244 (1996).

16. AMY collab., B.J. Kim et al., Phys. Lett. B **325**, 248 (1994).

17. TOPAZ collab., H. Hayashii et al., Phys. Lett. B **314**, 149 (1993).

18. OPAL collab.,K. Ackerstaff et al., Z. Phys. C **73**, 433 (1997).

19. P. Aurenche et al., Prog. Theor. Phys. **92** 175, (1994);
    T. Kleinwort, G. Kramer, hep-ph/9610489, preprint DESY 96-223.

20. J. Binnewies, B.A. Kniehl, G. Kramer, Phys. Rev. D **52**, 4947 (1995).

21. H1 collab., I. Abt et al., Phys. Lett. B **328**, 176 (1994);
    ZEUS collab., M. Derrick et al., Z. Phys. C **67**, 227 (1995).

22. G.T. Bodwin, E. Braaten, G.P. Lepage, Phys. Rev. D **51**, 1125 (1995).

23. P. Cho, A.K. Leibovich, Phys. Rev. D **53**, 150 (1996);**D53**, 6203 (1996).

24. G.P. Lepage et al., Phys. Rev. D **46**, 4052 (1992).

25. M. Krämer, Nucl. Phys. B **459**, 3 (1996).

26. M. Cacciari, M. Krämer, Phys. Rev. Lett. **76**, 4128 (1996).

27. H1 collab, S. Aid et al., Nucl. Phys. B **472**, 3 (1996).

28. ZEUS collab., L. Stanco, talk at the International Workshop on Deep Inelastic Scatterring, Rome, 1996.

29. M. Cacciari, M. Krämer, hep-ph/9609500, Talk given at Workshop on Future Physics at HERA, Hamburg, Germany, 30-31 May 1996.

30. M. Beneke, I.Z. Rothstein, M.B. Wise, hep-ph/9705286, preprint CERN-TH/97-86.

31. R. Godbole, D.P. Roy, K. Sridhar, Phys. Lett. B **373**, 328 (1996).

32. B.A. Kniehl, G. Kramer, hep-ph/9702406, preprint DESY 97-012; hep-ph/9703280, preprint DESY 97-036.

33. M. Cacciari, M. Greco, M. Krämer, Phys. Rev. D **55**, 7126 (1997).

DIJET PRODUCTION IN PHOTON-PHOTON COLLISIONS AT $\sqrt{s}_{ee} = 161$ AND 172 GEV

ROLAND BÜRGIN

for the OPAL collaboration

Universität Freiburg, Hermann-Herder-Straße 3,

D-79104 Freiburg, Germany

Dijet production is studied in collisions of quasi-real photons radiated by the LEP beams at e^+e^- centre-of-mass energies $\sqrt{s}_{ee} = 161$ and 172 GeV. Jets are reconstructed using a cone jet finding algorithm in the range $|\eta^{jet}| < 2$ and $E_T^{jet} > 3$ GeV. The angular distributions of direct and double-resolved processes and the inclusive two-jet cross-section are measured. They are compared to next-to-leading order perturbative QCD calculations and the prediction of the leading order Monte Carlo generators PYTHIA and PHOJET.

1 Introduction

The production of dijet events in the collision of two quasi-real photons is used to study the structure of the photon and different QCD predictions. The measurement of inclusive jet cross-sections and the comparison with next-to-leading order (NLO) QCD calculations and different photon structure functions can constrain the relatively unknown gluonic content of the photon.

2 Event selection and jet finding

To select a data sample of two-photon events the following set of cuts was applied. The sum of all energy deposits in the electromagnetic calorimeter (ECAL) and the hadronic calorimeter (HCAL) has to be less than 45 GeV. The visible invariant hadronic mass, W_{ECAL}, measured in the ECAL has to be greater than 3 GeV. The missing transverse energy of the event measured in the ECAL and the forward calorimeters has to be less than 5 GeV. At least 5 tracks must have been found in the tracking chambers. Events with detected scattered electrons (single-tagged or double-tagged events) are excluded from the analysis.

The results of the cone jet finding algorithm depend on the minimal transverse energy E_T^{min} and the cone size $R = \sqrt{(\Delta\eta)^2 + (\Delta\phi)^2}$ with the pseudorapidity $\eta = -\ln\tan(\theta/2)$ and the azimuthal angle ϕ. Here the values were chosen to be $R = 1$ and $E_T^{min} = 3$ GeV. The jet pseudorapidity in the laboratory frame is required to be within $|\eta^{jet}| < 2$.

After applying all cuts and requiring at least two jets 2681 events remain in the data corresponding to an integrated luminosity of 20 pb^{-1}. For the simulation of two-photon interactions the Monte Carlo generators PYTHIA [1] and PHOJET [2] have been used. The mean Q^2 of the selected Monte Carlo events is 0.06 GeV^2. About 1.2 % of the events in the data sample are expected to be e$^+$e$^-$ annihilation events with hadronic final states and 0.2 % electron-photon events.

3 Angular distributions in direct and resolved events

A pair of variables, x_γ^+ and x_γ^-, can be defined which is related to the fraction of the photon energy participating in the hard scattering:

$$x_\gamma^+ = \frac{\displaystyle\sum_{\text{jets}=1,2} (E + p_z)}{\displaystyle\sum_{\text{hadrons}} (E + p_z)} \quad \text{and} \quad x_\gamma^- = \frac{\displaystyle\sum_{\text{jets}=1,2} (E - p_z)}{\displaystyle\sum_{\text{hadrons}} (E - p_z)}, \tag{1}$$

where p_z is the momentum component along the z axis of the detector and E is the energy of the jets or hadrons. If an event contains more than two jets, the two jets with the highest E_T^{jet} values are taken. Samples with large direct and double-resolved contributions can be separated by requiring both x_γ^+ and x_γ^- to be larger than 0.8 (denoted as $x_\gamma^\pm > 0.8$) or both values to be smaller than 0.8 (denoted as $x_\gamma^\pm < 0.8$), respectively [3].

The transverse energy flow around the jet axis for double-resolved events is expected to show additional activity outside the jet due to the photon remnants compared to the direct events. Figure 1 therefore shows the transverse energy flow around the jets with respect to the jet direction for data samples with different $x_\gamma^\pm$ cuts. The pseudorapidity difference is defined by:

$$\Delta\eta' = k(\eta - \eta^{\text{jet}}).$$

The factor k is chosen event-by-event to be $k = +1$ for events with $x_\gamma^+ > x_\gamma^-$ and $k = -1$ for events with $x_\gamma^+ < x_\gamma^-$. Due to the definition of $\Delta\eta'$ there is always more of the remnant found at $\Delta\eta' < 0$ and the enhancement due to the additional transverse energy flow at negative and positive $\Delta\eta'$ is asymmetric. The jets in the data sample with $x_\gamma^\pm > 0.8$ are more collimated and there is almost no activity outside the jet whereas the transverse energy flow of two-jet events with $x_\gamma^\pm < 0.8$ shows additional activity outside the jets.

In the centre-of-mass system of the interacting partons or bare photons the parton scattering angle θ^* is defined as the angle between the jet axis of

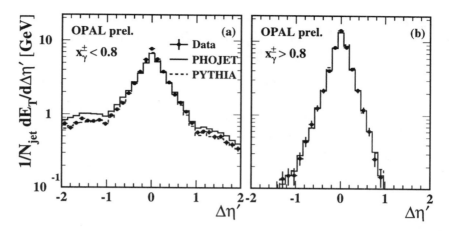

Figure 1: Uncorrected energy flow transverse to the beam direction measured relative to the direction of each jet in two-jet events. Jets from data samples with a large contribution of (a) double-resolved and (b) direct events according to their x_γ^+ and x_γ^- values are shown. The energy flow is integrated over $|\Delta\phi| < \pi/2$. Statistical errors only are shown.

the jets originating from the outgoing partons and the axis of the incoming partons or bare photons. The angular distribution of the jets can be used to check the separation between the different event classes using a variable which is not directly correlated to the definition of x_γ^+ and x_γ^-. In the dijet centre-of-mass frame one expects different angular distributions for direct and double-resolved events. An estimator of the angle between the jets and the parton-parton axis in the dijet centre-of-mass frame can be formed from their pseudorapidities. The variable $\cos\theta^*$ is calculated as

$$\cos\theta^* = \tanh\left(\frac{\eta^{\text{jet1}} - \eta^{\text{jet2}}}{2}\right).$$

Since the ordering of the jets is arbitrary, only $|\cos\theta^*|$ can be measured. The matrix elements of elastic parton-parton scattering processes have been calculated in LO[4]. The cut on E_T^{jet} restricts the accessible range of values of $|\cos\theta^*|$. Requiring the invariant mass of the dijet system to be larger than 12 GeV ensures that values of $|\cos\theta^*| < 0.85$ are not biased by the E_T^{jet} cut. The boost of the two-jet system in the z direction is defined by $\bar{\eta} = (\eta^{\text{jet1}} + \eta^{\text{jet2}})/2$. The detector resolution on $|\cos\theta^*|$ deteriorates significantly for events with $|\bar{\eta}|$ larger than 1. These events were therefore rejected by requiring $|\bar{\eta}| < 1$.

Figure 2 shows the $|\cos\theta^*|$-distribution of events with $x_\gamma^\pm > 0.8$ and of events with $x_\gamma^\pm < 0.8$. The dependence on the Monte Carlo models used

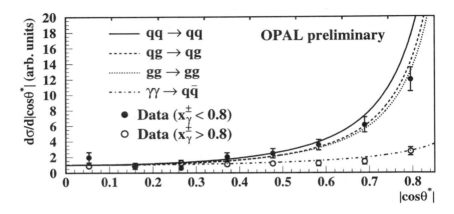

Figure 2: Angular distribution of events with large direct and large double-resolved contributions according to the separation with x_γ^+ and x_γ^-. The data are compared to QCD matrix element calculations [4]. The data are normalised to have an average value of 1 in the first three bins and the curves are normalised to be 1 at $\cos(0)$.

is taken into account by adding the difference between the results obtained with PYTHIA, which are taken to be the central values, and PHOJET to the systematic error. The error bars show the statistical and the systematic errors added in quadrature. The events with $x_\gamma^\pm > 0.8$ show a small rise with $|\cos\theta^*|$, whereas the events with $x_\gamma^\pm < 0.8$ show a much stronger rise in $|\cos\theta^*|$. The data points of the events with $x_\gamma^\pm < 0.8$ are compared with the prediction of a QCD matrix element calculation of the interaction of quarks or gluons in the photon. The matrix elements with a relevant contribution to the cross-section where antiquarks are involved instead of quarks show a similar behaviour as the examples shown. The QCD matrix element calculations agree well with the data points of the data samples with large direct and large double-resolved contribution.

4 Inclusive two-jet cross-sections

The inclusive two-jet cross-section is measured using a cone jet finding algorithm with a cone size $R = 1$. The data were corrected for the selection cuts, the resolution effects of the detector and the background from non-signal processes. In Fig. 3, the inclusive two-jet cross-section is shown as a function of E_T^{jet}. The bin sizes, which are indicated by the vertical lines at the top of the figure, approximately reflect the experimental resolution.

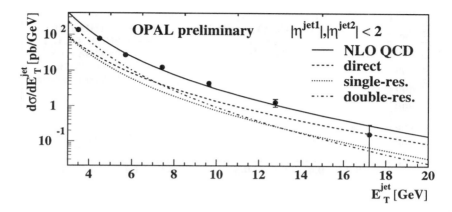

Figure 3: The inclusive two-jet cross-section as a function of E_T^{jet} for jets with $|\eta^{\text{jet}}| < 2$ compared to the NLO calculation by Kleinwort and Kramer[5]. The direct, single-resolved and double-resolved cross-sections and the sum (continuous line) are shown separately.

The E_T^{jet} distribution is compared to an NLO perturbative QCD calculation of the inclusive two-jet cross-section by Kleinwort and Kramer[5] who use the NLO GRV parametrisation of the photon structure function[6]. Their calculation was repeated for the kinematic conditions of this analysis. The direct, single- and double-resolved parts and their sum are shown separately. The resolved cross-sections dominate in the region $E_T^{\text{jet}} \lesssim 8$ GeV, whereas, at high E_T^{jet} the direct cross-section is largest. The data points are in good agreement with the calculation except in the first bin where the NLO calculation is not reliable due to IR singularities. The uncertainties due to the modelling of the hadronisation process are expected to contribute mainly at low E_T^{jet} values.

The inclusive two-jet cross-section, which is dominated by the low E_T^{jet} events, depends on the parton density function of the photon which mainly differs in the assumptions on the gluon part of the photon. In 40 to 60 % of all processes at least one gluon from the photon interacts depending on the parton density function used. This leads to different predictions of the inclusive two-jet cross-section. The inclusive two-jet cross-section as a function of $|\eta^{\text{jet}}|$ is shown in Fig. 4. The inclusive two-jet cross-section predicted by the two Monte Carlo models differ significantly even if the same photon structure function is used. This model dependence currently reduces the sensitivity to the parametrisation of the photon structure function. The GRV-LO and SaS-1D parametrisations[6,7] describe the data equally well, but the LAC1 parametrisation[8] overestimates the inclusive two-jet cross-section significantly.

126

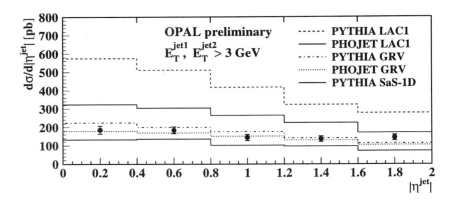

Figure 4: The inclusive two-jet cross-section as a function of $|\eta^{\text{jet}}|$ for jets with $E_T^{\text{jet}} > 3$ GeV.

5 Conclusions

The distribution of the parton scattering angle θ^* of data samples with large direct and double-resolved contributions separated experimentally using the variables x_γ^+ and x_γ^- have been compared to the relevant QCD matrix element calculations. The inclusive two-jet cross-sections were measured as a function of E_T^{jet} and $|\eta^{\text{jet}}|$. The E_T^{jet} dependent two-jet cross-section is in good agreement with an NLO QCD calculation. The GRV-LO and SaS-1D parametrisations describe the inclusive two-jet cross-section equally well. The LAC1 parametrisation overestimates the inclusive two-jet cross-section significantly.

1. T. Sjöstrand, Comp. Phys. Commun. 82 (1994) 74; T. Sjöstrand, LUND University Report, LU-TP-95-20 (1995).
2. R. Engel and J. Ranft, Phys. Rev. D54 (1996) 4244; R. Engel, Z. Phys. C66 (1995) 203.
3. OPAL Collaboration, K. Ackerstaff et al., Z. Phys. C73 (1997) 433.
4. B. L. Combridge et al., Phys. Lett. B70 (1977) 234; D. W. Duke and J. F. Owens, Phys. Rev. D26 (1982) 1600.
5. T. Kleinwort, G. Kramer, DESY-96-035 (1996); T. Kleinwort, G. Kramer, Phys. Lett. B370 (1996) 141.
6. M. Glück, E. Reya and A. Vogt, Phys. Rev. D46 (1992) 1973; M. Glück, E. Reya and A. Vogt, Phys. Rev. D45 (1992) 3986.
7. G. A. Schuler and T. Sjöstrand, Z. Phys. C68 (1995) 607.
8. H. Abramowicz, K. Charchula and A. Levy, Phys. Lett. B269 (1991) 458.

JETS IN REAL AND VIRTUAL PHOTOPRODUCTION

H. RICK

(for the H1 Collaboration)

DESY, Notkestraße 85, D-22607 Hamburg, Germany. rick@mail.desy.de

Measurements of jet cross sections from real and virtual photon-proton scattering are presented, based on recent results from the H1 experiment at HERA. For the case of real photoproduction, differential cross sections of di-jet events are shown as a function of the transverse energy of the jets and the reconstructed momentum fraction of the struck parton from the photon. Based on these cross sections, an effective leading order parton density of the photon is extracted as a function of the transverse momentum scale of the jets. In virtual photoproduction, single inclusive jet cross sections are presented as a function of the jet transverse energy and the photon virtuality.

1 Introduction

HERA's electron beam is accompanied by a flux of real and virtual photons whose partonic structure reveals itself via the formation of jets with large transverse momentum when scattering off the constituents of the proton. The large center of mass energy and the wide range of energies and virtualities of these photons make the HERA collision experiments a unique opportunity to study the hadronic structure of the photon as well as its dependence on the two scales p_{T}^2 and Q^2 which represent the squared transverse momentum in the partonic process and the photon virtuality.

The first of the two analyses presented here investigates the p_{T}^2 dependence of the jet cross section and the parton distribution of quasireal photons at $Q^2 \approx 0$, while the second analysis deals with the Q^2 evolution of the virtual photon–proton jet cross section in bins of the transverse jet energy.

1.1 Experimental setup

A detailed description of the H1 detector can be found in [1]. In the analyses presented here, hadronic jets are identified in the H1 liquid argon calorimeter, which covers polar angles between 4° and 150° with respect to the proton beam direction. The scattered electron in virtual photon-proton scattering events and part of the hadronic final state at angles larger than 150° is seen in the backward electromagnetic calorimeter. In the case of real photoproduction, the scattered electron escapes unseen by the central detector through the beam hole. The signals from the tracking detectors inside the calorimeter system are used for reconstructing the position of the interaction vertex and to support the calorimetric measurement of the hadronic energy flow.

The data used for these analyses were taken during the 1994 run period with an integrated luminosity of $2.9\,\mathrm{pb}^{-1}$. For the analysis of virtual photon–proton scattering the event sample was complemented by a special run of $120\,\mathrm{nb}^{-1}$ which was taken in 1995 with the interaction vertex shifted by 70 cm with respect to the nominal vertex position, extending the acceptance of the backward calorimeter for the scattered electron down to photon virtualities of $Q^2 = 0.65\,\mathrm{GeV}^2$.

2 Di-jets in real photoproduction

In the following analysis of di-jet events from real photoproduction, jets were found by a cone algorithm [2] using a cone with radius R=0.7 in the plane of azimuthal angle ϕ and pseudorapidity η. Events were accepted in which at least 2 jets were found with transverse energies above 8 GeV each. The two jets with the highest transverse energies found in an event were used for approximate reconstruction of the kinematics of the underlying partonic process.

The cross section as a function of the parton momentum fraction in the photon x_γ and the transverse momentum p_{T} of the jets was corrected in a two-step procedure. In a first step, the data were corrected for the smearing of the detector in order to obtain the cross section for di-jet production. This cross section was then corrected further for effects of fragmentation, higher order parton radiation and underlying event energy in order to extract the leading order parton density in the photon.

2.1 Differential di-jet cross sections

The double-differential cross section for di-jet production as a function of the reconstructed parton momentum fraction in the photon x_γ^{jets} and the transverse energy E_T of the second highest E_T jet in the event is shown in figure 1. The result is given as an ep cross section for the kinematic region defined by the cuts that are listed in the figure caption. The error bars include the full systematic error which is dominated by the uncertainty in the calibration of the calorimeter for hadronic energy measurement. This error is between 15% and 30% of the cross section, with the largest uncertainty occurring in the lowest x_γ^{jets} bins. A variation of the parameters of the two-dimensional unfolding procedure [3] which was used for correcting the data causes an uncertainty below 10%, and the uncertainty in the determination of the triggering efficiency for jet events contributes another 10% to the relative systematic error.

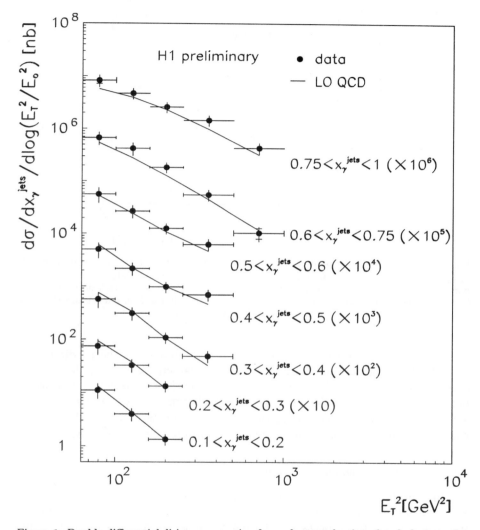

Figure 1: Double-differential di-jet cross section from photoproduction of real photons. Jet finding is based on the hadronic final state using a cone algorithm with a cone radius of 0.7 units in the plane of pseudorapidity η and azimuthal angle φ. The cross section is given as a function of the logarithm of the squared transverse energy $\log(E_T^2/E_0^2)$ ($E_0 = 1\,\text{GeV}$) of the jet with the second highest E_T, in bins of the parton momentum fraction in the photon which was reconstructed from the transverse energies (E_{T1}, E_{T2}) and pseudorapidities (η_1, η_2) of the two jets: $x_\gamma^{\text{jets}} = (E_{T1}e^{-\eta_1} + E_{T2}e^{-\eta_2})/(2yE_e)$. The jet pseudorapidities were restricted to the range $-0.5 < \eta_{1,2} < 2.5$ and $|\eta_1 - \eta_2| < 1$ in the HERA laboratory system. The scaled photon energy in units of the incoming electron energy $y = E_\gamma/E_e$ was required to be in the range $0.2 < y < 0.83$, and the photon virtuality Q^2 was below $Q^2 = 4\,\text{GeV}^2$.

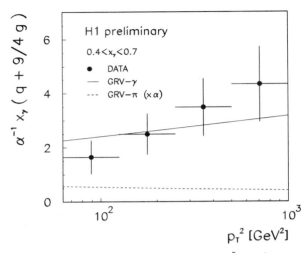

Figure 2: The effective photon parton distribution $x_\gamma \tilde{f}(x_\gamma, p_\mathrm{T}^2) = x_\gamma(q(x_\gamma, p_\mathrm{T}^2) + 9/4\,g(x_\gamma, p_\mathrm{T}^2))$ is shown as a function of the transverse momentum scale p_T^2, averaged over parton momentum fractions in the range $0.4 < x_\gamma < 0.7$. The data (black dots with error bars) are compared to the GRV parameterisation of the photon (full curve) and the pion (dashed, scaled by a factor α).

In figure 1 the measured cross section is compared to the prediction of the PYTHIA [4] generator using the GRV [5] parameterisations of the photon and proton parton distributions. The comparison shows reasonable agreement between the model and the data over the whole range of x_γ^{jets} and E_T shown, with some possible deviations in the region of large x_γ^{jets} where the photon parton distribution is not well constrained from previous measurements.

2.2 The effective parton density of the photon

In contrast to measurements of the photon structure function F_2 at e^+e^- experiments, which corresponds to a sum over the quark densities in the photon, resolved photon processes at HERA are sensitive to both the quark and the gluon [6] densities in the photon. In this jet analysis however, jets originating from final state quarks cannot be distinguished experimentally from those originating from gluons, so that quark and gluon densities cannot be determined separately. Therefore the so-called **S**ingle **E**ffective **S**ubprocess approximation [7] is used here, which implies the definition of an effective parton distribution of the photon $\tilde{f}^\gamma(x_\gamma, p_\mathrm{T}^2) = \sum_q (q^\gamma(x_\gamma, p_\mathrm{T}^2) + \bar{q}^\gamma(x_\gamma, p_\mathrm{T}^2)) + \frac{9}{4}g^\gamma(x_\gamma, p_\mathrm{T}^2)$. Here q^γ and g^γ are the quark and gluon parton densities in the photon. The sum runs over all quark flavours, the factor $\frac{9}{4}$ represents the strength of the gluon-gluon coupling relative to the gluon-quark coupling. With this definition, the differential di-jet cross section as a function of the parton momentum fractions x_γ and x_p in photon and proton, the scaled photon energy in units of the incident electron energy $y = E_\gamma/E_e$ and the scattering angle θ^* of the final state partons in their center of mass frame with respect to the beam axis factorizes approximately as follows:

$$\frac{d^4\sigma}{dy\, dx_\gamma\, dx_p\, d\cos\theta^*} \approx \frac{1}{32\pi s_{ep}}\, \frac{f_{\gamma/e}(y)}{y}\, \frac{\tilde{f}_\gamma(x_\gamma, p_T^2)}{x_\gamma}\, \frac{\tilde{f}_p(x_p, p_T^2)}{x_p}\, |M_{SES}(\cos\theta^*)|^2$$

In this expression, $f_{\gamma/e}$ is the photon flux of the beam electron, $\tilde{f}_\gamma$ and $\tilde{f}_p$ are the effective parton densities of photon and proton, and M_{SES} is the matrix element for the effective subprocess, which can be approximated by the matrix element for the process $qq' \to qq'$ with a t-channel gluon exchange.

In order to extract the effective parton density of the photon $\tilde{f}_\gamma(x_\gamma, p_T^2)$ from the data, the corrected di-jet cross section given in the previous paragraph was corrected to the parton variables x_γ and p_T in a second unfolding step. For estimation of the model dependent uncertainties which are inevitably introduced by an interpretation of the data in terms of a leading order model, this last step was repeated several times using PYTHIA simulations with different parameter settings, or the simulation of the PHOJET[8] generator. The difference between the models tested mainly concerns variations of the underlying event energy as modelled by multiple parton interactions, and of higher order QCD effects, which are modelled by a parton shower mechanism. A more detailed discussion of these effects is given in [9] and [10]. In the region around $x_\gamma \approx 0.5$, the variation of the result with these alternative models is around 10% of the parton density.

The unfolded effective parton density of the photon is shown in figure 2 as a function of the squared transverse momentum transfer p_T^2 in the hard scattering process, and averaged over parton momentum fractions in the range $0.4 < x_\gamma < 0.7$. The parton density is compared to the effective photon parton density which was calculated from the GRV parameterisation. As an approximation of the vector meson dominance model of the photon, the GRV pion parton density is also shown, scaled by the factor α. The measured parton density shows a rise with the transverse momentum scale p_T^2 which is clearly different from the pion curve both in shape and in absolute rate. This difference between the photon and typical hadrons is caused by the pointlike coupling of the photon to quark-antiquark-pairs. It has been observed in measurements of the photon structure function F_2 at e^+e^- experiments (e.g.,[11]), and is here now directly verified for the first time in photoproduction at an ep experiment.

132

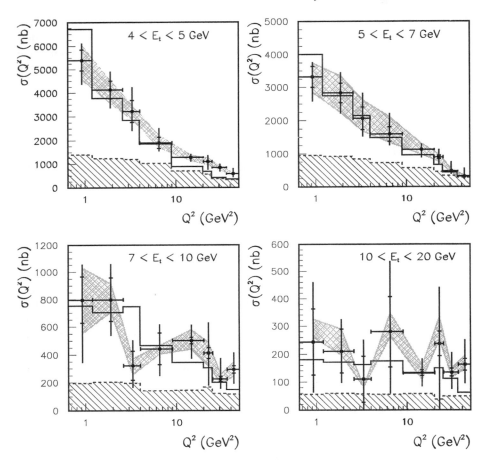

Figure 3: Single inclusive jet cross section from virtual photoproduction as a function of the photon virtuality Q^2, in bins of the jet transverse energy E_t. Jets were found in the pseudorapidity range $-2.5 < \eta^* < -0.5$ in the photon–proton center of mass frame, using a k_T clustering algorithm. The data are presented as γp cross sections, normalized to the flux of virtual photons that are radiated off the beam electron in the y range $0.3 < y < 0.6$. The data points are shown with statistical errors (inner error bars) and the quadratic sum of statistical and systematic errors (full error bars) and are compared to the prediction of the HERWIG model with the direct photon component only (hatched histogram) and the sum of direct and resolved contributions (full line). The shaded band indicates the systematic error induced by the uncertainty in the calibration of the calorimeter.

3   Jets in virtual photoproduction

For the case of virtual photons, resolved-photon processes are expected to dominate the jet production cross section as long as the transverse energy scale E_t of the jets is much larger than the virtuality of the photon Q^2 ($E_t^2 \gg Q^2$), while they become more and more suppressed with increasing Q^2. In the limit $Q^2 \gg E_t^2$ the cross section can be described by the classical deep-inelastic scattering picture of a pointlike photon. This behaviour is verified in the following virtual photon analysis, which is based on jets found by a k_T clustering algorithm in the virtual photon–proton center of mass frame. Figure 3 shows the single inclusive jet cross section as a function of the photon virtuality Q^2, in bins of the jet transverse energy E_t. The cross section is shown as a γp cross section, corrected for detector effects, and divided by the flux of virtual photons from the incident electron. It is compared to the prediction of the virtual photon–proton model of the HERWIG [12] generator which implements a continuous suppression of the resolved photon component with increasing Q^2. The pure pointlike, direct photon component, which is shown separately as hatched histograms, is not sufficient to describe the measured jet rate, while the complete model including the resolved part gives a much better prediction of the jet cross section both in shape and absolute normalisation.

This preliminary result already gives an indication for a resolved contribution even at large photon virtualities $Q^2 \gg 0$. The next step for future studies in this interesting field could consist in a direct reconstruction of the underlying parton kinematics in order to measure the parton distribution in virtual photons in a similar way as it is being done for the real photon.

References

1. H1 Collab., I. Abt *et al*, *Nucl. Instrum. Methods* A **386**, 310 (1997).
2. J. Huth *et al*, Fermilab-Conf-90/249-E (1990).
3. G. D'Agostini, *Nucl. Instrum. Methods* A **362**, 487 (1995).
4. T. Sjöstrand, *Comput. Phys. Commun.* **82**, 74 (1994).
5. M. Glück, E. Reya, A. Vogt, *Z. Phys.* C **53**, 127,651 (1992).
6. H1 Collab., T. Ahmed *et al*, *Nucl. Phys.* B **445**, 195 (1995).
7. B.L. Combridge, C.J. Maxwell, *Nucl. Phys.* B **239**, 429 (1984).
8. R. Engel, J. Ranft, *Phys. Rev.* D **54**, 4244 (1996).
9. H1 Collab., S. Aid *et al*, *Z. Phys.* C **70**, 17 (1996).
10. M. Erdmann, "The Partonic Structure of the Photon", Springer Tracts in Mod. Phys. 138, Berlin, Springer (1997).
11. AMY Collab., S.K. Sahu *et al*, *Phys. Lett.* B **346**, 208 (1995).
12. G. Marchesini *et al*, *Comput. Phys. Commun.* **67**, 465 (1992).

DIJET CROSS SECTIONS AND RAPIDITY GAPS BETWEEN JETS IN PHOTOPRODUCTION AT HERA

M. HAYES

On behalf of the ZEUS Collaboration

H. H. Wills Physics Laboratory, Tyndall Avenue, Bristol BS8 1TL UK

Dijet cross sections from the original 1994 ZEUS data analysis are shown compared to NLO calculations. New 1995 cross sections are shown compared to Monte Carlo predictions. The fraction of dijet events with a rapidity gap inbetween the jets is also presented for the new 1995 data.

In e^+p scattering at HERA, an almost real photon ($P^2 \approx 0$, where P^2 is the negative four momentum squared of the photon) can be emitted from the positron with momentum fraction y and collide with the proton. At leading order (LO) there are two distinct types of process: (a) where all of the photon interacts directly with the proton (direct process) and (b) where the photon resolves into partons which interact with the proton (resolved process). Both processes can produce two high E_T jets which provide a hard scale, meaning that they should be calculable in perturbative QCD. In this contribution we report on two different dijet cross section measurements. Another possibility is resolved hard scattering with the exchange of a colour singlet object. A measurement of the fraction of rapidity gap events compared to normal dijet events is presented, which probes these processes.

The present results are based on 2.6 pb^{-1} of the data taken during 1994 HERA running and on 5.7 pb^{-1} from the 1995 data. In both years HERA was running with 820 GeV protons and 27.5 GeV positrons.

Photoproduction processes are separated from other processes by the requirement that no positron is found in the main detector. This corresponds to a cut of $P^2 < 4 \text{GeV}^2$ and gives a median $P^2 \approx 10^{-3} \text{GeV}^2$.

Jets are located using the energy deposit pattern in the uranium-scintillator calorimeter. Results presented here use both the cone type and the clustering type of jet finding algorithms. Two types of cone algorithm (EUCELL and PUCELL) are used in ZEUS. Both involve moving a cone around in $\eta - \phi$ [a] space. Both comply with the snowmass convention. The clustering algorithm (KTCLUS[1]) uses an E_T recombination scheme to build jets from 'clusters' of nearby particles.

---

[a] $\eta = -\ln\tan(\theta/2)$, where θ is polar angle measured from the proton direction and ϕ is the azimuthal angle.

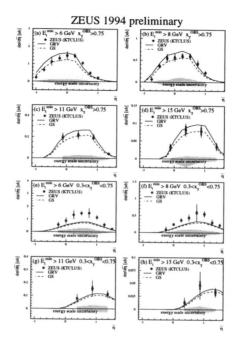

Figure 1: Dijet cross sections $d\sigma/d\overline{\eta}$. The thin (thick) error bars represent systematic (statistical) errors. The shaded band is the uncertainty in the calorimeter energy scale.

1   Dijet Cross Sections

The first set of cross sections presented are based on the 1994 HERA running. Dijet events are found as detailed above using the clustering algorithm. The jets are also required to lie in the range $-1.375 < \eta^{jet} < 1.875$. The cut $\Delta\eta = |\eta_1 - \eta_2| < 0.5$ is applied to increase the correlation with the parton momenta. The cross section was measured as a function of $\overline{\eta} = (\eta_1 + \eta_2)/2$, which is the boost of the dijet system in the lab..

The e^+p cross sections $d\sigma/d\overline{\eta}$ are presented in figure 1 integrated over $E_T^{jet} > 6, 8, 11, 15$ GeV in two regions of x_γ^{OBS} [b] : (a)-(d) $x_\gamma^{OBS} > 0.75$ corresponding to mostly direct and (e)-(h) $0.3 < x_\gamma^{OBS} < 0.75$ corresponding

---

[b]In LO the fraction of photon's momentum taking part in the scattering can be estimated using $x_\gamma^{OBS} = \sum_{jets} E_T^{jet} e^{-\eta^{jet}} / (2yE_e)$ where E_e is the energy of the incoming positron.

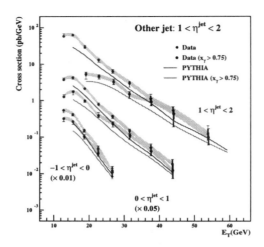

Figure 2: ZEUS Preliminary 1995 dijet cross sections $d\sigma/dE_T$; one of the jets is required to be forward ($1 < \eta^{jet} < 2$). In the 1995 plots the thick error bars are statistical and the thin ones are statistical and systematic added in quadrature. The shaded band represents the uncertainty in the calorimeter energy scale.

to mostly resolved. The cross sections are compared to next-to-leading-order (NLO) calculations by Klasen and Kramer[2]. The calculations are shown for two photon structure function sets, GRV and GS. For $x_\gamma^{OBS} > 0.75$ the NLO calculations agree well with the data for $E_T > 8$ GeV although at present differentiation between photon structure functions is not possible. For the lowest E_T graph, $\overline{\eta} < 0$ agrees with the GS set, but at higher $\overline{\eta}$ the data agrees with the GRV set. For $0.3 < x_\gamma^{OBS} < 0.75$ the data lies above the calculation for the first two graphs. However the agreement is good for $E_T > 11$ GeV. Again no differentiation between photon structure functions is possible.

The second set of cross sections presented are based on the 1995 HERA running. Dijet events are found as above using a cone algorithm. The jets are also required to lie in the range $-1 < \eta^{jet} < 2$. Both jets are required to have $E_T > 11$ GeV. The following graphs are all symmetrized in η_{jet}, both jets being plotted twice for each of their η values. E_T always refers to the highest E_T^{jet}[3].

The e^+p cross sections $d\sigma/dE_T$ are presented in figure 2. One of the jets is required to be forward ($1 < \eta^{jet} < 2$), and the three sets of points show entries

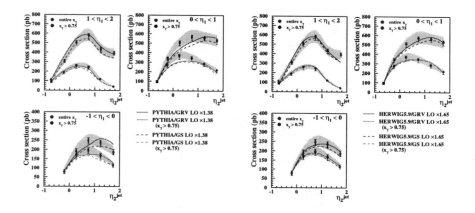

Figure 3: ZEUS preliminary 1995 dijet cross sections $d\sigma/\eta_2$. The extra cut $E_T > 14$ GeV has been applied to the leading jet. Errors as in figure 2.

for the other jet being in three separate parts of the detector ($1 < \eta^{jet} < 2$, $0 < \eta^{jet} < 1$ or $-1 < \eta^{jet} < 0$). A subset of the data ($x_\gamma^{OBS} > 0.75$) is also plotted separately. PYTHIA curves are also plotted for each set of points. The graph shows that at high E_T the dominant contribution is from direct processes. The Monte Carlo shape appears to agree well with the data, although the overall normalization is low.

The e^+p cross sections $d\sigma/\eta_2$ are presented in figure 3. The graphs show the pseudorapidity of the other jet, given that one jet is in a definite area of the detector ($1 < \eta^{jet} < 2$, $0 < \eta^{jet} < 1$ or $-1 < \eta^{jet} < 0$). The extra cut $E_T > 14$ GeV has been applied to the leading jet. Again, the entire data set is plotted as well as the subset $x_\gamma^{OBS} > 0.75$. These are compared to two PYTHIA curves [left plots] corresponding to the two photon structure function sets, GRV and GS. The PYTHIA lines have been scaled, by eye, to the data. HERWIG is shown in the right set of plots. Both Monte Carlos show good agreement with the data when considering the calorimeter uncertainty scale. However, PYTHIA appears more forward when requiring one jet to be in the middle or rear. HERWIG agrees well with the shape formed by the data points.

2 Rapidity Gaps Between Jets

It was shown[4] that there exists a class of dijet events with large separation between jets with no significant energy deposits between the jet cone edges.

138

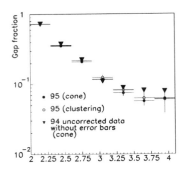

Figure 4: Uncorrected preliminary data showing the gap fraction. Error bars represent statistical errors. The gap fraction based on 1994 data is also shown for comparison.

Standard direct and resolved processes can produce these 'gap' events by random particle multiplicity fluctuations. However, these are expected to become less likely exponentially with increasing gap width ($\Delta\eta$). A surplus of events above this exponential decrease is described by the exchange of an unknown colour singlet.

Figure 4 shows the fraction of dijet events with a gap (the gap fraction), i.e. the number with a gap divided by the total number of dijet events. An $E_T^{jet} > 6$ GeV was used with both types of jet finders. A cut of $\overline{\eta} < 0.75$ is also applied. A gap is defined as the absence of a cluster of calorimeter cells with total transverse energy of greater than 250 MeV. The gap fractions agree well with both jet finders and the 1994 data published result. A levelling out of the gap fraction is seen for $\Delta\eta > 3.0$, rather than an exponential fall off, indicating the exchange of a colour singlet.

References

1. S. Catani et al., *Nucl. Phys.* B406, 187 (1993).
2. M. Klasen, G. Kramer, *DESY-96-246, hep-ph/9611450*
3. For the motivation behind these measurements see the contribution by P. Aurenche in these proceedings.
4. ZEUS Collaboration, *Phys. Lett. B369 (1996) 55-68. hep-ex/9510012*

JET SHAPES AND MULTIJET EVENTS IN HARD PHOTOPRODUCTION AT HERA

E.J. STRICKLAND

(On behalf of the ZEUS Collaboration)

Department of Physics and Astronomy, University of Glasgow,
Glasgow G12 8QQ, Scotland

Jet shapes and multijet events in quasi-real photon-proton collisions have been studied using the ZEUS detector at HERA. Measured jet shapes are compared to a LO parton shower Monte Carlo prediction, with and without multi-parton interactions, and NLO QCD calculations. The x_γ distribution and 3-jet to 2-jet inclusive production ratio are shown for events with multijet final states.

1   Introduction

The study of e^+p collisions at HERA provides many opportunities to study quasi-real photon-proton collisions. At leading order (LO) QCD, the photon can either interact directly with a parton from the proton (direct process) or fluctuate into a hadronic state which acts as a source of partons which scatter off those in the proton (resolved process).

Jets observed experimentally correspond to a reasonable approximation to final state partons, enabling comparison with theoretical calculations to be made. Experimentally, in the case of events with two or more jets, it is possible to define an observable quantity, x_γ^{obs},

$$x_\gamma^{obs} = \sum_{jets} \frac{E_T^{jet} e^{-\eta^{jet}}}{2yE_e} \tag{1}$$

which is accessible experimentally, well-defined at higher orders and can be interpreted at lowest order as the fraction of the photon's momentum which goes into the hard scatter.

Two analyses by the ZEUS Collaboration are presented here. The first investigates the internal structure of jets as a means to probe the mechanism responsible for changing a final state parton into an experimentally observed jet; the other studies some features of events with multijet final states.

2   Jet Shapes in Hard Photoproduction

Jets are searched for with a cone algorithm with radius $R = 1$ in pseudorapidity[a](η) - azimuth(φ) space and selected with transverse energy, E_T^{jet}, > 14 GeV

---

[a]The pseudorapidity is defined as $\eta = -ln(tan\frac{\theta}{2})$, where the polar angle θ is taken with respect to the proton beam direction.

and $-1 < \eta^{jet} < 2$. In this study, pairs of overlapping jets are merged together if the common energy exceeds 75% of the total energy of the lower energy jet. The jet shape, $\psi(r)$, is defined by [2]:

$$\psi(r) = \frac{1}{N_{jets}} \sum_{jets} \frac{E_T(r)}{E_T(R)} \qquad (2)$$

where R is the radius of the jet defining cone, $E_T(r)$ is the transverse energy within an inner cone of radius r and N_{jets} is the total number of jets in the sample.

Figure 1 shows reasonable agreement between measured jet shapes and predictions from the LO parton shower Monte Carlo event generator PYTHIA [3] in the region $-1 < \eta^{jet} < 1$. In the forward region, however, the data are significantly broader than the predictions. The PYTHIA predictions based on a LO calculation and subsequent fragmentation of single partons using the LUND string model [4] are significantly narrower than the data, indicating that, at the transverse energies studied here, the shape of jets is strongly dictated by parton radiation and cannot be explained by hadronization alone.

The evolution of the jet shape at $r=0.5$ with η^{jet} and E_T^{jet} is shown in Fig. 2. The data show that jets become broader as η^{jet} increases, becoming less quark-like and more gluon-like. The addition to PYTHIA of multi-parton interactions (MI), a model which allows more than one interaction between the partons from the proton and photon, improves the agreement with the data in the two high η^{jet} bins. Figure 2(b) shows that the measured jet shape becomes narrower as E_T^{jet} increases, a possible effect of decreasing α_s.

At LO QCD, a jet is associated with one parton only and therefore has no internal structure. The lowest non-trivial order contribution to the jet shape is given by next-to-leading order (NLO) QCD calculations for the reaction $AB \rightarrow$ jet $+ X$.

Figure 3 compares the data with NLO QCD calculations of jet shapes [5][6]. On the theoretical side, an attempt was made to simulate the merging and overlapping procedures of the experimental jet algorithm by introducing at the parton level a parameter R_{SEP} [2] which is related to the separation of two partons in $\eta - \varphi$ space. In the region $E_T^{jet} > 17$ GeV the jet shapes are reproduced well by the calculations with $R_{SEP} = 1.4$. The magnitude of the uncertainty in the theoretical expectation is given by the spread of the calculations with $R_{SEP} = 1.4$ and 2.0.

3 Multijet Events in Hard Photoproduction

Dijet studies in hard photoproduction have extensively tested QCD predictions and studies of multijet events would provide a means of testing QCD at higher

ZEUS 1994

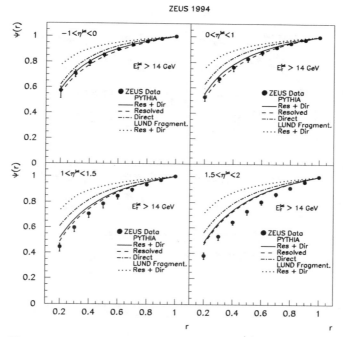

Figure 1: The measured jet shapes, $\psi(r)$, for jets in the E_T^{jet} range above 14 GeV in different η^{jet} regions are shown and compared to PYTHIA. The predictions of PYTHIA without initial and final state parton radiation are also included ('LUND Fragment').

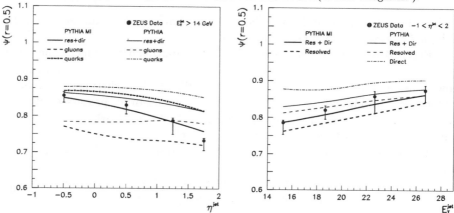

Figure 2: $\psi(r=0.5)$, left (a), as a function of η^{jet} for jets with $E_T^{jet} > 14$ GeV and compared to predictions from PYTHIA for quark jets only, gluon jets only and all jets (also shown with multi-parton interactions - PYTHIA MI) and right (b), as a function of E_T^{jet} for jets with $-1 < \eta^{jet} < 2$.

142

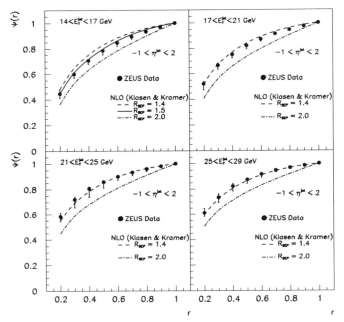

Figure 3: The measured jet shape, $\psi(r)$, for jets in the range $-1 < \eta^{jet} < 2$ in different E_T^{jet} regions. Also shown are the predictions for the jet shapes based upon the NLO QCD calculations by M. Klasen and G. Kramer with various values of R_{SEP}.

order. Here, jets are found using the k_T algorithm[78] and events selected with 3 high E_T jets: $E_T^{jet} > 6$ GeV and $\eta^{jet} < 1.5$.

Figure 4(a) shows the uncorrected x_γ^{obs} distribution defined using the three highest E_T jets in the event. The data are peaked at high x_γ^{obs} with a tail to low values and are in general agreement with PYTHIA predictions. The slight differences at high and low x_γ^{obs} may be due to higher-order processes relevant to 3-jet production which are not included in the Monte Carlo. The low x_γ^{obs} tail shows the need to include resolved processes.

The inclusive 3-jet to 2-jet ratio as a function of $\sum E_T^{jet}$[9] is shown in Figure 4(b),

$$\frac{\sigma_3}{\sigma_2} = \frac{\sigma(\gamma p \to njets + X; n \geq 3)}{\sigma(\gamma p \to njets + X; n \geq 2)} \tag{3}$$

where the sum is over all jets passing the selection cuts. The data rise initially due to the increase in the phase-space available for 3-jet production and then level off. The prediction from PYTHIA is in broad agreement with the data within the large systematic errors.

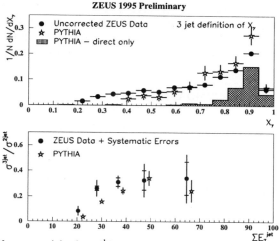

Figure 4: Shown here are, (a), the x_γ^{obs} distribution with purely statistical errors and (b), the 3 to 2 jet inclusive ratio.

4 Conclusions

Comparison between data and PYTHIA show that jet shapes in photoproduction are governed strongly by QCD parton radiation. Their description by PYTHIA is improved by the addition of multi-parton interactions. NLO QCD calculations agree with the data using an R_{SEP} parameter of ≈ 1.4.

Photoproduced multijet events have been observed. Comparison with a LO parton shower Monte Carlo indicates that both direct and resolved events are needed to describe the x_γ^{obs} distribution. It is hoped that development of a NLO Monte Carlo and increased statistics will enable further studies to discriminate between the predictions of different models.

References

1. ZEUS Collab., M. Derrick et al., *Phys. Lett.* **B348** (1995) 665.
2. S.D. Ellis, Z. Kunszt and D.E. Soper, *Phys. Rev. Lett.* **69** (1992) 3615.
3. H.-U. Bengtsson and T. Sjöstrand, *Comp. Phys. Comm.* **46** (1987) 43; T. Sjöstrand, *Comp. Phys. Comm.* **82** (1994) 74.
4. G. Gustafson, B. Andersson and C. Petersen, *Z. Phys.*, C1 (1979), 105.
5. G. Kramer and S.G. Salesch, *Phys. Lett.* **B317** (1993) 218, *Phys. Lett.* **B333** (1994) 519.
6. M. Klasen and G. Kramer, preprint DESY-97-002.
7. S. Catani, Yu.L. Dokshitzer, M.H. Seymour and B.R. Webber, *Nucl. Phys* **B406** (1993) 187.
8. S.D. Ellis, D.E. Soper, *Phys. Rev.* **D48** (1993) 3160.
9. E. Gallas, preprint FERMILAB-CONF-96-304-EF.

PHOTOPRODUCTION OF HIGH TRANSVERSE MOMENTUM CHARGED PARTICLES AND A COMPARISON OF STRANGENESS PRODUCTION IN PHOTOPRODUCTION AND DEEP INELASTIC SCATTERING

DAVID MILSTEAD

For the H1 Collaboration

Oliver Lodge Laboratory, The University of Liverpool, Liverpool, UK.

Photon-proton interactions with $Q^2 < 10^{-2}$ GeV^2 (photoproduction) and deep inelastic scattering (DIS) interactions with photon virtualities $Q^2 > 10$ GeV^2 are studied at the high energy electron-proton collider HERA. Inclusive charged particle spectra in photoproduction are compared to LO QCD calculations and shown to be sensitive to the partonic structure of the photon. K^0 and Λ properties in photoproduction and in DIS are shown and compared with NLO QCD calculations.

1 Introduction

With the ep collider at HERA it is possible to study in the same experiment the hadronic final state of photon-proton interactions for a range of photon virtualities giving an insight into partonic structure of the photon and proton. In photoproduction, the measurement of the high p_T particles can tag hard partonic interactions which can be used to constrain the quark and gluon densities of the photon down to an approximate lower limit of x_γ, the fraction of the photon energy carried by the interacting parton , of $x_\gamma > \frac{p_T e^{-\eta}}{2E_\gamma}$, where p_T and η are the transverse momentum and pseudorapidity of the observed hard particle and E_γ is the exchanged photon energy. The study of strange particle production gives an increased sensitivity at high p_T to charm and gluon interactions while at low p_T a comparison of strangeness production between photoproduction and DIS can test the universality of the fragmentation process.

2 HERA and H1

The results presented in this report are based on data taken in 1994 with the H1 detector at HERA, which collides beams of 27.5 GeV positrons and 820 GeV protons, and corresponds to an integrated luminosity of 1.3 pb^{-1}. A detailed description of the detector can be found elsewhere [1] and only the components relevant to the analyses presented here are described. Photoproduction events are selected by identifying positrons scattered at low angle in the H1 electron tagger, the acceptance of which restricts the kinematic range of y and Q^2, the fractional energy and photon virtuality, to $0.3 < y < 0.7$ and $Q^2 < 0.01$ GeV^2. Positrons scattered at larger angles into the H1 Backward Electromagnetic Calorimeter are used to detect DIS events with Q^2 above several GeV^2. Charged tracks are measured in the central track detector and are used to tag K^0 and Λ [a] particles by reconstructing secondary vertices from the weak decays $K_s^0 \longrightarrow \pi^+\pi^-$ and $\Lambda \longrightarrow p\pi^-$, $\overline{\Lambda} \longrightarrow \overline{p}\pi^+$.

3   Charged Particles in Photoproduction

Figure 1 shows the differential charged particle cross-section in photoproduction [2] as a function of transverse momentum, p_T, compared with a LO QCD calculation. The photoproduction data are defined in the kinematic intervals of $0.3 < y < 0.7$ and $Q^2 < 0.01$ GeV^2.

The cross-section is shown for particles with transverse momenta above 2 GeV and is integrated over the pseudorapidity region $| \eta | < 1.0$

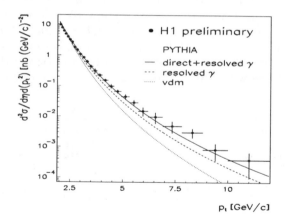

Figure 1: The differential charged particle cross-section $d\sigma/dp_T$ in the interval $| \eta | < 1$ for charged particles with $p_T > 2$ GeV, compared to PYTHIA using GRV-LO photon and proton parton densities

The QCD calculation was based on the event generator PYTHIA [3] with multiple parton interactions. The GRV-LO parameterisation of the parton dis-

---

[a]Unless otherwise stated, all references in this report to K^0, Λ will implicitly mean $K^0 + \overline{K^0}$, $\Lambda + \overline{\Lambda}$

tributions for the photon and the proton were used. The data were normalised to the calculation of direct and resolved processes and exceeds the data by 20% at transverse hadron momenta $p_T = 2$ GeV though is consistent with the measurement above $p_T = 2.5$ GeV. Also shown are the relative contributions of the direct, Vector Dominance Model (VDM) and anomalous photon components. The GRV-LO [4] pion parton density parameterisations were used to calculate the VDM component. The VDM contribution was normalised together with the direct photon component to give the total predicted cross-section at $p_T = 2$ GeV and the anomalous contribution then results from the difference between the total calculated cross-section and the VDM plus direct photon components.

With this calculation the anomalous photon component contributes about 50% at transverse momenta above 6 GeV and the direct and anomalous components dominate the cross-section for p_T above 3.5 GeV.

In figure 2, the charged particle differential pseudorapidity cross-section $d\sigma/d\eta$ is shown for particles with transverse momenta above 2 GeV. The corresponding interval of the parton energy fraction can be estimated to be between $x_\gamma(\eta = 1) \approx 0.05$ and $x_\gamma(\eta = -1) \approx 0.4$ on average. A comparison is made with PYTHIA with two different parton distribution functions: GRV-LO(figure 2a) and LAC1 [5](figure 2b). The GRV-LO prediction gives a cross-section too large at negative rapidities (high x_γ) but falling short for higher rapidities (low x_γ). The LAC1 prediction shown is seen to substantially exceed the data for $\eta > 0$. The calculated gluon contribution in the photon is shown as a dotted line with LAC1 predicting a steep rise not matched by the data.

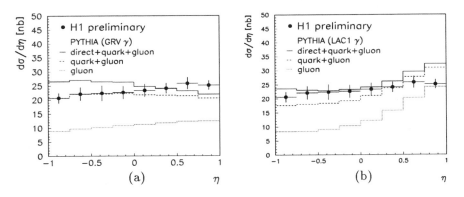

Figure 2: The differential charged particle cross-section $d\sigma/d\eta$ in photoproduction compared to PYTHIA with the GRV-LO(a) and LAC1(b) photon parton parameterisations

4   Strangeness Production

Figure 3 shows the differential K^0 cross-section [7] as a function of p_T in photoproduction in the kinematic range $0.3 < y < 0.6$, $Q^2 < 0.01$ GeV^2 and is shown for the K^0 kinematic interval $0.5 < p_T < 5.0$ GeV and $| \eta | < 1.3$. A comparison is made to analytical NLO calculations [6] using quark and gluon fragmentation functions from e^+e^- data. The predictions assume that the four scales used in the calculation are equal and are alternatively set to $p_T/2$, p_T and $2p_T$. For p_T above 3 GeV, where the calculation is considered to be reliable, good agreement with the data is observed.

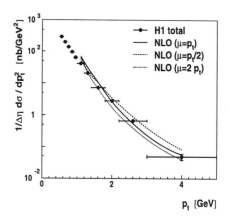

Figure 3: The differential K^0 cross-section as a function of p_T^2 in photoproduction compared to NLO calculations

It is of interest to compare strangeness rates in photoproduction with those in deep inelastic scattering (DIS) processes, where Q^2 is larger than several GeV^2. Though particle rates are expected to be Q^2 independent in the central rapidity region of the photon-proton centre of mass system, differences are expected in the photon fragmentation region [8].

Since the relative contribution of low mass diffractive events in photoproduction and DIS events are very different, these were removed by insisting on a minimum amount of energy in the forward going (proton) region [7]. The remaining sample is termed non-diffractive.

Figure 4 shows the K^0 multiplicity as a function of p_T^* and the K^0 and Λ multiplicity as a function of rapidity, y^*, in non-diffractive photoproduction and DIS interactions [7]. The DIS data lie in the range $10 < Q^2 < 70$ GeV^2,

$0.3 < y < 0.6$, giving an average photon virtuality, $\langle Q^2 \rangle = 23$ GeV^2. These results are presented the photon-proton rest frame, where the exchanged photon defines the longitudinal $+z^*$ axis and are restricted to the region $0.5 < p_T^* < 5$ GeV, $1.3 < y^* < 2.8$ for the K^0 results and $0.6 < p_T^* < 5$ GeV, $1.3 < y^* < 2.8$ for the Λ spectra.

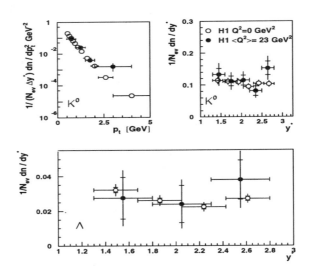

Figure 4: The K^0 and Λ rates in non-diffractive photoproduction and DIS as a function of p_T^{*2} (K^0, top left), y^* (K^0, top right) and y^* (Λ, bottom).

The K^0 rate is seen to be independent of Q^2 in this phase space region though there is a suggestion of a hardening of the K^0 transverse momenta spectra for DIS compared to photoproduction processes. Similarly, the differential multiplicity in η is shown in figure 4 for Λ production in non-diffractive DIS and photoproduction. Within the larger statistical and systematic errors, the rate of Λ production is also seen to be independent of Q^2.

5   Conclusion

Charged particle cross-sections in photoproduction interactions have been presented and compared to QCD LO predictions and have been shown to be sensitive to the partonic structure of the photon and proton. Strangeness production in non-diffractive photoproduction interactions is found to be similar to that in and DIS processes and agree well with QCD NLO calculations.

References

1. T. Ahmed it et al., Nucl. Inst. and Meth **A386** (1996) 310;
2. W. Hoprich, diploma thesis, Hiedelberg (1995) ;
3. T. Sjostrand *et al.*, Comp. Phys. Comm. **82** (1994) 74;
4. M. Gluck *et al.*, Phys. Rev. **D46** (1992) 1973;
5. H. Abramowicz *et al.*, Phys. Lett. **B269** (1991) 458;
6. J. Binneweis *et al.*, Phys. Rev. **D53** (1996) 3573;
7. S. Aid *et al.*, Submitted to Z. Phys. **C** (1997);
8. J. D. Bjorken *et al.*, Phys. Rev. **D8** (1973) 1341.

OBSERVATION OF ISOLATED HIGH-E_T PHOTONS IN PHOTOPRODUCTION AT HERA.

A.W. VAICIULIS

Physics Department, University of Wisconsin
1150 University Avenue, Madison, WI 53706
Representing the ZEUS Collaboration

Events with an isolated prompt photon with high transverse energy, accompanied by a balancing jet, have been observed for the first time in photoproduction at HERA using the ZEUS detector. The fraction of the incoming photon energy participating in the production of the prompt photon and the jet shows a strong peak near unity, consistent with LO QCD Monte Carlo predictions. A cross section for the process is presented and found to be in good agreement with a recent NLO calculation.

1   Introduction

In photoproduction at HERA, two major classes of $2 \rightarrow 2$ process can be defined in lowest order QCD, depending on how the photon interacts with a parton in the proton: direct, in which the photon interacts as a pointlike particle in the hard subprocess, and resolved, in which the photon provides a quark or gluon which then interacts. The outgoing products of these subprocesses are most commonly quarks or gluons, which at high transverse energy (E_T) can give rise to two observed jets (dijet events). However, final states containing a high E_T jet together with a high E_T photon are also possible. Such photons are known as "prompt" photons to distinguish them from those produced via particle decays. In the kinematic region accessible at HERA, the direct channel in prompt photon processes is expected to be dominated by the direct Compton process $\gamma q \rightarrow \gamma q$ (fig.1a). The main predicted contributions to the resolved processes are $qg \rightarrow q\gamma$ and $q\bar{q} \rightarrow g\gamma$.[1,2]

A further source of prompt photons is dijet events in which an outgoing quark radiates a high E_T photon. In measuring prompt photon processes, these radiative contributions are largely suppressed by restricting the measurement to prompt photons that are isolated from other particles in the event. Such a condition is needed to reduce experimental backgrounds from neutral mesons in jets.

Fixed target studies[3] have provided a first confirmation of prompt photon processes in photoproduction, at a level consistent with QCD expectations. At HERA, the highly asymmetric beam energies ($E_e \times E_p = 27.5$ GeV $\times$ 820 GeV), together with the detector coverage, restrict the main sensitivity of the

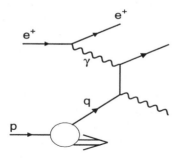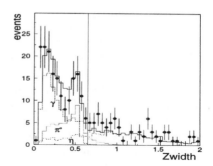

Figure 1: (a) Direct LO diagram in hard photoproduction producing an outgoing prompt photon. The corresponding dijet diagram may be obtained by replacing the final-state photon by a gluon. (b) Distribution of Zwidth for prompt photon candidates and γ, π°, η fitted Monte Carlo (see text).

resolved processes to the quark content of the photon [4,5], together with the quark and gluon contents of the proton. A particular virtue of prompt photon processes is that the observed final-state photon emerges directly from the hard scatter, without the intermediate hadronisation by which a final state quark or gluon forms an observable jet. The above considerations, together with the availability of recent NLO calculations [6,7], make prompt photon processes an attractive and relatively clean means for studying QCD, despite the low cross sections.

¿From 6.36pb^{-1} of data taken in e^+p running in 1995 with the ZEUS detector at HERA, we have identified a class of events showing the characteristics of hard prompt photon processes in quasi-real γp collisions. This is the first observation of prompt photons at γp center of mass energies an order of magnitude higher than those previously employed. The data are compared with leading order Monte carlo predictions and a NLO QCD calculation.

2 Event Selection

The ZEUS apparatus is described elsewhere.[8] Of particular importance in the present work are the barrel part of the uranium-scintillator calorimeter (BCAL) and the central tracking detector (CTD). The BCAL consists of an electromagnetic section (BEMC) backed by a hadronic section; the BEMC consists of projective cells of ≈ 20 cm length and ≈ 5 cm width. This width is not small enough to resolve the photons from the processes $\pi^\circ \to 2\gamma$, $\eta \to 2\gamma$, and

$\eta \rightarrow 3\pi^\circ$ on an event by event basis. It does, however, enable a partial discrimination between single photons and the decay products of neutral mesons. Because of this discriminating power the photon is required to be detected in the BCAL, thus restricting the photon pseudorapidity to the approximate range $-0.75 < \eta < 1.0$.

A ZEUS electron finding algorithm was used to identify possible photon signals in BCAL with $5 < E_T(\gamma) < 10$ GeV. Above ≈ 10 GeV the separation of the two photons from a π° decay is so small that the resulting BEMC signal is very similar to a single photon signal. A cone jet finding algorithm [9] was used to identify jets, using the entire ZEUS calorimeter system, with $E_T(jet)$ > 4.5 GeV, pseudorapidity $-1.5 < \eta < 1.7$ and unit cone radius. Events with an observed DIS electron were removed, restricting the present analysis to incoming photons of virtuality $Q^2 \leq 1$ GeV^2.

A photon candidate was rejected if a track pointed within 0.3 radian of it; high E_T positrons and electrons were thus removed, including those that underwent hard radiation in the material between the interaction point and the BCAL. An isolation cone was now imposed around the photon candidate: within a cone of unit radius in (η, ϕ), the total E_T from other particles was required not to exceed $0.1E_T^\gamma$.

3 Signal/Background Separation Using Shower Shapes

Electromagnetic signals in the calorimeter that do not arise from charged particles arise predominantly from photons and from decays of π° and η mesons. Two shape-dependent quantities were studied in order to distinguish photon, π° and η signals. These were (i) the energy weighted mean width of the BEMC cluster in Z and (ii) the fraction Fmax of the photon candidate energy found in the most energetic cell in the cluster. In figure 1b the Zwidth quantity (in units of BEMC cell width) is shown for the data and three types of single particle Monte Carlo. Events with Zwidth > 0.65 were rejected because there is no photon signal above this value. Fmax for the remaining events is shown in figure 2a. The relative amounts of γ, π°, and η Monte Carlo were fit to the data for Z width > 0.65 (determines η contribution) and all Fmax bins. The experimental data are well fitted to a sum (solid line) of the Monte Carlo shapes, and a photon component is demanded by the fit. The γ and π° Monte Carlo Z width and Fmax shapes were compared to data (DIS positrons, π° from $\rho^\pm$) and reasonable agreement was found.

We perform a background subtraction on the assumption that the data may be expressed as a sum of photon signal plus neutral meson background as indicated in figure 2a. The Fmax distribution of figure 2a was divided

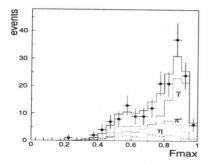 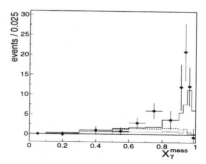

Figure 2: (a) Distribution of Fmax for prompt photon candidates and γ, π°, η fitted Monte Carlo (see text). (b) x_γ^{meas} of prompt photon events after background subtraction. Points = data; dotted histogram = MC radiative contribution; dashed = radiative + resolved; solid = radiative + resolved + direct. Errors are statistical only.

into two parts at Fmax = 0.75, a signal enhanced region above this value, and a background enhanced region below. ¿From the shapes of the Monte Carlo distributions, one can calculate the probabilities that a given photon or neutral meson will generate an entry in either region. In this way, any quantity of interest can be plotted after background subtraction based on the Fmax plot.

4 Results

The fraction x_γ of the incoming photon momentum that contributes to the production of the high E_T photon and jet is studied. Using the definition in [10], x_γ^{meas} was plotted (fig 2b). Also shown are the corresponding Pythia Monte Carlo expectations for the following processes: (i) dijet events in which an outgoing quark radiates an isolated high E_T photon; (ii) resolved prompt photon production; (iii) direct prompt photon production. The Monte Carlo distributions are normalised to the same integrated luminosity as the data. For clarity, the plotted histograms show (i), (i)+(ii) and (i)+(ii)+(iii). The error bars on the data points are statistical only. The Monte Carlo distribution is similar to the data in shape and magnitude. We identify the strong peak near unity with the direct Compton process. It is not possible to make conclusions concerning the presence of a resolved photon component, except to remark that the observed numbers of events at low x_γ^{meas} are consistent with the level expected. For $x_\gamma^{\text{meas}} \geq 0.8$, the number of events in the signal is 57.6. The background distribution is consistent with zero for $x_\gamma^{\mathrm{meas}} > 0.9$. Below this value the average is two counts per 0.025 interval.

We quote a cross section for the process

$$ep \rightarrow e + \gamma_{\mathrm{prompt}} + \mathrm{jet} + X$$

with $x_\gamma^{\mathrm{meas}} \geq 0.8$. Here, γ_{prompt} denotes a final state isolated prompt photon with $5 \leq E_T^\gamma < 10$ GeV and $-0.7 \leq \eta^\gamma < 0.8$; jet denotes a "hadron jet" with $E_T^{\mathrm{jet}} \geq 5$ GeV, $-1.5 \leq \eta^{\mathrm{jet}} \leq 1.8$. Limits of $0.16 < y^{\mathrm{true}} < 0.8$ and $Q^2 < 1\mathrm{GeV}^2$ were applied in the hadron level event definition. The correction factor from Pythia Monte Carlo is 1.69. With the above definitions, a cross section of 15.3±3.8±1.8 pb is obtained, where the errors are statistical and systematic respectively. The systematic error is dominated by the 8% contribution due to the uncertainty in the calorimeter calibration.

This result can be compared with NLO calculations at the parton level of Gordon [11] (using a LO radiative contribution), evaluated under the same kinematic conditions as used above. Using the GS [12] and GRV [13] NLO photon parton densities, integrated cross sections of 13.17 (14.05) pb and 16.58 (17.93) pb respectively are obtained, where the first value is calculated at a QCD scale $Q^2 = E_T^{\gamma\,2}$ and the second, parenthesized value at $Q^2 = 0.25\,E_T^{\gamma\,2}$. These values cover the range of theoretical uncertainty of each calculation. The experiment and theory are in good agreement.

Conclusions

We have observed for the first time isolated high E_T photons, accompanied by balancing jets, in photoproduction at HERA. The x_γ^{meas} distribution of the events is in good general agreement with LO QCD expectations as calculated using PYTHIA. The measured cross section for prompt photon production in ep collisions, satisfying the conditions defined above, is 15.3±3.8±1.8 pb, in good agreement of a recent NLO calculation of the process.

Acknowledgments

I wish to thank the other members of the ZEUS Collaboration as well as the DESY directorate and staff for their encouragement and support. The outstanding efforts of the HERA machine group in providing improved luminosities in 1995 are much appreciated.

References

1. A. C. Bawa and W. J. Stirling, J. Phys. **G14**, 1353 (1988).
2. A. C. Bawa, M. Krawczyk and W. J. Stirling, Z. Phys. **C50**, 293 (1991).
3. NA14 Collaboration, P. Astbury et al., Phys. Lett. **152B**, 419 (1985).
4. L. E. Gordon and J. K. Storrow, Z. Phys. **C63**, 581 (1994).
5. P. J. Bussey, proc. *Photon 95,* Sheffield, ed. D. J. Miller et al. (World Scientific, 1996), 47.
6. L. E. Gordon and W. Vogelsang, Phys. Rev. **D52**, 58 (1995).
7. L. E. Gordon, Argonne Report, ANL-HEP-CP-96-50.
8. ZEUS Collaboration, M. Derrick et al., Phys. Lett. **B297**, 404 (1992).
9. ZEUS Collaboration, M. Derrick et al., Phys. Lett. **B348**, 665 (1995).
10. ZEUS Collaboration, M. Derrick et al., Phys. Lett. **B322**, 287 (1994).
11. L. E. Gordon, these proceedings and private communication.
12. L. E. Gordon and J. K. Storrow, Nucl. Phys. **B489**, 405 (1997).
13. M. Glück, E. Reya and A. Vogt, Phys. Rev. **D46**, 1973 (1992).

VIRTUAL PHOTON STRUCTURE FROM JET PRODUCTION

J. CHÝLA, J. CVACH

Institute of Physics of the Academy of Sciences,
Na Slovance 2, Prague 8, 18040, Czech Republic

Some aspects of extracting the information on the structure of virtual photons from jet production in ep and e^+e^- collisions are discussed.

1   Virtual particles - why, where and how?

Measuring the dependence of the structure of the photon at short distance on its virtuality provides new information on strong interaction dynamics. The results of first attempts in this direction have recently been reported[1]. Presently the structure of virtual photons can be investigated via the deep inelastic scattering or jet production in $\gamma\gamma$ collisions at LEP, or in jet production in γp collisions at HERA. In jet studies the internal structure of the photon manifests itself through the resolved photon contribution to hard γp or $\gamma\gamma$ collisions. Measuring the deviation of jet cross–sections from expectations of a structureless photon provides information on the distribution functions $f_{i/\gamma}(x, M^2, P^2)$ of partons inside the photon of virtuality P^2, probed at the distance $1/M$. In Fig. 1a we compare the integrated cross–sections for the DIS and dijet production

$$\sigma^{\mathrm{DIS}}(M^2) \equiv \int_{M^2} \mathrm{d}Q^2 \int \mathrm{d}x \frac{\mathrm{d}\sigma(x, Q^2)}{\mathrm{d}x\mathrm{d}Q^2}, \quad \sigma^{\mathrm{jets}}(M^2) \equiv \int_M \mathrm{d}p_T \int \mathrm{d}\eta \frac{\mathrm{d}\sigma(\eta, p_T)}{\mathrm{d}\eta\mathrm{d}p_T}$$

in e^+e^- collisions at LEP 2 for photons with $P^2 < 1$ GeV^2. The hard scale is identified with the standard Q in DIS and p_T in jet production. The curves in Fig. 1a show that up to moderate scales jet production is more effective than DIS, while for M^2 above 40 GeV^2 DIS has larger cross–section. Although both cross–sections decrease with increasing P^2, their ratio is essentially independent of it. To obtain reasonable statistics of a few thousands of events it will be necessary to use jets with transverse momenta down to 3-4 GeV. In [2] we discussed the possibilities offered by the HERA upgrade for the measurement of basic features of the virtual photon structure via the jet production. Here we elaborate on two important aspects of this problem.

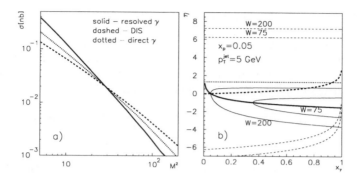

Figure 1: Integrated cross–sections of γ with $Q^2 \leq 1$ GeV^2 for the DIS and jet production in e^+e^- collisions at LEP 2, using the GRV structure functions for the photon and disregarding any detector efficiencies (a), kinematical ranges of the pseudorapidity of jets (solid lines) and beam remnants at HERA (dashed) (b). In (b) the thick solid and dashed lines indicate the centers of the respective intervals and the dotted one the end of the H1 detector.

2 WW approximation and the structure of the virtual photon

The measured electroproduction cross–sections at the CMS energy $\sqrt{S}$ are related to those of the photoproduction via the WW approximation as

$$d\sigma(e + p \rightarrow e' + X; S) = \int \int dy dP^2 f_{\gamma/e}(y, P^2) d\sigma(\gamma + p \rightarrow X; yS, P^2),$$

where $f_{\gamma/e}(y, P^2)$ is the unintegrated distribution function of virtual photons inside an electron. This relation holds for P^2 much smaller than the scale of the $\gamma + p \rightarrow X$ process. If this latter process is characterized by the hard scale Q, its cross–section can in turn be expressed in terms of the convolution of integrated parton distribution functions (pdf) $f_{i/\gamma}(x_\gamma, Q^2, P^2)$ of the photon with those of the proton, $f_{j/p}(x_p, Q^2)$, and partonic hard scattering cross–section σ_{ij}. Because virtual photons can be transverse as well as longitudinal, there are two independent fluxes. Neglecting subdominant terms we have

$$f^T_{\gamma/e}(x, P^2) = \frac{\alpha}{2\pi} \frac{1 + (1-x)^2}{x} \frac{1}{P^2} \equiv \frac{F^T(x)}{P^2},$$
$$f^L_{\gamma/e}(x, P^2) = \frac{\alpha}{2\pi} \frac{2(1-x)}{x} \frac{1}{P^2} \equiv \frac{F^L(x)}{P^2}.$$

As $P^2 \rightarrow 0$, $f^{T,L}_{i/\gamma}$ behave as

$$f^T_{i/\gamma}(x, Q^2, P^2) = f^{real}_{i/\gamma}(x, Q^2) + (P^2/\mu_T^2) h^T_i(x, Q^2) + O(P^4),$$

$$f_{i/\gamma}^L(x, Q^2, P^2) = (P^2/\mu_L^2)h_i^L(x, Q^2) + O(P^4),$$

where $\mu_{T,L}$ are some parameters. In most of existing phenomenological analyses [a] of the photon structure its longitudinal componennt f^L has been neglected. This is, however, consistent only if we at the same time neglect also the dependence of $f_{i/\gamma}^T(x, Q^2, P^2)$ on the virtuality P^2! Indeed, as

$$f_{\gamma/e}^T(P^2) \otimes f_{i/\gamma}^T(Q^2, P^2) = (1/P^2)F^T \otimes f_{i/\gamma}^{\rm real}(Q^2) + (1/\mu_T^2)F^T \otimes h_i^T(Q^2),$$
$$f_{\gamma/e}^L(P^2) \otimes f_{i/\gamma}^L(Q^2, P^2) = (1/\mu_L^2)F^L \otimes h_i^L(Q^2),$$

$f_{\gamma/e}^L$ contributes terms of the same order as the subleading, $O(P^2)$, term in $f_{\gamma/e}^T$! Thus to investigate P^2 dependence of photon structure, we <u>must</u> take into account also its longitudinal component. Details will be discussed in [10]. The P^2 dependence of the photon pdf has recently been addressed in a number of papers [5,6,7,9]. For instance, in [6] the virtuality dependence of $f_{\gamma/e}^T$ is assumed to be given by a simple multiplicative suppression factor L

$$f_{q/\gamma}^T(x, Q^2, P^2) = L(Q^2, P^2, P_c^2)f_{q/\gamma}^{\rm real}(x, Q^2), \ L \equiv \frac{\ln\left((Q^2 + P_c^2)/(P^2 + P_c^2)\right)}{\ln\left((Q^2 + P_c^2)/P_c^2\right)}.$$

As for $P^2 \to 0$, $L \approx 1 - (P^2/P_c^2)/\ln(Q^2/P_c^2)$, the parameter P_c plays the role of μ_T. For the gluon the suppression factor is taken as L^2. This simple ansatz, incorporated in HERWIG event generator, was used in [2].

3 Jets vs. the underlying event in ep collisions at HERA

Also at HERA the studies of resolved photon processes with P^2 above, say, 0.5 GeV^2, will require using jets with E_T down to about 5 GeV^2. The properties of such low E_T jets can, however, be significantly distorted by the presence of soft particles produced in the *soft underlying event* (sue), which appears, in one form or another, in all event generators. For instance, the H1 found [11] significant disagreement between their data on jets with $E_T^{\rm jet} \approx 7$ GeV and PYTHIA and HERWIG event generators <u>without</u> the sue. For PYTHIA this discrepancy disappeared when the multiple interaction option with a very small partonic $p_T^{\rm min} = 1.2$ GeV was used. The presence of sue may also be the cause of the discrepancy between NLO calculations of dijet cross–sections in photoproduction and ZEUS data [12,13] in the region $x_\gamma \leq 0.75$, $E_T^{\rm jet} \leq 10$ GeV.

In HERWIG the sue is modelled as the soft interaction of two beam remnant clusters, which accompanies the basic hard parton–parton scattering. The

---

[a]The relevance of the longitudinal part $f_{\gamma/e}^L$ has recently been been discussed in [4].

main effect of this soft collision is the redistribution of the (usually large) longitudinal energy of the two beam remnant clusters. Without sue these remnant clusters decay into just a few particles, separated by a large rapidity gap. In a sue event this longitudinal energy is redistributed among many softer particles which populate central region in pseudorapidity and thus provide "pedestal" under the jets. The strength and frequency of the sue is governed by two parameters, which can be tuned to data. As there are so far no conclusive results on the magnitude of sue needed by the data we performed our studies for two extreme options: no sue and sue in each event and with all the energy of beam remnants used up for the soft collision. The differences between these two scenarios, shown in Figs. 2,3, illustrate the importance of a good quantitative understanding of nonjet physics for the determination of jet properties.

We defined jets using the CDF cone algorithm with $R = 1$ and required $E_T \geq 5$ GeV in γp CMS. The crucial question is how much transverse energy of the sue populates the region in η where jets are found. For a given $x_\gamma \equiv (E_T^{(1)} \exp(-\eta_1) + E_T^{(2)} \exp(-\eta_2))/2E_\gamma$, x_p, W and p_T^{jet} simple kinematics allows us to determine the intervals of η^{jet} and η^{remn}, populated by jets and by soft particles from beam remnant fragmentation respectively. In Fig. 1b they correspond, as a function of a x_γ and for fixed typical $x_p = 0.05$, $p_T^{\text{jet}} = 5$ GeV and two values of $W = 75, 200$ GeV, to intervals on the y axis between the solid (for jets) and dashed curves (for beam remnants). We see that except for x_γ very close to 1, jets can bath in a pool of soft particles from beam fragmentation. Whether they indeed do so depends on the way beam remnants fragment. In Fig. 2 we show, for events with and without sue, normalized lego-plots of E_T as a function of η^{jet} and x_γ for jets and η^{remn} and x_γ for particles from beam remnants. Without the sue jets and beam remnants overlap significantly only for large x_γ, while for events with the sue they do so for all values of x_γ. Moreover, the amount of transverse energy under the jets coming from beam remnant fragmentation is almost negligible for events without the sue, but becomes quite sizeable for the sue option. There is always some transverse energy under the jets which distorts its properties, but above certain value it makes the theoretical predictions unstable and thus unreliable. Too much transverse energy from sue leads to fake hard jets, which significantly increase the corresponding cross–section. We studied this effect in HERWIG by generating events with p_T^{part} of the basic partonic subprocess starting from 2 GeV and looked for jets with E_T between 5 and 12 GeV. The results, plotted in Fig. 3a, show that without the sue (dashed curves), the contributions to jets with a given E_T^{jet} come mainly from partons with $p_T^{\text{part}} \doteq E_T^{\text{jet}} + 1$ and drop off rapidly below and more slowly above E_T^{jet}. Summing the contributions of all events with $p_T^{\text{part}} > 2$ GeV yields the dashed curves in Fig. 3b. The jet cross–sections

160

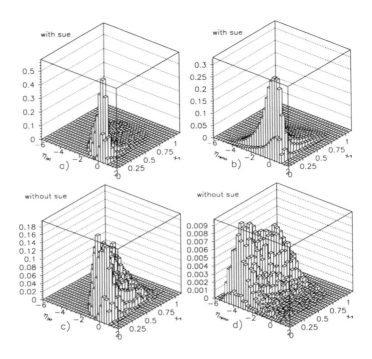

Figure 2: Transverse energy flow per event as a function of x_γ and pseudorapidity of jets or particles from beam remnants in events with (a,b) and without (c,d) the sue.

are reasonably stable with respect to the variation of the minimal partonic p_T^{min} down to $E_T^{jet} = 5$ GeV. For events with sue the situation, described by solid curves in Fig. 3, is substantially different. Even events with $p_T = 2$ GeV can fake jets with E_T^{jet} below 10 GeV and this probability in fact increases with decreasing p_T^{part}! A closer scrutiny shows that these fake hard jets are characterized by almost no correlation between the momenta of basic hard parton scattering process and the observed jets. Only for E_T^{jet} above roughly 10 GeV we get the situation analogous to that of dashed curves. The integrated jet cross–sections in Fig. 3b are then highly unstable with respect to the minimal partonic p_T^{min}, which makes the theoretical predictions unreliable. In order to make sensible comparisons between theory and data the amount of transverse energy under the jets (jet pedestals) must be determined experimentally and subtracted from measured jets transverse energy. This is in particular true for comparisons at the NLO, where theoretical calculations are available on

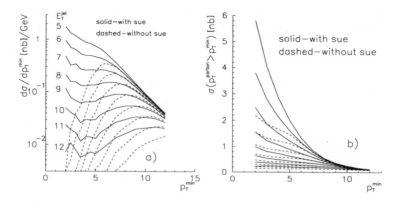

Figure 3: The contribution of a given events with given p_T^{part} to the cross–section for production of jets with E_T^{jet} between 5 and 12 GeV (a) and sums of these contribution above a given minimal partonic p_T^{min} (b).

partonic level only. Comparing theoretical prediction directly with observed jets makes sense only if the theory describes quantitatively also the transverse energy flow <u>outside</u> the jets. This point will be discussed in more detail in [10].

This work has been supported by the Grant Agency of the AS of the Czech Republic under the grants No. A1010602 and A1010619.

References

1. C. Foudas, in Proceedings *DIS96*, ed. G. D'Agostini and A. Nigro, World Scientific 1997, p. 275, T. Ebert, ibid., p. 272
   T. Ebert and H. Rick, these Proceedings
2. J. Chýla and J. Cvach in Proceedings *Future Physics at HERA*, ed. G. Ingelman, A. De Roeck, R. Klanner (World Scientific, 1996), p. 545.
3. G. Schuler, CERN-TH/96-297.
4. F. Borzumati and G. Schuler, *Z. Phys.* C **58**, 139 (1993).
5. M. Drees and R. Godbole, *Phys. Rev.* D **50**, 3124 (1994).
6. G. Schuler and T. Sjöstrand, *Phys. Lett.* B **376**, 193 (1996).
7. M. Glück, E. Reya and M. Stratmann, *Phys. Rev.* D **51**, 3220 (1995).
8. J. Chýla and J. Cvach, in preparation.
9. S. Aid et al. (H1 Collab.), *Z. Phys.* C **70**, 17 (1996)
10. R. Saunders, talk at the *DIS97 Conference*, Chicago, April 1997.
11. P. Aurenche, these Proceedings.

PROBING THE STRUCTURE OF VIRTUAL PHOTON IN THE DEEP INELASTIC COMPTON PROCESS AT HERA

MARIA KRAWCZYK, A. ZEMBRZUSKI

*Institute of Theoretical Physics, University of Warsaw, ul. Hoza 69,
00-681 Warsaw, Poland*

The sensitivity of the Deep Inelastic Compton (DIC) scattering at HERA to the structure of the virtual photon is discussed. It is demonstrated that the gluonic content of the virtual photon can be pinned down by measuring the photons with $p_T \sim 5$ GeV in the proton direction.

1 Introduction

The Deep Inelastic Compton (DIC) process provides the opportunity to probe at HERA the structure of the real photon, as was pointed out in [1,2,3,4,5 a]. The ability to probe the structure of the photon (and the proton) in the tagged and untagged events at HERA was studied in paper [3] with the conclusion that in order to separate the contribution arising from the gluonic content of the (real) photon the tagged condition is preferred.

The first attempt to describe the DIC process at HERA using the structure of the virtual photon can be found in [6,7], where the EPA approach was compared with the calculation, where the virtual photon interacts directly or by its partonic content. Results obtained for the virtual photon were based on the naive Parton Model formulae only for quarks.

Here we examine, using the GRS (LO) [9] parton parametrization for the virtual photon, the usefulness of DIC process to study at HERA the structure of a virtual photon, in particular the gluonic content of virtual photon. The recent study have showed that the parton distributions of the virtual photon can be tested at HERA via tagged single high E_T jet or $b\bar{b}$ production [10].

2 Deep Inelastic Compton Scattering at HERA Collider

We investigate an inclusive DIC process in which photons with large transverse momentum, $p_T \gg \Lambda_{QCD}$, are produced in electron(positron)-proton collision:

$$ep \rightarrow e\gamma X. \tag{1}$$

---

[a]The sensitivity to the quark fragmentation into the photon in the DIC process has been studied as well, see [2].

We will limit ourself to events with the tagged electrons, and small momentum transfers between them. In such case DIC process proceeds via the virtual photon-proton scattering:

$$\gamma^* p \to \gamma X, \tag{2}$$

with the (positive) virtuality of the initial photon equal to $-p^2 = P^2$.

The direct photon interaction corresponds to the following subprocess

$$\gamma^* q_p \to \gamma q, \tag{3}$$

where the initial photon interacts with a quark from the proton (the Born approximation).

The corresponding resolved photon processes, i.e. where the photon interacts through its partonic constituents, involving the partonic constituents of the initial and/or final photons are as follows:

- single resolved initial photon

$$g_{\gamma^*} q_p \to \gamma q, \tag{4}$$

$$q_{\gamma^*} g_p \to \gamma q, \tag{5}$$

$$q_{\gamma^*} \bar{q}_p \to \gamma g \tag{6}$$

$$\bar{q}_{\gamma^*} q_p \to \gamma g \tag{7}$$

- single resolved final photon (fragmentation into the photon)

$$\gamma^* g_p \to q\bar{q} \tag{8}$$

$$\gamma^* q_p \to gq \tag{9}$$

- double resolved photons

$$g_{\gamma^*} g_p \to gg \tag{10}$$

$$q_{\gamma^*} g_p \to qg, \, etc. \tag{11}$$

In this presentation we limit ourself to the process involving (single) resolved initial photon, where we expect to see the effect due to the gluonic content in the virtual photon $P^2 \neq 0$. The full discussion will be given elsewhere [7].

3 Calculation of the Cross Section

The differential cross section for the deep inelastic electron-proton scattering with a photon in the final state, eq. 1, can be written in the following way:

$$E_e E_\gamma \frac{d\sigma^{ep\to e\gamma X}}{d^3 p_e d^3 p_\gamma} = \Gamma \left(E_\gamma \frac{d\sigma^{\gamma^* p\to \gamma X}}{d^3 p_\gamma}|_T + \epsilon E_\gamma \frac{d\sigma^{\gamma^* p\to \gamma X}}{d^3 p_\gamma}|_L \right). \tag{12}$$

where $E_e(E_\gamma)$ and $p_e(p_\gamma)$ are energy and momentum of the final state electron(photon). Coefficients Γ and $\epsilon\Gamma$ (functions of energy and momentum of the electron in initial and final states; see [11]) can be interpreted as the probability of emitting by the initial electron a virtual photon polarized transversely and longitudinally, respectively.

Since the cross section for the reaction $ep \to e\gamma X$ is dominated by the exchane of photons with small virtuality, one can neglect a contribution due to the longitudinal polarization (see also [6]). Assuming that exchanged photons have only transverse polarization we obtain:

$$E_e E_\gamma \frac{d\sigma^{ep\to e\gamma X}}{d^3 p_e d^3 p_\gamma} = \Gamma E_\gamma \frac{d\sigma^{\gamma^* p\to \gamma X}}{d^3 p_\gamma}|_T. \tag{13}$$

Flux Γ can be found in [11,7] and the invariant cross section (we skip the subscrpt T below) $E_\gamma \frac{d\sigma^{\gamma^* p\to \gamma X}}{d^3 p_\gamma}$ has a form:

- for the direct (Born) process:

$$\left(E_\gamma \frac{d\sigma^{\gamma^* p\to \gamma X}}{d^3 p_\gamma} \right)_{dir} = \sum_{q,\bar{q}} \int_0^1 dx_p \; f_{q/p}(x_p, \tilde{Q}^2) \; E_\gamma \frac{d\hat{\sigma}^{\gamma^* q\to \gamma q_p}}{d^3 p_\gamma}, \tag{14}$$

- for processes involving the resolved initial photon:

$$\left(E_\gamma \frac{d\sigma^{\gamma^* p\to \gamma X}}{d^3 p_\gamma} \right)_{res} \tag{15}$$

$$= \sum_{i,j} \int_0^1 dx_\gamma \int_0^1 dx_p f_{i/\gamma^*}(x_\gamma, \tilde{Q}^2, P^2) \; f_{j/p}(x_p, \tilde{Q}^2) \; \left(E_\gamma \frac{d\hat{\sigma}^{ij\to \gamma k}}{d^3 p_\gamma} \right),$$

$f_{i/\gamma^*}(x_\gamma, \tilde{Q}^2, P^2)$ is a (i) parton distribution in the virtual photon with a virtuality equal to P^2 at scale $\tilde{Q}^2$. The cross sections $\hat{\sigma}$ correspond to the partonic subprocesses.

In the calculation we take into consideration the virtuality $(-P^2)$ of the photon emitted by the electron as it follows from the kinematics of the process.

4   Results

In the calculation we used the GRS (LO) parton parametrizations for the parton distributions in the virtual photon [9] and the GRV (LO) set of the quark and the gluon demsities for the proton [12].

Calculations were performed for the energy of the HERA accelerator: $S_{ep} = 98400$ GeV^2. We assumed the number of flavours $f = 4$, the QCD parameter $\Lambda_{QCD} = 0.2$ GeV, and the energy scale in Eqs. 14-15 equal to the transverse momentum of the final photon: $\tilde{Q} = p_T$.

We calculated the cross section for the transverse momentum of the final photon equal to 5 GeV and for the fixed energy of the initial photon: $E_\gamma = 0.5 E_e$ (so the y variable was equal to 0.5). The rapidity dependence was studied for the various values of P^2 between 0.03 to 2.5 GeV^2. [b]

The results for the $E_\gamma \frac{d\sigma^{ep \to e\gamma X}}{d^3 p_\gamma dP^2 dy}$ for the subprocesses Eqs. 3 and 4 for three values of P^2 are presented in Fig.1a as a function of the rapidity [c] in the electron-proton center of mass system. In Fig.1b the comparison of the different contributions to the considered cross section is plotted for the $P^2 = 0.25$ GeV^2.

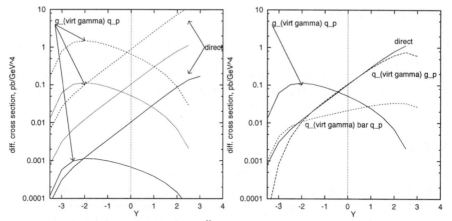

Figure 1: a) The cross section $E_\gamma \frac{d\sigma^{ep \to e\gamma X}}{d^3 p_\gamma dP^2 dy}$ for subprocesses: direct (3) and $g_{\gamma^*} q_p \to \gamma q$ (4) at the P^2=0.03, 0.25 and 2.5 GeV^2 (dotted, dashed and solid line). b) The same for subprocesses: (3) and (4) (solid lines), (5) (dashed line) and (6+7) (dotted line) at P^2=0.25 GeV^2.

[b]Note that tagging of the final electron helps to distinguish the direct contribution from the resolved ones.

[c]The rapidity Y is equal to $Y = -\ln tg \frac{\theta}{2}$, where θ is the angle between the momentum of the photon in the final state and the momentum of the electron in the initial state.

The clear dominace of the contribution due to gluonic content of the virtual photon in the proton direction is seen for the considered range of virtuality of initial photon. We check that this holds also for smaller P^2 values. [d]

The discussion based on the full set of diagrams, wider P^2 range and others parton parametrizations will be given elesewhere[8]. Note that the interference with the Bethe-Heitler process, discussed in [13], seems to be small for $p_T = 5$GeV and in the region of the rapidity where the gluonic content of the virtual photon plays a dominante role[14].

5 Conclusions

Tagged DIC events at HERA were studied using the GRS(LO) and GRV(LO) parton parametrizations for the direct and resolved virtual photon subprocesses. The contribution due to gluonic content of the virtual photon was found to dominate in the direction of the proton as compared to others subprocesses. This can have important consequences for the possibility of measuring the gluon content of the virtual photon at HERA.

Acknowledgments

One of us (MK) would like to thank organizers of the very fruitful conference. We are grateful to Stan Brodsky for pointing the reference [13] and useful discussions. We thank M. Stratman and A. Vogt for sending us the Fortran code with the parton parametrizations. Supporting by the Polish Committee for Scientific Research, Grant No 2P03B18209.

References

1. M. Krawczyk, Acta Physica Pol. **B21** (1990) 999.
2. A. C. Bawa, M. Krawczyk, W. J. Stirling, Z. Phys. **C50** (1991) 293.
3. A. C. Bawa and M. Krawczyk, Probing the structure of proton and photon in deep inelastic Compton process at HERA and LEP/LHC, Proc. "Physics at HERA", Hamburg 1991, vol. 1, p. 579, and IFT 91/17.
4. P. Aurenche, et al. , proceeding of the HERA Workshop, Hamburg 1987, p. 561 and *Z. Phys.* C56 (1992) 589
5. L. E. Gordon, J. K. Storrow, *Z. Phys.* C63 (1994) 581

---

[d]Due to smooth behaviour of the GRS parametrization in the limit $P^2 \to 0$ we were able to perform the calculation also below Λ^2_{QCD}.

6. A. Zembrzuski and M. Krawczyk, On the validity of the equivalent photon approximation and the structure of a virtual photon, Proc. "Physics at HERA", Hamburg 1991, vol. 1, p. 617, and Warsaw Univ. IFT 91/15.

7. A. Zembrzuski, The $ep \rightarrow e\gamma X$ process at HERA. Structure of photon, Msc Thesis, Warsaw University 1991

8. M. Krawczyk and A. Zembrzuski, in preparation

9. M. Glück, E. Reya and M. Stratmann, *Phys. Rev.* D51 (1995) 3220

10. M. Glück, E. Reya and M. Stratmann, *Phys. Rev.* D54 (1996) 5515; D. de Florian, C. Garcia Canal, R.Sassot, CERN-TH/96-234 (hep-ph/9608438); M. Klasen, G. Kramer, B. Plotter, DESY 97-0.39(hep-ph/9703302); B. Plotter, DESY 97-138 (hep-ph/9707319)

11. F. Halzen , A. D. Martin, Quarks and Leptons, John Wiley & Sons, 1984

12. M. Glück, E. Reya and A. Vogt, *Z. Phys.* C67 (1995) 433

13. S.J.Brodsky, private communication and S.J.Brodsky, J. F. Gunion, R. L. Joffe, *Phys. Rev.* D6 (1972) 2487

14. P. Jankowski and M. Krawczyk, in preparation

A NLO MONTE CARLO GENERATOR FOR PHOTOPRODUCTION OF JETS AT HERA

L. BOURHIS, M. FONTANNAZ

Laboratoire de Physique Théorique et Hautes Energies [a]
Université de Paris XI, bâtiment 211
F-91405 Orsay Cedex, France

J.PH. GUILLET

Laboratoire de Physique Théorique ENSLAPP [b] *- Groupe d'Annecy*
LAPP, IN2P3-CNRS, B.P. 110
F-74941 Annecy-le-Vieux Cedex, France

We present Next Leading Log QCD calculations for the photoproduction of jets at HERA. They are implemented as a Monte-Carlo generator able to compute easily any infra-red safe cross sections for 1 or 2 jet observables using various jet reconstruction algorithms. Some applications are discussed.

1 Description of the method

To calculate Next Leading Log QCD corrections, we used a "phase space slicing method" adapted from a previous method developped to deal with the production of two high-p_T hadrons in hadrons collisions [1]. We start from the $2 \rightarrow 3$ partonic squared matrix elements and virtual corrections evaluated by Ellis and Sexton [2]. Let us consider a generic real process $1 + 2 \rightarrow 3 + 4 + 5$ where 5 is the parton with the smallest p_T. The integration over the phase space of 5 leads to colinear and infrared singularities. In order to extract them we cut its phase space in several parts : part I where p_{T5} is less than some cut p_{Tm} and part II where $p_{T5} > p_{Tm}$. The part II is divided in three parts : IIa (resp. IIb) where the parton 5 is within a cone around parton 3 (resp. 4) called C_3 (resp. C_4), IIc where the parton 5 is outside C_3 and C_4. The parton 5 is in C_i if $((\phi_5 - \phi_i)^2 + (\eta_5 - \eta_i)^2)^{\frac{1}{2}} < R_c$. Here η is the pseudo-rapidity and ϕ is the azimuthal angle. Part I contains infra-red singularities and collinear singularities and parts IIa and IIb contain collinear singularities in the final state whereas the part IIc is finite. The infra-red singularities are cancelled by the corresponding ones in the virtual terms. The initial collinear singularities are factorised in the parton distributions and the final collinear singularities

---

[a]Laboratoire associé au CNRS - URA 0063.

[b]URA 14-36 du CNRS, associée à l'Ecole Normale Supérieure de Lyon, et au Laboratoire d'Annecy-le-Vieux de Physique des Particules.

disappear when integrating on the relative momentum between the parton 5 and the parton with which it is collinear due to energy momentum sum rules.

The finite parts remaining after the cancellation of singularities have been analytically computed using a Maple [3] program. Large logarithms $\log p_{Tm}$, $\log^2 p_{Tm}$ and $\log R_c$ appears in the collinear and infrared contributions. They are cancelled by similar terms from the part IIc so that the total cross section is independent of this unphysical cuts. It should be notice that we have kept only the logarithmic terms.

Using the Monte-Carlo package BASES [4], our program generates quasi $2 \rightarrow 2$ events corresponding to collinear, Born and virtual contributions and $2 \rightarrow 3$ events corresponding to part IIc. For the latter ones, a jet algorithm is applied. Finally, these events are histogrammed [5] in order to give any cross sections we are interested in. We take $p_{Tm} \ll p_{T3,4}^{min}$ and $R_c \ll 1$ such that the $2 \rightarrow 2$ events give two jets with the same kinematic whatever jets definition we use. Indeed in region I, parton 5 is soft and give no jet. There is then two jets J_a and J_b with $p_a \approx p_3$ and $p_b \approx p_4$ when neglecting p_5. In region IIa because R_c is small, we have again two jets J_a (containing parton 3 and 5) and J_b with $p_{Ta} \approx p_{T3} + p_{T5}, \eta_a \approx \eta_3, \phi_a \approx \phi_3$ and $p_b = p_4$. The situation is symmetric in the region IIb. These approximations are valid with currently used jet definitions (such as Snowmass or k_T algorithm) providing p_{Tm} and R_c verify the aformentionned inequalities.

2   Dijets cross sections and the photon structure function

In this section, we present some numerical results for dijet cross section. We use the kinematical conditions of the ZEUS collaboration : $Q^2 < 4 \ GeV^2$ and $0.2 < y < 0.8$ where $y = E_\gamma/E_e$. The spectrum of the quasi-real photon was approximated by the Weizsäcker-Williams formula. We have used the ABFOW proton densities [6] wich is a NLL parametrisation in the $\overline{MS}$ scheme and $\Lambda^{(4)} = 0.230 \ GeV$. We use the KTCLUST algorithm to build jets. If not specified the followings cuts on the phase space of the two jets with the highest p_T are used :

$$p_T > 9.2 \ GeV \quad -1 < \eta < 2 \tag{1}$$

Following the strategy of the ZEUS collaboration [8] which defines the variable $x_\gamma^{obs} = (p_{T3}e^{-\eta_3} + p_{T4}e^{-\eta_4})/2E_\gamma$, we can study the cross section $d\sigma/dx_\gamma^{obs}$. At Leading Log accuracy, introducing the square matrix element $|M(ab \rightarrow 34)|^2$ of the $a + b \rightarrow p_3 + p_4$ scattering and the parton distributions in the photon

F_γ^a and the proton F_p^b, it reads

$$\frac{d\sigma}{dx_\gamma^{obs}} = \sum_{a,b} F_\gamma^a(x_\gamma^{obs}) \int_0^1 \frac{dy}{y} dp_T^2 d\eta_3 d\eta_4 \delta \left(x_\gamma^{obs} - \frac{p_T \left(e^{-\eta_3} + e^{-\eta_4} \right)}{2yE_e} \right)$$
$$\times F_e^\gamma(y) F_p^b(x_p) |M(ab \to 34)|^2. \qquad (2)$$

F_e^γ is the Weizsäcker-Williams distribution and $x_p = p_T(e^{\eta_3} + e^{\eta_4})/\sqrt{s}$. Thus the dijet cross section written as a function of x_γ^{obs} is proportional to the parton distribution in the photon $F_\gamma^a(x_\gamma^{obs})$.

Next to Leading Log QCD corrections to the LL expression (2) blur its simple kinematics. There are contributions with three jets in the final state, and x_γ^{obs} is no longer the argument of F_γ^a. Moreover, this definition of x_γ^{obs} constrains the phase space integration too much. An inclusive dijet cross section can only be function of p_T, η_3 and η_4 ; the transverse momentum of the second jet cannot be observed without spoiling IR compensation between the virtual and real HO cross section.

Let us consider for example the direct contribution of fig. 1. In the colinear limit, x_γ^{obs} becomes the fraction of the photon energy taken by the parton 2. So when x_γ^{obs} goes to 1, terms behaving like $P_{\gamma q}(x_\gamma^{obs}) \log(1 - x_\gamma^{obs})$ appears , where $P_{\gamma q}$ is the splitting kernel of photon into quark, giving a integrable IR singularity.

We therefore propose the following variable

$$x_\gamma^{LL} = p_{T3} \left(e^{-\eta_3} + e^{-\eta_4} \right) /2E_\gamma \qquad (3)$$

The distribution $d\sigma/dx_\gamma^{LL}$ is less singular than $d\sigma/dx_\gamma^{obs}$ because only one transverse momentum appears in its definition but it remains singular. The fig. 2 shows the singular behavior of these two observables for the direct term near $x_\gamma = 1$. One can see that the infrared singularity occurs only at values of x_γ very close to 1. Currently experimentalists integrate the x_γ^{obs} variable over the range $[0.75 - 1]$. So this problem should not blur the phenomenological application of NLL calculations to this kind of experimental results.

In the LL approximation, x_γ^{LL} is the fraction of energy taken by the parton from the photon (notice that x_γ^{LL} can be larger than one at NLL) ; it is important to check how much the HO corrections change this simple picture, and if the determination of $F_\gamma^a(x_\gamma)$ from $d\sigma/dx_\gamma^{LL}$ remains accurate.

We have computed the observable $d\sigma/dx_\gamma^{LL}$ in two factorisation schemes, the so called DIS_γ and $\overline{MS}$ ones, using for the former case the GRV parton densities for the photon [9] and for the latter the AFG distributions [10]. We can see that both the direct and resolved part are very different in this two

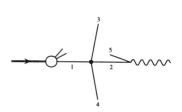

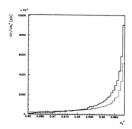

Figure 1:

Figure 2: Distribution $d\sigma/dx_\gamma^{obs}$ (full line) and $d\sigma/dx_\gamma^{LL}$ (dashed line) for the direct term in the $\overline{MS}$ scheme with the cuts (1).

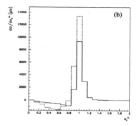
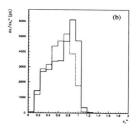
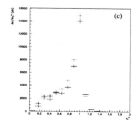

Figure 3: Cross sections $d\sigma/dx_\gamma^{LL}$ for the direct (a) and resolved (b) contribution and their sum (c) with the cuts (1). Full lines (resp. dashed lines) correspond to $\overline{MS}$ scheme and AFG photon densities (resp. DIS_γ scheme and GRV photon densities.)

schemes (fig. 3), but that this difference is much smaller for the total cross section which is factorisation scheme independent. The remaining difference comes from different hadronic input in the two sets of distribution. It should be noticed that the contribution at $x_\gamma^{obs} = 1$ in the direct term contains a delta function, and so the mean value of the bin containing this point depends on the width of the bin.

We have also looked for the influence of the gluon content of the photon on $d\sigma/dx_\gamma^{LL}$. We compare the full observable with a cross section for which we have artificially set the gluon distribution to zero (fig. 4). When allowing rapidities to be between -1 and 2, the two predictions are quite similar. But when one constrains the rapidity range, very different behaviours appear between complete cross section and cross section without gluons. For rapidities between 1 and 2, the gluon appears to play a great role. But experimentaly, this region corresponds to jets in the forward direction of the proton, where the underlying events create both experimental and theoritical difficulties.

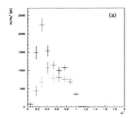 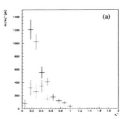

Figure 4: Cross sections $d\sigma/dx_\gamma^{LL}$ for the resolved contribution without the gluon (dashed lines) and with it (full line).The cuts on the rapidity of the two high p_T jets are $0.5 < \eta < 2$ (a) and $1 < \eta < 2$ (b).

3 Conclusion

We have build a Monte Carlo generator which produces partonic configurations with which any IR safe cross sections can be easily computed. We present some applications to the phenomenology of the variable x_γ^{obs} and show that it leads to some IR singularities. Therefore we introduce another variable x_γ^{LL} and we show that the distribution $d\sigma/dx_\gamma^{LL}$ is very sensitive to the gluon content of the photon when selecting jets in the forward direction.

References

1. P. Chiappetta, R. Fergani and J. Ph. Guillet, Z. Phys. **C69** (1996) 443.
2. R.K. Ellis and J.C. Sexton, Nucl. Phys **B269** (1986) 445.
3. B. W. Char et al., Maple V Language Reference Manual, Springer Verlag.
4. S. Kawabata, Comput.Phys.Commun. **88** (1995) 309.
5. HBOOK Reference Manual, Applications Software Group, Computing and Network Division, CERN.
6. ABFOW collaboration, Phys. Rev. **D39** (1989) 3275.
7. M. Klasen and G. Kramer, Preprint Desy 95-226, Phys. Lett. **B366** (1996) 385.
8. M. Derrick et al., ZEUS collaboration, Phys. Lett. **B348** (1995) 665.
9. M. Gluck, E. Reya, A. Vogt, Phys. Rev. **D45** (1992) 3986.
10. P. Aurenche, J.P. Guillet, M. Fontannaz, Z. Phys.**C64** (1994) 621.

ISOLATED PROMPT PHOTON PLUS JET PHOTOPRODUCTION AT HERA

L. E. GORDON

Argonne National Laboratory, 9700 S. Cass Avenue, Argonne,
IL 60439, USA

The cross section for photoproduction of a prompt photon in association with a jet is studied in Next-to-Leading Order at the DESY ep collider HERA. The effect of various cuts imposed on the cross section by the ZEUS collaboration including isolation cuts on the photon is examined. Comparisons with the ZEUS preliminary data using various parametrizations of the photon structure function is made, and good agreement is found. The preliminary data is not yet precise enough to make a distinction between various models for the photon structure function.

1 Introduction

It has long been anticipated that the DESY ep collider HERA would provide a good opportunity to study prompt photon production in photoproduction processes [1]. Over the past few years various studies of this process have been performed with continuous improvements in their theoretical precision [2,3,4,5]. In the most recent studies [5,6] the inclusive cross section for producing a single photon was calculated fully in NLO with isolation effects incorporated. In [5,6] an approximate but nevertheless very accurate analytic technique [7,8] for including isolation effects in the NLO calculation, including the fragmentation contributions was used. This analytic technique is only applicable to single inclusive prompt photon production and cannot be applied when a jet is also observed.

The ZEUS Collaboration have begun analyzing prompt photon data [9] and have first chosen to look for events with a jet balancing the transverse momentum (p_T^γ) of the photon. In order to compare with this data a new calculation is necessary which will be described in outline in the next section.

In all the previous studies of prompt photon production at HERA, one of the common themes was the possibility of using it for measuring the photon distribution functions, particularly the gluon distribution, $g^\gamma(x, Q^2)$ which is presently very poorly constrained by the available data. This latter fact is still true even with the availability of jet photoproduction data at both HERA and TRISTAN. Prompt photon production is particularly attractive since it is dominated in Leading Order (LO) by the hard scattering subprocess $qg \rightarrow \gamma q$, resulting in a cross section which is very sensitive to the gluon distribution.

At HERA the situation is rather more complicated than at hadron colliders by two factors. Firstly there are two particles involved in the reaction, namely the quasi-real photon emitted by the electron which scatters at a small angle, as well as the proton. Both particles have distinct gluon distribution functions g^γ and g^p, hence two different qg initiated subprocess are present, $q^p g^\gamma \to \gamma q$ and $q^\gamma g^p \to \gamma q$. Since they contribute to the cross section in different regions of pseudo-rapidity, η, it has been proposed that this may provide a means of separating them experimentally, but this has proven to be very difficult experimentally. Secondly, there are two types of contributions to the cross section in photoproduction processes, usually labelled the direct and resolved contributions. In the former case the quasi-real photon participates directly in the hard scattering subprocess and gives up all its energy, while in the latter, resolved, case it interacts via its partonic substructure. Thus the resolved subprocesses are sensitive to the photon structure functions whereas the direct are not. Again it was proposed that they may be separated experimentally with suitable rapidity cuts. A study performed in [4] has shown that since the initial photon energy is not fixed but forms a continuous spectrum, then even this separation is not straightforward. Separation of resolved and direct processes is better achieved by tagging of the spectator jet from the resolved photon.

2   The Inclusive Photon Plus Jet Cross Section

In addition to the direct and resolved photon contributions to the cross section there are the non-fragmentation and fragmentation contributions. In the former case the observed final state photon is produced directly in the hard scattering whereas in the latter it is produced by long distance fragmentation off a final state parton. The fragmentation processes involve the fragmentation functions which require a non-perturbative input from experiment and have not been satisfactorily measured up to now.

The only direct non-fragmentation process contributing to the cross section in LO is the so called QCD Compton process

$$\gamma q \to \gamma q$$

and the direct fragmentation processes are

$$\gamma q \to g q \quad \text{and} \quad \gamma g \to q \bar{q}.$$

As discussed in many places (see eg. [5]) the photon fragmentation function is formally $O(\alpha_{em}/\alpha_s)$, thus although the hard subprocess cross sections in the fragmentation case are $O(\alpha_{em}\alpha_s)$, after convolution with the photon fragmentation functions the process is $O(\alpha_{em}^2)$, the same as the the non-fragmentation part.

At NLO for the non-fragmentation part there are the virtual corrections to the LO Compton process plus the additional three-body processes

$$\gamma q \rightarrow \gamma g q \quad \text{and} \quad \gamma g \rightarrow \gamma q \bar{q}.$$

In addition there are $O(\alpha_s)$ corrections to the fragmentation processes to take into account, but in this calculation these processes are included in LO only. It has been shown in [5] that the fragmentation contributions are not as significant here as at hadron colliders which generally have higher cms energies and are reduced drastically when isolation cuts are implemented. Thus ignoring NLO corrections to the fragmentation contributions while in principle inconsistent will not lead to a large numerical error.

In the resolved case, for non-fragmentation there are only the two processes

$$q g \rightarrow \gamma q \quad \text{and} \quad q \bar{q} \rightarrow \gamma g.$$

in LO. At NLO there are virtual and three-bofy corrections to these as well as other three-body processes, eg. $gg \rightarrow \gamma q \bar{q}$ etc. for a complete list of these plus the fragmentation processes see eg. [5].

The calculation was performed using the phase space slicing method which makes it possible to perform photon isolation exactly as well as to implement the jet definition. Details of the calculation can be found in ref.[10]. Following the ZEUS experiment, the cone isolation method is used, which restricts the hadronic energy allowed in a cone of radius $R_\gamma = \sqrt{\Delta\phi^2 + \Delta\eta^2}$, centred on the photon to be below the value ϵE_γ, where E_γ is the photon energy. The fixed value $\epsilon = 0.1$ is used which corresponds to the value used in the ZEUS analysis.

The cone algorithm is used to define the jet. This defines a jet as hadronic energy deposited in a cone radius $R_J = \sqrt{\Delta\phi^2 + \Delta\eta^2}$. If two partons form the jet then the kinematic variables are combined to form that of the jet according to the formulae $p_J = p_1 + p_2$, $\eta_J = (\eta_1 p_1 + \eta_2 p_2)/p_J$ and $\phi_J = (\phi_1 p_1 + \phi_2 p_2)/p_J$. In the ZEUS analysis $R_\gamma = 1.0$ and $R_J = 1.0$ are chosen and we therefore use these values.

In order to estimate the flux of quasi-real photons from the electron beam the Weiszacker-Williams approximation is used. Thus the 'electron structure function' $f_e(x_e, Q^2)$ is given by a convolution of the photon structure function $f^\gamma(x_\gamma, Q^2)$ and the Weiszacker-Williams function

$$f_{\gamma/e}(z) = \frac{\alpha_{em}}{2\pi}\left[\frac{1+(1-z)^2}{z}\ln\frac{Q^2_{max}(1-z)}{m_e^2 z^2} - 2m_e^2 z^2\left\{\frac{(1-z)}{m_e^2 z^2} - \frac{1}{Q^2_{max}}\right\}\right]$$

$$(1)$$

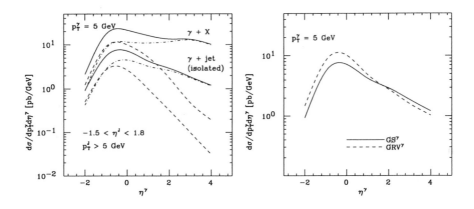

Figure 1: (a) Comparison of differential cross section for single γ and $\gamma + jet$. (b) Differential cross section with HERA (ZEUS) cuts for GRV and GS96 photon distributions.

by

$$f_e(x_e, Q^2) = \int_{x_e}^1 \frac{dz}{z} f_{\gamma/e}(z) f^\gamma \left(\frac{x_e}{z}, Q^2 \right).\tag{2}$$

Following the ZEUS analysis the value $Q^2_{max} = 1$ GeV^2 is used throughout.

3   Numerical Results

The numerical results presented in this section are obtained using the GS96 [11] photon distribution functions, the CTEQ4M [12] parton distributions for the proton and the GRVLO [13] fragmentation functions as standard. Futhermore the two-loop expression for α_s is used, four-flavours of quarks are assumed active and the factorization/renormalization scales are taken to be equal to the photon p_T ($Q^2 = (p_T^\gamma)^2$). The maximum virtuality of the initial state photon is fixed at $Q^2_{max} = 1$ GeV^2 as chosen by the ZEUS Collaboration. Using the above parameters the fragmentation contribution constituted less than 20% of the cross section at $p_T^\gamma = 5$ GeV before isolation and falls rapidly with increasing p_T^γ. After isolation this figure is reduced by 85%. The higher order corrections enhances the cross section $O(20\%)$ before isolation. Imposing the ZEUS p_T, rapidity, and isolation cuts on the inclusive single photon cross section results in a drop in the cross section by more then a factor of 3 as shown in fig.1a . This severely reduces the accuracy of the measurement and makes it less likely that it will be useful in distinguishing between the available photon distribution function parametrizations. But as fig.1b shows if enough statistics can be accumulated in the negative rapidity region the possibility still exists to discriminate between the GRV [14] and GS parametrizations.

Table 1 shows predictions for the resolved and direct contributions to the cross section in pb and their sum for various choices of parameters. In order to obtain a sample of direct events the ZEUS Collaboration have imposed the cut $x_\gamma \geq 0.8$ on their data. This cut which is also imposed on the results in Table 1, favours the direct contributions since they contribute at $x_\gamma = 1$, but there is still a contribution from the resolved processes and hence some sensitivity to the photon distributions chosen. In addition the cuts 5 GeV $\leq p_T^\gamma \leq 10$ GeV, $p_T^J \geq 5$ GeV, $-1.5 \leq \eta^J \leq 1.8$, $-0.7 \leq \eta^\gamma \leq 0.8$ and $0.16 \leq z = E_\gamma/E_e \leq 0.8$ along with the isolation cuts and jet definitions discussed in section 2 are imposed.

The first column of numbers gives the results for the standard choice of parameters, while the 2nd and 3rd columns show the effect of changing the scales. The results show a remarkable stability to scale changes. This is in contrast to eg. the p_T^γ distribution which generally shows significant scale sensitivity. The 4th and 5th columns show the effect of changing the photon and proton distribution functions used respectively. In the latter case there is hardly any changes in the predictions, while in the former case the changes are very significant. Since with these cuts the cross section is mostly sensitive to the quark distributions in the photon at large-x then it may potentially be used to discriminate between the GS96 and GRV photon parametrizations which differ most significantly in this region. The preliminary experimental value given by the ZUES Collaboration of $17.1 \pm 4.5 \pm 1.5$ pb agrees remarkably well with the NLO theoretical predictions but the errors quoted are still too large to make any distinction between GS and GRV.

4 Conclusions

A NLO calculation of isolated single photon plus jet production at HERA was presented and compared to the preliminary data from the ZEUS Collaboration and good agreement was found. The kinematic cuts chosen favour the direct contribution but there is still a significant sensitivity to the quarks distributions in the photon at large-x. At the moment the error in the data is still too large to

Table 1: Total $\gamma + jet$ cross section with HERA cuts (see text).

	STD	$Q^2 = (p_T^\gamma)^2/4$	$Q^2 = 4(p_T^\gamma)^2$	GRV$^\gamma$	MRSR1
RES	3.31	2.60	4.95	6.72	3.44
DIR	9.86	11.45	8.18	9.86	9.34
SUM	13.17	14.05	13.13	16.58	12.78

distinguish between the GRV and GS96 photon distributions, but it is expected that accumulation of more data will soon remedy this situation.

Acknowledgments

I am indebted to E. L. Berger for helping me to secure funds to attend the Photon'97 conference and to the Planning Committee for waiving the registration fee. This work was funded in part by the US Department of Energy, Division of High Energy Physics, Contract No. W-31-109-ENG-38.

References

1. P. Aurenche *et al.*, *Z. Phys.* C **24**, 309 (1984).
2. A. C. Bawa, M. Krawczyk, W.J. Stirling, *Z. Phys.* C **50**, 293 (1991).
3. P. Aurenche *et al.*, *Z. Phys.* C **56**, 589 (1993).
4. L.E. Gordon , J.K. Storrow, *Z. Phys.* C **63**, 581 (1994).
5. L.E. Gordon, W. Vogelsang, *Phys. Rev.* D **52**, 58 (1995).
6. L.E. Gordon, W. Vogelsang, Proc. of 'Int Workshop on Deep Inelastic Scattering and Related Phenomena' Rome, Italy, April 15-19, 1996.
7. L.E. Gordon, W. Vogelsang, *Phys. Rev.* D **50**, 1901 (1994).
8. M. Glück, L.E. Gordon, E. Reya, W. Vogelsang, *Phys. Rev. Lett.* **73**, 388 (1994).
9. Zeus Collab., these proceedings.
10. L. E. Gordon, 'Prompt Photons plus Jet at HERA in Next-to-Leading Order QCD' ANL-HEP-PR-97-42.
11. L.E. Gordon , J.K. Storrow, *Nucl. Phys.* B **489**, 405 (1997).
12. CTEQ Collab., H. Lai *et al.*, *Phys. Rev.* D **55**, 1280 (1997).
13. M. Glück, E. Reya, A. Vogt, *Phys. Rev.* D **48**, 116 (1993).
14. M. Glück, E. Reya, A. Vogt, *Phys. Rev.* D **45**, 3986 (1992).

INCLUSIVE D^* and J/ψ INELASTIC PHOTOPRODUCTION AT HERA

L.K. GLADILIN

Inst. of Experimental Physics II, University of Hamburg, Luruper Chaussee 149, D-22761 Hamburg, Germany

on behalf of the ZEUS Collaboration

Inclusive $D^{*\pm}$ and J/ψ inelastic photoproduction has been measured with the ZEUS detector. D^* cross sections are compared with two next-to-leading order perturbative QCD predictions. For a calculation using a massive charm scheme the predicted cross sections are smaller than the measured ones. A recent calculation using a massless charm scheme is in agreement with the data. Cross sections of J/ψ inelastic photoproduction have been compared with next-to-leading order perturbative QCD calculations and QCD predictions in semihard approach.

1 Introduction

Heavy quark photoproduction can be used to probe perturbative QCD calculations with a hard scale stemming from the heavy quark mass and the high transverse momentum of the produced parton. At leading order (LO) in QCD two types of processes are responsible for the production of heavy quarks: the direct photon processes, where the photon participates as a point-like particle which interacts with a parton from the incoming proton, and the resolved photon processes, where the photon is a source of partons, one of which scatters off a parton from the proton. Charm quarks present in the parton distributions of the photon, as well as of the proton, lead to processes like $cg \rightarrow cg$, which are called charm flavour excitation. In next-to-leading order (NLO) QCD only the sum of direct and resolved processes is unambiguously defined. Two types of NLO calculations using different approaches are available for comparison with measurements of charm photoproduction at HERA. The massive charm approach [1] assumes light quarks to be the only active flavours within the structure functions of the proton and the photon, while the massless charm approach [2,3] also treats charm as an active flavour.

The data presented here correspond to integrated luminosities of $\mathcal{L} = 2.99 \pm .05$ pb^{-1} and $\mathcal{L} = 6.32 \pm .07$ pb^{-1} taken by the ZEUS detector [4] at HERA in 1994 and 1995 respectively. Charm was tagged by D^* (2010) or J/ψ mesons identified in the final state via their charged decay products detected in the Central Tracking Detector (CTD). Cross sections were measured in the photoproduction range of photon virtualities $Q^2 < 4\ GeV^2$ ($Q^2_{median} \sim$

$5 \cdot 10^{-4}\ GeV^2$) within γp center-of-mass energy regions $115 < W < 280\ GeV$ for D^* and $50 < W < 180\ GeV$ for J/ψ mesons. Q^2 and W were determined from energy deposits in the uranium calorimeter (CAL).

2 $D^{*\pm}(2010)$ Inclusive Photoproduction

$D^{*\pm}$ decays into $D^0\pi_s$ with D^0 decaying into $(K\pi)$ or $(K\pi\pi)$ states have been selected by means of mass difference method [6] within the restricted kinematic range: $p_\perp(D^*) > 3\ GeV$ and $-1.5 < \eta(D^*) < 1.0$. Here $p_\perp(D^*)$ is D^* transverse momentum and its pseudorapidity is $\eta(D^*) = -ln(tan\frac{\theta}{2})$, where θ is the polar angle with respect to the proton beam direction.

The total number of D^* mesons observed with 1995 data (Fig.1) are 321 ± 25 and 408 ± 60 decays into $(K\pi)\pi_s$ and $(K\pi\pi)\pi_s$ states respectively. Integrated over the restricted kinematic range cross section has been measured to be $\sigma(e^+p \rightarrow D^{*\pm}X) = 10.1\pm0.8\pm^{0.7}_{0.4}$ nb and $\sigma(e^+p \rightarrow D^{*\pm}X) = 11.8\pm1.7$ nb with $(K\pi)\pi_s$ and $(K\pi\pi)\pi_s$ decay modes respectively. The results are in agreement with our previous measurements [5].

Differential cross sections in W, $p_\perp(D^*)$ and $\eta(D^*)$ (Fig.2) have been compared to NLO QCD calculations in 'massive' [1] and 'massless' [2] charm approaches. Results of "massless charm" calculations agree with data in shape and magnitude while "massive charm" ones underestimate data by 30-50% depending on the charm quark mass and scale μ.

To obtain additional information on the charm production mechanism a jet analysis of charm events has been performed. Using a cone(EUCELL) or a cluster (KT) algorithm and requiring at least two jets with $E_\perp > 4GeV$ and $\eta < 2.4$ the fraction of photon energy participating in hard interaction can be estimated as $x_\gamma^{OBS} = \frac{\Sigma_{2jets}(E_\perp * e^{-\eta})_{jet}}{2E_e y}$. A comparison of observed (uncorrected for detector effects) x_γ distribution (Fig.3) with leading order HERWIG Monte Carlo predictions demonstrates significant contribution of resolved processes ($x_\gamma^{OBS} < 0.75$) to D* production in the measured kinematic range.

3 J/ψ Inelastic Photoproduction

The inelastic reaction $e^+p \rightarrow J/\psi X$ was studied via detection of J/ψ meson decays into e^+e^- or $\mu^+\mu^-$ pairs. The signal observed in $\mu^+\mu^-$ mass spectrum is shown in Fig.4 a.

Contributions from background resolved photon process and proton diffractive dissociation are minimized using J/ψ inelasticity variable $z = \frac{P_p \cdot P(J/\psi)}{P_p \cdot P_e}$, where P_p, P_e and $P(J/\psi)$ are 4-momenta of proton and electron beams and

J/ψ meson. Requiring $z < 0.9$ together with $p_\perp(J/\psi) > 1$ GeV keeps proton diffractive dissociation negligible and requiring $z > 0.4$ rejects the main part of the resolved photon background. Measured ep cross sections are extrapolated in z down to 0 and then converted into γp cross sections. Within the large measurement errors, experimental cross sections in W and z (Fig.4 b,c) are reproduced in shape and magnitude by NLO QCD [7] and SemiHard Approach (SHA)in QCD [8] calculations. In both calculations, $c\bar{c}$ hadronization into J/ψ was described by the color singlet (CS) model. For z distribution, calculations were repeated in LO using the color octet (CO) model with a normalization fixed by CDF data [9]. CO contribution to inelastic J/ψ photoproduction appears to be too large for the region $0.7 < z < 0.9$ as compared to data (Fig.4 c).

4 Summary

Inclusive D^* and J/ψ inelastic photoproduction cross sections have been measured and comparisons with theory have been made. D^* inclusive cross sections are reproduced in shape and magnitude by NLO QCD calculations in the "massless charm" approach. "Massive charm" results are below the data. x_γ^{OBS} distribution demonstrates a significant contribution of resolved processes to D^* production in the measured kinematic range. The CS model calculations in QCD at NLO and using the SHA, agree with the J/ψ inelastic photoproduction cross sections to within the large experimental errors, whereas the CO model LO calculations predict too large conribution of the CO mechanism to J/ψ production with respect to the ZEUS data.

References

1. S.Frixione et al., *Nucl. Phys.* B454, 3 (1995).
2. B.A.Kniehl et. al., *DESY* **96-210**.
3. M.Cacciary et. al., *DESY* **96-146**.
4. ZEUS Collab., M.Derrick et al.,*Phys. Lett.* B349, 225 (1995).
5. ZEUS Collab., J.Breitweg et al.,*Phys. Lett.* B401, 192 (1997).
6. S.Nussinov,*Phys. Rev. Lett.35, 1672 (1975)*;
   G.J.Feldman et al.,Phys. Rev. Lett.38, 1313 (1977).
7. M.Kramer et al., *Phys. Lett.* B348, 657 (1995), *Nucl. Phys.* B459, 3 (1996).
8. V.A.Saleev, N.P.Zotov, *Mod. Phys. Lett* **A9**, 151 (1994); *ibid* **A11**, 25 (1996).
9. CDF Colab., F.Abe et al.,*Phys. Rev. Lett.69, 3704 (1992)*;
   CDF Colab., A.Sansoni, FERMILAB-CONF-**95/262-E**

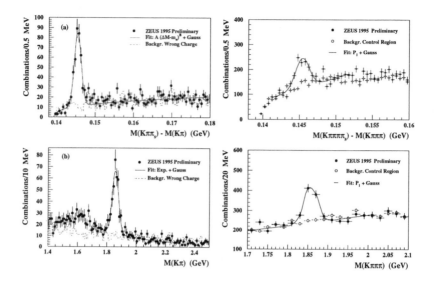

Figure 1: D^* photoproduction signals.

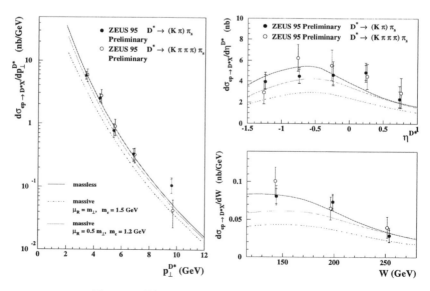

Figure 2: D^* inclusive photoproduction cross sections.

ZEUS 95 D$^*\to$(Kπ)π_s Preliminary

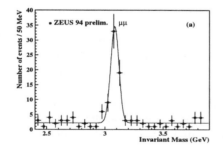

Figure 3: Observed x_γ distributions.

(a) $\mu^+\mu^-$ msss spectrum (points) fitted to Gauss plus constant distribution (curve).

(b,c) cross sections as functions of W, z compared with NLO QCD (solid lines) and SHA (dashed lines) calculations.

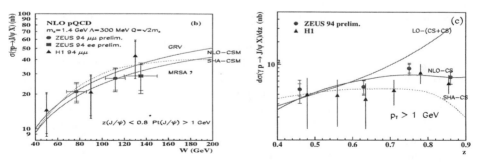

Figure 4: Inelastic J/Ψ photoproduction signal and cross sections.

MEASUREMENT OF THE INCLUSIVE CHARM PRODUCTION IN $\gamma\gamma$ COLLISIONS AT LEP

VALERY P. ANDREEV [a]

Department of Physics and Astronomy,
Louisiana State University,
Baton Rouge, LA 70803, USA

(on behalf of the L3 Collaboration)

Inclusive charm production in $\gamma\gamma$ collisions has been studied with the L3 detector at the LEP collider. Charmed hadrons were identified by muons from their semi-leptonic decays. The cross section of charm production has been measured at average center of mass energies 91 GeV (LEP1) and 161+172 GeV (LEP2). The results of the cross section measurement are in agreement with QCD prediction.

1 Introduction

The production of heavy quarks in gamma-gamma collisions consists mainly of charm quarks. The production of beauty quarks is expected to be suppressed by more than two orders of magnitude [1]. Measurement of charm production in $\gamma\gamma$ collisions provides a test of QCD and is especially attractive as in heavy quark physics one can rely on perturbative calculations. The "hadronic" nature of photons can be studied more easily with the increase of e^+e^--collider energies. At LEP2 energies "pointlike" and "hadronic" (resolved) photons contribute equally to the cross section [1]. The production rate of the charm quarks in $\gamma\gamma$ collisions depends on the mass of charm quark and the gluon density in the photon. Precise measurements of the process $\gamma\gamma \rightarrow c\bar{c}$ could better constrain those important physical parameters. Measurements of the charm production in two-photon collisions were done at PEP,PETRA,TRISTAN and LEP1 energies [2,3,4,5,6,7,8]. The published results of different experiments were extrapolated to the total charm cross sections for the purpose of comparison at "Physics at LEP2" workshop [9]. Experiments at KEK have measured higher cross sections than predicted by theory (even with Next to Leading Order(NLO) corrections taken into account). Measurement of charm production rate at LEP1 by ALEPH [8] is compatible with the direct production $\gamma\gamma \rightarrow c\bar{c}$ in the Born approximation and with QCD prediction which includes radiative corrections to the direct process and a contribution when one of the photons is first resolved into quark and gluon constituents.

---

[a] on leave from Petersburg Nuclear Physics Institute,
e-mail address: Valeri.Andreev@cern.ch

In this paper we present the result of the measurement of $e^+e^- \to e^+e^-c\bar{c}X$ cross section by the L3 experiment at LEP1 and for the first time at LEP2 energies. To identify the presence of charm quark a tagging by muons from semi-leptonic decays has been used.

2   Measurement of inclusive charm production

Data samples collected by L3 at $\sqrt{s} = 91$ GeV (total integrated luminosity of 80 pb^{-1} in the period 1994-95) and at $\sqrt{s} = 161$, 172 GeV (total integrated luminosity of 21 pb^{-1} in the period 1996) have been analyzed. The L3 detector has been described in detail in Ref. [10].

The event selection consists of two steps. One needs first to select hadronic final states produced in $\gamma\gamma$ collision and second to tag charm quarks. Hadronic two-photon events are selected by the following cuts: we require at least four tracks in each event, visible energy to be in the range $2 < E_{vis} < 60$ GeV ($<$ 40 GeV at LEP1), energy in the electro-magnetic calorimeter to exceed 0.5 GeV, invariant visible mass to be greater than 3 GeV and thrust to be smaller than 0.95. The invariant visible mass of the event is calculated from the four-momentum vectors of the measured particles. All particles are considered to be pions except for the electro-magnetic clusters identified as photons. The analysis is limited to anti-tagged events; which are selected by excluding events where the most energetic cluster in the L3 luminosity monitor has an energy greater than 0.43 E_{beam}. Two more cuts are applied to the LEP1 data. We require the number of calorimetric clusters to be greater than ten and transverse momentum imbalance to be smaller than 5 GeV/c (to suppress further $\tau\tau$ background).

This selection leaves 63330 events in the LEP2 data. Monte Carlo prediction at this stage is 65986 $\gamma\gamma \to$ hadrons events (PYTHIA[11]) and 0.3% of events in total of other types ($qq, ee\tau\tau, \tau\tau, WW$). For LEP1 data corresponding numbers are 137320 events in the data, 125482 events $\gamma\gamma \to$ hadrons (PYTHIA) and 4.1% of events in total of other types ($qq, ee\tau\tau, \tau\tau$). A comparison of different distributions also shows good agreement between data and Monte Carlo. In Figure 1a) we plot the measured visible mass spectrum for LEP2 data after hadronic events selection ($c\bar{c}$ purity is only 10 % at this step).

Tagging of charm quarks in this analysis is based on the detection of muons in the L3 muon chambers. This implies a lower cut on muon momentum of 2 GeV/c as only such muons can penetrate through calorimeters to muon chambers. In order to suppress a contribution of muons from annihilation processes we require the muon momentum to be smaller than 7 GeV/c for LEP1 and 15 GeV/c for LEP2 data. Figure 1b) shows the transverse momentum of

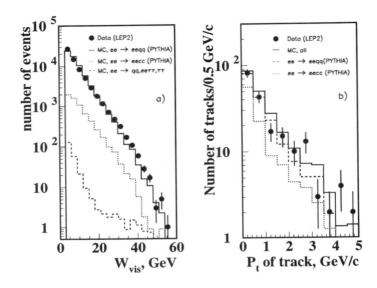

Figure 1: Spectra of visible mass of events after hadronic selection (1a) and transverse momentum of tracks after final selection (1b).

tracks spectrum for LEP2 data after all selection cuts have been applied.

After applying all cuts, 43 inclusive muon events have been observed in the LEP1 and 29 events in the LEP2 data. One event in LEP1 data has two (same sign) muon candidates. Monte Carlo prediction is 32.6 events for LEP1 and 28.8 events for LEP2 luminosities. It accounts for contributions from two-photon process $e^+e^- \rightarrow e^+e^-\gamma^*\gamma^* \rightarrow e^+e^-q\bar{q}$ and annihilation process $e^+e^- \rightarrow Z,\gamma \rightarrow hadrons$ (both simulated with PYTHIA), $e^+e^- \rightarrow \tau^+\tau^-$ (KORALZ [12]), $e^+e^- \rightarrow e^+e^-\tau^+\tau^-$ (Vermaseren [13]) and at LEP2 also $e^+e^- \rightarrow W^+W^-$ (KORALW [14]). Cosmic ray events were rejected by visual scan. All the contributions are listed in Table 1.

Total cross section of inclusive charm production was obtained by using selection efficiency and $c\bar{c}$ purity of $\gamma\gamma \rightarrow$ hadrons events given by the PYTHIA Monte Carlo, which includes contributions from direct and resolved processes. In total, $25.5 \pm 6.6(stat)$ (LEP1) and $12.2 \pm 5.4(stat)$ (LEP2) events remained after background subtraction. Selection efficiencies were estimated to be $(0.60 \pm 0.14)\,10^{-3}$ at LEP1 and $(0.73 \pm 0.17)\,10^{-3}$ at LEP2 energies. Trigger efficiencies were derived from the data itself using a set of indepen-

Table 1: Background composition for charm production measurement.

LEP energy [GeV]	Number of expected events	Background source
$\sqrt{s} = 91$	10.9 ± 1.4	$e^+e^- \rightarrow e^+e^- q\bar{q}$
	5.4 ± 2.7	$e^+e^- \rightarrow q\bar{q}$
	1.2 ± 0.5	$e^+e^- \rightarrow e^+e^- \tau^+\tau^-$
$\sqrt{s} = 161, 172$	8.2 ± 1.1	$e^+e^- \rightarrow e^+e^- q\bar{q}$
	7.0 ± 0.8	$e^+e^- \rightarrow e^+e^- \tau^+\tau^-$
	0.8 ± 0.1	$e^+e^- \rightarrow \tau^+\tau^-$
	0.6 ± 0.3	$e^+e^- \rightarrow q\bar{q}$
	0.2 ± 0.1	$e^+e^- \rightarrow W^+W^-$

dent triggers. Trigger efficiencies were found to be 95.7 ± 1.2 % for LEP1 and 93.5 ± 0.7 % for LEP2 data. Altogether total cross section measurement is $553 \pm 142(stat) \pm 141(syst)$ pb at LEP1 and $848 \pm 373(stat) \pm 231(syst)$ pb at LEP2 energies. Systematic errors arise from uncertainty on background subtraction and selection efficiencies. We have also made an estimate of $c\bar{c}$ selection efficiency using the MC program [13] of J.A.M. Vermaseren for the Quark Parton Model (QPM) production of charm quarks which were $(0.43 \pm 0.05) \, 10^{-3}$ at LEP1 and $(0.79 \pm 0.11) \, 10^{-3}$ at LEP2 energies. This is compatible within errors with PYTHIA numbers and provides an estimate for possible systematics from model dependence. Vermaseren Monte Carlo uses the exact $2 \rightarrow 4$ matrix elements calculation for $e^+e^- \rightarrow e^+e^- f\bar{f}$ via $\gamma\gamma$ collisions (direct process only).

In Figure 2 we show the results for the measurement of the total inclusive charm production cross section compared to other measurements [9] and to the predictions of Ref.[1]. Dashed lines correspond to the QPM prediction while solid lines show the QCD prediction calculated to the NLO accuracy. Our results are in agreement with QCD predictions.

Uncertainty for the theory prediction is due to charm mass variation. The highest values of prediction come from using a charm mass of 1.3 GeV/c^2; the lowest values correspond to a charm mass of 1.7 GeV/c^2. The open $c\bar{c}$ threshold energy is set to 3.8 GeV. The QPM (Born direct process) prediction depends only on the heavy-quark mass and the QCD coupling constant. The plotted theory prediction was calculated with the photon structure function of Glück-Reya-Vogt [15]. Using parametrization by Drees-Grassie [16] for the quark and gluon densities of the photon results in a decrease of the cross section by 3% for high mass and by 9% for low mass. The renormalization scale was

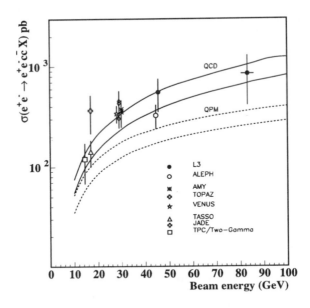

Figure 2: Charm production cross section in two-photon collisions. Dashed lines correspond to the QPM prediction while solid lines show the QCD prediction calculated to the NLO accuracy[1]. Data points at TRISTAN and LEP energies were artificially splited by 1 GeV to avoid merging.

chosen to be a charm mass. The change in the renormalization scale from m_c to $2m_c$ decreases QCD prediction by roughly 15% and by 30% respectively. It means that in order to measure the mass of c-quark one will need to separate direct process from resolved photon contribution. With currently available statistics it is premature to put a constraint on the mass of charm quark. Full LEP2 statistics could provide such a possibility.

3 Conclusions

The cross section of inclusive charm production in $\gamma\gamma$ collisions has been measured with L3 detector at LEP1 and for the first time at LEP2 energies. The values of the cross sections have been found to be

$$\sigma_{LEP1}^{ee \rightarrow eecX} = 553 \pm 142 \text{ (stat) } \pm 141 \text{ (syst) pb}$$

$$\sigma_{LEP2}^{ee \to eeccX} = 848 \pm 373 \text{ (stat)} \pm 231 \text{ (syst) pb}$$

The results are consistent with QCD predictions.

Acknowledgments

We would like to thank Alex Finch and Michael Krämer for providing us with a source code for cross section calculation and kind explanations. The author is grateful to Maria N. Kienzle-Focacci and Roger R. McNeil for useful discussions and encouragement. Special thanks to John H. Field for his suggestions and comments.

References

1. M. Drees, M. Krämer, J. Zunft and P.M. Zerwas, *Phys. Lett.* B **306**, 371 (1993).
2. JADE Collab., W. Bartel et al., *Phys. Lett.* B **184**, 288 (1987).
3. TPC/Two-Gamma Collab., M. Alston-Garnjost et al., *Phys. Lett.* B **252**, 499 (1990).
4. TASSO Collab., W. Braunschweig et al., *Z. Phys.* C **47**, 499 (1990).
5. TOPAZ Collab., R. Enomoto et al., *Phys. Lett.* B **328**, 535 (1994), *Phys. Rev.* D **50**, 1879 (1994), *Phys. Lett.* B **341**, 99 (1994), *Phys. Lett.* B **341**, 341 (1994).
6. VENUS Collab., S. Uehara et al., *Z. Phys.* C **63**, 213 (1994).
7. T. Nozaki (AMY Collab.), in Proceedings of PHOTON 95, Sheffield (1995), S. Cartwright, D. Miller and V.A. Khose *eds* (World Scientific).
8. ALEPH Collab., D. Buskulic et al., *Phys. Lett.* B **255**, 595 (1995).
9. M. Cacciari et al., in CERN 96-01 Physics at LEP2, edited by G. Altarelli, (1996), v.1, p. 334.
10. L3 Collab., B. Adeva et al., *Nucl. Instrum. Methods* A **289**, 35 (1990).
11. T. Sjöstrand, *Comput. Phys. Commun.* **82**, 74 (1994).
12. S. Jadach, B.F.L. Ward and Z. Was, *Comput. Phys. Commun.* **79**, 503 (1994).
13. J.A.M. Vermaseren, *Nucl. Phys.* B **229**, 347 (1983).
14. M. Skrzypek, S. Jadach, W. Placzek and Z. Was, *Comput. Phys. Commun.* **94**, 216 (1996).
15. M. Glück, E. Reya and A. Vogt, *Phys. Rev.* D **46**, 1973 (1992).
16. M. Drees and K. Grassie, *Z. Phys.* C **28**, 451 (1985).

SEARCH FOR SINGLE LEPTOQUARK PRODUCTION IN ELECTRON-PHOTON SCATTERING AT $\sqrt{s} = 161$ AND 172 GEV

STEFAN SÖLDNER-REMBOLD

for the OPAL collaboration

Universität Freiburg, Hermann-Herder-Str. 3,
D-79104 Freiburg i. Br., Germany

A search for a first generation scalar leptoquark (LQ) has been performed using the data collected by the OPAL detector in 1996 at e^+e^- centre-of-mass energies $\sqrt{s}$ of 161 and 172 GeV. It is assumed that a single leptoquark can be produced in the process eq→ LQ, where the initial state quark originates from a hadronic fluctuation of a quasi-real photon which has been radiated by one of the LEP beams. Lower limits at the 95 % confidence level on the mass of a first generation scalar leptoquark of 131 GeV for $\beta = 0.5$ and $\beta = 1$, coupling values λ larger than $\sqrt{4\pi\alpha_{\text{em}}}$ and leptoquark charges $-1/3$ or $-5/3$ are obtained.

1   Kinematics and Monte Carlo Simulations

Leptoquarks are coloured spin 0 or spin 1 particles carrying both baryon and lepton quantum numbers. Recently it has been suggested to search for leptoquarks in electron-photon collisions at LEP [1]. The photon, which has been radiated by one of the LEP beams, serves as a source of quarks through its fluctuations into hadronic states. The electron-quark interaction produces a leptoquark which is assumed to decay subsequently into an electron or a neutrino and a quark.[a]

In electron-photon scattering first generation leptoquarks of charge $-1/3$, $-5/3$, $-2/3$ and $-4/3$ can be produced. The cross-section to produce charge $-2/3$ and $-4/3$ leptoquarks is suppressed, since there is less d quark content in the photon than u quark. The limits will therefore be given for leptoquark charges $-1/3$ or $-5/3$. The cross-sections in eγ scattering for both charge states are identical, since it is equally probable to find a u or a $\overline{u}$ quark in the photon. In principle this search is also sensitive to electron-charm states, since the probability for a photon to split into c$\overline{c}$ or u$\overline{u}$ is expected to be about equal for leptoquark masses $M >> m_c$. Furthermore it has been assumed that either left or right handed couplings to fermions vanish. The cross-sections in eγ scattering for both couplings are identical, whereas the branching ratio

---

[a]Charge conjugation is implied throughout this paper and positrons are referred to as electrons

β into eq final states is 1 for right handed couplings and 1/2 for left handed couplings [2].

The total cross-section for the production of scalar leptoquarks of mass M is a convolution of the Weizsäcker-Williams effective photon distribution $f_{\gamma/e}(z, Q^2_{max})$, with z being the momentum fraction carried by the photon, and the parton distribution functions $f_{q/\gamma}(x, \mu^2)$ of the photon, evaluated at the scale $\mu = M$ [1]:

$$\sigma(e^+e^- \rightarrow LQ + X) = \frac{\lambda^2 \pi}{2s} \int_{M^2/s}^{1} \frac{dz}{z} f_{\gamma/e}(z, Q^2_{max}) f_{q/\gamma}(M^2/(zs), M^2). \quad (1)$$

The Monte Carlo simulation of this process is done with PYTHIA 5.722 [3,4]. In the simulation the maximum photon virtuality Q^2_{max} used in the Equivalent Photon Approximation equals $s/4$, but the simulated photon is always real ($Q^2 = 0$). The GRV parametrisation [5] of the parton distribution functions was used. In the kinematic region relevant for leptoquark production the variations of the cross-section due to the different parameterisations are small. Interference effects with deep-inelastic eγ scattering are also neglected. The total cross-section in PYTHIA for $\sqrt{s} = 172$ is about 10–20 % lower than the cross-sections given for $\sqrt{s} = 175$ in Ref. 1. Vector leptoquarks can currently not be simulated with PYTHIA. The limits are therefore given only for scalar leptoquarks. The standard PYTHIA Monte Carlo has been modified to include LQ $\rightarrow \nu_e$d decays in addition to the standard LQ $\rightarrow$ eu decays.

2 Event Analysis

Jets were reconstructed using a cone jet finding algorithm with a cone size $R = 1$ and a cut on the minimum transverse jet energy E_T of 15 GeV. Tracks and calorimeter clusters were used as input for the jet finding algorithm and for determining the missing transverse energy $\not{E}_T$ of the event. A matching algorithm between tracks and clusters is applied. The electron was identified using the standard OPAL neural net electron identification [6]. All relevant Standard Model background processes were studied using Monte Carlo generators. The total data sample corresponds to an integrated luminosity of 20.5 pb^{-1}.

2.1 The electron plus hadronic jet channel

For this channel the identified electron with the largest momentum was assumed to be the electron from the leptoquark decay. The electron is usually reconstructed as a jet. Candidate events were selected based on the following cuts:

- In order to reduce background from deep-inelastic $e\gamma$ and $e^+e^- \to \tau^+\tau^-$ events, exactly two jets must have been found in the event ($n_j = 2$).

- A large number of $e^+e^- \to \tau^+\tau^-$ and $e^+e^- \to e^+e^-$ events are rejected by requiring a minimum number of 5 reconstructed tracks ($n_{ch} \geq 5$). In addition, the ratio $E_{ECAL}/\sqrt{s}$ has to be less than 0.9, where E_{ECAL} is the energy in the electromagnetic calorimeter.

- The missing transverse energy $\not{E}_T$ must be less than 15 GeV in order to reduce background from $\tau^+\tau^-$ and W^+W^- pair production.

- An isolation cut is applied on the identified electron. The jet with the smallest angular distance to the electron is chosen to be the electron jet. The difference between the energy E_e^j of this jet and the energy E_e of the electron must be less than 4 GeV. Most multihadronic $e^+e^- \to q\bar{q}$ events are removed by this cut.

- Events where an electron was scattered at a small angle are rejected by requiring for the angle of the electron $|\cos\theta_e| < 0.85$.

- The total multiplicity n_q of the quark jet must be $n_q \geq 7$, where n_q is the total number of tracks and calorimeter clusters associated to this jet.

The cuts on the transverse momenta of the jets and on the angle $|\cos\theta_e|$ of the electron reduce significantly the sensitivity to find a leptoquark which is lighter than approximately $M_Z/2$, the region excluded by the LEP1 searches. These cuts are necessary to reduce the background from deep-inelastic $e\gamma$ events which becomes increasingly important at small masses.

After all cuts we expect a background of 5.2 ± 0.4 events from all Standard Model processes. In the data four events are observed with jet-jet invariant masses M_{jj} of 36, 37, 62 and 98 GeV. In Fig. 1a the M_{jj} distribution of the four candidate events is shown together with the sum of all Monte Carlo background distributions. Also shown is a possible leptoquark signal for $\lambda = \sqrt{4\pi\alpha_{em}}$ and different LQ masses. The mass distribution of the candidate events is consistent with the expectation from the background Monte Carlo simulation.

2.2 The neutrino plus hadronic jet channel

This search has to be optimized for a single hadronic jet in the detector. Its transverse energy E_T^j must be balanced by the neutrino. The cuts are therefore:

- In order to reject events with large missing transverse energy due to badly measured tracks, the ratio of the energy E_{ECAL} to the total visible energy E_{vis} has to be larger than 20 %.

- Exactly one jet has to be found ($n_j = 1$) with $E^j_T > 15$ GeV. The jet direction in the laboratory frame is required to lie within a pseudorapidity range $|\eta^j| < 2$ to reject events where a single jet, usually due to an electron, was found in the forward detectors.

- $n_{ch} \geq 5$ and $n_q \geq 7$.

- The missing transverse energy $E\!\!\!/_T$ must be greater than 15 GeV and it should be mainly due to the jet. Therefore we require $|E^j_T - E\!\!\!/_T| < 3$ GeV and $E^j/E_{vis} > 0.5$.

Since no additional cuts on electron variables are necessary, the efficiency to detect a leptoquark is higher in the $\nu_e q'$ than in the eq channel. For $M = 100$ GeV the efficiency is about 61 % in the $\nu_e q'$ and 55 % in the eq channel.

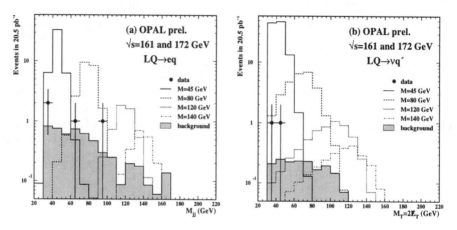

Figure 1: Number of (a) LQ $\rightarrow$ eq and (b) LQ $\rightarrow \nu_e q'$ events expected with $\lambda = (4\pi\alpha_{em})^{1/2}$ in 20.5 pb^{-1} of data after all cuts for $M = 45, 80, 120$ and 140 GeV (histograms) and the candidate events (data points). The sum of all background contributions expected from the simulation of the Standard Model processes is also shown normalized to the data luminosity.

The leptoquark mass was reconstructed by calculating the transverse mass $M_T = 2E\!\!\!/_T$. The transverse mass M_T of the two candidate events at 38 and 46 GeV is shown in Fig. 1b together with the background distribution from the simulation. The expected background rate is 1.81 ± 0.05 events. The transverse mass distribution for a leptoquark production cross-section using $\lambda = \sqrt{4\pi\alpha_{em}}$ is also indicated.

3   Mass Limit for a Scalar Leptoquark

The systematic error includes (a) the luminosity measurement with 1 %, (b) the model dependence of the leptoquark fragmentation with 4 %, (c) the electron identification efficiency with 2 % and (d) the Monte Carlo statistics with 1 %. The model dependence of the leptoquark fragmentation was estimated by varying the cut on the average charged multiplicity by one unit in the Monte Carlo while keeping it fixed in the data.

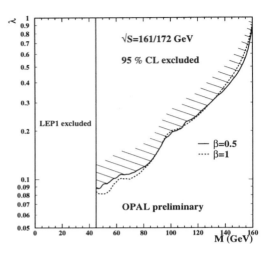

Figure 2: Upper limit at 95 % CL of the coupling λ as a function of the mass M of the scalar LQ.

The limit was obtained separately for $\beta = 1$ and for $\beta = 0.5$. The 95 % confidence level (CL) upper limit was calculated taking into account the candidates, the background, the experimental resolution and the systematic errors. The cross-section was determined using PYTHIA. The upper limit at 95 % CL of the coupling λ as a function of the leptoquark mass M is given in Fig. 2. The mass limits are $M > 131$ GeV for both $\beta = 0.5$ and $\beta = 1$ and for $\lambda = \sqrt{4\pi\alpha_{em}}$.

References

1. M. A. Doncheski, S. Godfrey, Phys. Lett. B393 (1997) 355; hep-ph/9703285 and private communications.
2. W. Buchmüller, R. Rückl, D. Wyler, Phys. Lett. B191 (1987) 442.
3. T. Sjöstrand, Comp. Phys. Commun. 82 (1994) 74.
4. C. Friberg, E. Norrbin, T. Sjöstrand, LU-TP-97-04 (hep-ph/9704214).
5. M. Glück, E. Reya, A. Vogt, Phys. Rev. D46 (1992) 1973; Phys. Rev. D45 (1992) 3986.
6. OPAL Collaboration, G. Alexander et al., Z. Phys. C70 (1996) 357.
7. J. Kalinowski, R. Rückl, H. Spiesberger, P. M. Zerwas, DESY 97-038 (hep-ph/9703288).

Session C

Exclusive Processes in $\gamma\gamma$ Interactions

EXCLUSIVE PHOTON-PHOTON PROCESSES

S. J. BRODSKY

Stanford Linear Accelerator Center,
Stanford University, Stanford, California 94309

Exclusive $\gamma\gamma \rightarrow$ hadron pairs are among the most fundamental processes in QCD, providing a detailed examination of Compton scattering in the crossed channel. In the high momentum transfer domain (s, t, large, θ_{cm} for t/s fixed), these processes can be computed from first principles in QCD, yielding important information on the nature of the QCD coupling α_s and the form of hadron distribution amplitudes. Similarly, the transition form factors $\gamma^*\gamma$, $\gamma^*\gamma \rightarrow \pi^0, \eta^0, \eta', \eta_c \ldots$ provide rigorous tests of QCD and definitive determinations of the meson distribution amplitudes $\phi_H(x, Q)$. We show that the assumption of a frozen coupling at low momentum transfers can explain the observed scaling of two-photon exclusive processes.

1 Introduction

Exclusive two-photon processes provide highly valuable probes of coherent effects in quantum chromodynamics. For example, in the case of exclusive final states at high momentum transfer and fixed θ_{cm} such as $\gamma\gamma \rightarrow p\bar{p}$ or meson pairs, photon-photon collisions provide a timelike microscope for testing fundamental scaling laws of PQCD and for measuring distribution amplitudes, the fundamental wavefunctions of hadrons. [1] At very high energies $s >> -t$, diffractive processes such as $\gamma\gamma \rightarrow$ neutral vector (or pseudoscalar) meson pairs with real or virtual photons can test the QCD Pomeron (or the $C = -1$ exchange Odderon) in a detailed way utilizing the simplest possible initial state. [2] In the case of low momentum transfer processes, the comparison of the two-photon decay width for a given $C = +$ resonance with its inferred two-gluon width provides an indirect discovery tool for gluonium. As discussed at this conference by H. Paar, [3] CLEO has reported a very small upper limit for the coupling $\Gamma(\gamma\gamma \rightarrow f_J^0(1220))$ due to the absence of a signal for $K_s K_s$ decays, whereas a large $gg \rightarrow f_J^0(1220)$ coupling is inferred from Mark III and BES observations of $J/\psi \rightarrow \gamma f_J^0$ decays. Using Chanowitz's "stickiness" criteria, [4] this points to a gluonium interpretation of the f_J^0.

Traditionally, $\gamma\gamma$ data has come from the annihilation of Weisäcker–Williams effective photons emitted in $e^- e^\pm$ collisions. Data for $\gamma\gamma \rightarrow$ hadrons from $ep \rightarrow e'p'R^0$ events at HERA has also now become available. The HERA diffractive events will allow studies of photon and pomeron interference effects in hadron-induced amplitudes. As emphasized by Klein, [5] nuclear-coherent $\gamma\gamma \rightarrow$ hadrons reactions can be observed in heavy-ion collisions at RHIC or the LHC, *e.g.* $Z_1 Z_2 \to Z_1 Z_2 \pi^+ \pi^-$. Eventually $\gamma\gamma$ collisions will be studied at TeV energies with back-scattered laser beams, allowing critical probes of Standard Model and supersymmetric processes with polarized photons in exclusive channels such as Higgs production $\gamma\gamma \to W^+ W^-$, and $\gamma\gamma \to W^+ W^- W^+ W^-$.[6]

2 Hard Exclusive Two-Photon Reactions

Exclusive two-photon processes such as $\gamma\gamma \to$ hadron pairs and the transition form factor $\gamma^* \gamma \to$ neutral mesons play a unique role in testing quantum chromodynamics because of the simplicity of the initial state. [1] At large momentum transfer the direct point-like coupling of the photon dominates at leading twist, leading to highly specific predictions which depend on the shape and normalization of the hadron distribution amplitudes $\phi_H(x_i, Q)$ the basic valence bound state wavefunctions. The most recent exclusive two-photon process data from CLEO [7] provides stringent tests of these fundamental QCD predictions.

Exclusive processes are particularly challenging to compute in QCD because of their sensitivity to the unknown non-perturbative bound state dynamics of the hadrons. However, in some important cases, the leading power-law behavior of an exclusive amplitude at large momentum transfer can be computed rigorously via a factorization theorem which separates the soft and hard dynamics. The key ingredient is the factorization of the hadronic amplitude at leading twist. As in the case of inclusive reactions, factorization theorems for exclusive processes [1,8,9] allow the analytic separation of the perturbatively-calculable short-distance contributions from the long-distance non-perturbative dynamics associated with hadronic binding. For example, the amplitude $\gamma\gamma \to \pi^+ \pi^-$ factorizes in the form

$$\mathcal{M}_{\gamma\gamma \to \pi^+ \pi^-} = \int_0^1 dx \int_0^1 dy \, \phi_\pi(x, \widetilde{Q}) \, T_H(x, y, \widetilde{Q}) \, \phi_\pi(y, \widetilde{Q}) \tag{1}$$

where $\phi_\pi(x, \widetilde{Q})$ is in the pion distribution amplitude and contains all of the soft, nonperturbative dynamics of the pion $q\bar{q}$ wavefunction integrated in relative transverse momentum up to the separation scale $k_\perp^2 < \widetilde{Q}^2$, and T_H is the quark/gluon hard scattering amplitude for $\gamma\gamma \to (q\bar{q})(q\bar{q})$ where the outgoing quarks are taken collinear with their respective pion parent. To lowest order in α_s, the hard scattering amplitude is linear in α_s. The most convenient definition of the coupling is the effective charge $\alpha_V(Q^2)$, defined from the potential for the scattering of two infinitely heavy test charges, in analogy to the definition of the QED running coupling. Another possible choice is the effective charge $\alpha_R(s)$, defined from the QCD correction to the annihilation cross section: $R_{e+e-\to\text{hadrons}}(s) \equiv R_0(1 + \alpha_R(s)/\pi)$. One can relate α_V and α_R to $\alpha_{\overline{MS}}$ to NNLO using commensurate scale relations [10].

The contributions from non-valence Fock states and the correction from neglecting the transverse momentum in the subprocess amplitude from the non-perturbative region are higher twist, $i.e.$, power-law suppressed. The transverse momenta in the perturbative domain lead to the evolution of the distribution amplitude and to next-to-leading-order (NLO) corrections in α_s. The contribution from the endpoint regions of integration, $x \sim 1$ and $y \sim 1$, are power-law and Sudakov suppressed and thus can only contribute corrections at higher order in $1/Q$. [1]

The distribution amplitude $\phi(x, \widetilde{Q})$ is boost and gauge invariant and evolves in $\ln \widetilde{Q}$ through an evolution equation [1]. It can be computed from the integral over transverse momenta of the renormalized hadron valence wavefunction in the light-cone gauge at fixed light-cone time [1]:

$$\phi(x,\widetilde{Q}) = \int d^2\vec{k_\perp}\, \theta\left(\widetilde{Q}^2 - \frac{\vec{k_\perp}^2}{x(1-x)}\right) \psi^{(\widetilde{Q})}(x,\vec{k_\perp}). \tag{2}$$

A physical amplitude must be independent of the separation scale $\widetilde{Q}$. The natural variable in which to make this separation is the light-cone energy, or equivalently the invariant mass $\mathcal{M}^2 = \vec{k_\perp}^2/x(1-x)$, of the off-shell partonic system [11,1]. Any residual dependence on the choice of $\widetilde{Q}$ for the distribution amplitude will be compensated by a corresponding dependence of the NLO correction in T_H. In general, the NLO prediction for exclusive amplitude depends strongly on the form of the pion distribution amplitude as well as the choice of renormalization scale μ and scheme.

The QCD coupling is typically evaluated at quite low scales in exclusive processes since the momentum transfers has to be divided among several constituents. In the BLM procedure, the scale of the coupling is evaluated by absorbing all vacuum polarization corrections with the scale of the coupling or by taking the experimental value integrating over the gluon virtuality. Thus, in the case of the (timelike) pion form factor the relevant scale is of order $Q^{*2} \sim e^{-3}\mathcal{M}^2_{\pi\pi-} \cong \frac{1}{20}\mathcal{M}^2_{\pi+\pi-}$ assuming the asymptotic form of the pion distribution amplitude $\phi_\pi^{\text{asympt}} = \sqrt{3} f_\pi\, x(1-x)$. At such low scales, it is likely that the coupling is frozen or relatively slow varying.

In the BLM procedure, the renormalization scales are chosen such that all vacuum polarization effects from the QCD β function are re-summed into the running couplings. The coefficients of the perturbative series are thus identical to the perturbative coefficients of the corresponding conformally invariant theory with $\beta = 0$. The BLM method has the important advantage of "presumming" the large and strongly divergent terms in the PQCD series which grow as $n!(\alpha_s \beta_0)^n$, *i.e.*, the infrared renormalons associated with coupling constant renormalization [12,13]. Furthermore, the renormalization scales Q^* in the BLM method are physical in the sense that they reflect the mean virtuality of the gluon propagators [13,14,15,16]. In fact, in the $\alpha_V(Q)$ scheme, where the QCD coupling is defined from the heavy quark potential, the renormalization scale is by definition the momentum transfer caused by the gluon. Because the renormalization scale is small in the exclusive $\gamma\gamma$ processes discussed here, we will argue that the effective coupling is nearly constant, thus accounting for the nominal scaling behavior of the data [17,18].

The heavy-quark potential $V(Q^2)$ can be identified via the two-particle-irreducible scattering amplitude of test charges, *i.e.*, the scattering of an infinitely heavy quark and antiquark at momentum transfer $t = -Q^2$. The relation

$$V(Q^2) = -\frac{4\pi C_F \alpha_V(Q^2)}{Q^2}, \tag{3}$$

with $C_F = (N_C^2 - 1)/2N_C = 4/3$, then defines the effective charge $\alpha_V(Q)$. This coupling provides a physically-based alternative to the usual $\overline{MS}$ scheme. As in the corresponding case of Abelian QED, the scale Q of the coupling $\alpha_V(Q)$ is identified with the exchanged momentum. The scale-fixed relation between α_V and the conventional $\overline{MS}$ coupling is

$$\alpha_V(Q) = \alpha_{\overline{MS}}(e^{-5/6}Q)\left(1 - \frac{2C_A}{3}\frac{\alpha_{\overline{MS}}}{\pi} + \cdots\right), \tag{4}$$

above or below any quark mass threshold. The factor $e^{-5/6} \simeq 0.4346$ is the ratio of commensurate scales between the two schemes to this order. It arises because of the conventions used in defining the modified minimal subtraction scheme. The scale in the $\overline{MS}$ scheme is thus a factor ~ 0.4 smaller than the physical scale. The coefficient $2C_A/3$ in the NLO term is a feature of the non-Abelian couplings of QCD; the same coefficient would occur even if the theory were conformally invariant with $\beta_0 = 0$. Recent lattice calculations have provided strong constraints on the normalization and shape of $\alpha_V(Q^2)$. [19] The J/ψ and Υ spectra have been used to determine the normalization:

$$\alpha_V^{(3)}(8.2 \text{ GeV}) = 0.196(3), \tag{5}$$

where the effective number of light flavors is $n_f = 3$. The corresponding modified minimal subtraction coupling evolved to the Z mass using Eq. (4) is given by

$$\alpha_{\overline{MS}}^{(5)}(M_Z) = 0.115(2). \tag{6}$$

This value is consistent with the world average of 0.117(5), but is significantly more precise. These results are valid up to NLO.

Ji, Pang, Robertson, and I [20] have recently analyzed the pion transition form factor $F^{\gamma^*\gamma} \rightarrow \pi^0$ obtained from $e\gamma \rightarrow e'\pi^0$, the timelike pion form obtained from $e^+e^- \rightarrow \pi^+\pi$, and the $\gamma\gamma \rightarrow \pi^+\pi^-$ processes, all at NLO in α_V. The assumption of a nearly constant coupling in the hard scattering amplitude at low scales provides an explanation for the phenomenological success of dimensional counting rules for exclusive processes; $i.e.$, the power-law fall-off follows the nominal scaling of the hard scattering amplitude $\mathcal{M}_{\rm had} \sim T_H \sim [p_T]^{4-n}$ where n is in the total number of incident and final fields entering T_H. The transition form factor has now been measured up to $Q^2 < 8$ GeV^2 in the tagged two-photon collisions $e\gamma \rightarrow e'\pi^0$ by the CLEO and CELLO collaborations. In this case the amplitude has the factorized form

$$F_{\gamma M}(Q^2) = \frac{4}{\sqrt{3}} \int_0^1 dx \phi_M(x, Q^2) T_{\gamma \rightarrow M}^H(x, Q^2), \tag{7}$$

where the hard scattering amplitude for $\gamma\gamma^* \rightarrow q\bar{q}$ is

$$T_{\gamma M}^H(x, Q^2) = \frac{1}{(1-x)Q^2} (1 + \mathcal{O}(\alpha_s)). \tag{8}$$

The leading QCD corrections have been computed by Braaten [21]; however, the NLO corrections are necessary to fix the BLM scale at LO. Thus it is not yet possible to rigorously determine the BLM scale for this quantity. We shall here assume that this scale is the same as that occurring in the prediction for F_π. For the asymptotic distribution amplitude we thus predict

$$Q^2 F_{\gamma\pi}(Q^2) = 2f_\pi \left(1 - \frac{5}{3} \frac{\alpha_V(Q^*)}{\pi}\right). \tag{9}$$

As we shall see, given the phenomenological form of α_V we employ (discussed below), this result is not terribly sensitive to the precise value of the scale.

An important prediction resulting from the factorized form of these results is that the normalization of the ratio

$$R_\pi(Q^2) \equiv \frac{F_\pi(Q^2)}{4\pi Q^2 |F_{\pi\gamma}(Q^2)|^2} \tag{10}$$

$$= \alpha_{\overline{MS}}(e^{-14/6}Q) \left(1 - 0.56 \frac{\alpha_{\overline{MS}}}{\pi}\right) \tag{11}$$

$$= \alpha_V(e^{-3/2}Q) \left(1 + 1.43 \frac{\alpha_V}{\pi}\right) \tag{12}$$

$$= \alpha_R(e^{5/12 - 2\zeta_3}Q) \left(1 - 0.65 \frac{\alpha_R}{\pi}\right) \tag{13}$$

is formally independent of the form of the pion distribution amplitude. The $\alpha_{\overline{MS}}$ correction follows from combined references [21,22,23]. The next-to-leading correction given here assumes the asymptotic distribution amplitude.

We emphasize that when we relate R_π to α_V we relate observable to observable and thus there is no scheme ambiguity. Furthermore, effective charges such as α_V are defined from physical observables and thus must be finite even at low momenta. A number of proposals have been suggested for the form of the QCD coupling in the low-momentum regime. For example, Petronzio and Parisi [24] have argued that the coupling must freeze at low momentum transfer in order that perturbative QCD loop integrations be well defined. Mattingly and Stevenson [25] have incorporated such behavior into their parameterizations of α_R at low scales. Gribov [26] has presented novel dynamical arguments related to the nature of confinement for a fixed coupling at low scales. Zerwas [27] has noted the heavy quark potential must saturate to a Yukawa form since the light-quark production processes will screen the linear confining potential at large distances. Cornwall [28] and others [29,30] have argued that the gluon propagator will acquire an effective gluon mass m_g from non-perturbative dynamics, which again will regulate the form of the effective couplings at low momentum. We shall adopt the simple parameterization

$$\alpha_V(Q) = \frac{4\pi}{\beta_0 \ln\left(\frac{Q^2 + 4m_g^2}{\Lambda_V^2}\right)}, \tag{14}$$

which effectively freezes the α_V effective charge to a finite value for $Q^2 \leq 4m_g^2$.

We can use the non-relativistic heavy quark lattice results [19,31] to fix the parameters. A fit to the lattice data of the above parameterization gives $\Lambda_V = 0.16$ GeV if we use the well-known momentum-dependent n_f [32]. Furthermore, the value $m_g^2 = 0.19$ GeV^2 gives consistency with the frozen value of α_R advocated by Mattingly and Stevenson [25]. Their parameterization implies the approximate constraint $\alpha_R(Q)/\pi \simeq 0.27$ for $Q = \sqrt{s} < 0.3$ GeV, which leads to $\alpha_V(0.5 \text{ GeV}) \simeq 0.37$ using the NLO commensurate scale relation between α_V and α_R. The resulting form for α_V is shown in Fig. 1. The corresponding predictions for α_R and $\alpha_{\overline{MS}}$ using the CSRs at NLO are also shown. Note that for low Q^2 the couplings, although frozen, are large. Thus the NLO and higher-order terms in the CSRs are large, and inverting them perturbatively to NLO does not give accurate results at low scales. In addition, higher-twist contributions to α_V and α_R, which are not reflected in the CSR relating them, may be expected to be important for low Q^2 [33].

It is clear that exclusive processes such as the photon to pion transition form factors can provide a valuable window for determining the magnitude

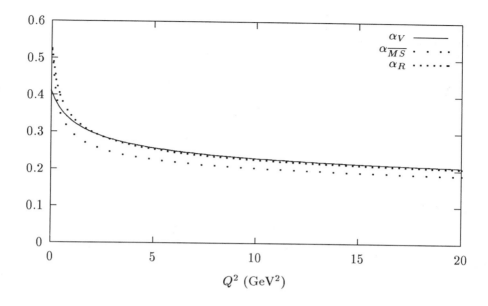

Figure 1: The coupling function $\alpha_V(Q^2)$ as given in Eq. (14). Also shown are the corresponding predictions for $\alpha_{\overline{MS}}$ and α_R following from the NLO commensurate scale relations.

and the shape of the effective charges at quite low momentum transfers. In particular, we can check consistency with the α_V prediction from lattice gauge theory. A complimentary method for determining α_V at low momentum is to use the angular anisotropy of $e^+e^- \to Q\overline{Q}$ at the heavy quark thresholds[34]. It should be emphasized that the parameterization (14) is just an approximate form. The actual behavior of $\alpha_V(Q^2)$ at low Q^2 is one of the key uncertainties in QCD phenomenology.

As we have emphasized, exclusive processes are sensitive to the magnitude and shape of the QCD couplings at quite low momentum transfer: $Q_V^{*2} \simeq e^{-3}Q^2 \simeq Q^2/20$ and $Q_R^{*2} \simeq Q^2/50$ [35]. The fact that the data for exclusive processes such as form factors, two photon processes such as $\gamma\gamma \to \pi^+\pi^-$, and photoproduction at fixed $\theta_{c.m.}$ are consistent with the nominal scaling of the leading-twist QCD predictions (dimensional counting) at momentum transfers Q up to the order of a few GeV can be immediately understood if the effective charges α_V and α_R are slowly varying at low momentum. The scaling of the exclusive amplitude then follows that of the subprocess amplitude T_H with effectively fixed coupling. Note also that the Sudakov effect of the end point region is the exponential of a double log series if the coupling is frozen, and thus is strong.

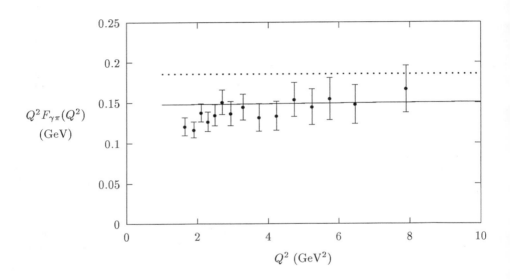

Figure 2: The $\gamma \to \pi^0$ transition form factor. The solid line is the full prediction including the QCD correction [Eq. (15)]; the dotted line is the LO prediction $Q^2 F_{\gamma\pi}(Q^2) = 2f_\pi$.

In Fig. 2, we compare the recent CLEO data [7] for the photon to pion transition form factor with the prediction

$$Q^2 F_{\gamma\pi}(Q^2) = 2f_\pi \left(1 - \frac{5}{3} \frac{\alpha_V(e^{-3/2}Q)}{\pi} \right). \qquad (15)$$

The flat scaling of the $Q^2 F_{\gamma\pi}(Q^2)$ data from $Q^2 = 2$ to $Q^2 = 8$ GeV^2 provides an important confirmation of the applicability of leading twist QCD to this process. The magnitude of $Q^2 F_{\gamma\pi}(Q^2)$ is remarkably consistent with the predicted form, assuming the asymptotic distribution amplitude and including the LO QCD radiative correction with $\alpha_V(e^{-3/2}Q)/\pi \simeq 0.12$. Radyushkin [36], Ong [37] and Kroll [38] have also noted that the scaling and normalization of the photon-to-pion transition form factor tends to favor the asymptotic form for the pion distribution amplitude and rules out broader distributions such as the two-humped form suggested by QCD sum rules [39]. One cannot obtain a unique solution for the non-perturbative wavefunction from the $F_{\pi\gamma}$ data alone. However, we have the constraint that

$$\frac{1}{3}\langle\frac{1}{1-x}\rangle\left[1 - \frac{5}{3}\frac{\alpha_V(Q^*)}{\pi}\right] \simeq 0.8 \tag{16}$$

(assuming the renormalization scale we have chosen in Eq. (9) is approximately correct). Thus one could allow for some broadening of the distribution amplitude with a corresponding increase in the value of α_V at low scales.

We have also analyzed the $\gamma\gamma \to \pi^+\pi^-, K^+K^-$ data. These data exhibit true leading-twist scaling (Fig. 3), so that one would expect this process to be a good test of theory. One can show that to LO

$$\frac{\frac{d\sigma}{dt}(\gamma\gamma \to \pi^+\pi^-)}{\frac{d\sigma}{dt}(\gamma\gamma \to \mu^+\mu^-)} = \frac{4|F_\pi(s)|^2}{1 - \cos^4\theta_{c.m.}} \tag{17}$$

in the CMS, where $dt = (s/2)d(\cos\theta_{c.m.})$ and here $F_\pi(s)$ is the *time-like* pion form factor. The ratio of the time-like to space-like pion form factor for the asymptotic distribution amplitude is given by

$$\frac{|F_\pi^{(\text{timelike})}(-Q^2)|}{F_\pi^{(\text{spacelike})}(Q^2)} = \frac{|\alpha_V(-Q^{*2})|}{\alpha_V(Q^{*2})}. \tag{18}$$

If we simply continue Eq. (14) to negative values of Q^2 then for $1 < Q^2 < 10$ GeV^2, and hence $0.05 < Q^{*2} < 0.5$ GeV^2, the ratio of couplings in Eq. (18) is of order 1.5. Of course this assumes the analytic application of Eq. (14). Thus if we assume the asymptotic form for the distribution amplitude, then we predict $F_\pi^{(\text{timelike})}(-Q^2) \simeq (0.3 \text{ GeV}^2)/Q^2$ and hence

$$\frac{\frac{d\sigma}{dt}(\gamma\gamma \to \pi^+\pi^-)}{\frac{d\sigma}{dt}(\gamma\gamma \to \mu^+\mu^-)} \simeq \frac{.36}{s^2}\frac{1}{1 - \cos^4\theta_{c.m.}}. \tag{19}$$

The resulting prediction for the combined cross section $\sigma(\gamma\gamma \to \pi^+\pi^-, K^+K^-)^a$ is shown in Fig. 3, along with CLEO data [7]. Considering the possible contribution of the resonance $f_2(1270)$, the agreement is reasonable.

We also note that the normalization of α_V could be larger at low momentum than our estimate. This would also imply a broadening of the pion distribution amplitude compared to its asymptotic form since one needs to

---

^{a}The contribution from kaons is obtained at this order simply by rescaling the prediction for pions by a factor $(f_K/f_\pi)^4 \simeq 2.2$.

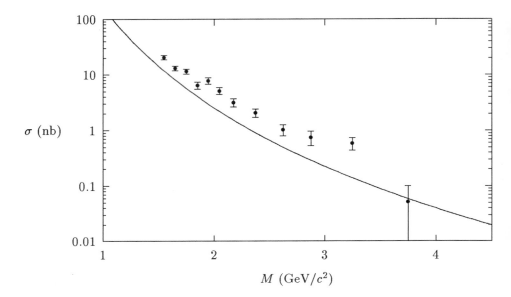

Figure 3: Two-photon annihilation cross section $\sigma(\gamma\gamma \rightarrow \pi^+\pi^-, K^+K^-)$ as a function of CMS energy, for $|\cos\theta^*| < 0.6$.

raise the expectation value of $1/(1-x)$ in order to maintain consistency with the magnitude of the $F_{\gamma\pi}(Q^2)$ data. A full analysis will then also require consideration of the breaking of scaling from the evolution of the distribution amplitude. In any case, we find no compelling argument for significant higher-twist contributions in the few GeV regime from the hard scattering amplitude or the endpoint regions, since such corrections violate the observed scaling behavior of the data.

The analysis we have presented here suggests a systematic program for estimating exclusive amplitudes in QCD (including exclusive B-decays) which involve hard scattering. The central input is $\alpha_V(0)$, or

$$\overline{\alpha_V} = \frac{1}{Q_0^2} \int_0^{Q_0^2} dQ'^2 \alpha_V(Q'^2), \quad Q_0^2 \leq 1 \ \text{GeV}^2, \tag{20}$$

which largely controls the magnitude of the underlying quark-gluon subprocesses for hard processes in the few-GeV region. In this work, the mean coupling value for $Q_0^2 \simeq 0.5$ GeV^2 is $\overline{\alpha_V} \simeq 0.38$. The main focus will then be to determine the shapes and normalization of the process-independent meson and baryon distribution amplitudes.

3 Conclusions

The leading-twist scaling of the observed cross sections for exclusive two-photon processes and other fixed θ_{cm} reactions can be understood if the effective coupling $\alpha_V(Q^*)$ is approximately constant in the domain of Q^* relevant to the underlying hard scattering amplitudes. In addition, the Sudakov suppression of the long-distance contributions is strengthened if the coupling is frozen because of the exponentiation of a double log series. We have also found that the commensurate scale relation connecting the heavy quark potential, as determined from lattice gauge theory, to the photon-to-pion transition form factor is in excellent agreement with $\gamma e \rightarrow \pi^0 e$ data assuming that the pion distribution amplitude is close to its asymptotic form $\sqrt{3} f_\pi x(1-x)$. We also reproduce the scaling and approximate normalization of the $\gamma\gamma \rightarrow \pi^+\pi^-$, K^+K^- data at large momentum transfer. However, the normalization of the space-like pion form factor $F_\pi(Q^2)$ obtained from electroproduction experiments is somewhat higher than that predicted by the corresponding commensurate scale relation. This discrepancy may be due to systematic errors introduced by the extrapolation of the $\gamma^* p \rightarrow \pi^+ n$ electroproduction data to the pion pole.

Acknowledgments

Much of this talk is based on collaborations with Peter Lepage, Hung Jung Lu, Chueng Ji, Dave Robertson, and Alex Pang, and I thank them for helpful conversations. This work is supported in part by the U.S. Department of Energy under contract no. DE–AC03–76SF00515.

References

1. S. J. Brodsky and G. P. Lepage, *Phys. Rev. Lett.* **53**, 545 (1979); *Phys. Lett.* **87B**, 359 (1979); G. P. Lepage and S. J. Brodsky, *Phys. Rev.* **D22**, 2157 (1980).
2. I.F. Ginzburg, D.Yu. Ivanov, and V.G. Serbo these proceedings, and e-Print hep-ph/9508309.
3. H. Paar, these proceedings.
4. M. Chanowitz, *Nucl. Instrum. Meth.* **A355** 42, (1995), e-Print hep-ph/9407231, and references therein.
5. S. Klein, e-Print, nucl-th/9707008 and these proceedings.

6. S. J. Brodsky and P. M. Zerwas, *Nucl. Instrum. Meth.* **A355** 19, (1995), e-Print hep-ph/9407362, and references therein. Se also G. Jikia, these proceedings.
7. J. Dominick, *et al.*, Phys. Rev. **D50**, 3027 (1994). See also, J. Gronberg *et al.* CLNS-97-1477, (1997), e-Print hep-ex/9707031 and V. Savinov, these proceedings.
8. A. V. Efremov and A. V. Radyushkin, *Theor. Math. Phys.* **42**, 97 (1980).
9. S. J. Brodsky and G. P. Lepage, in *Perturbative Quantum Chromodynamics*, A. H. Mueller, Ed. (World Scientific, 1989).
10. H. J. Lu and S. J. Brodsky, *Phys. Rev.* **D48**, 3310 (1993).
11. C.-R. Ji, A. Pang, and A. Szczepaniak, *Phys. Rev.* **D52**, 4038 (1995).
12. A. H. Mueller, *Nucl. Phys.* **B250**, 327 (1985).
13. P. Ball, M. Beneke and V. M. Braun, *Phys. Rev.* **D52**, 3929 (1995).
14. S. J. Brodsky, G. P. Lepage, and P. B. Mackenzie, *Phys. Rev.* **D28**, 228 (1983).
15. G. P. Lepage and P. B. Mackenzie, *Phys. Rev.* **D48**, 2250 (1993).
16. M. Neubert, *Phys. Rev.* **D51**, 5924 (1995); *Phys. Rev. Lett.* **76**, 3061 (1996).
17. C.-R. Ji, A. Sill and R. Lombard-Nelsen, *Phys. Rev.* **D36**, 165 (1987).
18. C.-R. Ji and F. Amiri, *Phys. Rev.* **D42**, 3764 (1990).
19. C. T. H. Davies *et. al.*, *Phys. Rev.* **D52**, 6519 (1995).
20. S. J. Brodsky, C.-R. Ji, A. Pang, and D. Robertson, SLAC-PUB-7473, (1997).
21. E. Braaten and S.-M. Tse, *Phys. Rev.* **D35**, 2255 (1987).
22. F. M. Dittes and A. V. Radyushkin, *Sov. J. Nucl. Phys.* **34**, 293 (1981); *Phys. Lett.* **134B**, 359 (1984).
23. R. D. Field, R. Gupta, S. Otto and L. Chang, *Nucl. Phys.* **B186**, 429 (1981).
24. G. Parisi and R. Petronzio, *Phys. Lett.* **95B**, 51 (1980).
25. A. C. Mattingly and P. M. Stevenson, *Phys. Rev.* **D49**, 437 (1994).
26. V. N. Gribov, Lund Report No. LU-TP 91-7, 1991 (unpublished).
27. K. D. Born, E. Laermann, R. Sommer, P. M. Zerwas, and T. F. Walsh, *Phys. Lett.* **329B**, 325 (1994).
28. J. M. Cornwall, *Phys. Rev.* **D26**, 1453 (1982).
29. A. Donnachie and P. V. Landshoff, *Nucl. Phys.* **B311**, 509 (1989).
30. M. Gay Ducati, F. Halzen and A. A. Natale, *Phys. Rev.* **D48**, 2324 (1993).
31. A. X. El-Khadra, G. Hockney, A. Kronfeld and P. B. Mackenzie, *Phys. Rev. Lett.* **69**, 729 (1992).

32. D. V. Shirkov and S. V. Mikhailov, *Z. Phys.* **C63**, 463 (1994).
33. V. M. Braun, "QCD renormalons and higher twist effects," hep-ph/9505317.
34. S. J. Brodsky, A. H. Hoang, J. H. Kuhn and T. Teubner, *Phys. Lett.* **359B**, 355 (1995).
35. N. Isgur and C. H. Lewellyn-Smith, *Phys. Rev. Lett.* **52**, 1080 (1984); *Phys. Lett.* **217B**, 535 (1989); *Nucl. Phys.* **B317**, 526 (1989).
36. A. V. Radyushkin, *Acta Phys. Polon.* **B26**, 2067 (1995).
37. S. Ong, *Phys. Rev.* **D52**, 3111 (1995).
38. P. Kroll and M. Raulfs, *Phys. Lett.* **387B**, 848 (1996).
39. V. L. Chernyak and A. R. Zhitnitsky, *Phys. Rep.* **112**, 173 (1984).

MEASUREMENTS OF THE MESON-PHOTON TRANSITION FORM FACTORS OF LIGHT PSEUDOSCALAR MESONS AT LARGE MOMENTUM TRANSFER

V. SAVINOV (representing the CLEO Collaboration)

Stanford Linear Accelerator Center,

MS61, P.O. Box 4349, Stanford, CA, 94309, USA

(e-mail: savinov@lns62.lns.cornell.edu)

Using the CLEO II detector, we have measured the form factors associated with the electromagnetic transitions $\gamma^*\gamma \to$ meson. We have measured these form factors in the momentum transfer ranges from 1.5 to 9, 20, and 30 GeV^2 for π^0, η, and η', respectively.

1 Introduction

Production of even C-parity hadronic matter in e^+e^- scattering provides a unique opportunity to study the properties of strong interactions. To leading order in quantum electrodynamics (QED) these processes are described as the interaction between two photons emitted by the scattered electrons. Although in e^+e^- scattering the probe and the target are both represented by photons that are carriers of the electromagnetic force, these space-like photons can produce a pair of quarks that interact strongly and are observed in the form of hadrons. Therefore, by measuring the four-momenta of the scattered electrons we can study the dynamics of strong interactions. The quantities of interest in these studies are the form factors associated with the transitions between the photons and the hadrons.

In this paper we briefly describe the final results of our measurements [1,2] of the differential cross sections for the production of a single pseudoscalar meson in e^+e^- scattering: $e^+e^- \to e^+e^-\mathcal{R}$, where $\mathcal{R}$ is a π^0, η or η'. We measure these cross sections in a "single-tagged" experimental mode where one of the scattered electrons is detected ("tagged"), while the other electron is scattered at a very small angle and therefore remains undetected ("untagged"). The mesons produced in e^+e^- scattering are observed through their decays to various fully reconstructed final states. The tagged electron emits a highly off-shell photon (γ^*), whereas the untagged electron emits a nearly on-shell photon (γ). We measure the dependence of the meson production rate on the squared momentum transfer Q^2 carried by the highly off-shell photon. This momentum transfer is determined by energy-momentum conservation as applied to the tag: $Q^2 \equiv -(p_b - p_t)^2 = 2E_bE_t(1 - \cos\theta_t)$, where p_b and p_t

are the four-momenta of the incident beam-energy electron and the tag, E_b and E_t are corresponding energies, and θ_t is the scattering angle. From the measurements of the differential rates $d\sigma(e^+e^- \to e^+e^-\mathcal{R})/dQ^2$ we obtain the transition form factors $\mathcal{F}_{\gamma^*\gamma\mathcal{R}}$ that describe the effect of the strong interaction in the $\gamma^*\gamma \to \mathcal{R}$ transition amplitudes.

To relate the differential cross sections to the transition form factors we employ the theoretical framework developed by V.M. Budnev et al.[3] (BGMS formalism). In BGMS the process $e^+e^- \to e^+e^-\mathcal{R}$ is divided into two parts: $e^+e^- \to e^+e^-\gamma^*\gamma$ and $\gamma^*\gamma \to \mathcal{R}$. The first part is completely calculable in QED and the second part is defined in terms of the transition form factors $\mathcal{F}_{\gamma^*\gamma\mathcal{R}}(Q^2)$. In the case of pseudoscalar mesons there is only one form factor. At zero momentum transfer this form factor is expressed as:

$$|\mathcal{F}_{\gamma^*\gamma\mathcal{R}}(0)|^2 = \frac{1}{(4\pi\alpha)^2} \frac{64\pi\Gamma(\mathcal{R} \to \gamma\gamma)}{M_\mathcal{R}^3}, \qquad (1)$$

where α is the QED coupling constant, $M_\mathcal{R}$ is the mass and $\Gamma(\mathcal{R} \to \gamma\gamma)$ is the two-photon partial width of the meson $\mathcal{R}$. The transition form factors cannot be calculated directly from Quantum Chromodynamics (QCD). However, these form factors have been estimated[4,5,6,7] using theoretical methods based on the perturbative QCD (PQCD)[8] and the sum rules[9].

Brodsky and Lepage employed PQCD to find the asymptotic behavior of the $\gamma^*\gamma \to \mathcal{R}$ transition form factors in the limit $Q^2 \to \infty$[10]:

$$\lim_{Q^2 \to \infty} Q^2 \mathcal{F}_{\gamma^*\gamma\mathcal{R}}(Q^2) = 2f_\mathcal{R}, \qquad (2)$$

where $f_\mathcal{R}$ is the meson decay constant. In addition, it has been predicted that in this limit any mesonic wave function evolves to the asymptotic wave function of unique shape[8,11,12].

While PQCD predicts the form factors of the $\gamma^*\gamma \to \mathcal{R}$ transitions at large momentum transfer, the behavior of these form factors in the limit $Q^2 \to 0$ can be determined from the axial anomaly[13,14] in the chiral limit of QCD. For π^0 and η the axial anomaly yields[10]:

$$\lim_{Q^2 \to 0} \mathcal{F}_{\gamma^*\gamma\mathcal{R}}(Q^2) = \frac{1}{4\pi^2 f_\mathcal{R}}, \qquad (3)$$

to leading order in $m_u^2/M_\mathcal{R}^2$ and $m_d^2/M_\mathcal{R}^2$ where m_u and m_d are the masses of the u and d quarks. This prediction does not hold with the same precision for η' due to the larger value of the s-quark mass. In addition, even if the s-quark mass were small, this prediction might be broken for η' because this particle is an unlikely candidate for the Goldstone boson[15,16].

Finally, to approximate the soft non-perturbative region of Q^2 a simple interpolation between $Q^2 \to 0$ and $Q^2 \to \infty$ limits has been proposed [10]:

$$\mathcal{F}_{\gamma^* \gamma \mathcal{R}}(Q^2) \sim \frac{1}{4\pi^2 f_{\mathcal{R}}} \frac{1}{1 + (Q^2/8\pi^2 f_{\mathcal{R}}^2)}. \tag{4}$$

We have measured the transition form factors $\mathcal{F}_{\gamma^* \gamma \mathcal{R}}$ in the space-like regions of the momentum transfer between 1.5 and 9 GeV^2 for π^0, 1.5 and 20 GeV^2 for η, and 1.5 and 30 GeV^2 for η'. We report the measurements of the transition form factors of π^0, η, and η' using the decays: $\pi^0 \to \gamma\gamma$, $\eta \to \gamma\gamma$, $\eta \to \pi^0\pi^0\pi^0 \to 6\gamma$, $\eta \to \pi^+\pi^-\pi^0 \to \pi^+\pi^- 2\gamma$, $\eta' \to \rho^0\gamma \to \pi^+\pi^-\gamma$, $\eta' \to \pi^+\pi^-\eta \to \pi^+\pi^- 2\gamma$, $\eta' \to \pi^0\pi^0\eta \to 6\gamma$, $\eta' \to \pi^+\pi^-\eta \to 2\pi^+2\pi^- 2\gamma$, $\eta' \to \pi^0\pi^0\eta \to 5\pi^0 \to 10\gamma$, $\eta' \to \pi^0\pi^0\eta \to 3\pi^0\pi^+\pi^- \to \pi^+\pi^- 6\gamma$, and $\eta' \to \pi^+\pi^-\eta \to \pi^+\pi^- 3\pi^0 \to \pi^+\pi^- 6\gamma$. We have analyzed the last two decay chains of η' together since they are observed in the same final state $\pi^+\pi^- 6\gamma$.

The data sample employed in our analysis corresponds to an integrated e^+e^- luminosity of 2.88 ± 0.03 fb^{-1} collected at e^+e^- center-of-mass energy around 10.6 GeV with the CLEO-II detector [17,18] at CESR.

2 Analysis Procedure

To measure the products of the differential cross sections and branching fractions for each decay chain we use the following analysis procedure. Data events that pass all selection criteria [2] are used to form the Q^2 distribution where the value of Q^2 for each event is estimated from energy-momentum conservation for this event (the experimental method we use to estimate the value of Q^2 for each event is described in detail elsewhere [1,2]). Next we divide the event yields into Q^2 intervals. For each Q^2 interval we obtain the number of signal events in data from the fit to the invariant mass distribution. Then we estimate and subtract the (small) feed-down background [2]. Finally we correct the background-subtracted number of signal events for the detection efficiency. The signal line shapes used in the fits and the detection efficiencies are determined from the detector simulation for each Q^2 interval. To extract the transition form factors we compare the measured and the predicted values of the cross sections. Namely, for each Q^2 interval, we measure the form factors $\mathcal{F}_{\gamma^* \gamma \mathcal{R}}^{data}(\tilde{Q}^2)$ from: $|\mathcal{F}_{\gamma^* \gamma \mathcal{R}}^{data}(\tilde{Q}^2)|^2 = \sigma(data)/\sigma(MC)|\mathcal{F}_{\gamma^* \gamma \mathcal{R}}^{MC}(\tilde{Q}^2)|^2$, where $\mathcal{F}_{\gamma^* \gamma \mathcal{R}}^{MC}(\tilde{Q}^2)$ is the approximation for the Q^2-dependent part of the form factor in Monte Carlo (MC) simulation, and $\sigma(data)$ and $\sigma(MC)$ are the cross sections for this Q^2 interval measured in data and predicted using numerical integration, respectively. The transition form factors are measured at $\tilde{Q}^2$

where the differential cross sections achieve their mean values according to the results of numerical integration.

The Q^2-dependent part of the $\gamma^*\gamma^* \to \mathcal{R}$ transition form factors in our two-photon MC simulation program is approximated by:

$$|\mathcal{F}_{\gamma^*\gamma^*\mathcal{R}}(Q^2)|^2 \;\; = \;\; \frac{1}{(4\pi\alpha)^2} \frac{64\pi\Gamma(\mathcal{R} \to \gamma\gamma)}{M_{\mathcal{R}}^3} \frac{1}{(1 + Q^2/\Lambda_{\mathcal{R}}^2)^2}, \qquad (5)$$

where the pole-mass parameter $\Lambda_{\mathcal{R}} = 770$ MeV.

3   Results

In Figures 1 and 2 we compare our results with the theoretical predictions. In these figures we also show the results of the CELLO experiment [19] and the asymptotic prediction of PQCD given by Eqn. 2. For both experimental results the error bars represent the statistical errors only. To plot the results of the theoretical predictions we use their published analytical forms. To estimate the values of the meson decay constants $f_{\mathcal{R}}$ we use Eqns. 1 and 3 and the tabulated two-photon partial widths of the studied mesons [20].

Finally, for each meson $\mathcal{R}$, where $\mathcal{R}$ is π^0, η, or η', we derive the values of the pole-mass parameters $\Lambda_{\mathcal{R}}$ which we use to represent our results in a simple phenomenological form. For each meson we fit all our results for $|\mathcal{F}_{\gamma^*\gamma\mathcal{R}}(Q^2)|^2$ with the function given by Eqn. 5 and obtain the values of the pole-mass parameters $\Lambda_{\mathcal{R}}$ shown in Table 1. In this table, for each measurement, the first error is statistical, the second error represents the systematic uncertainties of our measurement and the third error reflects the experimental error in the value of the two-photon partial width of the meson. The results of the fits are also shown in Figures 1 and 2.

We use the measured values of the parameters Λ_{π^0} and Λ_{η} to compare the soft non-perturbative properties of π^0 and η. This is a legitimate comparison because the asymptotic prediction given by Eqn. 2 and the chiral limit given by Eqn. 3 are expected to hold for both π^0 and η. From the comparison between the measured values of Λ_{π^0} and Λ_{η} we conclude that the Q^2 shapes of the $\gamma^*\gamma \to$ meson transition form factors of π^0 and η are nearly identical, which strongly indicates the similarity between the wave functions of these mesons.

The results of our measurements for the production of η' demonstrate that if this particle were a $q\bar{q}$ bound state and the QCD chiral limit given by Eqn. 3 held for this meson, the Q^2-dependence of the transition form factor of η' and consequently its wave function would be significantly different from these non-perturbative properties of either π^0 or η.

4 Conclusions

We have measured the form factors associated with the electromagnetic transitions $\gamma^*\gamma \to$ meson in the regions of momentum transfer from 1.5 to 9, 20, and 30 GeV^2 for π^0, η, and η', respectively. These are the first measurements above 2.7 GeV^2 for π^0 and above 7 GeV^2 for η and η'.

Our measurement for π^0 unambiguously distinguishes among various theoretical predictions for the form factors of the $\gamma^*\gamma \to \pi^0$ transition. We have demonstrated that the non-perturbative properties of π^0 and η agree with each other which indicates that the wave functions of these two mesons are similar. In the η' analysis we have shown that the non-perturbative properties of η' differ substantially from those of π^0 and η. Our measurement for η' provides important information for future theoretical investigations of the structure of this particle.

References

1. V. Savinov, PhD thesis, University of Minnesota, Minneapolis, 1997, Unpublished.
2. J. Gronberg et al., CLEO Coll., CLNS 97/1477, Submitted to PRD.
3. V.M. Budnev et al., Phys. Rep. **C15** (1975) 181.
4. P. Kroll, Universität Wuppertal preprint WU B 94-17..
5. R. Jakob et al., J. Phys. **G22** (1996) 45.
6. F.-G. Cao et al., Phys. Rev. **D53** (1996) 6582.
7. A.V. Radyushkin and R. Ruskov, Nucl. Phys. **B481** (1996) 625.
8. G.P. Lepage and S.J. Brodsky, Phys. Rev. **D22** (1980) 2157.
9. M.A. Shifman, et al., Nucl. Phys. **B147** (1979) 385.
10. S.J. Brodsky and G.P. Lepage, Phys. Rev. **D24** (1981) 1808.
11. A.V. Efremov and A.V. Radyushkin, Phys. Lett. **B94** (1980) 245.
12. V.L. Chernyak and A.R. Zhitnitsky, Phys. Rep. **112** (1984) 173.
13. S. Adler, Phys. Rev. **177** (1969) 2426.
14. J. Bell and R. Jackiw, Nuovo. Cim. **A60** (1969) 47.
15. L.H. Ryder, Quantum Field Theory, p.297, Cambridge University Press, 1986.
16. S. Coleman, Aspects of Symmetry, Cambridge University Press, 1985.
17. Y. Kubota et al., CLEO Coll., Nucl. Inst. and Meth. **A320** (1992) 66.
18. C. Bebek et al., CLEO Coll., Nucl. Inst. and Meth. **A302** (1992) 261.
19. H.-J. Behrend et al., CELLO Coll., Z. Phys. **C49** (1991) 401.
20. Particle Data Group, L. Montanet et al., Review of Particle Properties, Phys. Rev. **D54** (1996) 1.

Table 1: Values of the pole-mass parameters Λ_{π^0}, Λ_η and $\Lambda_{\eta'}$.

Decay chain	$\Lambda_\mathcal{R}$ (MeV)
$\pi^0 \to \gamma\gamma$	$776 \pm 10 \pm 12 \pm 16$
Simultaneous fit to three decay chains for η	$774 \pm 11 \pm 16 \pm 22$
Simultaneous fit to seven decay chains for η'	$859 \pm 9 \pm 18 \pm 20$

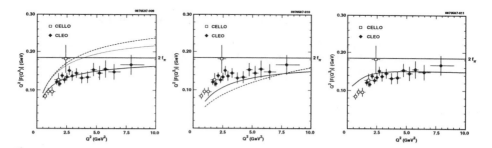

Figure 1: Comparison of the results (points) for π^0 with the theoretical predictions [5,6,7] (from left to right). Two figures on the left show the predictions with the asymptotic wave function [8,11,12] (solid curves) and the CZ wave function [12] (dashed curves). The dotted curve shows the prediction made with the CZ wave function when its QCD evolution is taken into account.

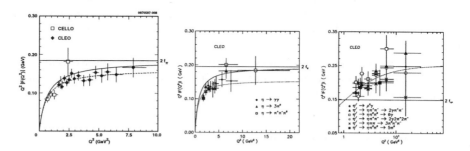

Figure 2: Pole-mass parameter fits (dashed lines) to CLEO results for (from left to right) π^0, η, and η'. The solid curves (where shown) are the interpolations given by Eqn. 4.

VECTOR MESON PRODUCTION IN $\gamma\gamma$ INTERACTIONS AT LEP WITH THE L3 DETECTOR

Á. CSILLING

Research Institute for Particle and Nuclear Physics (KFKI-RMKI)
Budapest, Konkoly-Thege u. 29.-33., 1121 Hungary

on behalf of the L3 Collaboration

Vector Meson Production in untagged $\gamma\gamma$ collisions has been studied with the L3 detector at the LEP e^+e^- collider. Exclusive $\rho - \rho$ production was studied in $\pi^+\pi^-\pi^+\pi^-$ events for $0.5 < W < 8$ GeV. Exclusive $\rho - \omega$ and inclusive ρ and ω production was also observed. The $K_s^0 K^\pm \pi^\mp$ final state with $K_s^0 \to \pi^+\pi^-$ was examined in the resonance region.

1 Introduction

In this work we present the summary of two different analyses currently in progress using data collected by the L3 Experiment[1] at the LEP collider.

An important component of the total hadronic two photon cross-section comes from the interaction of Vector Mesons produced as a quantum fluctuation of the incoming photons. This can be tested directly by the observation of the exclusive production of two Vector Mesons: $e^+e^- \to e^+e^-\rho^0\rho^0$ or $\rho^0\omega^0$.

The second measurement, $e^+e^- \to e^+e^-K_s^0 K^\pm \pi^\mp$, is intended to help in the better interpretation of some specific resonances. One example is the $\eta(1440)$, which is copiously produced in the J/Ψ radiative decays, but no signal was found in two-photon processes, indicating a small two-photon width that favours a glueball interpretation.

All the results included in this work are preliminary, as this write-up represents a snapshot of the work going on in these two specific directions and not the results of a finished study.

2 Vector Meson Production at High W

The interaction of two quasi-real photons at low energies can be described by the Vector Meson Dominance Model (VDM), while at higher energies by perturbative QCD (PQCD). These two regimes were combined into a single model by G. Schuler and T. Sjöstrand.[2] The predictions of this model are included in the PYTHIA Monte-Carlo program,[3] used throughout this analysis.

Table 1: Comparison of experiments studying the $\gamma\gamma \to \rho^0\rho^0$ process. Shown are the number of 4-track $\gamma\gamma$ events observed, the number of exclusive 4π events and selected $\rho^0\rho^0$ events, together with the e^+e^- luminosity and the centre-of-mass energy.

	4 tracks	4 π	$\rho^0\rho^0$	L_{ee} (pb^{-1})	$\sqrt{s}$ (GeV)
L3 (1994)	20771	2754	1940	49.7	91
L3 (1996a)	4485	1354	944	10.9	161
L3 (1996b)	4690	1453	1012	10.3	172
L3 Total	29946	5561	3896	70.9	91 − 172
ARGUS [4]		5701		242	10.2
CELLO [5]			910	11.2	34
PLUTO [6]		2272		28.7	34.7
TASSO [7]		1722		40.9	14 − 36.6
TPC/2γ [8]		4814		73	29

2.1 Event Selection

We studied 4-track events, where all tracks satisfied some quality criteria ($p_t >$ 100 MeV, DCA $\leq$ 10 mm, $N_{hits} \geq 12$). The untagged exclusive $\pi^+\pi^-\pi^+\pi^-$ final state was identified by an antitag condition ($E_{LUMI} < 30$ GeV) and a cut on the transverse momentum balance ($\Sigma\vec{p}_t(\pi_i) < 0.05$ GeV$^2/c^2$, $i = 1,4$). By fitting a linear function to this distribution we estimated the non-exclusive background coming from events with undetected particles to be around 25%. $\rho^0\rho^0$ events were separated from the non-resonant background by the requirement $M(\rho^0_{1,2}) < 1.1$ GeV.

The number of events selected at three values of beam energy are shown in table 1 together with data obtained by other experiments that have studied the same final state. Note that earlier experiments concentrated their study on the threshold region, dominated by a controversial resonance, while our analysis is intended to study the high mass region. This is possible due to the large energy and luminosity of LEP.

2.2 Results

Figure 1 shows the invariant mass (W) distribution of the exclusive 4-track events together with the same distribution for the $\rho^0\rho^0$ events at $\sqrt{s} = 91$ GeV, the value of the Z peak and for high energy data at $\sqrt{s} = 161$ and 172 GeV. At low W the phase-space forces all events to be identified as $\rho^0\rho^0$, while as we go to higher W regions the non-resonant 4π channel becomes dominant.

218

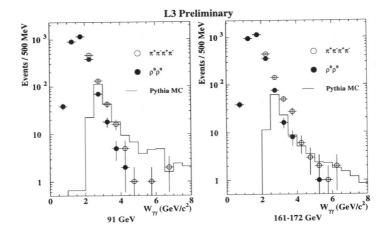

Figure 1: Mass distribution of 4π and $\rho^0\rho^0$ events compared with the PYTHIA prediction.

The solid line shows the prediction of PYTHIA generated in the region above $W = 2.5$ GeV. A discrepancy between the Monte-Carlo and data at 91 GeV can be observed, while the agreement is better at higher energies. A possible explanation for this difference is a change of the trigger efficiency, which was not taken into account.

2.3 Outlook

With the increase of LEP energy and luminosity enough statistics will be collected in the high mass region to allow the study of the ρ^0 momentum transfer and angular distribution in bins of W, where a change of behaviour is expected. In order to compare directly with QCD model predictions the differential $\gamma\gamma \rightarrow \rho^0\rho^0$ cross-section has to be extracted. The study of charged ρ meson production could also provide useful information.

We have observed the process $\gamma\gamma \rightarrow \rho^0\omega^0$ followed by $\rho^0 \rightarrow \pi^+\pi^-$ and $\omega^0 \rightarrow \pi^+\pi^-\pi^0$, with $\pi^0 \rightarrow \gamma\gamma$. The number of events observed is smaller and also dominated by low masses.

The study of inclusive ρ^0 and ω^0 production promises very high statistics, but the presence of a large background requires further studies for an efficient background rejection.

3 $K_s^0 K^\pm \pi^\mp$ Final State

In the $\gamma\gamma \rightarrow R \rightarrow K_s^0 K^\pm \pi^\mp$ channel, followed by $K_s^0 \rightarrow \pi^+\pi^-$, various resonances can be studied. The $\eta(1440)$ is copiously produced in the J/Ψ radiative decays, but not in two-photon processes. This small two-photon coupling suggests that it can be a glueball candidate. The $\Gamma_{\gamma\gamma}^{\eta_c}$ radiative width of the η_c charmonium state can also be measured in this process.

3.1 Event Selection

The data sample collected over the years 1991-95 by the L3 detector at 91 GeV centre-of-mass energies of LEP corresponds to an integrated luminosity of 114.35 pb^{-1}. Selected events contain exactly 4 tracks (with $p_t > 100$ MeV and $N_{hits} \geq 12$) and at least one secondary vertex separated by more than 3 mm from the primary vertex. To select exclusive events the antitag condition ($E_{LUMI} < 35$ GeV) and the transverse momentum balance ($\Sigma \vec{p}_t(\pi_i) < 0.04$ GeV$^2/c^2$, $i = 1, 4$) were required. Non-exclusive background was estimated by fitting a linear function to this last distribution. The angle α between the flight path and momentum direction of the K_s^0 candidate defined in the transverse plane had to be less than 75 mrad, and its invariant mass was required to lie between 460 and 530 MeV. Background was estimated from the sidebands of this mass distribution.

3.2 Results

The Dalitz-plot of the $K\pi$ and $K_s^0\pi$ invariant masses together with the two projections is shown in figure 2 *(left)*, for the 469 events selected without $K - \pi$ identification, with two entries per event. Both invariant mass distributions are dominated by the $K^*(892)$, but in case of the $K_s^0 - \pi$ distribution a second enhancement in the region of the $K_2^*(1430)$ is also visible.

Figure 2 *(right)* shows the $K_s^0 K^\pm \pi^\mp$ invariant mass distribution of the 214 events remaining after $K^\pm - \pi^\mp$ identification based on dE/dx. The dashed line indicates the background calculated from the K_s^0 sidebands and the solid line includes also background from non-exclusive processes with undetected particles, estimated from the distribution of the total momentum balance in the transverse plane.

The absence of a resonance-like structure in the region of the $\eta(1440)$ supports its glueball interpretation. The slight enhancement around 3 GeV can be interpreted as the signal from the charmonium state η_c.

220

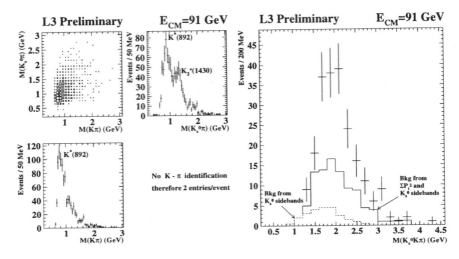

Figure 2: *(Left)* Dalitz-plot of the $K\pi$ and $K_s^0\pi$ invariant masses together with the two projections, with two entries per event. *(Right)* $K_s^0 K^\pm\pi^\mp$ invariant mass, where the dashed line indicates background calculated from the K_s^0 sidebands and the solid line includes also background from non-exclusive processes with undetected particles.

Acknowledgements

I would like to express my gratitude to Gerhard Schuler, Maria N. Kienzle-Focacci and John H. Field for useful discussions and encouragement. The author also wishes to thank László Boldizsár for providing his results on the $K_s^0 K^\pm\pi^\mp$ channel.

This work was partly funded by the Hungarian Scientific Research Fund under grant number OTKA T-019181 and OTKA F-023259 and the Eötvös Fellowship of the Hungarian Fellowship Board.

1. B. Adeva *et al*, *Nucl. Instrum. Methods* A **289**, 35 (1990).
2. G. Schuler and T. Sjöstrand, *Z. Phys.* C **73**, 677 (1997).
3. T. Sjöstrand, *Comput. Phys. Commun.* **82**, 74 (1994).
4. H. Albrecht *et al*, *Z. Phys.* C **50**, 1 (1991).
5. H.-J. Behrend *et al*, *Z. Phys.* C **21**, 205 (1984).
6. C. Berger *et al*, *Z. Phys.* C **38**, 521 (1988).
7. M. Althoff *et al*, *Z. Phys.* C **16**, 13 (1982).
8. H. Aihara *et al*, *Phys. Rev.* D **37**, 28 (1988).

RESONANCES IN MULTI-PHOTON FINAL STATES IN POSITRON PROTON SCATTERING AT HERA

S. TAPPROGGE for the H1 Collaboration

Institut für Hochenergiephysik, Universität Heidelberg
Schröderstr. 90, 69120 Heidelberg, GERMANY

A first search for exclusive production of C=+1 mesons at HERA using data taken with the H1 detector in 1996 is presented. The process is expected to be dominated by photon-photon fusion, but may also be induced by Odderon ($\mathcal{O}$) exchange. Utilizing its backward calorimeter SPACAL, H1 is able to measure mesons decaying into multi-photon final states and to investigate these for exclusive production.

1 Introduction

Properties of soft hadron-hadron interactions at high energies are known to be well described by Regge theory provided that the exchange of a trajectory with the quantum numbers of the vacuum and an intercept $\alpha(t = 0) \approx 1$ and C parity $+1$ (called "Pomeron" – $I\!P$) is introduced. However, no direct evidence has been found at high energies (where subleading trajectories do no longer contribute) for an exchange with $\alpha(t = 0) \approx 1$ but with $C = -1$ (called "Odderon" – $\mathcal{O}$). Contributions from an Odderon trajectory can be investigated e.g. when comparing antiproton-proton with proton-proton scattering.

At HERA the existence of an Odderon trajectory could result, as suggested by Schäfer, Nachtmann, and Mankiewicz [1], in the production of pseudoscalar mesons with $C = +1$ in addition to their production via the two photon fusion process. Figure 1 shows the two processes, taking as an example the η_c meson. The cross section in case of the η_c however is expected to be smaller than 10 pb. Thus Schäfer et al. suggest to measure the cross section ratio for

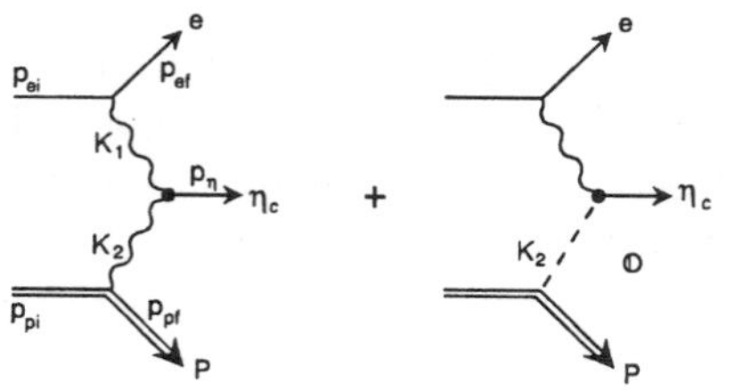

Figure 1: Processes contributing to the exclusive production of $C = +1$ mesons at HERA (taken from [1]):photon-photon fusion (left part) and photon-Odderon fusion (right part).

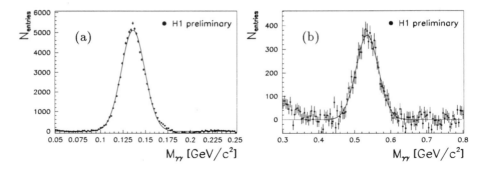

Figure 2: Invariant mass spectra of inclusively produced γ-γ pairs (after background subtraction): in the π^0 mass region (a), with a minimal energy for each photon of at least 1 GeV, and in the η mass region (b), with a minimal energy for each photon of at least 1.5 GeV.

exclusive production of η's and η''s, since a larger cross section is expected and in their model, the sensitivity to the Odderon induced process differs for η and η'. Assuming the coupling to the meson for photon-Odderon fusion to be proportional to the product of the electric charge and the baryon number of the quarks composing the meson, the η' – being dominantly the singlet state with respect to flavour $SU(3)$ – gets only a small contribution, whereas the η – dominantly the octet state – gets a large contribution.

2   Detector Performance

The data used were taken in 1996 with the H1 detector at HERA (27.5 GeV positrons on 820 GeV protons) and amount to an integrated luminosity of about 5 pb^{-1}. They are based on a trigger demanding a signal in the positron calorimeter of the H1 luminosity system and a localized energy deposit in the backward calorimeter (SPACAL) of more than 1.5 GeV. This corresponds to a kinematic range of $0.3 < y < 0.7$ and $Q^2 < 0.01 \text{GeV}^2/c^2$.

The lead/scintillating fibre calorimeter SPACAL [2] has a sampling term of $7\%/\sqrt{E/\text{GeV}}$ and, due to its fine granularity, a position resolution of about 5 mm at 1 GeV. Together with the low energy threshold (≈ 100 MeV) this allows for a precise measurement of mesons decaying into multi-photon final states, e.g. of the π^0 and the η mesons in their 2γ decay mode, as shown in Figure 2. Here the invariant mass spectra of inclusively produced photon pairs are shown, yielding clear signals of π^0 (a) and η (b) mesons. The signal of

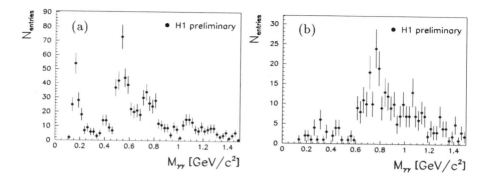

Figure 3: Invariant mass spectrum of candidates for photon pairs, where each photon has an energy of at least 0.7 GeV and $(E - p_z c)_{e\gamma\gamma} > 50$ GeV is required: (a) events with a vertex, (b) events without a vertex.

the π^0 meson has been used for a calibration of the SPACAL in the photon energy range of 0.1 to 1.5 GeV to correct for energy losses. The central values of the Gaussian fit – after this correction – amount to 136 MeV/c^2 for π^0 and 535 MeV/c^2 for η. The measured width of the invariant mass distribution is $\sigma \approx 13$ MeV/c^2 for π^0 and $\sigma \approx 31$ MeV/c^2 for η, demonstrating the good performance of the detector. No inclusive signal of $\eta' \to \gamma\gamma$ has been found.

3 Search for Exclusive Meson Production

The acceptance of the positron calorimeter of the luminosity system ($0.3 < y < 0.7$) restricts the meson energy in the laboratory frame to lie between 8 and 20 GeV and kinematically forces the production of the meson in the backward direction (positron beam). The selected events consist of the scattered positron (being tagged in the luminosity system), two photons within the angular acceptance of the SPACAL, and an elastically scattered proton which escapes detection in the main detector. To ensure no losses in the backward direction, a cut on the variable[a] $(E - p_z c)_{e\gamma\gamma} > 50$ GeV is applied, as calculated from the scattered positron and the two photons, to exclude events with inclusive meson production.

Requiring in addition a reconstructed vertex, i.e. is at least one charged

---

[a]The proton beam direction defines the $+z$-axis, leading to the expected value of twice the positron beam energy for $(E - p_z c)_{e\gamma\gamma}$, where E is the energy and p_z the longitudinal momentum along the z-axis.

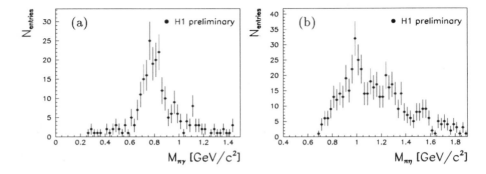

Figure 4: (a): Invariant mass spectrum of candidates for exclusively produced γ-π^0 pairs in the ω mass region (photon energy $E > 0.8$ GeV and $(E - p_z c)_{e\pi^0\gamma} > 49$ GeV). (b): Invariant mass spectrum of candidates for exclusively produced η-π^0 pairs (photon energy $E > 1$ GeV and $(E - p_z c)_{e\eta\pi^0} > 49$ GeV).

track in the detector, results in the invariant mass spectrum of photon pairs as shown in Figure 3 (a). Clear signals of the π^0 and the η mesons are observed, no indication for a signal of the η' meson is found. At about 800 MeV/c^2 a "bump" is observed, which will be discussed below.

By requiring no charged particles to be found in the central detector – thus selecting events without a reconstructed vertex, compatible with exclusive meson production – leads to the invariant mass spectrum of photon pairs as shown in Figure 3 (b). No signal of exclusively produced η and η' mesons is observed, nor of π^0. However, the resonance-like structure at an invariant mass of about 800 MeV/c^2 has become more pronounced. This is interpreted as being due to elastic photoproduction of ω mesons and their subsequent decays into the $\gamma\pi^0$ final state, where only two out of the three photons are detected.

Figure 4 (a) shows the invariant mass spectra of γ-π^0 pairs (i.e. events with three photons out of which two form a π^0), after applying a mass constrained fit to the reconstructed π^0. A clear signal of the ω meson is observed, confirming the contribution from ω mesons to the two photon invariant mass spectrum. These data will be used to measure the photoproduction cross section for ω mesons at high values of W ($140 < W < 250$ GeV/c^2).

The non-observation of η mesons is compatible with the expectation from a pure two photon fusion process, given the small acceptance of the detector.

This excludes a large contribution from Odderon induced processes with cross sections substantially larger than the two photon fusion cross section. The magnitude of the observed ω signal supports these findings, since the acceptance is expected to be similar and the cross section for ω photoproduction due to Pomeron exchange is two to three orders of magnitude larger than the one for η mesons due to two photon fusion. In the case of the η' the small branching ratio of 2.12% further reduces the expected number of events by about one order of magnitude.

Figure 4 (b) shows the invariant mass spectra of η-π^0 pairs, where for both mesons a mass constrained fit has been applied. A signal of the $a_0(980)$ meson is observed. With tightened cuts, an indication of the $a_2(1320)$ is found. These mesons can also be used to search for Odderon induced processes at HERA.

4   Conclusions

In conclusion, a first search for contributions from Odderon induced production of $C = +1$ mesons at HERA has been performed. No signal for exclusive production of π^0, η and η' mesons has been obtained with the available statistics. The capability of the H1 detector to perform such a search and to study ω production at large W has been demonstrated, utilizing the new backward calorimeter which allows the detection of resonances decaying into multi-photon final states.

Acknowledgments

Helpful discussions with and the support by W. Kilian, O. Nachtmann and A. Schäfer are gratefully acknowledged. In addition, I want to thank F. Erné and the organizing committee for arranging an interesting and stimulating meeting in Egmond aan Zee.

This work is supported by the Bundesministerium für Bildung, Wissenschaft, Forschung und Technologie under contract number 6HD27I.

References

1. A. Schäfer, L. Mankiewicz, O. Nachtmann, *Diffractive η_c, η, η', J/ψ and ψ' Production in Electron-Proton Collisions at HERA Energies*, Proc. of the Workshop on Physics at HERA, Hamburg 1991, eds. W. Buchmüller and G. Ingelman, vol. 1, 243.
2. H1 SPACAL Group (R.D. Appuhn, et al.), *Nucl. Instrum. Methods* A **374**, 149 (1996).

STUDY OF THE GLUEBALL CANDIDATE $f_J(2220)$ AT CLEO

HANS P. PAAR[a]

Physics Department 0319
University of California San Diego
9500 Gilman Drive
La Jolla CA 92093-0319

The CLEO detector at the Cornell e^+e^- storage ring CESR was used to search for the two-photon production of the glueball candidate $f_J(2220)$ in its decay to $K_S K_S$. I present a restrictive upper limit on the product of the two-photon width and the $K_S K_S$ branching ratio $[\Gamma_{\gamma\gamma} B_{K_S K_S}]_{f_J(2220)} < 1.3\,\mathrm{eV}$, 95% CL. This limit is used to calculate a lower limit on the stickiness, a measure of the two-gluon coupling relative to the two-photon coupling, $S_{f_J(2220)} > 82$, 95% CL. This limit on the stickiness indicates that the $f_J(2220)$ is likely to have substantial glueball content.

1 Introduction

The unequivocal demonstration that glueballs exist would prove the existence of a new form of matter. In this report I describe an investigation[1,2] into the nature of the glueball candidate $f_J(2220)$.

The $f_J(2220)$ was discovered in radiative J/ψ decay[3] by the Mark III Collaboration at PEP in the early 80's. Although the $f_J(2220)$ has since been observed in hadronic collisions,[4,5,6,7] its production in radiative J/ψ decay has only recently been confirmed by the BES Collaboration who have observed[8] the $f_J(2220)$ in radiative J/ψ decay in four decay channels ($\pi^+\pi^-$, $p\bar{p}$, K^+K^-, and $K_S K_S$). The experiments favor a spin 2 assignment to the $f_J(2220)$ but this is not firmly established. The production in a glue-rich environment and the similar decay rates into final states that contain non-strange or strange particles[8] make the $f_J(2220)$ a promising candidate for a glueball. Because the $f_J(2220)$ is not near a $q\bar{q}$ meson and is narrow, it is not expected to mix with $q\bar{q}$ mesons and might therefore even be a candidate for a pure glueball (a hadron in which *all* valence partons are gluons). QCD predicts (using lattice calculations) that a glueball with spin 2 exists and that it should have a mass near $2.2\,\mathrm{GeV}$.[9]

A pure glueball will couple to photons only through its sea quarks. Therefore its two-photon coupling is expected to be weak. The absence of two-photon production of the $f_J(2220)$ would thus be a strong indicator of a glueball nature of the $f_J(2220)$. A search for the two-photon production of the $f_J(2220)$,

[a]e-mail: hpaar@ucsd.edu

decaying into $K_S K_S$ with each $K_S \to \pi^+ \pi^-$, was performed using the CLEO II detector at the Cornell $e^+ e^-$ storage ring CESR. Below I describe the analysis procedures in Sec. 2, the results in Sec. 3, and their interpretation in Sec. 4.

2 Detector, Event Selection, and Simulation

The CLEO II detector[10] is a general purpose detector that provides charged particle tracking, precision electromagnetic calorimetry, charged particle identification, and muon detection. Charged particle detection over 95% of the solid angle is provided by three concentric wire chambers in a magnetic field of 1.5 T giving a momentum resolution $\sigma_p/p = 0.5\%$ at $p = 1\,\text{GeV}$. The driftchambers are surrounded by a time of flight system and a CsI based electromagnetic calorimeter giving an energy resolution $\sigma_E/E = 4\%$ for 100 MeV electromagnetic showers. A superconducting coil and muon detectors surround the calorimeter. Several redundant triggers provided efficient registration of fourprong events. The CESR ring operated at a center-of-mass energy of approximately 10.6 GeV. The results in this paper are based upon $3.0\,\text{fb}^{-1}$ of data.

The event selection required events to have exactly four tracks whose sum of charges is zero, to have an event energy less than 6.0 GeV, to have the transverse component of the vector sum of the tracks to be less than 0.2 GeV, and to have $\pi^+ \pi^-$ pairs whose vertices have a separation in the plane perpendicular to the beam of at least 5 mm. The momenta of the four tracks at their respective vertices are used to calculate two pion-pair masses $(m_{\pi^+\pi^-})_1$ and $(m_{\pi^+\pi^-})_2$. A lego-plot of the pion-pair masses is shown in Fig. 1. There are two entries per event corresponding to the exchange of labels 1 and 2. There is a strong enhancement near the (m_{K_S}, m_{K_S}) point. The $m_{\pi^+\pi^-}$ mass resolution near the K_S mass is 3.3 MeV. $K_S K_S$ events are selected by requiring both pion-pair masses to be within a circle of radius 10 MeV from the (m_{K_S}, m_{K_S}) point.

The event simulation made use of the BGMS[11] formalism for the event generation and GEANT for the detector simulation. Mass and width of the $f_J(2220)$ were obtained by averaging MarkIII[3] and BES[8] results: $m_{f_J(2220)} = 2234 \pm 6$ MeV and $\Gamma_{f_J(2220)} = 19 \pm 11$ MeV. A Breit-Wigner lineshape was used. The detector simulation generates raw data that is processed through the same event reconstruction and analysis procedures as the real data. The trigger simulation used the raw data to determine which triggers, if any, fired for a given event. The efficiency is found to be 7.0% for spin 2, helicity 0 and 15% for spin 2, helicity 2.

228

3 Results

The $K_S K_S$ pair mass is formed for the events that pass the cuts listed in Sec. 2. Fig. 2 shows the the $K_S K_S$ pair mass distribution. It has a significant $f_2'(1525)$ signal but no visible $f_J(2220)$ signal.

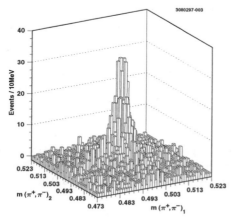

Figure 1: $(m_\pi^+ \pi^-)_1$ versus $(m\pi^+\pi^-)_2$. Each data event has two entries corresponding to exchange of the labels 1 and 2.

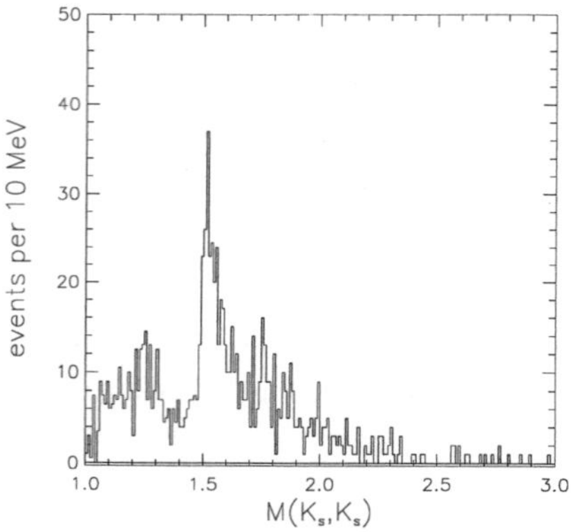

Figure 2: $K_S K_S$ pair mass distribution.

The mass region near the $f_J(2220)$ is shown in detail in Fig. 3. In the absence of a signal, an upper limit is set as follows. The background is fitted with a linear function from 2.05 to 2.35 GeV, excluding a safely large ± 40 MeV region centered on 2234 MeV. This gives an average background of 1.8 ± 0.3 events per 10 MeV. The signal region is determined by maximizing the ratio ϵ^2/B where ϵ is the fraction of the signal and B the expected number of background events within that region. This leads to a signal region of ± 18 MeV (centered on 2234 MeV) with $\epsilon = 70\%$.

There are four events within the signal region while the background is estimated to be 6.5 events. The standard PDG technique[12] for extracting an upper limit gives 4.9 events, 95% CL. The curve in Fig. 3 is the sum of the background and a signal of 4.9 events. With the assumption that the ratio $\Gamma_{\gamma\gamma}^{2,2} : \Gamma_{\gamma\gamma}^{2,0} = 6 : 1$[13] we obtain

$$[\Gamma_{\gamma\gamma} B_{K_S K_S}]_{f_J(2220)} < 1.3 \text{ eV}, \, 95\% \text{ CL} \tag{1}$$

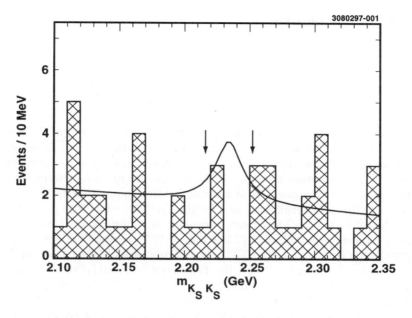

Figure 3: $K_S K_S$ pair mass distribution near the mass of the $f_J(2220)$. The arrows indicate the signal region. The solid line is the sum of a fit to the background and a signal that corresponds to the 95% CL upperlimit of 4.9 events.

When the mass and width of the $f_J(2220)$ are varied by 6 and 11 MeV respectively (one standard deviation), the upper limit ranges from 1.2 to 1.8 eV. The upper limits include the effects of systematic uncertainties in the trigger (8%), the tracking (7%), the event selection (7%), and the background subtraction (16%). Other sources of systematic error, such as the photon formfactor used in the simulation, are negligible. Because of its similarity to the $f_J(2220)$, the $f_2'(1525)$ decaying into $K_S K_S$ was analyzed using the same analysis procedures. A value for $\Gamma_{\gamma\gamma} B_{K_S K_S}$ was measured that is within one standard deviation of the PDG[12] value of 22 eV.

4   Interpretation

The upper limit $[\Gamma_{\gamma\gamma} B_{K_S K_S}]_{f_J(2220)} < 1.3$ eV, 95% CL indicates that the $f_J(2220)$ is likely to have a significant glueball content. To make this statement more quantitative, we make use of the stickiness S, introduced by Chanowitz.[14] Stickiness is a measure of the ratio of the two-gluon and the two-photon coupling of a particle. It is defined as

$$S_X = \frac{|\langle X|gg\rangle|^2}{|\langle X|\gamma\gamma\rangle|^2} \tag{2}$$

$$= N_\ell \left(\frac{m_X}{k_{J/\psi \to \gamma X}}\right)^{2\ell+1} \frac{\Gamma(J/\psi \to \gamma X)}{\Gamma(X \to \gamma\gamma)} \tag{3}$$

The parameter $k_{J/\psi \to \gamma X}$ is the energy (in the J/ψ rest frame) of the photon produced in the radiative J/ψ decay. The factor with the $2l+1$ in the exponent is a phase space factor that removes trivial dependence upon the mass of the particle X. The quantum number ℓ is the relative angular momentum between the two gluons or photons. N_ℓ is a normalization factor that is chosen such that the stickiness is normalized to 1 for the $f_2(1270)$ which has $\ell = 0$ and for the η which has $\ell = 1$. Thus glueball content of a particle is defined relative to these particles. A value of $(2.2 \pm 0.6) \times 10^{-5}$ is obtained for $\Gamma[J/\psi \to \gamma f_J(2220)] B[f_J(2220) \to K_S K_S]$ by combining results from Mark III[3] and BES.[8] Using our upper limit (1), the branching ratio $B[f_J(2220) \to K_S K_S]$ cancels, and we find a lower limit $S_{f_J(2220)} > 82, 95\%\,\mathrm{CL}$. Statistical and systematic errors are incorporated into this result.

Other particles with large stickiness are (from largest to smallest) the $f_J(1710)$ ($S > 25$, 95% CL), the $f_2'(1525)$ ($S = 14.5 \pm 3.7$), and the η' ($S = 2.9 \pm 0.3$). The $f_J(1710)$ is generally considered a glueball candidate. Without glueball content, the largest value of stickiness is obtained by assuming that a particle consists of down and strange valence quarks and antiquarks because the two-photon width depends upon the fourth power of the quark charges. This gives a stickiness of about 10-15. Only the stickiness of the $f_J(2220)$ is comfortably above that value.

In general, particles with a small two-photon width have also small radiative J/ψ branching ratios. Examples include radial and angular excitations. The $f_J(2220)$ can not have spin 1 because its production in radiative J/ψ decay shows that it has $C = +1$ while $\pi^+\pi^-$ in an $L = 1$ state have $C = -1$. It is possible to construct a particle consisting of a superposition of $u\bar{u}$, $d\bar{d}$, and $s\bar{s}$ quarks and antiquarks with coefficients such that its two-photon coupling is arbitrarily small. I consider such a fortuitous cancellation 'unlikely'.

5   Conclusion

I present in this report evidence for the likely glueball nature of the $f_J(2220)$. The arguments rest upon the restrictive upper limit of the product of the two-photon width and the $K_S K_S$ branching ratio $[\Gamma_{\gamma\gamma} B_{K_S K_S}]_{f_J(2220)} < 1.3\,\mathrm{eV}$,

95% CL. Using its production rate in glue-rich radiative J/ψ decay this upper limit leads to a large lower limit on its stickiness $S_{f_J(2220)} > 82$, 95% CL. This large value is difficult to understand if the valence partons of the $f_J(2220)$ are only quarks and antiquarks. Therefore, the $f_J(2220)$ is likely to have a substantial glueball content.

Additional supporting evidence comes from the fact the the $f_J(2220)$ has similar decay rates into final states that contain non-strange or strange particles and from the fact that lattice QCD calculations give a value for the mass of a spin 2 glueball near 2.2 GeV.

Acknowledgments

I gratefully acknowledge the effort of the CESR staff in providing the luminosity and running conditions necessary to make this measurement possible and my CLEO colleagues upon whose effort this work is based. This work was supported by the Department of Energy, the National Science Foundation, and others. Finally, I would like to thank the organizers of Photon 97 for a well-organized and fruitful conference held in a beautifull environment.

References

1. R. Godang *et al* (CLEO Collaboration), CLEO preprint 93-3 (1997).
2. D.W. Bliss, PhD thesis (1997), UC San Diego, La Jolla CA, unpublished.
3. R. Baltrusaitis *et al* (Mark III Collaboration), *Phys. Rev. Lett.* **56**, 107 (1986).
4. Alde *et al* (GAMS Collaboration), *Phys. Lett.* B **177**, 120 (1986).
5. D. Aston *et al* (LASS Collaboration), *Phys. Lett.* B **215**, 199 (1988).
6. B.V. Bolonkin *et al* (MSS Collaboration), *Nucl. Phys.* B **309**, 426 (1988).
7. J.E. Augustin *et al* (DM2 Collaboration), *Phys. Rev. Lett.* **60**, 2238 (1988).
8. J.Z. Bai *et al* (BES Collaboration), *Phys. Rev. Lett.* **76**, 3502 (1996).
9. C. Michael, hep-lat/9605243 (1966) and references therein; C. Morningstar, M. Peardon, hep-lat/9704011 (1997) and references therein.
10. Y. Kubota *et al* (CLEO Collaboration), *Nucl. Instr. Meth.* A **320**, 66 (1992).
11. V.M. Budnev *et al* (BGMS), *Phys. Rep.* **15C**, 181 (1975).
12. R.M. Barnett *et al* (Particle Data Group), *Phys. Rev.* D **54**, (1996).
13. M. Poppe, *Int. Jour. Mod. Phys.* **A1**, 545 (1986).
14. M.Chanowitz in *VIth International Workshop on Photon-Photon Collisions*, ed. R. Lander (World Scientific, Singapore, 1984).

RESONANCE FORMATION IN TWO-PHOTON COLLISIONS WITH THE L3 DETECTOR AT LEP

S. BRACCINI

University of Geneva,
24, Quai Ernest Ansermet,
CH-1211 Genève 4, Switzerland

e-mail: Saverio.Braccini@cern.ch

representing the

L3 Collaboration

We report on the study of the formation of several resonances with the L3 detector at LEP. The $\eta'(958)$ and its form factor are studied in the $\pi^+\pi^-\gamma$ final state. The $\pi^+\pi^-\pi^0$ final state shows evidence for the formation of the $a_2(1320)$ and its radial recurrence around 1750 MeV. The spectrum is dominated by a $J^{PC}=2^{++}$ wave. We observe the $f_2(1270)$ in $\gamma\gamma \to \pi^+\pi^-$ and the f_2-a_2 interference in $\gamma\gamma \to K\bar{K}$. The formation of the $f_2'(1525)$ is studied in the $K_s^0 K_s^0$ final state where there is evidence for a possible radially excited state around 1750 MeV.

1 Introduction

The LEP e^+e^- collider is a good laboratory to investigate the formation of resonances in two-photon collisions. The high beam energy permits to separate easily the background from annihilation process with a visible energy cut and gives access to higher masses and cross sections. The centre-of-mass energy of the LEP machine was increased in 1996 from the Z mass up to 172 GeV. The L3 experiment is described in detail elsewhere [1].

2 The η' and its Form Factor

We search [2] for $\gamma\gamma \to \eta' \to \pi^+\pi^-\gamma$ selecting events with two opposite charged tracks and an isolated electromagnetic cluster with energy larger than 140 MeV. We require $|\vec{p_T}(\pi^+\pi^-\gamma)|^2 < 0.01$ GeV^2 to select exclusive events and $|\vec{p_T}(\pi^+\pi^-)|^2 > 0.001$ GeV^2 to reduce the background from $\gamma\gamma \to l^+l^-$. Since $\eta' \to \rho\gamma$ decay mode largely dominates, non resonant background is reduced by requiring $|\cos\theta_\pi^*| < 0.94$ in the ρ rest frame. The $\pi^+\pi^-\gamma$ mass spectrum is shown in fig. 1(a) where the enhancement around 1250 MeV is due to $a_2(1320) \to \pi^+\pi^-\pi^0$ when one photon goes undetected. This contamination is subtracted by a Monte Carlo simulation using PDG values for the η' mass and width. The $\Gamma_{\gamma\gamma}(\eta')$ is determined by fitting the mass spectrum with the Monte

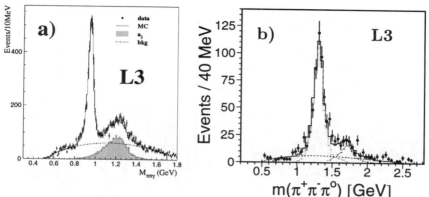

Figure 1: a) The $\pi^+\pi^-\gamma$ mass spectrum. b) The $\pi^+\pi^-\pi^0$ mass spectrum.

Carlo expected shape for the η', the background for the a_2 and a third order polynomial. We measure $\Gamma_{\gamma\gamma}(\eta') = 4.17\pm0.10\pm0.21$ keV. The electromagnetic η' form factor is studied using tagged and untagged events. For the untagged mode the Monte Carlo simulation demonstrates that $Q^2 = |\vec{p_T}(\pi^+\pi^-\gamma)|^2$ within the experimental resolution. The cross section is measured as a function of Q^2. We observe its characteristic decrease due to the luminosity function and η' form factor. The form factor can be parametrised as $F(Q^2) \sim (\frac{1}{1+Q^2/\Lambda^2})^2$ with $\Lambda = 0.903 \pm 0.046 \pm 0.034$ GeV.

3 The $\pi^+\pi^-\pi^0$ Final State

We search for $\gamma\gamma \to \pi^+\pi^-\pi^0$ selecting events[3] with two opposite charged tracks and two isolated electromagnetic clusters with energy larger than 80 MeV and $m_{\gamma\gamma}$ between 105 and 165 MeV. We require $|\vec{p_T}(\pi^+\pi^-\pi^0)|^2 < 0.0015$ GeV^2. The $\pi^+\pi^-\pi^0$ mass spectrum (fig. 1(b)) is dominated by the formation of the $a_2(1320)$ tensor meson. A clear enhancement is visible around 1750 MeV where the study of the total transverse momentum shows evidence for an exclusive process. We therefore divide the data sample into two mass ranges: form 1 up to 1.55 GeV, in order to study the a_2, and from 1.55 up to 2.1 GeV. The study of the angular distributions shows the a_2 formation is dominated by a $J^{PC}=2^{++}$ helicity 2 wave. The helicity 2 fraction is measured to be $0.92\pm0.05\pm0.05$. For the radiative width we measure $\Gamma_{\gamma\gamma}(a_2) = 0.98 \pm 0.05 \pm 0.09$ keV. We perform a spin-parity analysis in the high mass region for the $\rho\pi$ and the $f_2\pi$ decay

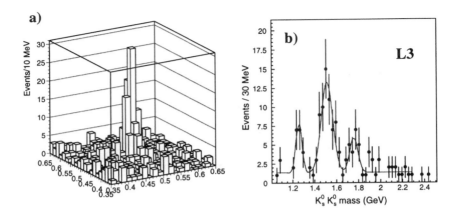

Figure 2: a) $m(\pi^+\pi^-)$ at one secondary vertex versus $m(\pi^+\pi^-)$ at the other secondary vertex. b) The $K_s^0 K_s^0$ mass spectrum.

modes. Also this region is found to be dominated by a $J^P=2^+$ helicity 2 wave. This can be interpreted as the formation of a radial recurrence of the a_2 for which we measure $\Gamma_{\gamma\gamma}(a_2') \times BR(\pi^+\pi^-\pi^0) = 0.29\pm0.04\pm0.02$ keV in agreement with the most recent theoretical predictions[4]. The $J^P(\lambda)=2^-(0)$ wave is found to be compatible with zero and we derive $\Gamma_{\gamma\gamma}(\pi_2) \times BR(\pi^+\pi^-\pi^0) < 0.072$ keV at 90% confidence level.

4 The $K_s^0 K_s^0$ Final State

In order to study $\gamma\gamma \rightarrow K_s^0 K_s^0 \rightarrow \pi^+\pi^-\pi^+\pi^-$, we select[5] events with four charged tracks, charge balance and no photons. Exclusive events are selected by requiring $|\vec{p_T}(\pi^+\pi^-\pi^+\pi^-)|^2 < 0.1$ GeV^2. There must be two $\pi^+\pi^-$ pairs forming two secondary vertices[6] at a distance larger than 3 mm from the beam axis and with the angle between the flight direction of each K_s^0 candidate and the total transverse momentum vector of the two outgoing tracks smaller than 0.3 rad. Fig. 2(a) shows the mass of one pair versus the mass of the other pair: a clear clustering is found corresponding to exclusive $K_s^0 K_s^0$ production. The $K_s^0 K_s^0$ mass spectrum (fig. 2(b)) shows clear evidence for the formation of the $f_2'(1525)$ tensor meson. f_2-a_2 destructive interference[7] around 1300 MeV is observed. The enhancement of 3 standard deviations around 1750 MeV is probably due to the formation of a radially excited state of the f_2', according to theoretical predictions[4]. For the $f_2'(1525)$ the detection

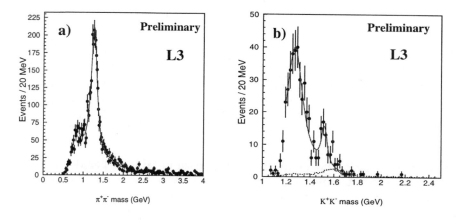

Figure 3: a) The $\pi^+\pi^-$ mass spectrum. b) The K^+K^- mass spectrum.

and trigger efficiencies are evaluated by Monte Carlo simulation. We measure $\Gamma_{\gamma\gamma}(f_2') \times Br(f_2' \to K\bar{K})$=0.093± 0.018± 0.022 keV under the hypothesis of a pure helicity-2 and $\Gamma_{\gamma\gamma}(f_2') \times Br(f_2' \to K\bar{K})$=0.198± 0.040± 0.050 keV for a pure helicity-0 state. The study of the angular distribution in the two-photon centre-of-mass system favours helicity-2 formation over helicity-0, according to theoretical predictions [8].

5 The $\pi^+\pi^-$ and the K^+K^- Final States

Exclusive two charged track events are dominated by $\gamma\gamma \to e^+e^-$ and $\gamma\gamma \to \mu^+\mu^-$. In order to identify different charged particles an artificial neural network technique has been developed using track momentum, ionization loss (dE/dx), electromagnetic and hadron calorimeter information. Exclusive events are selected by requiring $|\vec{p_T}(t^+t^-)|^2 < 0.06$ GeV^2. In fig. 3 mass spectra are shown for identified $\pi^+\pi^-$ and K^+K^- pairs. The $\pi^+\pi^-$ spectrum is dominated by the formation of the $f_2(1270)$ tensor meson. The K^+K^- spectrum shows f_2-a_2 constructive interference [7] around 1300 MeV and the formation of the $f_2'(1525)$ tensor meson.

6 Conclusions

The study of the formation of several resonances is performed with the

Table 1: Summary of the results.

Resonance	Decay	$\mathcal{L}$ (pb^{-1})	Mass (MeV)	$\Gamma_{\gamma\gamma}$(keV)
$\eta'(958)$	$\pi^+\pi^-\gamma$	129	952±1	4.17±0.10±0.21
$a_2(1320)$	$\pi^+\pi^-\pi^0$	140	1323±4	0.98±0.05±0.09
$f_2'(1525)$	$K\bar{K}$	140	1515±10	(0.093±0.018±0.022)/BR
$a_2'(1750)$	$\pi^+\pi^-\pi^0$	140	1752±21	(0.029±0.04±0.02)/BR

L3 detector at LEP. Our results are summarised in table 1. For the η' a form factor parameter $\Lambda = 0.903 \pm 0.046 \pm 0.034$ GeV is measured. The $\pi^+\pi^-\pi^0$ final state is dominated by a $J^{PC}=2^{++}$ wave while there is no evidence for a $J^P=2^-$ state. The enhancement around 1750 MeV can be interpreted as the formation of the $a_2'(1750)$, radial recurrence of the $a_2(1320)$. We observe the f_2-a_2 interference in the $K\bar{K}$ final state. The $K_s^0 K_s^0$ final state shows a possible signal from a radially excited state of the f_2' around 1750 MeV.

Acknowledgments

I would like to express my gratitude to the two-photon physics group of the L3 collaboration in particular to M.N. Focacci-Kienzle, J.H. Field, B. Monteleoni, S.R. Hou, C.H. Lin, P. Ladron de Guevara and R. Rizzo.

References

1. L3 Collab., B. Adeva et al., *Nucl. Instrum. Methods* A **289**, 35 (1990); L3 Collab., O. Adriani et al., *Phys. Rep.* **236**, 1 (1993).
2. To be published in *Phys. Lett.* B.
3. S. R. Hou, *L3 Note 1854*. To be published in *Phys. Lett.* B.
4. C. R. Münz, *Nucl. Phys.* A **609**, 364 (1996).
5. S. Braccini, *"Studio delle interazioni fotone-fotone con il rivelatore L3 al LEP"*, Tesi di Laurea, University of Florence, Italy (1995); L3 Collab., M. Acciarri et al., *Phys. Lett.* B **363**, 118 (1995).
6. F. Becattini, Ph. D. Thesis, University of Florence, Italy (1996).
7. H. J. Lipkin, *Nucl. Phys.* B **7**, 321 (1968).
8. B. Schrempp-Otto et al., *Phys. Lett.* B **36**, 463 (1971); G. Köpp et al., *Nucl. Phys.* B **70**, 461 (1974); P. Grassberger and R. Kögerler, *Nucl. Phys.* B **106**, 451 (1976).

TWO-PHOTON PHYSICS AT THE ARGUS

G. MEDIN

Institute Jozef Stefan
Jamova 39, 1111 Ljubljana, Slovenia

On behalf of the ARGUS Collaboration

Two photon production of $K^+\pi^-K^-\pi^+$, $K_s^0\pi^0K^\pm\pi^\mp$ and $K_s^0K_s^0\pi^+\pi^-$ was studied using the ARGUS detector at the e^+e^- storage ring DORIS II at DESY. The data were analysed using the maximum likelihood method. In particular, two-photon production of $K^{*0}\bar{K}^{*0}$ was extracted from the final states $K^+\pi^-K^-\pi^+$ and $K_s^0\pi^0K^\pm\pi^\mp$, and the production of $K^{*+}K^{*-}$ from $K_s^0K^\pm\pi^\mp\pi^0$ and $K_s^0K_s^0\pi^+\pi^-$. A partial wave analysis was performed on the $K^+\pi^-K^-\pi^+$ state. It was found that the reaction $\gamma\gamma \to K^{*0}\bar{K}^{*0}$ is dominated by the partial wave with spin, parity and helicity $(J^P, J_z) = (2^+, 2)$.

1 Introduction

Measurement of two-photon production of pairs of vector mesons is a direct test of vector dominance models. On the other hand, it is a unique way to study possible $qq\bar{q}\bar{q}$ states. It has been suggested[1,2] that the large ratio between measured cross sections for the reactions $\gamma\gamma \to \rho^0\rho^0$ and $\gamma\gamma \to \rho^+\rho^-$ indicate a possible interference between isospin 0 and isospin 2 states, both positioned close to the reaction threshold. It would, therefore, be interesting to see how large is the ratio between cross sections for the reactions $\gamma\gamma \to K^{*0}\bar{K}^{*0}$ and $K^{*+}K^{*-}$ where isospin 0 and 1 intermediate states are possible.

Two photon production of $K^{*0}\bar{K}^{*0}$ and $K^{*+}K^{*-}$ was already measured by the ARGUS collaboration[3,4]. The analyses were performed on a data sample corresponding to the integrated luminosity of 243 pb^{-1}. The low statistics did not allow a partial wave analysis of $K^*\bar{K}^*$ pair. The present analyses are based on a larger data sample and use a maximum likelihood method.

2 Data Selection

The studies of two-photon reactions $\gamma\gamma \to K^+\pi^-K^-\pi^+$, $K_s^0\pi^0K^\pm\pi^\mp$ and $\gamma\gamma \to K_s^0K_s^0\pi^+\pi^-$ presented in this paper were carried out using the ARGUS detector at the e^+e^- storage ring DORIS II at DESY. The data correspond to an integrated luminosity of 456 pb^{-1} collected at beam energies between 4.7 GeV and 5.3 GeV. The ARGUS detector, its trigger and its particle identification system are described elsewhere[5].In what follows, only main features of the analyses are presented, while details can be found in Ref. [6].

Candidate events for the forementioned reactions had to satisfy the following conditions. Pions and kaons had to be consistent with the corresponding mass hypothesis, by requiring the combined likelihood ratio from specific ionisation and time-of-flight measurements to exceed 1%. Photons were identified by clusters in the calorimeter not associated with the charge tracks. A neutral pion was identified by a photon pair with the invariant mass close to the nominal π^0 mass. The allowed mass difference was 70 MeV. K_s^0 mesons were reconstructed from $\pi^+\pi^-$ pairs. In order to increase the efficiency, separate secondary vertices for K_s^0 were not required. The maximum allowed mass difference $|m_{\pi^+\pi^-} - m_{K_s^0}|$ was 12 MeV for accepted K_s^0 candidates. A cut on the total transverse momentum, $|\sum_i \vec{P}_{T,i}| < 100$ MeV/c, was applied to suppress the background.

3   Results of Analyses and Discussion

$\gamma\gamma \to K^+\pi^- K^-\pi^+$

After imposing the selection criteria, 1112 $K^+\pi^- K^-\pi^+$ events remained in $W_{\gamma\gamma}$ between 1.5 and 3.0 GeV of which 37% represent background contributions as found by simulation. About 84 % of the total background events came from the reactions with $\pi^+\pi^-\pi^+\pi^-$ in the final state.

The $K^+\pi^- K^-\pi^+$ data was analysed in the three steps. First we performed a mass likelihood fit in 6 bins covering mass region between 1.5 and 3.0 GeV. The mass likelihood fit included uniformly phase space distributed $K^{*0}\bar{K}^{*0}$, $K^{*0}K^-\pi^+$ + cc and $K^+\pi^- K^-\pi^+$ channels. The decay matrix element for the mentioned uniformly space distributed states does not include angular dependence. It contains the Breit-Wigner amplitude to account for the $K^{*0}(\bar{K}^{*0})$ mass correlations. In order to determine the distribution of background events into various cross sections, the background events were subject to the same fit as the measured data. It was found that 84 % of background events migrated to $\gamma\gamma \to K^+\pi^- K^-\pi^+$ and only 5 % to $\gamma\gamma \to K^{*0}\bar{K}^{*0}$. This procedure for the determination of background contribution was used in all presented analyses. The analysis of $\gamma\gamma \to K^+\pi^- K^-\pi^+$ shows that about 15% of the total cross section is due to the reaction $\gamma\gamma \to K^{*0}\bar{K}^{*0} \to K^+\pi^- K^-\pi^+$.

In the second step of the $K^+\pi^- K^-\pi^+$ analysis the spin-parity structure of $K^{*0}\bar{K}^{*0}$ was determined. A *partial wave analysis* included five $K^{*0}\bar{K}^{*0}$ waves with different spin-parities $(J^P, J_z) = (0^+, 0)$, $(0^-, 0)$, $(2^+, 0)$, $(2^+, 2)$, $(2^-, 0, S = 1)$, and two phase space distributed $K^{*0}K^-\pi^+$ + cc and $K^+\pi^- K^-\pi^+$. This 7 parameter fit was performed in one single $W_{\gamma\gamma}$ bin between 1.75 and

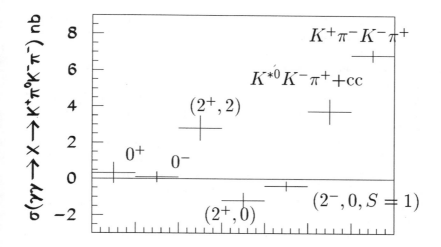

Figure 1: Cross sections for the reactions that contribute to the $K^+\pi^-K^-\pi^+$ production: $\gamma\gamma \to K^{*0}\bar{K}^{*0}(J^P) \to K^+\pi^-K^-\pi^+$ and isotropic $\gamma\gamma \to K^{*0}K^-\pi^+ + cc \to K^+\pi^-K^-\pi^+$, $\gamma\gamma \to K^+\pi^-K^-\pi^+$. Only statistic errors are shown.

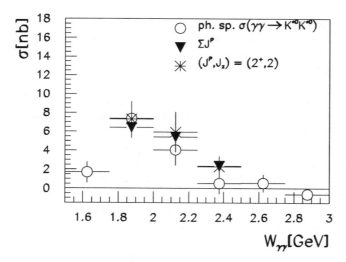

Figure 2: Cross section for the sum of the $(J^P, J_z) = (0^+, 0), (0^-, 0), (2^+, 2)$ partial waves of the reaction $\gamma\gamma \to K^{*0}\bar{K}^{*0}$ (full triangles), cross section for the $(2^+, 2)$ partial wave of $\gamma\gamma \to K^{*0}\bar{K}^{*0}$ (stars) and cross section assuming phase space distribution of $K^{*0}\bar{K}^{*0}$ waves (open cicles).

2.25 GeV. Fig. 1 shows the cross sections obtained from the fit. The cross section for the $J^P = 2^+$, with helicity 2 wave is dominant. The contributions from negative parities 0^- and 2^- are small. The helicity 0 component of 2^+ is suppressed over helicity 2, which is known to be the case for tensor meson production in $\gamma\gamma$ reactions.

In the third step, we excluded from the fit partial waves $(2^+, 0)$ and $(2^-, 0, S = 1)$ that were consistent with zero in the previous analysis. This five parameter fit was performed in three $W_{\gamma\gamma}$ bins covering two-photon invariant mass between 1.75 GeV and 2.5 GeV. Fig. 2 shows the total cross section for the reaction $\gamma\gamma \to K^{*0}\bar{K}^{*0}$ that was obtained by adding $(0^+, 0)$, $(0^-, 0)$, $(2^+, 2)$ partial waves. The cross section for the partial wave $(2^+, 2)$ that dominates the $K^{*0}\bar{K}^{*0}$ production is also shown in Fig. 2. For comparison, the cross section for $K^{*0}\bar{K}^{*0}$ obtained in the first step of analysis is presented in Fig. 2, too.

It is interesting to note that the cross section for the reaction $\gamma\gamma \to K^{*0}\bar{K}^{*0}$ has its maximum close to the interaction threshold, an efect that was previously observed in the reaction $\gamma\gamma \to \rho^0\rho^0$.

$\gamma\gamma \to K_s^0\pi^0 K^{\pm}\pi^{\mp}$ and $\gamma\gamma \to K_s^0 K_s^0 \pi^+\pi^-$

The two-photon production of $K^{*+}K^{*-}$ pair was measured by analysing the final states $K_s^0\pi^0 K^{\pm}\pi^{\mp}$ and $K_s^0 K_s^0 \pi^+\pi^-$. In both analyses a mass likelihood fit was performed.

For $W_{\gamma\gamma}$ between 1.75 and 2.75 GeV the total number of selected $K_s^0\pi^0 K^{\pm}\pi^{\mp}$ and $K_s^0 K_s^0 \pi^+\pi^-$ events were 240 and 84, respectively. It was found that background events contributed 21% in the $K_s^0\pi^0 K^{\pm}\pi^{\mp}$ sample. No background events were found to contribute to the $K_s^0 K_s^0 \pi^+\pi^-$ data.

A five parameter fit was performed on the $K_s^0\pi^0 K^{\pm}\pi^{\mp}$ data in four $W_{\gamma\gamma}$ bins between 1.75 and 2.75 GeV. The fit included uniformly phase space distributed $K^{*0}\bar{K}^{*0}$, $K^{*+}K^{*-}$, $K^{*\pm}K_s^0\pi^{\mp}$, $K^{\pm}\pi^0 K^{*\mp}$ and $K_s^0\pi^0 K^{\pm}\pi^{\mp}$ channels. It was found that about 26% of the total integrated $\gamma\gamma \to K_s^0\pi^0 K^{\pm}\pi^{\mp}$ cross section in the mass region between 1.75 and 2.25 GeV is due to the production of charge $K^{*+}K^{*-}$ pair and only 4% due to production of neutral $K^{*0}\bar{K}^{*0}$.

The 3 parameter fit on $K_s^0 K_s^0 \pi^+\pi^-$ was performed in 3 bins covering the mass region between 1.75 and 2.5 GeV. About 60 % of the total integrated $\gamma\gamma \to K_s^0 K_s^0 \pi^+\pi^-$ cross section in this mass region is due to the production of $K^{*+}K^{*-}$.

The cross sections for $\gamma\gamma \to K^{*+}K^{*-}$ obtained from $K_s^0\pi^0 K^{\pm}\pi^{\mp}$ and $K_s^0 K_s^0 \pi^+\pi^-$ analyses are shown in Fig. 3. We see good agreement between them. An enhancement above the threshold was found in both analyses. The ratio between integrated $K^{*+}K^{*-}$ (derived by combining $K_s^0\pi^0 K^{\pm}\pi^{\mp}$ and

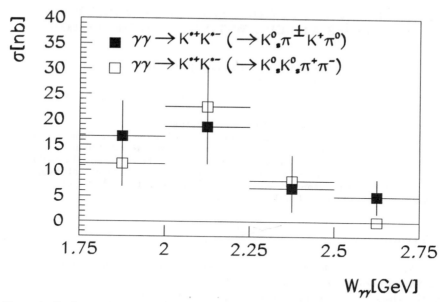

Figure 3: Background subtracted cross sections for the reaction $\gamma\gamma \to K^{*+}K^{*-}$ that was obtained analysing $K_s^0\pi^0 K^\pm\pi^\mp$ data (full squares) and $K_s^0 K_s^0\pi^+\pi^-$ data (open squares).

$K_s^0 K_s^0\pi^+\pi^-$ analyses) and $K^{*0}\bar{K}^{*0}$ (derived by combining $K^+\pi^- K^-\pi^+$ and $K_s^0\pi^0 K^\pm\pi^\mp$ analyses) cross sections was 4.50 ± 1.65. The measured ratio substantially depends on $W_{\gamma\gamma}$. In the mass region between 1.75 and 2.0 GeV ratio is 1.9 ± 0.9, while in the region between 2.0 and 2.25 GeV it is 7.9 ± 4.2.

References

1. H. Albrecht et al. (ARGUS), *Z. Phys.* **C50** (1991) 1
2. T. Zivko, *Measurement of Production of $\rho^0\rho^0$, $\rho^+\rho^-$ and $\omega\omega$ in Two-photon Interactions at the ARGUS Spectrometer*, Doctor thesis, University of Ljubljana, Slovenia (1994)
3. H. Albrecht et al., (ARGUS), *Phys. Lett.* **B198** (1987) 255
4. H. Albrecht et al., (ARGUS), *Phys. Lett.* **B212** (1988) 528
5. H. Albrecht et al., (ARGUS), *Nucl. Instr. Meth.* **A275** (1989) 1.
6. G. Medin, *Measurement of Production of $K^{*0}\overline{K}^{*0}$ and $K^{*+}K^{*-}$ in Two-Photon Interactions at the ARGUS Spectrometer*, Doctor thesis, University of Ljubljana, Slovenia (1997)

INCLUSIVE K_S^0 PRODUCTION IN TWO-PHOTON PROCESSES AT LEP 1 WITH DELPHI DETECTOR

W. DA SILVA, J. FAYOT, F. KAPUSTA

LPNHE, IN2P3 - CNRS Universites Paris VI et VII,
4 Place Jussieu, Tour 33, Rdc, 75252 PARIS Cedex 05, FRANCE

DELPHI Collaboration

The inclusive K_S^0 production was measured in two-photon interactions at LEP 1 with DELPHI detector. The data correspond to an integrated luminosity of 140 pb^{-1} at an average center of mass energy around the Z^0 mass. The visible K_S^0 transverse momentum differential cross section was studied with anti-tagged events. A resolved photon type enriched sub-sample was also studied. In the two cases, data were compared to theoretical predictions.

1 Introduction

The K_S^0 production in two photon physics has already been studied by the TOPAZ collaboration at TRISTAN [1]. One motivation of this study is to confirm the theoretical predictions and experimental results [2], concerning charm pair production in two-photon processes. At low P_T we are sensitive to nonperturbative QCD, whereas in the high P_T region, K_S^0 come mainly from $c\bar{c}$ and $s\bar{s}$ production (i.e. perturbative QCD).

Data were compared to two different Monte-Carlo : TWOGAM [3] and PHOJET [4]. The cross-section of two-photon events in TWOGAM is given by the sum of three components : direct (QPM), resolved photon contributions (QCD) and soft hadronic interactions (VDM). For resolved photon, GS2 with $PT_{min} = 1.85 \ GeV/c$, was used as parton density function. PHOJET is based on the Dual Parton Model combined with perturbative QCD to describe photon-photon interactions at high energies. The parton density function used for this generator is GRV-G-LO with $Q_0^2 = 0.25 \ (GeV/c^2)^2$. Both Monte-Carlo were interfaced with the DELPHI detector simulation program.

2 Event selection

Data used in this analysis were collected with the DELPHI detector at LEP 1 e^+e^- collider during the 1991-1995 year runs. The center of mass energies are between 88.6 and 94.6 GeV. The corresponding luminosity is about 140 pb^{-1}. DELPHI detector and its performances have been described in ref[5]. Selection of two-photon events was performed using the following criteria : number of charged tracks, with momentum greater than 0.4 GeV/c, greater than or

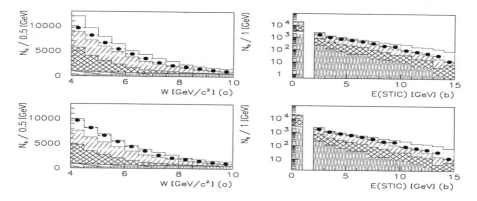

Figure 1: Comparison between data and Monte-Carlo predictions for the anti-tag selection without(upper) and with (lower) trigger efficiency. a) Invariant mass. b) Energies at low angle (STIC 1994-1995). Points are data and lines or hatched areas show the Monte-Carlo predictions - hatched areas are in the following order : Z^0 background + QPM + VDM + QCD - dotted line : Z^0 background + PHOJET.

equal to 4; total energy of charged tracks less than 12. GeV; total energy of charged tracks and neutrals below 20. GeV; invariant mass, computed with the charged and neutral tracks satisfaying the tracks selection criteria, between 4. GeV/c^2 and 10. GeV/c^2; total transverse momentum of charged and neutral tracks with respect to the beam direction less than 2.5 GeV/c; momentum of the most energetic charged track greater than or equal to 1 GeV/c (trigger condition); no neutral with energy greater than 20 GeV (anti-tag contition). A total of 48550 events satisfied these cuts. The main contamination comes from Z^0 hadronic events, which is estimated to 10.6 ± 1.7%. The visible $\gamma\gamma$ cross section is 309 ± 2 pb. For simulated events, trigger efficiency was taken into account. Its mean value is estimated to 93 ± 5%. Figure 1 shows the comparison between data and Monte-Carlo after selection cuts and illustrates the importance of trigger efficiency knowledge in DELPHI two-photon events. We also want to study a resolved photon type sub-sample. To tag these events, we used their specific topology : we required at least a 2 GeV energy deposition at low angle ($53 \leq \theta \leq 135\ mrad$) in the forward calorimeter (figure 1). These events are called remnant jet tagged events. The visible $\gamma\gamma$ cross section for remnant jet tagged events is 61.7 ± 0.7 pb. The fraction of resolved photon process increases from 45.7 ± 0.3% before the energy cut to 60.7 ± 0.7%.

3 K_s^0 production

Strangeness can be produced via direct or resolved processes. However, the direct term is supressed due to the strange quark charge, and the majority of the strangeness production arises from fragmentation processes. Strangeness can also come from the decay of c quark. Therefore, many sources contribute to the production of K_s^0 in two-photon events, and here is indicated the most important ones :

Fragmentation processes

"Primary" s quark : s g $\rightarrow$ s g + (γ s $\rightarrow$ g s + ...)

Decay of c quark : c $\rightarrow$ $\bar{K}^0$, γ γ $\rightarrow$ c $\bar{c}$ + (γ c $\rightarrow$ g c + ...)

VDM contribution.

The K_s^0 selection is based on its long life time and its decay into two charged pions. The K_s^0 secondary vertex is built and a candidate K_s^0 is accepted if it satisfies the following main conditions. The sign of charged tracks must be opposite. The momentum of charged tracks must be greater than 0.2 GeV/c. The secondary vertex is fitted and the two tracks are constrained to have a common intersection. The angle between the reconstructed V^0 and the beam axis must be between 40 and 140 degrees, and finally, the transverse momentum of the V^0 with respect to the beam direction must be greater than 0.6 GeV/c.

4 Results and discussion

With the previous selection, the invariant mass distribution of these $\pi^+\pi^-$ candidates is shown on figure 2. The signal to background ratio is quite good and a clear signal of K_S^0 is observed. The comparison is made with TWOGAM and PHOJET. The number of K_S^0 is obtained by a data fit. The invariant mass distribution is fitted by the sum of a constant term for the background and a gaussian distribution for the signal. The peak corresponds to 1041 ± 32 K_S^0 for the anti-tag sample (199 ± 15 for the remnant jet tag sample) and the resolution is about 4.8 MeV. The visible K_S^0 cross section is 6.8 ± 0.3 pb for the anti-tag sample (1.3 ± 0.2 pb for the remnant jet tag sample).

The visible K_S^0 P_T differential cross section was obtained from the numbers of reconstructed K_S^0 in each P_T bin. Each number results from a fitted invariant mass distribution using the same procedure as the one descibed above. For the anti-tag sample and the remnant jet sample we have compared the P_T distribution with two generators, TWOGAM and PHOJET, as can be seen in figure 2.

Now some observations can be made. The topology predicted by the theoretical models, PHOJET as well as TWOGAM are qualitatively in agreement

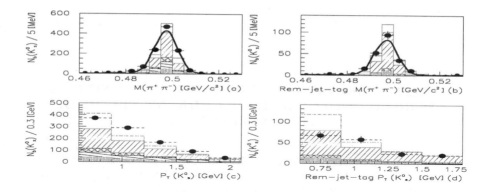

Figure 2: Comparaison between data and Monte-Carlo predictions for the anti-tag selection. a) K_s^0 in anti-tag events. b) K_s^0 in remnant jet tagged events. c) K_s^0 versus pt in anti-tagged events. d) K_s^0 versus pt in remnant jet tagged events.

with data. The shape of these distributions are similar. A slight excess of data over Monte-Carlo predictions is observed in the anti-tag sample, but the statistics is very low and the systematics are not taken into account, especially the trigger efficiency error. For the remnant-jet-tag sample, data and Monte-Carlo prediction are compatible within the statitical error except at low P_T. The main difference between TWOGAM and PHOJET comes from the low P_T region. At low P_T, the PHOJET K_S^0 production looks overestimated in the two samples, but the track efficiency and the trigger efficiency play an important rôle in this region and we must be very careful before concluding, in particular, trying to extract informations from the VDM region of K_S^0 production.

References

1. By TOPAZ Collaboration (R. Enomoto et al.) *Phys. Lett.* B **341**, 238 (1994).
2. By AMY Collaboration (T. Aso et al.) *Phys. Lett.* B **363**, 249 (1995); by TOPAZ Collaboration (R. Enomoto et al.) *Phys. Lett.* B **328**, 535 (1994); by VENUS Collaboration (S. Uehara et al.) *Z. Phys.* C **63**, 213 (1994).
3. DELPHI Collaboration DELPHI 90-35 PROG 152
4. R. Engel and J.Ranft *Phys. Rev.* D **54**, 4244 (1996).
5. DELPHI Collaboration, P. Abreu et al., "Performance of the DELPHI Detector" *Nucl. Instrum. Methods* A **378**, 57 (1996).

FIRST OBSERVATION OF PHOTON SPLITTING IN A STRONG COULOMB FIELD. CURRENT STATUS OF THE EXPERIMENT.

SH.ZH. AKHMADALIEV, G.YA. KEZERASHVILI, V.A. KISELEV,
S.G. KLIMENKO, V.M. MALYSHEV, A.L. MASLENNIKOV, A.M. MILOV,
A.I. MILSTEIN, N.YU. MUCHNOI, A.I. NAUMENKOV, $\boxed{\text{V.S. PANIN}}$,
S.V. PELEGANCHUK, G.E. POSPELOV, I.YA. PROTOPOPOV,
L.V. ROMANOV, A.G. SHAMOV, D.N. SHATILOV, E.A. SIMONOV,
YU.A. TIKHONOV
Budker Institute of Nuclear Physics,
630090, Novosibirsk, Russia

The experiment on photon splitting in a strong Coulomb field of a heavy nucleus has been performed at ROKK-1M facility at VEPP-4M collider. This high-order nonlinear QED process has never been observed in experiment. The experimental setup includes backscattering Compton gamma source, electron tagging system, low background collimation system, active target and liquid krypton calorimeter as photon detector. In the energy range of 120-450 MeV the statistics of $2.4 \cdot 10^9$ initial tagged photons falling on the BGO target has been collected. Analysis of 2/3 of the statistics gives 86 detected photon splitting events. The background is less than 20 %. In Monte-Carlo simulations based on the photon splitting cross section obtained with logarithmic accuracy ($\simeq$ 20 %) 125 events are found. Thus it is the first observation of the photon splitting process. Data analysis and comparison with more accurate theoretical predictions are in progress.

1 Introduction

Photon splitting (PS) is a nonlinear QED process, in which the initial photon transforms into two final photons via interaction with a virtual electron-positron pair in a Coulomb field of a nucleus (see Fig.1). In this process the total energy of the final photons is equal to the energy of the initial one.

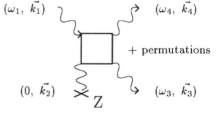

Figure 1: Lowest-order PS diagram.

At high energies $\omega_1 \gg m_e$ the main contribution to PS cross section comes from the region of small virtuality of Coulomb quanta. In this case the coplanarity angle φ between planes $(\vec{k}_1, \vec{k}_3)$ and $(\vec{k}_1, \vec{k}_4)$ is close to 180°. Photon splitting has not been observed up to now, though attemps have been made (see experiment[1] and articles[2,3], in which the wrong interpretation of the data in[1] was pointed out).

2 Experimental setup

The main ideas of our experimental aproach are the registration of both final photons and control of the balance between the sum of their energies and the energy of the initial photon. The PS cross section is quite small and peaked at small angles $\simeq 1/\gamma \ll 1$,where $\gamma = \omega_1/m_e$. Therefore, good collimation of the primary photon beam is required. Since one needs to separate incoming photons from scattered photons, the angular region below 2.4 mrad is enclosed by the dump and only photons scattered outside the dump shadow are to be registered. An analogous scheme of a PS experiment has been proposed in[4].

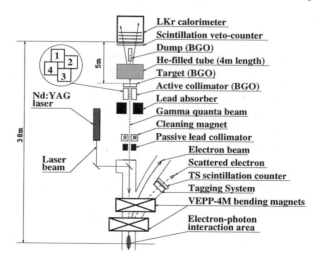

Figure 2: Principal scheme of the experimental setup.

The experimental setup is shown in Fig. 2. The ROKK-1M facility[5] is used as the intensive backscattering Compton source of gamma-quanta beam. The tagging system (TS)[6] allows one to tag the energy of the initial photon with an accuracy of about 1.3 %. The collimation of the photon beam is achieved by means of two collimators spaced at 13.5 m. The last collimator, intended to strip off the beam halo from the edges of the first one, is formed by four BGO crystals as shown in the separate view in Fig. 2. After passing through the collimation system the gamma beam is falling onto the target - BGO crystal of 1 X_o length. The incoming photons which passed the target without interaction and photons scattered through an angle less than 2.4 mrad are absorbed by the dump. All active elements of the beam channel (collimators, target, dump, scintillation counter in front of the calorimeter) set a veto signal in the trigger and their signals are later used in off-line analysis for background suppression. The signals from the target and the dump are also used to monitor the input gamma flux. We measure the energy in the final state with an accuracy of $2\%/\sqrt{E[GeV]}$ by means of the liquid krypton calorimeter (LKr) described in detail in [7]. Its double-sided strip structure enables us to get X and Y coordinates of the particles.

3   Preliminary results

We selected events which satisfied the following conditions:
• Absence of the signal in all active elements of the beam channel.
• Saturated balance between energy of the tagged photon and energy measured in the calorimeter.
• Two separate tracks in both X and Y coordinates found in the calorimeter.

The last condition strongly suppresses backgrounds with only one photon in the final state. The typical event which meets selection criteria is shown in Fig. 3. The experimental results are presented in Fig. 4 and in Tab. 1, together with Monte-Carlo simulation results based on a PS cross section calculated in the Weizsäcker-Williams approximation. The registration efficiency for PS events, averaged over energy spectrum of incoming photons, is 10%.

Table 1: Preliminary results of the PS experiment. Q is the number of incoming tagged photons. N_φ is the number of events in distribution over coplanarity angle φ after normalization to experimental statistics with target, see Fig. 4b.

DATA	TARGET	$Q, \cdot 10^9$	$N_{\varphi > 150°}$	$N_{\varphi < 150°}$
Experiment	$Bi_4Ge_3O_{12}$	1.16	86±9	13
Monte-Carlo PS	$Bi_4Ge_3O_{12}$	2.33	125±8	15
Experiment	no target	0.45	6.5±2	3.8

The quoted errors are only statistical ones. The agreement looks satisfactory, since the accuracy of theoretical approximation used is about 20%. Now we perform the simulation with the use of the PS cross section obtained recently in [8], which has essentially higher accuracy and is significantly smaller than the approximate one.

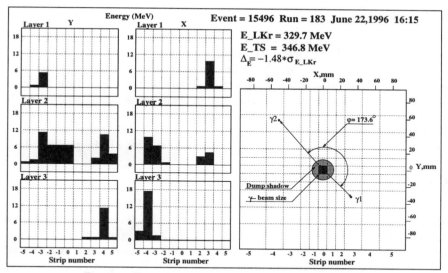

Figure 3: Tentative candidate to photon splitting events.

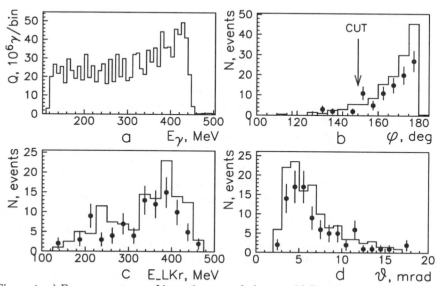

Figure 4: a) Energy spectrum of incoming tagged photons. b) Distribution over the coplanarity angle. c) Energy spectrum for coplanar events. d) Distribution over the minimal scattering angle for outgoing photons (coplanar events). Black circles – experiment, solid lines – MC simulation.

4 Conclusion

This experiment is the first observation of the photon splitting process in a strong Coulomb field of heavy nuclei. The preliminary results obtained with a most severe reconstruction algorithm show good separation of effect from background. Data analysis and Monte-Carlo simulations based on PS cross sections calculated with high accuracy are in progress. As a by-product of the PS experiment we have measured for the first time in the photon energy range of 120-450 MeV the differential cross section for Delbrück scattering. It is in good agreement with theoretical predictions and results will be published.

Acknowledgments

Authors wish to acknowledge the staff of the VEPP-4M accelerator complex for reliable work during the runs. We are thankful to V.N.Baier, A.E. Bondar and A.P. Onuchin for useful discussions and to V.M. Aulchenko and G.A. Savinov for their contribution to electronic equipment. We acknowledge A.Kh. Babaev and S.F. Ganzhur for their help in data acquisition. We express special thanks to V.P. Smakhtin who helped us to maintain the BGO crystals[a]. We are deeply grateful to A.N. Skrinsky and V.A. Sidorov for their permanent interest and support of this experiment.

References

1. G.Jarlskog *et al*, *Phys. Rev.* D **8**, 3813 (1973).
2. V.N. Baier *et al*, *Phys. Lett.* B **49**, 385 (1974).
3. R.M. Dzhilkibaev *et al*, *Pis'ma Zh. Exp. Teor. fiz.* **19**, 73 (1974) [*JETP Lett.* **19**, 47 (1974)]
4. A.I. Milstein, B.B. Woitsekhovski, It is possible to observe photon splitting in a strong Coulomb field. Preprint BINP 91-14, Novosibirsk, 1991.
5. G.Ya. Kezerashvili *et al*, in *AIP Conference Proceedings* **343**, 260, (American Institute of Physics, Woodbury, New York, 1995).
6. V.M. Aulchenko *et al*, *Nucl. Instrum. Methods* A **355**, 261 (1995).
7. V.M. Aulchenko *et al*, The test experiment with the prototype of LKr calorimeter at the tagged photon beam. Preprint BINP 95-96, Novosibirsk, 1995. Accepted for publication in *Nucl. Instrum. Methods* A. see also *Nucl. Instrum. Methods* A **379**, 475 (1996).
8. R.N. Lee, A.I. Milstein, V.M. Strakhovenko, High energy photon splitting in a strong Coulomb field. Preprint BINP 97-35, Novosibirsk, 1997.

---

[a] The BGO crystals grown by Czochralski low thermal gradient technique were provided by the Institute of Inorganic Chemistry, Novosibirsk.

PHOTOPRODUCTION OF NEUTRAL PION PAIRS IN THE COULOMB FIELD OF THE NUCLEUS

A.A. BEL'KOV, A.V. LANYOV

Particle Physics Laboratory, Joint Institute for Nuclear Research, 141980 Dubna, Moscow Region, Russia

M. DILLIG

Institut für Theoretische Physik III der Universität Erlangen-Nürnberg, D-91058 Erlangen, Germany

The total cross section for Coulomb photoproduction of neutral pion pairs in the reaction $\gamma A \rightarrow \pi^0 \pi^0 A$ is estimated within the effective chiral lagrangian approach. The amplitude of $\gamma\gamma^* \rightarrow \pi^0 \pi^0$ with one off-shell photon is calculated at $O(p^6)$ in the momentum expansion; in addition, nuclear absorption is taken into account. Besides its experimental feasibility, the results of the calculation demonstrate that the reaction $\gamma A \rightarrow \pi^0 \pi^0 A$ is a powerful source of information on the process $\gamma\gamma \rightarrow \pi^0 \pi^0$ close to threshold.

The nucleus Coulomb interaction method is an effective approach to study in high-energy experiments the low-energy electromagnetic properties of pions in the process $\gamma\gamma \rightarrow \pi\pi$. In this note we focus on the elementary process $\gamma\gamma \rightarrow \pi^0\pi^0$: the actual interest is caused both by experimental data [1] and recent progress in Chiral Perturbation Theory (ChPT) [2] up to and including $O(p^6)$. Its sensitivity to higher-order corrections makes this process a valuable source of the experimental information essential for the test of bosonized chiral lagrangians at $O(p^6)$. For the first time the reaction $\gamma A \rightarrow \pi\pi A$ was considered in this context in paper [3] with a one-loop amplitude of $\gamma\gamma \rightarrow \pi^0\pi^0$ at $O(p^4)$. In a recent paper [4] we extended and improved the previous calculations in a consistent way: we present results of a calculation of the nuclear Coulomb photoproduction of neutral pion pairs, where we include in the elementary amplitude $\gamma\gamma^* \rightarrow \pi^0\pi^0$ both off-shell corrections for the Coulomb virtual photon γ^* and contributions from ChPT up to $O(p^6)$, and where, in addition, nuclear structure and absorption are taken into account in the form factor for the nucleus.

The photoproduction of a $\pi^0\pi^0$ pair in the Coulomb field of a nucleus is schematically described by the diagram in Fig.1. The virtual photon $\gamma^*(q_2)$ for the interaction of the incident real photon with the stationary Coulomb field of the nucleus has zero energy and transfers only momentum: $q_2 = (0, \mathbf{q}_2)$.

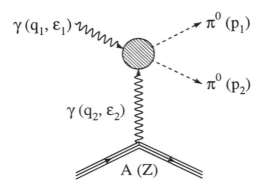

Fig. 1. Photoproduction of pion pairs in the Coulomb field of a nucleus.

Then the amplitude of the reaction $\gamma(q_1)A \to \pi^0(p_1)\pi^0(p_2)A$ has the form

$$T_C = 2M_A \frac{eZ_A}{|\mathbf{q}_2|^2} F_A(q_{2t}, q_{2l}) \epsilon^\mu T_{\mu 0}^{(\gamma\gamma^* \to \pi^0\pi^0)}, \tag{1}$$

where M_A and Z are, respectively, the mass and charge of the nucleus. In (1), the nuclear form factor $F_A(q_{2t}, q_{2l})$, which includes nuclear absorption, depends on transverse and longitudinal components of the momentum transfer $\mathbf{q}_2$ measured relative to the momentum $\mathbf{q}_1$ of the incident photon. $T_{\mu 0}^{(\gamma\gamma^* \to \pi^0\pi^0)}$ is the tensor component of the amplitude of the process $\gamma(q_1)\gamma^*(q_2) \to \pi^0(p_1)\pi^0(p_2)$.

From Lorentz and gauge invariances the general parameterization for the amplitude $T_{\mu 0}^{(\gamma\gamma^* \to \pi^0\pi^0)}$ at $O(p^6)$ has the form

$$
\begin{aligned}
T_{\mu\nu}^{(\gamma\gamma^* \to \pi^0\pi^0)} &= A(s,t,u;q_2^2)\left(\frac{\tilde{s}}{2}g_{\mu\nu} - q_{2\mu}q_{1\nu}\right) \\
&+ B(s,t,u;q_2^2)\left[2\tilde{s}\Delta_\mu\Delta_\nu - \nu^2 g_{\mu\nu} - 2\nu\left(\Delta_\mu q_{1\nu} - q_{2\mu}\Delta_\nu\right)\right] \\
&+ D(s,t,u;q_2^2)\left[\nu q_{2\mu}q_{2\nu} + \tilde{s}\Delta_\mu q_{2\nu} - q_2^2\left(\nu g_{\mu\nu} + 2\Delta_\mu q_{1\nu}\right)\right],
\end{aligned}
$$

where $\Delta_\mu = (p_1 - p_2)_\mu$, $s = (q_1 + q_2)^2 = (p_1 + p_2)^2$, $\tilde{s} = s - q_2^2$, $t = (p_1 - q_1)^2 = (q_2 - p_2)^2$, $u = (p_2 - q_1)^2 = (q_2 - p_1)^2$ and $\nu = t - u$. The calculation of the $\gamma\gamma^* \to \pi^0\pi^0$ amplitude at $O(p^6)$ of the momentum expansion of ChPTh involves tree-level, one-loop and two-loop diagrams of a chiral effective lagrangian (see papers [4,5] for more details).

The differential cross section for the photoproduction of a neutral pion

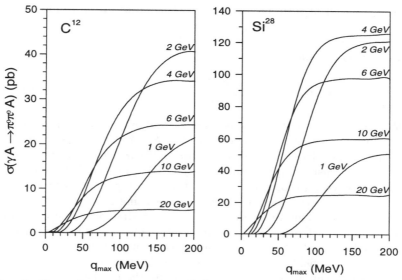

Fig. 2. Dependence of the $\gamma A \rightarrow \pi^0 \pi^0 A$ cross section on the momentum transfer cutoff q_{max} for different photon energies.

pair in the Coulomb field of a nucleus is defined as

$$d\sigma_C^{(\gamma A \rightarrow \pi\pi A)} = \frac{\delta^{(3)}(\mathbf{p}_1 + \mathbf{p}_2 - \mathbf{q}_1 - \mathbf{q}_2)\delta(E_1 + E_2 - \varepsilon)}{4\varepsilon M_A(2\pi)^5 8 E_1 E_2 M_A} \frac{1}{2}|T_C|^2 d^3\mathbf{p}_1 \, d^3\mathbf{p}_2 \, d^3\mathbf{q}_2$$

where E_i and $\mathbf{p}_i$ $(i = 1, 2)$ and ε are the energies and momenta of the pions and the energy of incident real photon, respectively. For large energies of the incident real photon and for small momentum transfers $|\mathbf{q}_2|$ to the recoil nucleus and neglecting the offshellness of the Coulomb photon and nuclear corrections, the method of equivalent photons allows us to relate the differential cross section for photoproduction of pion pairs on nuclei to the total cross section for the process $\gamma\gamma \rightarrow \pi\pi$:

$$\frac{d\sigma_C^{(\gamma A \rightarrow \pi\pi A)}}{ds} = \frac{\alpha}{\pi} Z^2 \log\left(\frac{\sqrt{s}}{2m_\pi}\right) \frac{1}{s} \sigma^{(\gamma\gamma \rightarrow \pi\pi)}(s) , \tag{2}$$

where $s \equiv m_{\pi\pi}^2$. In this limit equation (2) enables us to extract model-independent information on the process $\gamma\gamma \rightarrow \pi\pi$ from the experimental data on the nuclear Coulomb photoproduction of pion pairs. For a more general kinematics, the nuclear form factor and the offshellness of the Coulomb photon have to be taken into account, however.

The nuclear form factor $F_A(q_{2t}, q_{2l})$ in (1) can be estimated in the same approximation as in paper [6]:

$$F_A(q_t, q_l) = q_l R J_0(q_t R) K_1(q_l R) + \frac{(q_l R)^2}{q_t R} J_1(q_t R) K_0(q_l R) + \Delta F_A(q_t, q_l). \quad (3)$$

where R is the radius of the nucleus, and J_n and K_n $(n = 0, 1)$ are Bessel functions. In our estimates R is chosen to be $R = 1.12 A^{1/3}$ fm, where A is atomic weight of a nucleus. The first two terms in (3) arise from the integration over the three-dimensional space outside a cylinder of radius R of the nucleus. They reflect the assumption, that the nucleus is completely 'black' for the outgoing pions for impact parameters $b \leq R$, resulting in a cut $\theta(b - R)$, in the profile function. This drastic assumption is mediated by the correction term $\Delta F_A(q_t, q_l)$, which arises from the integration over the three-dimensional cylinder behind the nucleus and corresponds to the interaction of photons with the nuclear Coulomb field after passing through the nucleus.

Monte Carlo techniques were used to compute the total cross sections for the photoproduction of $\pi^0 \pi^0$-pairs in the Coulomb field of the carbon ($Z = 6$) and silicon nuclei ($Z = 14$). It is important to note that for a momentum transfer cutoff $q_{max} \equiv |q_2|_{max} \ll \varepsilon$, the effective mass of $\pi\pi$ system varies in the range $4m_\pi^2 \leq m_{\pi\pi}^2 \leq 2\varepsilon q_{max}$. The dependence of the total cross section of the reaction $\gamma A \to \pi^0 \pi^0 A$ on the momentum transfer cutoff q_{max} for different energies ε of the incident real photon is shown in Fig.2. In the calculation, the additional cutoff $m_{\pi\pi} \leq 700$ MeV was used, corresponding to the range of validity of the chiral theory.

The main background for the Coulomb photoproduction of $\pi^0 \pi^0$ pairs is the double pion photoproduction reaction on the nucleon $\gamma N \to \pi^0 \pi^0 N$ via the baryon resonance exchange mechanism [7]. In the photon energy region near $\varepsilon = 1$ GeV the total cross sections of the reactions $\gamma p \to \pi^0 \pi^0 p$ and $\gamma n \to \pi^0 \pi^0 n$ are dominated by diagrams with $\Delta(1232)$-isobar and resonance $N^*(1520)$. Our estimates have shown that in the case of an isoscalar target the coherent $\gamma N \to \pi^0 \pi^0 N$ background is strongly suppressed due to the self-cancell of the dominating diagrams of the elementary process while summing the amplitudes on protons and neutrons of the nucleus. The effect of such self-cancellation of diagrams is demonstrated in Fig.3. In Fig.3 we also show the photon energy dependence of the total cross sections for the coherent double pion photoproduction on the carbon and silicon nuclei (isoscalar targets) calculated with the Born nuclear electromagnetic form factor with symmetrized Fermi-density [9].

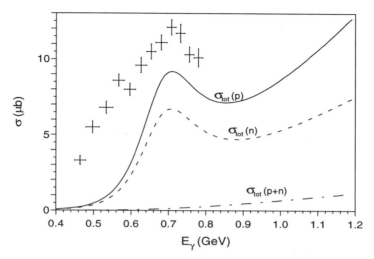

Fig. 3. Total cross sections of the reactions $\gamma p \rightarrow \pi^0 \pi^0 p$ (full curve) and $\gamma n \rightarrow \pi^0 \pi^0 n$ (dashed curve). Dash-dotted curve corresponds to the total cross section for the sum of the amplitudes on the proton and neutron. The experimental points for the reaction $\gamma p \rightarrow \pi^0 \pi^0 p$ were measured at DAΦNE[8].

To estimate the contribution of the reaction $\gamma N \rightarrow \pi^0 \pi^0 N$ to this part of the phase space which corresponds to the cutoffs introduced above for the Coulomb photoproduction of $\pi^0 \pi^0$ pairs, the additional cutoffs must be also taken into account: $m_{\pi\pi} \leq 700$ MeV and $\sqrt{-t_N} \leq q_{max}$, where $t_N = (p_1 - p_2)^2$, p_1 and p_2 are the momenta of nucleon in the initial and final states, respectively. The photon energy dependence of the cross sections for the carbon and silicon targets calculated with the cutoffs are shown in Fig.4. According to the symmetry properties of the background coherent reaction $\gamma A \rightarrow \pi^0 \pi^0 A$ on isoscalar nuclei [10], the two π^0 mesons prefer to propagate together in the CMS. The Monte-Carlo simulation shows that the additional suppression of the backgraund to the level lower than the Coulomb photoproduction can be easily achieved using some special angle cutoffs. To extract the signal of Coulomb photoproduction is possible in the experiment where a silicon detector is used as a sensitive target to develop a trigger on the nucleus recoil momentum.

Summarizing, we have found that for energies of the incident photon $\varepsilon \leq 4$ GeV and for momentum transfers $|\mathbf{q}_2| \leq 200$ MeV, $\pi^0 \pi^0$ pairs with $2m_\pi \leq m_{\pi\pi} \leq 700$MeV in the reaction $\gamma A \rightarrow \pi^0 \pi^0 A$ are produced with a cross section of typically $\sigma \approx 40$ pb and $\sigma \approx 120$ pb for carbon and silicon

256

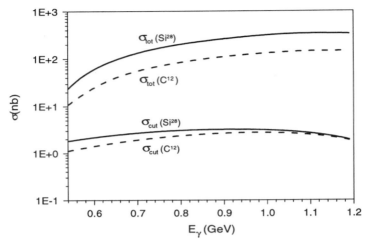

Fig. 4. Total cross sections of the double pion photoproduction reaction (σ_{tot}) and cross sections calculated with the additional cutoffs for coherent processes on the carbon (dashed curve) and silicon nuclei (full curve).

nuclei, respectively. Our results demonstrate that this reaction can be experimentally investigated with presently available photon beams as a new source of the low-energy data on the process $\gamma\gamma \to \pi^0\pi^0$.

References

1. Crystal Ball Collaboration (Marsiske H *et al.*) *Phys. Rev.* **D41**, 3324 (1990).
2. S. Bellucci, J. Gasser and M.E. Sainio, *Nucl. Phys.* **B423**, 80 (1994).
3. A.A. Bel'kov and V.N. Pervushin, *Sov. J. Nucl. Phys.* **40**, 616 (1984).
4. A.A. Bel'kov, M. Dillig and A.V. Lanyov, Preprint JINR E2-95-511, FAU-TP3-95/13, hep-ph/9512324.
5. A.A. Bel'kov, A.V. Lanyov and S. Scherer, *J. Phys.* **G22**, 1383 (1996).
6. G. Fäldt, D. Julius, H. Pilkuhn and A. Müllensiefen, *Nucl. Phys.* **B41**, 125 (1972).
7. J.A. Gomez Tejedor and E. Oset, *Nucl. Phys.* **A600** 413 (1996).
8. A. Braghieri *et al.*, *Phys. Lett.* **B363**, 46 (1995).
9. V.K. Lukyanov and Yu.S. Pol, *Fiz. Elem. Chastits At. Yadra*, 5 955 (1974) [*Sov. J. Part. Nucl.*, **5** (1974)].
10. E. Oset and S.S. Kamalov, *Preprint* FTUV/96-86, IFIC/96-95 (1996).

NEW DETERMINATION OF SCALAR MESON COUPLINGS TO TWO PHOTONS FROM $\gamma\gamma \to \pi\pi$ EXPERIMENTAL RESULTS

M. BOGLIONE

Dipartimento di Fisica Teorica, Universita' di Torino,
I.N.F.N, Sezione di Torino, Via P.Giuria 1, I-10125 Torino, Italy.

M.R. PENNINGTON

Centre for Particle Theory, University of Durham,
Durham DH1 3LE, U.K.

The scalar mesons in the 1 GeV energy region constitute the Higgs sector of the strong interactions. They are responsible for the masses of all light flavour hadrons. Their couplings to two photons, being a direct measure of the charges of their constituents, can illuminate their composition. A new amplitude analysis of experimental results on $\gamma\gamma \to \pi^+\pi^-$ and $\pi^0\pi^0$ will be presented. This updates the earlier analysis by Morgan and Pennington with the inclusion of the full Crystal Ball statistics and data from CELLO, significantly constraining the space of permitted solutions to just two narrow classes and allowing a new determination of the couplings of the $f_0(980)$, $f_0(1300) \to \gamma\gamma$.

1   Introduction

The excitations of a meson system by two photons, namely the processes $\gamma\gamma \to X$, represent a remarkably useful tool in the study of hadron spectroscopy. Because the two incident photons do not interact strongly, the reaction is particularly simple and clean, allowing a direct investigation of the structure of mesons in terms of their elementary constituents.

We start from the presently available $\gamma\gamma \to \pi\pi$ experimental information. The shape of the integrated cross-sections beautifully illustrates the dynamics of the process. At low energies, the photon sees the pion as a whole entity and couples to its charge. Consequently, the cross-section for $\gamma\gamma \to \pi^+\pi^-$ is pronounced at threshold, whereas the $\gamma\gamma \to \pi^0\pi^0$ cross-section is zero. When the energy increases, the shortening of its wavelength enables the photon to see the individual partonic constituents inside the pion; it couples to their charges, and causes them to resonate. Both the charged and neutral cross-sections are then dominated by the Breit-Wigner peak corresponding to the $f_2(1270)$ resonance.

We will consider the energy region from $\pi\pi$ threshold up to 1.4 GeV, in which only the $\pi\pi$ and $K\overline{K}$ channels need to be taken into account. Ideally, with complete information on all the possible angular correlations between the initial and final state directions and spins, we could decompose the cross sections into components with definite sets of quantum numbers. From these, we could then unambiguously deduce the couplings to two photons of all the resonances with those quantum numbers, not only the $f_2(1270)$ but also the more complicated scalar resonances $f_0(980)$ and $f_0(1300)$. Unfortunately, in the real world, experiments have only a limited angular coverage and the polarization of the initial state is not measured. This lack of information plays a crucial role in our analysis and affects the determination of the resonance couplings. The reason these couplings are so important is that they are directly proportional to the charges (to the fourth power) that the photon sees; so they give a picture of the inner nature of the mesons in terms of their elementary constituents.

Since 1990, when the last amplitude analysis of $\gamma\gamma \to \pi\pi$ was performed[1], new results on $\gamma\gamma \to \pi^+\pi^-$ from the CELLO collaboration[2], more detailed information on the scalar $\pi\pi$ final state interactions and increased statistics in the Crystal Ball experiment[3] on $\gamma\gamma \to \pi^0\pi^0$ have become available. These provide the impetus for a new analysis[4], the aim of which is to limit the number of possible solutions previously found and so obtain more stringent information particularly on the scalar sector. Our main goal is to perform a calculation, in an as model independent way as possible, while respecting all the fundamental constraints, not only unitarity, analyticity and crossing symmetry, but also low energy theorems and knowledge of final state interactions.

2 Formalism and constraints

The unpolarized cross-section for dipion production by two real photons is given by the contributions of two helicity amplitudes M_{++} and M_{+-} (the subscripts label the helicities of the incoming photons) :

$$\frac{d\sigma}{d\Omega} = \frac{1}{128\pi^2 s}\sqrt{1 - 4m_\pi^2/s}\,\left[\,|M_{++}|^2 + |M_{+-}|^2\right]. \tag{1}$$

These two helicity amplitudes can be decomposed into partial waves as

$$M_{++}(s, \theta, \phi) = e^2\sqrt{16\pi}\sum_{J\geq 0} F_{J0}(s)\,Y_{J0}(\theta, \phi)\,, \tag{2}$$

$$M_{+-}(s, \theta, \phi) = e^2\sqrt{16\pi}\sum_{J\geq 2} F_{J2}(s)\,Y_{J2}(\theta, \phi)\,. \tag{3}$$

The partial waves $F_{J\lambda}$ ($\lambda = 0, 2$) are the quantities we want to determine.

When $s \to 0$, Low's low energy theorem[5] tells us that each amplitude F goes to its Born contribution

$$F(s) \to B(s)\,, \quad s \to 0\,. \tag{4}$$

The Born amplitude is determined by one pion exchange and describes the process in which the energy of the photon is so low that it sees the pion as a whole and couples to its charge (the Born term for $\gamma\gamma \to \pi^0\pi^0$ is zero).

As soon as we move away from $s = 0$, final state interactions have to be included. These modify the Born amplitudes. This directly leads us to the second important constraint: unitarity. Unitarity plays a fundamental role in fixing the parametrization for the fit. It relates the two-photon processes $\gamma\gamma \to \pi\pi$ to other hadronic processes, like $\pi\pi \to \pi\pi$ and $\pi\pi \to K\overline{K}$, allowing us to input experimental information corresponding to these reactions. In this way, it constrains the partial wave amplitudes $F(\gamma\gamma \to \pi\pi)$ over the whole energy region we study. To see how, let us start from the elastic region, where the only possible intermediate state is $\pi\pi$ itself. Unitarity tells us that

$$\text{Im}F(\gamma\gamma \to \pi\pi) = F^*(\gamma\gamma \to \pi\pi)\,T(\pi\pi \to \pi\pi) \,. \tag{5}$$

This equation ensures *universality*, namely resonances which appear in $\pi\pi \to \pi\pi$ processes also appear in $\gamma\gamma \to \pi\pi$ and vice versa. From Eq.(7) follows Watson's theorem[6]: the phase of F equals the phase shift in T

$$\left.\begin{array}{l} F(\gamma\gamma \to \pi\pi) = |F|\,e^{\,i\Phi(s)} \\ T(\pi\pi \to \pi\pi) = \sin\delta(s)\,e^{\,i\delta(s)} \end{array}\right\} \;\Rightarrow\; \Phi(s) = \delta(s) \,, \tag{6}$$

which guarantees that the two pions scatter in the same way, however they are produced. If we consider a wider energy region, we have to take into account the $K\overline{K}$ intermediate state as well. Unitarity now requires

$$\text{Im}F(\gamma\gamma \to \pi\pi) = F^*(\gamma\gamma \to \pi\pi)T(\pi\pi \to \pi\pi) + F^*(\gamma\gamma \to K\overline{K})T(K\overline{K} \to \pi\pi). \tag{7}$$

Its general solution is usefully represented by

$$F(\gamma\gamma \to \pi\pi) = \alpha_1\,T(\pi\pi \to \pi\pi) + \alpha_2\,T(K\overline{K} \to \pi\pi) \,, \tag{8}$$

where α_1 and α_2 are essentially couplings functions, which are real smooth functions of energy. These are the quantities we are going to fit to the three sets of experimental data from Mark II[7], Crystal Ball[3,8], and CELLO[2] collaborations.

For lack of space we are unable to present here the plots showing our fits[4]. Suffice it to say that, thanks to the new inputs, only two classes of distinct solutions are found, instead of a large range of permitted scenarios[1]. In the first solution the $f_0(980)$ shows up as a pronounced peak in the cross-section, due to a dominant coupling to $\gamma\gamma \to K\overline{K}$ ($\alpha_2 \gg \alpha_1$), whereas in the second solution it produces a sharp dip, as a consequence of the larger coupling to $\gamma\gamma \to \pi\pi$ than to $\gamma\gamma \to K\overline{K}$ ($\alpha_1 \gg \alpha_2$), as illustrated in Fig. 1.

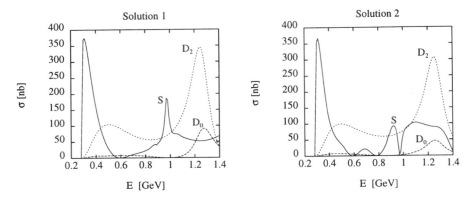

Figure 1: I=0 partial wave cross-sections from our two solutions.

3 Extraction of two-photon partial widths

The scalar resonance signals are not clean Breit-Wigners: interference phenomena and background activity considerably complicate their shapes. To calculate the couplings of the resonances to $\gamma\gamma$ reliably, the amplitudes F and $\mathcal{T}$ have to be analytically continued into the complex s-plane. Near each pole position they are dominated by their respective pole contributions and so their residues can be calculated there. From these, the couplings g_γ and the two-photon partial widths corresponding to each resonance can be extracted. The results are summarized in Table 1. We can compare these values with those found from theoretical estimates of the ratio between the two-photons widths of $q\bar{q}$ tensors and the corresponding scalars[9], Table 2. We then conclude that the $f_0(980)$ has too small a $\gamma\gamma$ coupling not only to be an $n\bar{n}$ state or a $K\overline{K}$ molecule, but also to be simply a pure $s\bar{s}$ state. More likely, hadronic intermediate states, both $\pi\pi$ and $K\overline{K}$, contribute to its peculiar features, as confirmed by other independent analyses. The two-photon partial width found for the $f_2(1270)$ is perfectly consistent with the value given in the Particle Data Tables of (2.8 ± 0.4) keV [10]. As far as the $f_0(1300)$ is concerned, its total width is so large that analytic continuation to the pole position is not reliable. Instead, we give a rough estimate of its two photon width, from the cross-section at real energies. This is consistent with it being an $n\bar{n}$ state.

Experimental improvements are needed to be able to differentiate between our two classes of solutions, to put more stringent constraints on the nature of the scalar mesons and to allow an extension of this analysis to a broader energy range, so that the very intriguing character of the $f_0(1500)$ can be investigated too. Data from CLEO and LEP, with their very high statistics and wide angular coverage, are eagerly awaited. They could boost our knowledge of the mysterious scalar sector.

Table 1: Two-photon partial widths in keV corresponding to the two classes of solutions.

	$\Gamma_{f_2(1270)}$	$\Gamma_{f_0(980)}$	$\Gamma_{f_0(1300)}$
Solution 1 (peak)	3.1	0.1-0.3	3.0
Solution 2 (dip)	2.6	0.3	4.7

Table 2: Two-photon partial widths in keV corresponding to $q\bar{q}$ conventional scalar states and $(K\overline{K})$ molecule.

	$\Gamma_{0^{++}}$
$n\bar{n}$	4.5
$s\bar{s}$	0.4
$K\overline{K}$	0.6

Acknowledgments

It is a pleasure for M.B. to thank the organizers of such an interesting and entertaining conference.

References

1. D. Morgan and M.R. Pennington, *Z. Phys.* C **48**, 623 (1990).
2. H.J. Behrend *et al.*, *Z. Phys.* C **56**, 381 (1992).
3. J.K. Bienlein, *Proc. IX Int. Workshop on Photon-Photon Collisions (San Diego 1992)*, ed. D. Caldwell and H.P. Paar (World Scientific), p. 241.
4. M. Boglione and M.R. Pennington (in preparation).
5. F.E. Low, *Phys. Rev.* **96**, 1428 (1954).
6. K.M. Watson *Phys. Rev.* **88**, 1163 (1952).
7. J. Boyer *et al.*, *Phys. Rev.* D **42**, 1350 (1990).
8. H. Marsiske *et al.*, *Phys. Rev.* D **41**, 3324 (1990).
9. T. Barnes, *Phys. Lett.* B **165**, 434 (1985).
10. Review of Particle Physics, Phys. Rev. D **54**, 30 (1996).

PREDICTIONS FOR THE $\eta_c\gamma$ TRANSITION FORM FACTOR

THORSTEN FELDMANN and PETER KROLL

Department of Theoretical Physics, University of Wuppertal,
D-42097 Wuppertal, Germany

The $\eta_c\gamma$ transition form factor is calculated in a model based on a modified hard scattering approach to exclusive reactions, in which transverse degrees of freedom are taken into account. For the η_c-meson a distribution amplitude of the Bauer-Stech-Wirbel type is used, where the two free parameters, namely the decay constant f_{η_c} and the transverse size of the wave function, are related to the Fock state probability and the width for the two-photon decay $\Gamma_{\eta_c \to \gamma\gamma}$.

1 Introduction

At large momentum transfer the hard scattering approach (HSA)[1] provides a scheme to calculate exclusive processes. Observables are described as convolutions of hadronic wave functions, which embody soft non-perturbative physics, and hard scattering amplitudes to be calculated from perturbative QCD.

One interesting class of such observables are the meson-photon transition form factors, which are at leading order of purely electromagnetic origin. Hence, the uncertainties related to the appropriate value of the strong coupling constant or the size of the (Feynman) contributions coming from the overlap of the soft wave functions are absent. For example, in case of the pion-photon transition form factor it has been shown recently that the experimental data can be well described by a distribution amplitude that is close to the asymptotic one;[2] and for the η and η' mesons a determination of the decay constants and the mixing angle from the measurement of their transition form factors is possible.[3]

Here we discuss the application of the HSA to the $\eta_c\gamma$ transition form factor. In this case the finite mass of the charmed quarks always provides a large scale which allows the application of the HSA even for zero virtuality of the probing photon, $Q^2 \to 0$. Then the HSA result for the transition form factor at $Q^2 = 0$ can be related to the decay width $\Gamma[\eta_c \to \gamma\gamma]$, whereas the shape turns out to be unique in the Q^2 region of experimental interest and for reasonable values of the valence Fock state probability $P_{c\bar{c}}$.

2 Modified Hard Scattering Approach

The $\eta_c\gamma$ transition form factor in the modified HSA [1,4] is defined in analogy to the $\pi\gamma$ form factor[2] in terms of a hard scattering amplitude T_H, a non-perturbative (light-cone) wave function Ψ_0 of the leading $|c\bar{c}\rangle$ Fock state and a Sudakov factor as

$$F_{\eta_c\gamma}(Q^2) = \int_0^1 dx \int \frac{d^2\vec{b}}{4\pi} \, \hat{\Psi}_0(x,\vec{b}) \, \hat{T}_H(x,\vec{b},Q) \, \exp\left[-\mathcal{S}(x,\vec{b},Q)\right] \quad (1)$$

Here $\vec{b}_\perp$ denotes the transverse size in configuration space, and x is the usual Feynman parameter. In the present case, the Sudakov factor $\exp[-\mathcal{S}]$ can be neglected for two reasons: First, due to the large quark mass the radiative corrections only produce soft divergences but no collinear ones. Secondly, in contrast to the light meson case where the Sudakov factor provides a consistent tool to suppress the contributions from the endpoint regions where perturbation theory becomes unreliable, the distribution amplitude $\phi(x)$ in the η_c meson is expected to be strongly peaked at $x = 1/2$, and the potentially dangerous endpoint regions are unimportant anyway. It is then more appropriate to use the Fourier transformed definition of the form factor,

$$F_{\eta_c\gamma}(Q^2) \simeq \int_0^1 dx \int \frac{d^2\vec{k}_\perp}{16\pi^3} \, \Psi_0(x,\vec{k}_\perp) \, T_H(x,\vec{k}_\perp,Q) \quad (2)$$

The hard scattering amplitude in leading order is up to conventional normalization constants calculated from the following Feynman diagrams ($\bar{x} = (1-x)$).

With one photon being almost on-shell $q_1^2 \simeq 0$ and the virtuality of the second photon denoted as $q_2^2 = -Q^2$, this leads to

$$T_H(x,\vec{k}_\perp,Q) = e_c^2 \, 2\sqrt{6} \, \frac{2}{x\,Q^2 + (x\bar{x} + \rho^2)\,M^2 + \vec{k}_\perp^2} + O(\alpha_s) \quad (3)$$

Here $p^2 = M^2$ and $\rho := m_c/M \simeq 0.5$, and e_c denotes the fractional charge of the charm quark.

For the wave function, it is reasonable to assume the following factorizing form

$$\Psi_0(x,\vec{k}_\perp) = \frac{f_{\eta_c}}{2\sqrt{6}} \, \phi(x) \, \Sigma(\vec{k}_\perp) \quad (4)$$

Here f_{η_c} is the decay constant (corresponding to $f_\pi = 133$ MeV), and $\phi(x)$ is the quark distribution amplitude (DA) in the meson. In the following we will use a form of the wave function adapted from Bauer, Stech and Wirbel [5]

$$\phi(x) = N_\phi(a) \, x \, \bar{x} \, \exp\left[-a^2 \, M^2 \, (x - 1/2)^2\right] \tag{5}$$

The normalization constant $N_\phi(a)$ is determined from $\int_0^1 dx \, \phi(x) = 1$. Note that this DA is concentrated around $x = 1/2$. Furthermore, Σ is a Gaussian shape function which takes into account the finite transverse size of a meson [a]

$$\Sigma(\vec{k}_\perp) = 16\pi^2 \, a^2 \, e^{-a^2 \, \vec{k}_\perp^2} \tag{6}$$

3   Fixing the Parameters

The parameters entering the wave function are constrained by the Fock state probability

$$1 \geq P_{c\bar{c}} = \int \frac{dx \, d^2\vec{k}_\perp}{16\pi^3} \, \left|\Psi_0(x, \vec{k}_\perp)\right|^2 \tag{7}$$

One expects $0.8 \leq P_{c\bar{c}} < 1$, and we find that for a given value of f_{η_c} the form factor only mildly depends on the value of $P_{c\bar{c}}$, such that we may use $P_{c\bar{c}} = 0.8$ as a constraint for the size parameter a which leads to $a \simeq 1$ GeV^{-1}, in consistence with typical estimates for the radius $\langle r^2 \rangle = 3 \, a^2 \simeq (0.4 \text{ fm})^2$ or the quark velocity $v^2 = 3/(Ma)^2 \simeq 0.3$.

For such values of a and M it makes sense to first consider the collinear limit $(aM)^2 \gg 1$ such that the wave function collapses to δ distributions around $x = 1/2$ and $\vec{k}_\perp = 0$. Accordingly,

$$F_{\eta_c\gamma}(Q^2) = e_c^2 \, f_{\eta_c} \, \frac{4}{M^2 + Q^2} \, \left(1 + O(1/a^2) + O(\alpha_s)\right) \tag{8}$$

Note that this structure of the form factor is similar to the vector meson dominance prediction.

The form factor at $Q^2 = 0$ is related to the decay rate $\Gamma[\eta_c \to \gamma\gamma]$ which still suffers from large experimental uncertainties [6]

$$\Gamma_{\eta_c\to\gamma\gamma} = \frac{e^4 M^3}{64\pi} \, \left|F_{\eta_c\gamma}(0)\right|^2 = \begin{cases} 7.5^{+1.6}_{-1.4} \text{ keV} & \text{(direct)} \\ (4.0 \pm 1.5 \text{ keV}) \cdot \frac{\Gamma_{\eta_c}^{\text{tot}}}{13.2 \text{ MeV}} & \text{(BR)} \end{cases} \tag{9}$$

---

[a]In fact, we use the same size parameter a for both, the distribution amplitude and the transverse shape. Strictly speaking, this equality only holds in the non-relativistic limit.

In the non-relativistic limit this can also be related to the partial width for $J/\Psi \to e^+e^-$ with $f_{\eta_c} \simeq f_{J/\Psi} \simeq 400$ MeV. However the α_s corrections are known to be large,[7] and the relativistic corrections are large and model dependent. Typically one finds[8,9,10] $f_{\eta_c}/f_{J/\Psi} = 1.2 \pm 0.1$ and $\Gamma_{\eta_c \to \gamma\gamma} = (5-7)$ keV. In the following, we will therefore use $\Gamma_{\eta_c \to \gamma\gamma}$ as a physical normalization for the form factor. In the region of experimental interest, $Q^2 \leq M^2$, we assume that the additional Q^2 dependence of the form factor which is induced by perturbative QCD corrections is small. For larger Q^2 the evolution of the wave function[1] and the α_s corrections to the hard scattering amplitude[11] will become important.

4   Results

Fig. 1 shows the scaled form factor $Q^2 F_{\eta_c\gamma}$ normalized to $\Gamma_{\eta_c \to \gamma\gamma} = 6$ keV. The

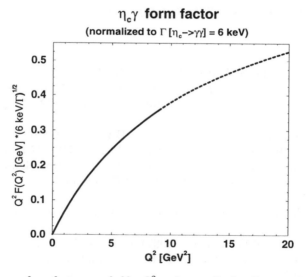

Figure 1: The $\eta_c\gamma$ form factor rescaled by Q^2 and normalized to $\Gamma_{\eta_c \to \gamma\gamma} = 6$ keV in leading order of the HSA. For $Q^2 > M^2$ (dashed line) the perturbative QCD corrections are expected to become important.

following conclusions can be drawn: The shape of the form factor predicted by the HSA approach is unique. It can be well approximated by

$$F_{\eta_c\gamma}(Q^2) \simeq \frac{F(0)}{1 + Q^2/(M^2 + 2\langle \vec{k}_\perp^2 \rangle)} \tag{10}$$

which takes into account the leading corrections to the collinear approximation, reducing the form factor at $Q^2 = 0$ by order 10%. In our case we have $M^2 + 2\langle \vec{k}_\perp^2 \rangle \simeq (3.2 \text{ GeV})^2$ which is not much larger than the value for the J/Ψ mass that one would have inserted in the VDM approach. Note that eq. (10) may be of particular use for the analysis of the decay width $\Gamma_{\eta_c \to \gamma\gamma}$.

The decay constant f_{η_c} enters the form factor as an overall factor. Thus, in principle one may determine its value from a precise measurement of $F_{\eta_c \gamma}$ and/or $\Gamma_{\eta_c \to \gamma\gamma}$. For this purpose also the perturbative corrections to the form factor at arbitrary Q^2 should be taken into account in a consistent way, which is to be analyzed in a forthcoming paper. In this context more precise information from other theoretical approaches (lattice, QCD sum rules) is of course welcome.

Acknowledgments

T.F. is supported by the *Deutsche Forschungsgemeinschaft*.

References

1. G. P. Lepage and S. J. Brodsky, Phys. Rev. **D22**, 2157 (1980).
2. P. Kroll and M. Raulfs, Phys. Lett. **B387**, 848 (1996), hep-ph/9605264.
3. R. Jakob, P. Kroll, and M. Raulfs, J. Phys. **G22**, 45 (1996), hep-ph/9410304.
4. J. Botts and G. Sterman, Nucl. Phys. **B325**, 62 (1989).
5. M. Wirbel, B. Stech, and M. Bauer, Z. Phys. **C29**, 637 (1985).
6. Particle Data Group, R. M. Barnett *et al.*, Phys. Rev. **D54**, 1 (1996).
7. R. Barbieri, E. d'Emilio, G. Curci, and E. Remiddi, Nucl. Phys. **B154**, 535 (1979).
8. M. R. Ahmady and R. R. Mendel, Z. Phys. **C65**, 263 (1995), hep-ph/9401327.
9. D. S. Hwang and G.-H. Kim, (1997), hep-ph/9703364.
10. K.-T. Chao, H.-W. Huang, J.-H. Liu, and J. Tang, (1996), hep-ph/9601381.
11. E. Braaten, Phys. Rev. **D28**, 524 (1983).

A GENERALIZATION OF THE BRODSKY-LEPAGE FORMALISM

L. HOURA-YAOU, P. KESSLER, J. PARISI

Laboratoire de Physique Corpusculaire, Collège de France
11, Place Marcelin Berthelot, F-75231 Paris Cedex 05, France

F. MURGIA

Istituto Nazionale di Fisica Nucleare, Sezione di Cagliari
Casella Postale 170, I-09042 Monserrato (CA), Italy

J. HANSSON

Department of Physics, Luleå University of Technology, S-95187 Luleå, Sweden

We present an approach that generalizes in a natural way the perturbative QCD formalism developed by Brodsky and Lepage for the study of exclusive hadronic processes to the case of $L \neq 0$ mesons. As an application of our approach we consider here the production of meson pairs, involving tensor and pseudotensor mesons, in photon-photon collisions.

In the last years a lot of theoretical work has been devoted to the study of hadronic exclusive processes at high transfer momentum, using factorization techniques and perturbative QCD (PQCD) [1]. While the PQCD formalism seems to be quite successful, it applies only to the case of hadrons with internal orbital angular momentum $L = 0$. Recently [2] we have proposed an approach which generalizes the PQCD formalism to the case of the production and/or decay of mesons with a $(q\bar{q})$ valence Fock state and with any value of the orbital angular momentum L.

In this contribution we give a short, qualitative presentation of our approach, and discuss its application to the case of meson pair production in photon-photon collisions. Predictions for the production of pseudoscalar and vector meson pairs have been already given by Brodsky and Lepage [3]. It is then interesting to extend this study to the production of other meson pairs, involving tensor and pseudotensor mesons.

Let us first recall how the helicity amplitudes for a generic exclusive hadronic process at high transfer momentum are evaluated in perturbative QCD [1]. Using factorization techniques, those amplitudes are expressed as a convolution among different contributions: *i)* A hard-scattering amplitude involving the valence partons of all participating hadrons, assumed to be, inside each hadron, in a collinear configuration; *ii)* Soft, nonperturbative distribution amplitudes (DA) for: *a)* finding the (collinear) valence partons in the incoming hadrons; *b)* the final partonic state to form the observed outgoing hadrons.

Notice that: *i)* Only leading Fock states are considered (i.e., $|q\bar{q}\rangle$ for mesons, $|qqq\rangle$ for baryons); *ii)* Valence parton masses are neglected (this, together with collinear configuration, forces the orbital angular momentum L of each hadron to be vanishing).

In our approach [2] we extend the PQCD formalism to the case of $L \neq 0$ mesons by combining it with a bound-state model of weakly bound valence quarks for the mesons involved. A general prescription can thus be given which relates the helicity amplitudes for the overall reaction (involving the observed mesons) to the partonic amplitudes (involving the collinear valence quarks of those mesons). This prescription implies the usual convolution of the partonic amplitude with the mesonic DA's, as discussed before. In addition, it involves also a convolution with the momentum-space wavefunction of the valence $q\bar{q}$ pair in each meson, given in the corresponding meson rest-frame. A Lorentz boost connects the rest frame of each meson with the center of mass frame of the initial particles; we assume that the mesons, as seen in this overall frame, are extreme-relativistic (this entails some simplifications in actual calculations). Another basic ingredient of our approach is the assumption that, for each meson, the momentum-space wavefunction of the valence $q\bar{q}$ pair is sharply peaked around zero, so that a series expansion in powers of the relative $q\bar{q}$ momentum can be made and only the leading terms have to be considered, in first approximation.

The following equation shows the resulting relationship between the overall and the partonic helicity amplitudes in the case of interest here, that is meson pair production in photon-photon collisions, $\gamma\gamma' \to QQ'$:

$$
\begin{aligned}
M^{LSJ\Lambda,\ L'S'J'\Lambda'}_{\lambda_\gamma\lambda_{\gamma'}}(E,\Theta) &= f_L^*\, f_{L'}^{\prime*} C^{L\ S\ J}_{0\ \Lambda\ \Lambda} C^{L'\ S'\ J'}_{0\ \Lambda'\ \Lambda'} \\
&\times \lim_{\beta,\ \beta' \to 0} \frac{1}{\beta^L \beta'^{L'}} \int \frac{d(\cos\theta)}{2} d^L_{0,0}(\theta) \int \frac{d(\cos\theta')}{2} d^{L'}_{0,0}(\theta') \\
&\times \int \frac{\Phi_N^*(x)dx}{\sqrt{x(1-x)}} \int \frac{\Phi_N'^*(x')dx'}{\sqrt{x'(1-x')}} T^{S\ \Lambda,\ S'\ \Lambda'}_{\lambda_\gamma\lambda_{\gamma'}}(E,\Theta,\beta,\beta',\theta,\theta',x,x') .
\end{aligned}
\tag{1}
$$

In this equation E and Θ are respectively the total energy and the scattering angle in the two-photon c.m. frame; L, S, J, Λ are the quantum numbers of meson Q (hereafter all corresponding labels with a prime refer to meson Q'); f_L is the normalization constant related to the Q meson bound-state wavefunction; $\beta = 2|\mathbf{k}|/M_Q$, θ, refer to the relative $q\bar{q}$ momentum, $\mathbf{k}$, inside meson Q, in its rest frame; $\Phi_N(x)$ is the Q meson distribution amplitude; x is the fraction of Q meson longitudinal momentum carried by quark q; finally,

d-matrices and Clebsch-Gordan coefficients come from opportunely combining the $q\bar{q}$ spin and relative angular momentum states to fit the Q meson quantum numbers. Notice also that in the partonic amplitude T the helicities of each $q\bar{q}$ pair have already been combined to give the required spin and helicity for the corresponding meson.

Let us stress that Eq. (1) reduces exactly to the usual PQCD result when $L = 0$.

The partonic helicity amplitude T in Eq. (1) can be evaluated at leading order in perturbative QCD. The normalization constants f_L, $f_{L'}$ may be fixed by evaluating within the same theoretical approach the two-photon decay widths $\Gamma(Q \to \gamma\gamma)$ and comparing them with the corresponding available experimental results. In order to check the dependence of our results on the meson DA's appearing in Eq. (1) we have considered several indicative choices: $i)$ For the pion, the asymptotic (ASY) DA, $\Phi_{N,\pi}^{ASY}(x) = 6x(1 - x)$, and the Chernyak-Zhitnitsky (CZ) DA, $\Phi_{N,\pi}^{CZ}(x) = 30x(1 - x)(2x - 1)^2$; $ii)$ For tensor and pseudotensor mesons the so-called nonrelativistic (NR) DA, $\Phi_N^{NR}(x) = \delta(x - 1/2)$, and a generalized asymptotic (GASY) DA, $\Phi_N^L(x) \propto x^{L+1}(1 - x)^{L+1}$, which is also required to get rid of possible divergences in the denominator of the partonic amplitudes (e.g., $\Phi_N^{L=1}(x) = 30x^2(1 - x)^2$ for tensor mesons, $\Phi_N^{L=2}(x) = 140x^3(1 - x)^3$ for pseudotensor mesons).

Let us now present some numerical results for the production of: $i)$ Tensor meson pairs; $ii)$ Pseudotensor meson pairs; $iii)$ Pairs made by a pion and a pseudotensor meson. A more complete discussion can be found in Ref. 2; here we limit ourselves to present some indicative examples.

In Fig. 1 the scaling differential cross section $E^8 d\sigma/dt$, as a function of $\cos^2\Theta$ is presented (Θ is the scattering angle in the two-photon c.m. frame). Results are given for a number of tensor meson pairs (using the GASY DA). For comparison, analogous results for pion pairs are also presented, using the asymptotic DA.

Tables 1 and 2 show, for all the meson pairs considered, the integrated cross sections (over the p_T of the mesons in the lab. frame, starting from a given minimum p_T) for the overall process $e^- e^+ \to e^- e^+ QQ'$, in two kinematical conditions, corresponding roughly to those of LEP2 and of a possible B-factory. Again, several choices for the meson DA's are considered.

¿From the results of Fig. 1 and Tables 1,2 (see also Ref. 2) one can make the following conclusions: $i)$ The results obtained do not depend strongly on the choice of the distribution amplitude for tensor and pseudotensor mesons; on the average, the GASY DA leads to results slightly (by a factor of 2 or 3) higher than the nonrelativistic one; $ii)$ As expected, the charged channels give rise to significantly higher yields than the neutral ones, and are then the favorite

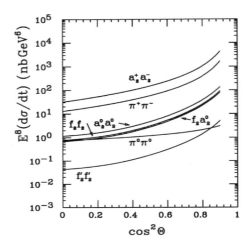

Fig. 1: Differential cross section $E^8\,[d\sigma/dt]$ in nb×GeV^6, as a function of $\cos^2\Theta$, for the process $\gamma\gamma \to QQ'$ involving the production of tensor-meson pairs; the generalized asymptotic (GASY) DA was used for tensor mesons; for comparison, analogous curves for $\gamma\gamma \to \pi^+\pi^-$ and $\gamma\gamma \to \pi^0\pi^0$, using the asymptotic DA are also shown.

candidates for experimental searches; *iii)* The production of the charged meson pairs here considered may become measurable with high-energy e^-e^+ colliders of the next generation, with integrated luminosities of about 10^{40} cm^{-2}.

Acknowledgments

This work has been partially supported by the EU program "Human Capital and Mobility" under contract CHRX-CT94-0450.

References

1. See, e.g., S.J. Brodsky and G.P. Lepage, in *Perturbative Quantum Chromodynamics*, ed. A.H. Mueller (World Scientific, Singapore, 1989).
2. L. Houra-Yaou, P. Kessler, J. Parisi, F. Murgia and J. Hansson, preprint hep-ph/9611337, *Z. Phys.* C, in press, 1997.
3. S.J. Brodsky and G.P. Lepage, *Phys. Rev.* **D24**,1808 (1981).

Table 1: Integrated cross sections (in 10^{-40} cm^2) for the process $e^- e^+ \rightarrow e^- e^+ QQ'$, at $\sqrt{s} = 200$ GeV, $p_T > 1$ GeV.

QQ'	$\sigma(e^- e^+ \rightarrow e^- e^+ QQ')$ $[10^{-40}$ cm$^2]$	
	NR	GASY
$f_2 \, f_2$	20.9	25.4
$a_2^0 \, a_2^0$	30.8	53.0
$f_2 \, a_2^0$	19.4	33.2
$f_2' \, f_2'$	0.6	1.1
$a_2^+ \, a_2^-$	291.0	1003.3
$\pi_2^0 \, \pi_2^0$	141.1	23.2
$\pi_2^+ \, \pi_2^-$	749.3	1418.2
$\pi_{\mathrm{CZ}}^0 \, \pi_2^0$	116.6	263.0
$\pi_{\mathrm{ASY}}^0 \, \pi_2^0$	35.2	104.1
$\pi_{\mathrm{CZ}}^+ \, \pi_2^-$	4167.0	6562.6
$\pi_{\mathrm{ASY}}^+ \, \pi_2^-$	1495.8	2368.5

Table 2: Same as table 1, but assuming: $\sqrt{s} = 10$ GeV, $p_T > 1$ GeV.

QQ'	$\sigma(e^- e^+ \rightarrow e^- e^+ QQ')$ $[10^{-40}$ cm$^2]$	
	NR	GASY
$f_2 \, f_2$	1.4	1.4
$a_2^0 \, a_2^0$	2.3	3.6
$f_2 \, a_2^0$	1.5	2.3
$f_2' \, f_2'$	0.04	0.06
$a_2^+ \, a_2^-$	20.1	68.6
$\pi_2^0 \, \pi_2^0$	10.0	1.6
$\pi_2^+ \, \pi_2^-$	41.6	72.4
$\pi_{\mathrm{CZ}}^0 \, \pi_2^0$	12.0	24.5
$\pi_{\mathrm{ASY}}^0 \, \pi_2^0$	3.0	8.8
$\pi_{\mathrm{CZ}}^+ \, \pi_2^-$	341.1	536.7
$\pi_{\mathrm{ASY}}^+ \, \pi_2^-$	122.0	193.2

$\gamma^*\gamma^* \to \pi^0$ REACTION AT LARGE PHOTON VIRTUALITIES

SARO ONG[a]

CEA/Saclay, DSM/DAPNIA, Service de Physique Nucléaire,
Centre d'Etudes de Saclay,
F-91191 Gif-sur-Yvette, France

The pion-photon transition form factor is related to the axial anomaly and, because of this connection, has a great physical interest. We have shown that pseudoscalar-meson production by two off-shell photons can be used to check the hard scattering approach of Brodsky and Lepage. Recently, A. Anselm et al. have proposed a new approach to this problem ; they reexamine the triangle diagram where the pion is treated as a composite particle. We emphasize the importance of precise measurements performed or planned at CLEO II and BaBar in the near future.

The prediction of Brodsky and Lepage[1] (BL) for the $\pi^0\gamma\gamma^*$ transition form factor has been found to be consistent with the CELLO data[2] and a recent experimental measurement[3] performed at CLEO II. However, those data are compatible as well with predictions based on the vector-meson dominance model (VMD).

Our study on pseudoscalar-meson production in $\gamma^*\gamma^*$ collisions[4] shows that it is possible to check the prediction of the pQCD hard-scattering approach[5] with high-luminosity e^+e^- colliders : CLEO II or $B\bar{B}$ factory. An interesting kinematic configuration is the symmetric one, where $Q'^2 = Q^2$; with $Q^2 = -q^2$, $Q'^2 = -q'^2$ (q, q' are the four-momenta of the photons). In that configuration, the form factor in the BL scheme becomes independent of the choice of the meson wave function. Notice that this form factor is $\sim Q^{-2}$, while the VMD predicts it to be $\sim Q^{-4}$.

The physical interest of this type of reaction was emphasized by various authors[6] who studied it in the framework of the algebra of bilocal currents.

A.V. Radyushkin and R. Ruskov[7] have also performed the calculation of the transition form factor $\gamma^*\gamma^* \to \pi^0$ in the framework of QCD sum rules. Their result is valid for small virtuality of one of the photons. For one photon on shell, their estimates are also in good agreement with existing experimental data[2,3]. In the same kinematic configuration, J. M. Gerard and T. Lahna[8] have calculated $F_{\pi\gamma^*}$, using the Bjorken-Johnson-Low theorem. They obtain the correct Q^2 behavior, but underestimate the magnitude.

Recently, A. Anselm et al.[9] have suggested a new approach to this problem. They have studied the $\pi^0\gamma^*\gamma^*$ vertex in the general picture of the triangle

---

[a]E-mail : ong@phnx7.saclay.cea.fr

diagram where the pion is treated as a composite particle, they were able to obtain an approximate expression of the form factor, for arbitrary values of Q^2 and Q'^2, without an explicit knowledge of the pion wave function.

We hereafter compare our results with those of Ref.[9] and it would be interesting to test these predictions experimentally.

Let us recall the expression for the transition form factor $F_{\pi\gamma^*}(Q^2, Q'^2)$, according to the Brodsky-Lepage scheme :

$$F_{\pi\gamma^*}(Q^2, Q'^2) = \frac{4}{\sqrt{3}} \int_0^1 dx \, \frac{\phi_\pi^*(x)}{Q^2 x + Q'^2(1-x)} \tag{1}$$

assuming Q^2 and/or $Q'^2 \gg m_\pi^2$, and taking into account the symmetry (due to invariance under charge conjugation) of the pion wave function $\phi_\pi(x)$ in x, $1-x$, the normalization condition of $\phi_\pi(x)$ reads :

$$\int_0^1 \phi_\pi(x) \, dx = f_\pi / 2\sqrt{3} \tag{2}$$

where $f_\pi = 93$ MeV is the pion decay constant.
Using the asymptotic wave function $\phi_\pi^{as}(x) = \sqrt{3} f_\pi x(1-x)$, we get[4]

$$F_{\pi\gamma^*}(Q^2, Q'^2) = 2f_\pi \frac{Q^4 - Q'^4 - 2Q^2 Q'^2 \ln(Q^2/Q'^2)}{(Q^2 - Q'^2)^3} \tag{3}$$

One immediately checks that this formula reduces to

$$F_{\pi\gamma}(Q^2) = \frac{2f_\pi}{Q^2} \tag{4}$$

when Q'^2 goes to zero.

Here, we focus on the scaling behavior of the transition form factor for large values of Q^2 and Q'^2 at a fixed Q^2/Q'^2 ratio. To facilitate the comparison with the results of Ref.[9], we reexpress (3) with a dimensionless function $G_1(\omega)$ where ω is a parameter defined by :

$$\omega = \frac{Q^2 - Q'^2}{Q^2 + Q'^2}$$

$$F_{\pi\gamma^*}(Q^2, Q'^2) = \frac{2f_\pi}{3 <Q^2>} \, G_1(\omega) \tag{5}$$

and

$$G_1(\omega) = \frac{3 \, [\, 2\omega + (1 - \omega^2)[\ln(1 - \omega) - \ln(1 + \omega)] \,]}{4\omega^3} \tag{6}$$

with $< Q^2 > = (Q^2 + Q'^2)/2$.

The behavior of the pion-photon transition form factor is somewhat different from the Chernyak-Zhitnitsky[10] wave function $\phi_\pi^{CZ}(x) = 5\sqrt{3}f_\pi x(1 - x)(1 - 2x)^2$. One obtains the same formula (5) with another function $G_2(\omega)$:

$$G_2(\omega) = \frac{5 \left[6\omega - 4\omega^3 + 3(1 - \omega^2)[\ln(1 - \omega) - \ln(1 + \omega)] \right]}{4\omega^5} \tag{7}$$

The authors of Ref.[9] obtain a similar expression for the dimensionless function $\phi(\omega)$ (denoted here as $G_3(\omega)$) without explicitly introducing the pion wave function :

$$G_3(\omega) = [(1 + \omega)\ln(1 + \omega) + (1 - \omega)\ln(1 - \omega)]/\omega^2 \tag{8}$$

We display for comparison in Fig. 1, for various values of $|\omega|$, the different $G_i(\omega)$ functions. One remarks that the prediction of the BL model with the asymptotic wave function is very close to that of Ref.[9] using quite different physical assumptions.

Notice that the two models reproduce exactly the operator product expansion (OPE) result[11] in the asymptotic region $Q^2 = Q'^2$ with $Q^2 \to \infty$.

$$F_{\pi\gamma^*}(Q^2, Q^2) = \frac{2f_\pi}{3Q^2} \tag{9}$$

It can be seen (Fig. 1), that the ratio between predictions for the form factor, based on the CZ and the asymptotic wave function respectively, varies between 1 and 5/3. A. S. Gorskii[12] has shown the possibility to obtain information on the pion wave function by combining a sum rule method with perturbative QCD at large photon virtualities. However, this sum rule method is valid only in the kinematic region $|\omega| \le 0.5$.

Brodsky and Lepage[1] have proposed a simple interpolation formula for the transition form factor, between its asymptotic expression (4) and the current-algebra prediction ($Q^2 \to 0$) :

$$F_{\pi\gamma}(Q^2) = \frac{1}{4\pi^2 f_\pi} \left(1 + \frac{Q^2}{\Lambda^2}\right)^{-1} \tag{10}$$

with $\Lambda^2 = 8\pi^2 f_\pi^2$.

Following this interpolation procedure, we write the formula (5) as

$$F_{\pi\gamma^*}(Q^2, Q'^2) = \frac{1}{4\pi^2 f_\pi} \left(1 + \frac{X^2}{\Lambda^2}\right)^{-1} \tag{11}$$

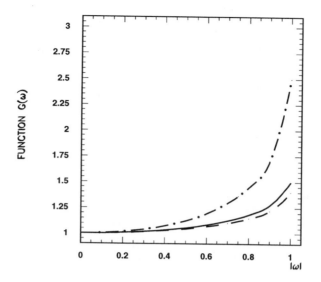

Figure 1: Function $G_i(\omega)$ vs $|\omega|$. $G_1(\omega)$ (solid line) ; $G_2(\omega)$ (dash-dotted line) ; $G_3(\omega)$ (dashed line).

with

$$X^2 = \frac{3 < Q^2 >}{G_1(\omega)} \tag{12}$$

In order to check the feasibility of measurements of the form factors at large photon virtualities, we have computed the cross section of the reaction $e^+e^- \rightarrow e^+e^-\pi^0$ with a c.m. energy of 10 GeV (chosen to be that of CLEO or of a $B\bar{B}$ factory) and an integrated luminosity $\int L \, dt = 10^{40}$ cm^{-2}, using interpolation formula (11). For $Q^2_{min} = Q'^2_{min} = 1$ GeV^2, one expects about 310 events and 71 events for $Q^2_{min} = 3$ GeV^2, $Q'^2_{min} = 1$ GeV^2 for example.

Such measurements should thus become feasible in a near future, allowing for a check of the asymptotic behavior of the pion-photon transition form factor at large photon virtualities.

Acknowledgments

The author would like to thank the theory group of DAPNIA/SPhN Saclay, for the warm hospitality extended to him. He is grateful to Prof. P. Kessler for constructive remarks.

References

1. S. J. Brodsky and G. P. Lepage, Phys. Rev. **D24** (1981) 1808.

2. CELLO Coll., H. J. Behrend et al., Z. Phys. **C49** (1991) 401.

3. CLEO II Coll., V. Savinov, Proceedings of the Workshop "Photon'95", Sheffield, UK (1995), edited by D. J. Miller, S. L. Cartwright and V. Khoze (World Scientific 1995), p. 203.
   See also the talk presented at this Conference by V. Savinov.

4. P. Kessler and S. Ong, Phys. Rev. **D48** (1993) R2974.

5. G. P. Lepage and S. J. Brodsky, Phys. Rev. Lett. **43** (1979) 545 ; Phys. Rev. **D22** (1980) 2157.
   V. L. Chernyak and A. R. Zhitnitsky, Yad. Fiz. **31** (1980) 1053 [Sov. J. Nucl. Phys. **31** (1980) 544] ; Phys. Rep. **112** (1984) 173.
   V. L. Chernyak, A. A. Ogloblin, I. R. Zhitnitsky, Z. Phys. **C42** (1989) 569.

6. H. Terazawa, Rev. Mod. Phys. **45** (1973) 615, and references therein.
   G. Köpp, T. F. Walsh, and P. Zerwas, Nucl. Phys. **B70** (1974) 461.

7. A. V. Radyushkin and R. Ruskov, Proceedings of the Workshop "Photon'95", Sheffield, UK (1995), edited by D. J. Miller, S. L. Cartwright and V. Khoze (World Scientific 1995), p. 250.
   See also the talk presented at this Conference by R. Ruskov.

8. J. M. Gerard and T. Lahna, Phys. Lett. **B356** (1995) 381.

9. A. Anselm, A. Johansen, E. Leader and L. Lukaszuk, HUTP-95/A037, hep-ph/9603444.

10. V. L. Chernyak and A. R. Zhitnitsky, Nucl. Phys. **B201** (1982) 492.

11. V. A. Novikov, M. A. Shifman, A. I. Vainshtein, M. B. Valoshin and V. I. Zakharov, Nucl. Phys. **B237** (1984) 525.

12. A. S. Gorskii, Yad. Fiz. **46** (1987) 938 [Sov. J. Nucl. Phys. **46** (1987) 537].

THE ASYMPTOTICS OF THE TRANSITION FORM FACTOR $\gamma\gamma^* \to \pi^o$ AND QCD SUM RULES

A.V. RADYUSHKIN[*†]

*Old Dominion University, Norfolk, VA 23529, USA;
Jefferson Lab, Newport News, VA 23606, USA

R. RUSKOV[†]

†Laboratory of Theoretical Physics, JINR, Dubna 141980, Russia

In this paper we present the result [1,2] of a direct QCD sum rule calculation of the transition form factor $\gamma\gamma^* \to \pi^0$ in the region of moderately large invariant momentum $Q^2 \geq 1\,GeV^2$ of the virtual photon. In contrast to pQCD, we make no assumptions about the shape of the pion distribution amplitude $\varphi_\pi(x)$. Our results agree with the Brodsky-Lepage proposal that the Q^2-dependence of this form factor is given by an interpolation between its $Q^2 = 0$ value fixed by the axial anomaly and $1/Q^2$ pQCD behaviour for large Q^2, with normalization corresponding to the asymptotic form $\varphi_\pi^{as}(x) = 6f_\pi x(1-x)$ of the pion distribution amplitude. Our prediction for the from factor $F_{\gamma^*\gamma^*\pi^0}(q_1^2 = 0, q_2^2 = -Q^2)$ is in good agreemnt with new CLEO data.

The transition $\gamma^*\gamma^* \to \pi^0$ of two virtual photons γ^* into a neutral pion provides an exceptional opportunity to test QCD predictions for exclusive processes. In the lowest order of perturbative QCD, its asymptotic behaviour is due to the subprocess $\gamma^*(q_1) + \gamma^*(q_2) \to \bar{q}(\bar{x}p) + q(xp)$ with x ($\bar{x}$) being the fraction of the pion momentum p carried by the quark produced at the q_1 (q_2) photon vertex. The relevant diagram resembles the handbag diagram of DIS, with the main difference that one should use the pion distribution amplitude (DA) $\varphi_\pi(x)$ instead of parton densities. This gives good reasons to expect that pQCD for this process may work at accessible values of spacelike photon virtualities. The asymptotic pQCD prediction is given by [3] ($\bar{x} = 1 - x$):

$$F_{\gamma^*\gamma^*\pi^0}^{as}(q^2, Q^2) = \frac{4\pi}{3} \int_0^1 \frac{\varphi_\pi(x)}{xQ^2 + \bar{x}q^2}\, dx \xrightarrow{q^2=0} \frac{4\pi}{3} \int_0^1 \frac{\varphi_\pi(x)}{xQ^2}\, dx \equiv \frac{4\pi f_\pi}{3Q^2}I. \quad (1)$$

Experimentally, the most important situation is when one of the photons is almost real $q^2 \approx 0$ [4,5]. In this case, necessary nonperturbative information is accumulated in the same integral I (see eq.(1)) that appears in the one-gluon-exchange diagram for the pion electromagnetic form factor [6,7,8].

The value of I is sensitive to the shape of the pion DA $\varphi_\pi(x)$, mainly to its end-point behaviour. In particular, using the asymptotic form $\varphi_\pi^{as}(x) = 6f_\pi x\bar{x}$ [6,7] gives $F_{\gamma\gamma^*\pi^0}^{as}(Q^2) = 4\pi f_\pi/Q^2$ for the asymptotic behaviour [3]. If one takes the Chernyak-Zhitnitsky form[8] $\varphi_\pi^{CZ}(x) = 30 f_\pi x \bar{x}(1-2x)^2$, the integral I increases by a sizable factor of 5/3, and this difference can be used for experimental discrimination between the two forms. One-loop radiative QCD corrections to eq.(1) are known [9,10] and they are under control.

For lower Q^2, power corrections become very important. Indeed, the asymptotic $1/Q^2$-behaviour cannot be true in the low-Q^2 region, since the $Q^2 = 0$ limit of $F_{\gamma\gamma^*\pi^0}(Q^2)$ is known to be finite and normalized by the $\pi^0 \to \gamma\gamma$ decay rate. Theoretically[11], $F_{\gamma\gamma^*\pi^0}(0) = 1/\pi f_\pi$. It is natural to expect that the leading term is close to a simple interpolation $\pi f_\pi F_{\gamma^*\pi^0}^{LO}(Q^2) = 1/(1 + Q^2/4\pi^2 f_\pi^2)$ between the $Q^2 = 0$ value and the large-Q^2 asymptotics. This interpolation agrees with experiment[4,5] and implies the asymptotic form[6,7] of the DA for accessible Q^2. It introduces a mass scale $s_o^\pi \equiv 4\pi^2 f_\pi^2 \approx 0.67 \, GeV^2$ close to m_ρ^2.

Consider a three-point correlation function[a]

$$\mathcal{F}_{\alpha\mu\nu}(q_1, q_2) = 2\pi i \int \langle 0|T\{j_\alpha^5(Y) J_\mu(X) J_\nu(0)\}|0\rangle e^{-iq_1 X} e^{ipY} d^4X \, d^4Y \,, \quad (2)$$

where J_μ is the EM current and the axial-vector current has a non-zero projection onto the neutral pion state. The amplitude $\mathcal{F}_{\alpha\mu\nu}(q_1, q_2)$ has a pole for $p^2 = m_\pi^2$ with residue proportional to the form factor of interest. The higher states include A_1 and higher broad pseudovector resonances. Due to asymptotic freedom, their sum for large s rapidly approaches the pQCD spectral density $\rho^{PT}(s, q^2, Q^2)$. Hence, the spectral density of the dispersion relation for the relevant invariant amplitude $\mathcal{F}(p^2, q^2, Q^2)$ can be written as $\rho(s, q^2, Q^2) = \pi f_\pi \delta(s - m_\pi^2) F_{\gamma^*\gamma^*\pi^0}(q^2, Q^2) + \theta(s - s_o)\rho^{PT}(s, q^2, Q^2)$, with the parameter s_o being the effective threshold for higher states. To construct a QCD sum rule, we calculate the three-point function $\mathcal{F}(p^2, q^2, Q^2)$ and then its SVZ-transform $\Phi(M^2, q^2, Q^2)$ as a power expansion in $1/M^2$ for large M^2.

The simplest case is when the smaller virtuality q^2 is large: $q^2, Q^2, -p^2 \geq 1 \, GeV^2$. Then, to produce a contribution with a power behaviour $(1/p^2)^N$, all three currents should be kept close to each other: all the intervals $X^2, Y^2, (X-Y)^2$ should be small. Taking into account the perturbative contribution and the condensate corrections, we obtain a QCD sum rule[1,2]. For $Q^2, q^2 \gg s_0$, keeping only the leading $O(1/Q^2, 1/q^2)$- terms we obtain:

$$F_{\gamma^*\gamma^*\pi^0}^{LO}(q^2, Q^2) = \frac{4\pi}{3f_\pi} \int_0^1 \frac{dx}{(xQ^2 + \bar{x}q^2)} \left\{ \frac{3M^2}{2\pi^2}(1 - e^{-s_0/M^2})x\bar{x} \right.$$

$$+ \frac{1}{24M^2}\langle\frac{\alpha_s}{\pi}GG\rangle[\delta(x) + \delta(\bar{x})]$$

---

[a] Actually, it is a common starting point both for pQCD and QCD SR approaches.

$$+ \frac{8}{81M^4} \pi \alpha_s \langle \bar{q}q \rangle^2 \left(11[\delta(x) + \delta(\bar{x})] + 2[\delta'(x) + \delta'(\bar{x})] \right) \Big\} . \tag{3}$$

Note, that the expression in curly brackets coincides with the QCD sum rule for the pion DA $f_\pi \varphi_\pi(x)$ (see, e.g., ref.[12]). Hence, the QCD sum rules approach is capable to reproduce the pQCD result (1).

An attempt to get a QCD sum rule for the integral I by taking $q^2 = 0$ in eq.(3) is ruined by power singularities $1/q^2$, $1/q^4$ in the condensate terms. The perturbative term in the small-q^2 region has logarithms $\log q^2$ which are a typical example of mass singularities (see, e.g.,[13]). All these infrared sensitive terms are produced in a regime when the hard momentum flow bypasses the soft photon vertex, i.e., the EM current $J_\mu(X)$ of the low-virtuality photon is far away from the two other currents $J(0), j^5(Y)$.

Observe also, that power singularities emerge precisely by the same $\delta(x)$ and $\delta'(x)$ terms in eq.(3) which generate the two-hump form for $\varphi_\pi(x)$ in the CZ-approach [8]. As shown in ref.[12], the $\delta^{(n)}(x)$ terms result from the Taylor expansion of nonlocal condensates like $\langle \bar{q}(0)q(Z) \rangle$.

Our strategy is to subtract all these singularities from the coefficient functions of the original OPE for the 3-point correlation function eq.(2). They are absorbed in this approach by *universal* bilocal correlators (see refs.[1,2]), which can be also interpreted as moments of the DAs for (almost) real photon $\int_0^1 y^n \phi_\gamma^{(i)}(y, q^2) \sim \Pi_n^{(i)}(q^2) = \int e^{iq_1 X} \langle 0|T\{J_\mu(X)\mathcal{O}_n^{(i)}(0)\}|0\rangle d^4X$, where $\mathcal{O}_n^{(i)}(0)$ are operators of leading and next-to-leading twist with n covariant derivatives [1,2]. The bilocal contribution to the 3-point function eq.(2) can be written in a "parton" form as a convolution of the photon DAs and some coefficient functions. The last originate from a light cone OPE for the product $T\{J(0)j^5(Y)\}$. The amplitude $\mathcal{F}$ is now a sum of its purely short-distance (SD) (regular for $q^2 = 0$) and bilocal (B) parts. Getting the $q^2 \to 0$ limit of $\Pi_n^{(i)}(q_1)$ requires a nonperturbative input.

After all modifications described above are made, we can write the QCD sum rule for the $\gamma\gamma^* \to \pi^0$ form factor in the $q^2 = 0$ limit:

$$\pi f_\pi F_{\gamma\gamma^* \pi^0}(Q^2) = \int_0^{s_0} \left\{ 1 - 2 \frac{Q^2 - 2s}{(s + Q^2)^2} \left(s_\rho - \frac{s_\rho^2}{2m_\rho^2} \right) \right.$$

$$+ \; 2 \frac{Q^4 - 6sQ^2 + 3s^2}{(s + Q^2)^4} \left(\frac{s_\rho^2}{2} - \frac{s_\rho^3}{3m_\rho^2} \right) \Big\} e^{-s/M^2} \frac{Q^2 ds}{(s + Q^2)^2}$$

$$+ \; \frac{\pi^2}{9} \langle \frac{\alpha_s}{\pi} GG \rangle \left\{ \frac{1}{2Q^2 M^2} + \frac{1}{Q^4} - 2 \int_0^{s_0} e^{-s/M^2} \frac{ds}{(s + Q^2)^3} \right\}$$

$$+ \frac{64}{27}\pi^3\alpha_s\langle\bar{q}q\rangle^2 \lim_{\lambda^2\to 0}\left\{\frac{1}{2Q^2M^4} + \frac{12}{Q^4m_\rho^2}\left[\log\frac{Q^2}{\lambda^2} - 2\right.\right.$$

$$+ \int_0^{s_0} e^{-s/M^2}\left(\frac{s^2+3sQ^2+4Q^4}{(s+Q^2)^3} - \frac{1}{s+\lambda^2}\right)ds\bigg]$$

$$- \frac{4}{Q^6}\left[\log\frac{Q^2}{\lambda^2} - 3 + \int_0^{s_0}e^{-s/M^2}\left(\frac{s^2+3sQ^2+6Q^4}{(s+Q^2)^3} - \frac{1}{s+\lambda^2}\right)ds\right]\bigg\}(4)$$

Here we model the bilocal contributions using the asymptotic form for the DAs of the ρ-meson and making them approximately dual to the corresponding pt-contribution. We use the standard values for the condensates and the ρ-meson

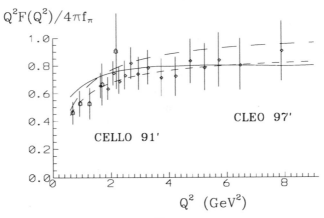

Figure 1:

duality interval $s_\rho = 1.5\,GeV^2$ [14]. Explicit fitting procedure in (4) favours the value $s_0 \approx 0.7\,GeV^2$ for the effective threshold [1,2]. Hence, our calculations support the local duality prescription [15].

In Fig.1, we present our curve (solid line) for $Q^2F_{\gamma\gamma^*\pi^0}(Q^2)/4\pi f_\pi$ calculated from eq.(4) for $s_0 = 0.7\,GeV^2$. One can observe very good agreement with the new CLEO data [5]. It is rather close to the Brodsky-Lepage interpolation formula [b] (long-dashed line) and the ρ-pole approximation (short-dashed line) $\pi f_\pi F^{VMD}(Q^2) = 1/(1+Q^2/m_\rho^2)$. It should be noted that the Q^2-dependence of the ρ-pole type emerges due to the fact that the pion duality interval $s_0 \approx 0.7\,GeV^2$ is numerically close to $m_\rho^2 \approx 0.6\,GeV^2$. In the region $Q^2 > Q_*^2 \sim 3\,GeV^2$, our curve for $Q^2F_{\gamma\gamma^*\pi^0}(Q^2)$ is practically constant, sup-

---

[b]In fact, such interpolation follows from the local duality considerations [15]

porting the pQCD expectation (1). The absolute magnitude of our prediction gives $I \approx 2.4$ for the I-integral with an accuracy of about 20%.

Comparing the value $I = 2.4$ with $I^{as} = 3$ and $I^{CZ} = 5$, we conclude that our result favours a pion DA which is narrower than the asymptotic form. Parametrizing the width of $\varphi_\pi(x)$ by a simple model $\varphi_\pi(x) \sim [x(1-x)]^n$, we get that $I = 2.4$ corresponds to $n = 2.5$. The second moment $\langle \xi^2 \rangle \equiv \langle (x - \bar{x})^2 \rangle$ for such a function is 0.125 (recall that $\langle \xi^2 \rangle^{as} = 0.2$ while $\langle \xi^2 \rangle^{CZ} = 0.43$) which agrees with the lattice calculation [16].

Acknowledgments

We are grateful to S.J.Brodsky, H.G.Dosch, A.V.Efremov, O.Nachtmann, D.J.Miller and V.Savinov for useful discussions and comments. The work of AR was supported by the US Department of Energy under contract DE-AC05-84ER40150; the work of RR was supported by Russian Foundation for Fundamental Research, Grant N° 96-02-17631.

References

1. A.V. Radyushkin and R.Ruskov, *Phys. Lett.* B **374**, 173 (1996).
2. A.V. Radyushkin and R.Ruskov, *Nucl.Phys.* B **481**, 625 (1996).
3. G.P.Lepage and S.J.Brodsky, *Phys.Rev.* D **22**, 2157 (1980).
4. CELLO collaboration, H.-J.Behrend et al., *Z. Phys.* C **49**, 401 (1991).
5. CLEO collaboration, preprint CLNS-97/1477 / CLEO-97-7 (1997).
6. A.V.Efremov and A.V.Radyushkin, JINR report E2-11983 (Oct 1978); *Phys.Lett.* B **94**, 245 (1980).
7. S.J.Brodsky and G.P.Lepage, *Phys.Lett.* B **87**, 359 (1979).
8. V.L.Chernyak and A.R.Zhitnitsky, *Phys.Reports* **112**, 173 (1984); *Nucl. Phys.* B **201**, 492 (1982); B **214**, 547(E) (1983).
9. E. Braaten, *Phys. Rev.* D **28** , 524 (1983).
10. E.P.Kadantseva, S.V.Mikhailov and A.V.Radyushkin, *Sov.J. Nucl.Phys.* **44**, 326 (1986).
11. S.L.Adler, *Phys.Rev.* **177**, 2426 (1969); J.S.Bell, R.Jackiw, *Nuovo Cim.* **A60**, 47 (1967).
12. S.V.Mikhailov and A.V.Radyushkin, *Phys.Rev.* D **45**, 1754 (1992).
13. R.K.Ellis et al., *Nucl. Phys.* B **152**, 285 (1979); G.Sterman, *Phys.Rev.* D **17**, 2773 (1978).
14. M.A.Shifman et al., *Nucl.Phys.* B **147**, 385, 448 (1979).
15. A.V. Radyushkin, *Acta Phys. Polon.* B **26**, 2067 (1995).
16. D.Daniel et al., *Phys.Rev.* D **43**, 3715 (1991).

EXACT AND COMPLETE MONTE-CARLO FOR $\gamma\gamma \to l^+l^-$

A. COURAU

Laboratoire de l'Accélérateur Linéaire, IN2P3-CNRS et Université de Paris-Sud,
F-91405 Orsay Cedex, France

C. CARIMALO

Laboratoire de Physique Corpusculaire, Collège de France, 11, Place Marcelin
Berthelot, F-75231 Paris Cedex 05, France

S. ONG

CEA/Saclay, DSM/DAPNIA, Service de Physique Nucléaire, Centre d'Etudes de
Saclay, F-91191 Gif-sur-Yvette, France

For lepton pair production through $\gamma\gamma$ collisions, a very fast Monte-Carlo program is presented. It generates all kinematical variables of all outgoing particles, according to the exact and complete differential cross section of the two-photon exchange graph, expressed within the helicity formalism by means of 20 helicity amplitudes. That Monte-Carlo program applies to any e^+e^- machine, from DAΦNE to LEP200 and beyond. Comparisons between various machines, acceptances and approximations are shown for some distributions.

The Monte-carlo program [1] here presented was originally developed in the context of $\gamma\gamma$ collisions at DAΦNE [2]. It was there essential to dispose of an exact and complete generation of muon pairs in order to control the experimental analysis and normalization of pion pair production near threshold, that provides important tests of Chiral Pertubation Theory. Let us also remind that in DAΦNE conditions there are large azimutal correlations that could be measured [3] (because of an unusual wide angular distribution of the scattered electrons) and that beams cross at angle. Of course, our generator applies as well to any ee machine from DAΦNE to LEP200 and beyond, for any beam configuration, and to any lepton pair production.

The Monte-Carlo program generates the 4-momenta of the 4 outgoing particles, namely (e^+, e^-, l^+, l^-), according to the exact and completely differentiated cross section of the 2 photon exchange graph, given the acceptance and beam configuration.

While the two photon exchange graph is treated in an exact way, there is however the following theoretical limitations : 1) contributions from other possible graphs are ignored 2) radiative corrections are not considered, though one must bear in mind that they may be significant in some experimental configurations 3) in case of $ee \to ee\tau\tau$ the tau polarization is not yet determined at the present stage 4) in case of $ee \rightarrow eeee$ the full antisymetrization of the identical $e^{\pm}$ is not taken into account.

No specific experimental limitations are required. However limits regarding the range of the l^+l^- invariant mass W, and angular acceptances of electrons and leptons can be set in the program. This allows the program to be fast whatever the chosen kinematical range. Let us note that requiring an angular acceptance is quite economical at very small W and large beam energy.

Within the helicity formalism [4], the differential cross section is written as :

$$d\sigma = dC \ H$$

$$dC = \frac{1}{2\pi^8} \ \frac{1}{2^{10}E_0^2} \ \frac{dx}{x} \ \frac{dx'}{x'} \ dQ^2 \ dQ'^2 \ d\Phi_1' \ d\Phi_2' \ \beta_l \ du \ d\phi_{el}$$

$$H = \frac{(4\pi\alpha)^4}{Q^4 \ Q'^4} \ \Sigma A_{m,\overline{m}} B_{m\overline{m},n\overline{n}} C_{n,\overline{n}} e^{i(m-\overline{m})\phi_{el}} \ e^{i(n-\overline{n})(\phi_{ee}-\phi_{el})}$$

where : $x = E_\gamma/E_0$, $x' = E_\gamma'/E_0$, E_γ, E_γ' and E_0 being the energies of either photon and that of the beam in the ee c-of-m frame ; $Q^2 = -q^2$ and $Q'^2 = -q'^2$ are the opposite of the 4-momenta squared of the photons ; Φ_1', Φ_2' are the respective azimutal angles of the scattered electrons e_1' and e_2' in the ee c-of-m frame ; ϕ_{ee} is the relative azimutal angle of $e_1'e_2'$ and ϕ_{el} that of $e'l$ in the $\gamma\gamma$ c-of-m frame ; $\beta_l = \sqrt{1 - 4m_l^2/W^2}$; $u = \cos\theta^\star$, $\theta^\star$ being the polar angle of l in $\gamma\gamma$ c-of-m frame ; $m\overline{m}$ $(n,\overline{n})$ are helicity indices of either exchanged photon; the A's and C's are helicity matrix elements associated with either $ee'\gamma$ vertex and the B's are helicity amplitudes describing the $\gamma^\star\gamma^\star$ subprocess.

Let us remind that, due to gauge invariance, the helicity matrix of each exchanged photon has 3×3 elements, so that the expression of the above factor H a priori contains 3^4 terms. In fact, using hermiticity, parity conservation and rotational invariance, that number is considerably reduced and one is led to a 20-term formula.

In the formula below, the various terms are listed according to their helicity content. Thus, the first five terms come from transverse photons while the remaining ones involve at least one longitudinal polarization. The analytical expressions of all these helicity amplitudes are too long to be given here, but they can be easily found inside the program itself where the same notations have been explicitly used. At this point, it is worth reminding that each subsript 0 implies a Q/W or a Q'/W factor in the corresponding amplitude.

$$2(A_{++}B_{++,++}C_{++} + A_{++}B_{++,--}C_{--})$$

$$\begin{array}{ll}
4(A_{++}B_{++,+-}C_{+-}) & \cos(2\phi_{ee} - \phi_{el}) \\
4(A_{+-}B_{+-,++}C_{++}) & \cos 2\phi_{el} \\
2(A_{+-}B_{+-,+-}C_{+-}) & \cos 2\phi_{ee} \\
2(A_{-+}B_{+-,-+}C_{-+}) & \cos(2\phi_{el} - \phi_{ee}) \\
4(A_{++}B_{++,+0}C_{+0} + A_{++}B_{++,0-}C_{0-}) & \cos(\phi_{ee} - \phi_{el}) \\
4(A_{+0}B_{+0,++}C_{++} + A_{0-}B_{0-,++}C_{++}) & \cos\phi_{el} \\
2(A_{+-}B_{+-,+0}C_{+0} + A_{+-}B_{+-,0-}C_{0-}) & \cos(\phi_{ee} + \phi_{el}) \\
2(A_{+0}B_{+0,+-}C_{+-} + A_{0-}B_{0-,+-}C_{+-}) & \cos(2\phi_{ee} - \phi_{el}) \\
2(A_{+-}B_{+-,0+}C_{0+} + A_{+-}B_{+-,-0}C_{-0}) & \cos(3\phi_{el} - \phi_{ee}) \\
2(A_{0+}B_{0+,+-}C_{+-} + A_{-0}B_{-0,+-}C_{+-}) & \cos(2\phi_{ee} - 3\phi_{el}) \\
4(A_{+0}B_{+0,+0}C_{+0} + A_{+0}B_{+0,0-}C_{0-}) & \cos\phi_{ee} \\
4(A_{+0}B_{+0,0+}C_{0+} + A_{+0}B_{+0,-0}C_{-0}) & \cos(2\phi_{el} - \phi_{ee}) \\
2(A_{++}B_{++,00}C_{00}) & \\
2(A_{00}B_{00,++}C_{++}) & \\
2(A_{+-}B_{+-,00}C_{00}) & \cos 2\phi_{el} \\
4(A_{00}B_{00,++}C_{++}) & \cos 2(\phi_{ee} - \phi_{el}) \\
4(A_{+0}B_{+0,00}C_{00}) & \cos\phi_{el} \\
2(A_{00}B_{00,+0}C_{+0}) & \cos(\phi_{ee} - \phi_{el}) \\
2(A_{00}B_{00,00}C_{00}) &
\end{array}$$

Such formula has been in the literature for a long time[4,5] . It exhibits 13 different azimutal dependences associated with 13 "structure functions". But the study of azimuthal correlations requires double-tag experiment.

Integrating over ϕ_{el} one gets a 3-term formula similar to that of Budnev et al.[6] :

$$d\sigma \sim D_o + D_1 \cos\phi_{ee} + D_2 \cos 2\phi_{ee}$$

Integrating over ϕ_{ee} one obtains another 3-term formula

$$d\sigma \sim D_0 + D_1' \cos\phi_{el} + D_2' \cos 2\phi_{el}$$

useful for single-tag experiment. That configuration practically amounts to an integration over ϕ_{ee} and to suppress the longitudinal components of the photon associated with the unseen electron. It leads to an expression similar to that of Hand for electroproduction, that was used to extract 3 QED structure functions from muon pair production[7].

Finally, if one integrates both over ϕ_{el} and ϕ_{ee} defining the polarization parameters of the photons $\epsilon = A_{00}/2A_{++}$ and $\epsilon' = C_{00}/2C_{++}$ one gets

$$d\sigma \sim D_0 \sim d\sigma_{TT} + \epsilon' d\sigma_{TL} + \epsilon d\sigma_{LT} + \epsilon\epsilon' d\sigma_{LL}$$

which for single-tag experiment leads to

$$d\sigma \sim d\sigma_{TT} + \epsilon d\sigma_{LT}$$

When $Q^2/W^2, Q'^2/W^2 \to 0$ one can derive approximations essentially relevant to no-tag experiment.

A dynamical approximation consists in neglecting all terms in Q^2/W^2, Q'^2/W^2 in helicity amplitudes. It only remains a simplified expression of the first one. The differential cross section can then be expressed as the product of two independent photon spectra and the cross section of the real $\gamma\gamma \to l^+l^-$ process. This is the "Double Equivalent Photon Approximation" (DEPA)

$$S(x,t)\frac{dx}{x}\frac{dt}{t} \ S(x',t')\frac{dx'}{x'}\frac{dt'}{t'}\ \frac{d\sigma_{\gamma\gamma}(W,u)}{du}$$
with $t = Q^2/Q^2_{min}, x = E_\gamma/E_0$.

Adding kinematical approximation to DEPA (neglecting the scattering angles of electrons so that the invariant mass and the rapidity of the $\gamma\gamma$ system are given by $(W/2E)^2 = x_1x_2$, $Y = \ln(x_1/x_2)/2)$, one can perform analytical integrations and then define $\gamma\gamma$ luminosity and "Williams-Weiszäcker"-type of analytical expressions of the cross section for the overall reaction.

Let us now describe the main features of the Monte-Carlo.

• The limits of parameters to be generated are determined from the acceptance.

• Both photons are generated according to the photon spectra $S(x,t)\frac{dx}{x}\frac{dt}{t}$. Thus one derives$(E_e, \Theta_e, \Phi')_{1,2}$ of both scattered electrons (Φ' being generated isotropically), and the 4-momentum and mass of the $\gamma\gamma$ system.

The decay of the $\gamma\gamma$ system in two leptons is generated in its rest frame system according to the real $\gamma\gamma \to l^+l^-$ cross section.

The 4-momenta of all particles are then determined in all various frames (Lab,ee c-of-m,$\gamma\gamma$ c-of-m), thanks to rotations and Lorentz boosts.

• Now, events are accepted or rejected according to the experimental cuts in the laboratory frame defined as input of the program

• For each accepted event, we compute for the given parameters the value of the exact differential cross-section and the value of the one used in the generation, and thereby correct its probability.

This program gives absolute normalization and generates individual events. However weighted events for exact and approximate cross-sections are stored in the program and various distributions can be extracted.

The figure shows for muon pair production at DAΦNE and LEP2 (50000 evts with $\cos\Theta_\mu \le 0.98$) the distribution of the scattered electron angle Θ_e, the ratio of the longitudinal contribution to the total cross-section versus this angle, and the azimuthal correlations between ϕ_{ee} and ϕ_{el}. One particularly notices at DAΦNE the wide Θ_e distribution, the small longitudinal contribution up to large Θ_e and the strong azimuthal correlations and distributions (look at the projections over ϕ_{ee} or ϕ_{el}).

286

This work was partly supported by The EEC., HCMP Contract CT920026.

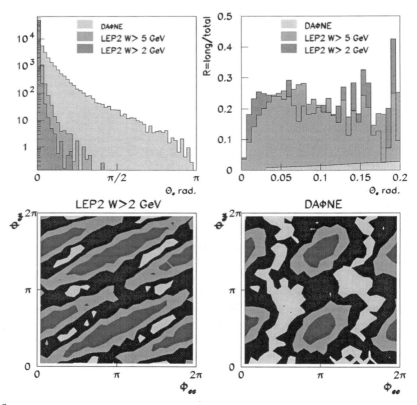

References

1. The program GG2L can be obtained from Courau@lal.in2p3.fr
2. The DAΦNE Physics Handbook, eds L. Maiani,G. Pancheri and N. Paver INFN,Frascati (1992) and references therein
3. G. Alexander et al.,Il Nuovo cimento 107A (1994) 837
   A. Courau, in Proceedings of the Photon'95, eds D.J. Miller, S.L. Cartwright and V. Khoze, World Scientific, 1995 p. 429
4. N. Arteaga et al., Phys. Rev. D52 (1995) 4920 and references therein.
5. V.N. Baier et al., Phys. Rep. 78 (1981) 293
6. V.M. Budnev et al., Phys. Rep. C15 (1975) 181
7. See these proceedings and E. Leonardi in Photon'95 p. 268

Session D

Diffractive and Elastic Scattering

DIFFRACTION (AT HERA) – AN INTRODUCTION

M. ARNEODO [a]

Università di Torino and INFN Cosenza,
via Giuria, 1, I-10125 Torino, Italy
arneodo@vxdesy.desy.de

Some general features of diffraction are presented and the motivations for studying diffraction in *ep* interactions are discussed.

1 The jargon

1.1 Introduction

Physics students first encounter the term "diffraction" in optics. Light of wavelength λ impinging on a black disk of radius R_0 produces on a distant screen a diffraction pattern, characterised by a large forward peak for scattering angle $\theta = 0$ (the "diffraction peak") and a series of symmetric minima and maxima, with the first minimum at $\theta_{min} \simeq \pm\lambda/(2R_0)$. The intensity I as a function of the scattering angle θ is given by

$$\frac{I(\theta)}{I(\theta = 0)} = \frac{[2J_1(x)]^2}{x^2} \simeq 1 - \frac{R_0^2}{4}(k\theta)^2, \tag{1}$$

where J_1 is the Bessel function of the first order, $x = kR_0 \sin\theta \simeq kR_0\theta$, with $k = 2\pi/\lambda$. The diffraction pattern is thus related to the size of the scattering centre and to the wavelength of the light beam.

The differential cross section $d\sigma/dt$ for proton-proton elastic scattering ($pp \rightarrow pp$) bears a remarkable resemblance to the diffraction pattern just described [1]:

$$\frac{d\sigma/dt(t)}{d\sigma/dt(t = 0)} \simeq \exp(bt) \simeq 1 - b(p\theta)^2, \tag{2}$$

where $|t| \simeq (p\theta)^2$ is the four-momentum transfer squared, p is the incident proton momentum and θ is the scattering angle. The t-slope b can be written as $b = R^2/4$, where once again R is related to the size of the target (in fact the quadratic sum of the projectile and target radii). A dip followed by a secondary maximum has also been observed, with the value of t at which the dip appears decreasing with increasing proton momentum. It is thus no wonder that the

---

[a] Alexander von Humboldt Fellow

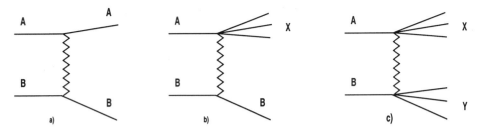

Figure 1: (a) Elastic scattering of hadrons A and B. (b) Single diffractive dissociation. (c) Double diffractive dissociation.

term diffraction is used for elastic pp scattering (and, as discussed below, for "soft" hadron-hadron reactions in general).

Diffraction in particle physics is a feature of hadron-hadron interactions and comes in three different varieties[1]: elastic (Fig. 1a), with the two hadrons emerging intact from the interaction, single diffractive dissociation (Fig. 1b), with either hadron being excited into a higher mass state (with the same quantum numbers as the initial hadron, but not necessarily a resonance), and double diffractive dissociation (Fig. 1c), where both hadrons are excited. In all cases the final state has two groups of particles well separated in polar angle, or pseudo-rapidity $\eta = -\ln\tan(\theta/2)$, leading to a "rapidity gap".

Diffractive interactions are thought to be mediated by an object, the "pomeron", that carries the quantum numbers of the vacuum, and in particular no colour charge. The nature of the pomeron is far from being understood and is the subject of this session.

1.2 Digression on Regge theory

In the language of Regge theory[3], hadron-hadron interactions can be understood in terms of the exchange of Regge trajectories. Take for example the reaction $\pi^- p \to \pi^0 n$. In order to conserve all relevant quantum numbers, only ρ, a_2 or g mesons can be exchanged in the t channel. Remarkably, the masses squared and the spins of these particles are related, as Fig. 2 shows.

The set of particles on the straight line in Fig. 2 is referred to as a "Regge trajectory" and is identified by the equation $J = \alpha(t) = \alpha(0) + \alpha't$, where $\alpha(0)$ and α' respectively are the intercept and the slope of the trajectory. The case just described corresponds to the reggeon ($I\!R$) trajectory which has $\alpha_{I\!R}(0) \simeq 0.5$ and $\alpha_{I\!R}' \simeq 1$ GeV^{-2}.

According to Regge theory, the cross section for the elastic interaction of hadrons A and B mediated by the exchange of a given trajectory is given by

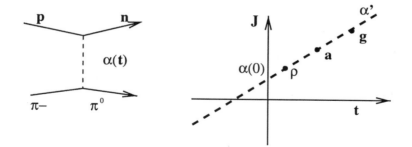

Figure 2: The reaction $\pi^- p \to \pi^0 n$ (left). The spin J of the particles that can be exchanged in the t channel as a function of $t = m^2$, with m the mass of the exchanged meson (right) (from [2]).

$$\frac{d\sigma_{el}^{AB}(s,t)}{dt} \propto \left(\frac{s}{s_0}\right)^{2\alpha(t)-2} \tag{3}$$

at fixed t; here s indicates the centre of mass energy squared. If $\alpha(t) = \alpha(0) + \alpha' t$, it then follows that

$$\frac{d\sigma_{el}^{AB}(s,t)}{dt} \propto \left(\frac{s}{s_0}\right)^{2\alpha(0)-2} \exp(bt), \tag{4}$$

with $b = b_0 + 2\alpha' \ln(s/s_0)$. The total cross section is related to the above via the optical theorem and is given by $\sigma_{tot}^{AB} \sim s^{\alpha(0)-1}$.

1.3 The pomeron

It is well known [1] that the total hadron-hadron cross section at high energies rises slowly with s. The reggeon trajectory just discussed would cause the total cross section to decrease with energy, since its intercept is about 0.5. Fits [4,5,6] to the hadron-hadron total cross section data indicate that the exchanged trajectory should have an intercept of about 1.1 (1.08 according to [4]) and a slope of approximately 0.25 GeV^{-2}. No known resonance corresponds to such trajectory, which is referred to as the pomeron ($I\!P$).

Typical features of pomeron exchange are the weak energy dependence of the cross section

$$\sigma_{tot} \sim s^{0.08} \tag{5}$$

(assuming $\alpha_{I\!P}$ from [4]) and the exponential t dependence

$$d\sigma_{el}/dt \sim \exp{(bt)}, \tag{6}$$

where $b \propto R_A^2 + R_B^2$ measures the size of the interacting hadrons and is a logarithmic function of s, $b = b_0 + 2\alpha_{I\!P}' \ln{(s/s_0)} \simeq b_0 + 0.5\ln{(s/s_0)}$ ("shrinkage of the diffractive cone").

The above is referred to as "soft" diffraction and the corresponding pomeron trajectory as the "soft pomeron". In this regime perturbative QCD (pQCD) cannot be applied.

2 Deep inelastic scattering and diffraction

Deep inelastic scattering (DIS) of charged leptons from protons proceeds via the exchange of a virtual photon (we neglect the contributions from Z_0 and W exchange) with negative four momentum squared $Q^2 = -q^2$ and energy ν in the proton rest frame. The photon is absorbed by a quark which, in the infinite momentum frame, carries a fraction $x = Q^2/2P \cdot q$ of the proton momentum; here P is the four momentum of the incoming proton and q is the four momentum of the exchanged photon. The photon-proton centre of mass energy is denoted by $W = \sqrt{(P+q)^2}$. The deep inelastic cross section $d^2\sigma/dxdQ^2$ is proportional to the structure function $F_2(x, Q^2)$ and depends on the function $R(x, Q^2)$. The latter is the ratio of the absorption cross sections for longitudinally and transversely polarised virtual photons; it depends on the partons' spin and in the Bjorken limit (Q^2 and ν large but Q^2/ν finite) tends to zero for spin 1/2 partons. In the quark-parton model, $F_2(x, Q^2) = \sum_i e_i^2 x f_i(x, Q^2)$, where the sum runs over all parton species, e_i denotes the electric charge of the ith parton species and f_i is its distribution function; F_2 is therefore sensitive to the momentum distribution of the partons in the proton.

Deep inelastic scattering is thus a probe of the partonic structure of the proton.

2.1 Why diffraction at HERA ?

Real and virtual photons exhibit hadronic properties since they can fluctuate into $q\bar{q}$ pairs (in the proton rest frame). To first approximation a $q\bar{q}$ pair with the quantum numbers of the photon is a vector meson (ρ^0, ω, ϕ,...). This forms the basis of the vector meson dominance model (VMD) [7].

Simple quantum-mechanical arguments can be used to show that the lifetime of the $q\bar{q}$ fluctuation is proportional to $1/x$ (i.e. to W^2). In addition, the transverse size of the pair is proportional to $1/Q^2$. Deep inelastic scattering at small x is thus dominated by the interaction of $q\bar{q}$ pairs – rather than of pointlike photons – with the proton. This offers the possibility of investigating hadron-hadron interactions, and notably diffraction, as a function of the transverse size of one of two hadrons. One can then have the deep inelastic equivalent of elastic reactions and single and double diffractive dissociation – simply the incoming hadron A of Fig. 1 is now the $q\bar{q}$ pair into which the virtual photon has fluctuated. The Regge formalism discussed earlier can be applied with s replaced by W^2.

Alternatively one can view diffractive scattering in DIS in the infinite momentum frame. In this case the virtual photon remains a pointlike object which scatters from the pomeron and probes its partonic structure.

2.2 What do we hope to see at HERA ?

As discussed above, the main advantage of studying diffraction at HERA is that the size of one of the hadrons can be decreased at will. It is then interesting to see if, as the size of this hadron becomes smaller (i.e. as the distances probed decrease), one observes a transition between the soft, VMD-like regime and a regime where perturbative calculations are valid.

Consider for instance elastic vector meson production, $ep \rightarrow eVp$. In the VMD case the photon behaves like a normal vector meson and interacts with the proton exchanging a soft pomeron with intercept $\alpha_{I\!P} \approx 1.1$. In the perturbative regime, the pomeron is viewed as a pair of gluons (a "gluon ladder"). The latter scenario has been proposed by various authors (cf. e.g.[8,9,10]). When either Q^2 or the vector meson mass squared, M_V^2, or $|t|$ are large, say $\gtrsim 1\,\mathrm{GeV}^2$, then the cross section becomes proportional to the gluon momentum density squared in the proton, $\sigma \propto [\bar{x}g(\bar{x}, \bar{q}^2)]^2$, where $\bar{x} = (Q^2 + M_V^2 + |t|)/W^2$ is the fraction of the proton's momentum carried by the gluon ladder and $\bar{q}^2 \simeq 0.2(Q^2 + M_V^2 + |t|)$ is the scale at which the gluon distribution is probed. The effective pomeron intercept depends on the gluon density and can be significantly larger than 1.1 (the "hard" pomeron).

3 Elastic vector meson production

We briefly summarise the experimental situation for elastic vector meson production. A detailed discussion of the recent HERA data can be found in [11–14]. Figure 3 shows the status of the field at $Q^2 \approx 0$ as it appeared before this conference.

3.1 Light vector mesons (ρ^0, ω, ϕ) at $Q^2 \approx 0$, $t \approx 0$

For elastic vector meson production, eq. (5) and the optical theorem give:

$$\sigma(\gamma p \to V p) \propto \frac{(W^2)^{2(\alpha_{I\!P}(0)-1)}}{b_0 + 2\alpha_{I\!P}' \ln(W^2/W_0^2)} \simeq W^{0.22}. \tag{7}$$

The recent HERA data [11,12] in conjunction with the results of the fixed target experiments (for a complete set of references see e.g. [15]) have confirmed the picture that was already apparent at Photon '95:

1. The W dependence of the cross section (cf. Fig. 3) is consistent with the expectations based on soft pomeron exchange.

2. The t dependence is exponential with a t-slope $b \sim 10$ GeV^{-2}; the evidence for shrinkage is for the moment far from compelling.

3. The produced vector meson seems to retain the helicity of the photon: s-channel helicity conservation (SCHC).

In this region it thus appears that the photon interacts softly with the proton, just as an ordinary hadron.

3.2 Heavy vector mesons (J/ψ) at $Q^2 \approx 0$, $t \approx 0$

The cross section for J/ψ photoproduction rises with W much faster than for light vector mesons: $\sigma \propto W^{0.8}$, implying an effective pomeron intercept of approximately 1.2. This result is consistent with the pQCD approaches described earlier. In this framework the rapid growth of the cross section with W is a reflection of the rise of the gluon density at small x.

The t dependence is exponential with a t-slope $b \sim 5$ GeV^{-2}, reflecting the fact that the J/ψ has a smaller size than the light vector mesons.

3.3 Light and heavy vector mesons at "large" Q^2, $Q^2 \approx 10$ GeV^2

In this case the situation is not clear. The early HERA data on ρ^0 and ϕ production in conjunction with the NMC fixed target data [16] indicated a rather steep W dependence of the cross section, inconsistent with the soft pomeron expectations. Recent data on ρ^0 production from the E665 Collaboration [17] at Fermilab are however at variance with the NMC results, and suggest (again together with the HERA measurements) a much shallower W dependence of the cross section. The HERA collider data alone are unfortunately not yet able to settle the question unambiguously.

The t dependence is exponential with a slope $b \sim 5$ GeV^{-2}, confirming the fact that at large Q^2 the transverse size of the $q\bar{q}$ pair is smaller than for $Q^2 = 0$.

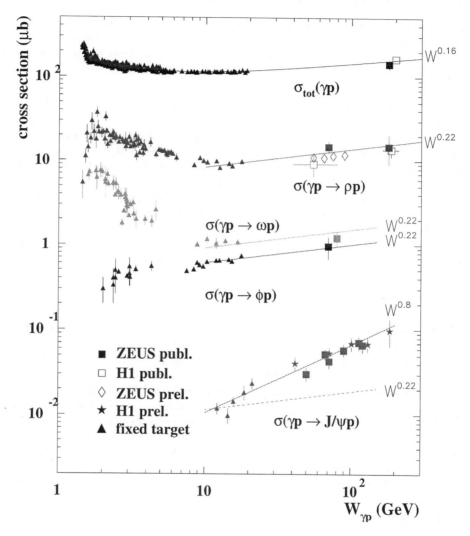

Figure 3: A compilation of vector meson photoproduction results as a function of W. The total photon-proton cross section is also shown. The lines are only meant to guide the eye and do not represent the result of fits to the data.

3.4 Conclusions and open questions on elastic vector meson production

In summary, at small Q^2 and for light vector mesons it is well established that the photon behaves as an ordinary vector meson. For J/ψ photoproduction a transition to a different regime appears to take place, at least as far as the W dependence is concerned.

Among the open questions to be addressed, we would like to list the following:

1. From the experimental point of view it remains to be seen if Q^2 and $|t|$ are on the same footing as M_V^2, i.e. if the scale relevant for vector meson production is really proportional to $Q^2 + M_V^2 + |t|$ as suggested by pQCD inspired models. With increasing Q^2 and $|t|$ one would then expect a rapid growth of the cross section with W as is observed for J/ψ photoproduction.

2. If this is the case, it is important to determine to what extent such behaviour of the cross section reflects a transition to a regime where pQCD holds: one should quantitatively verify that the rise of the cross section with W is related to the increase of the gluon density at small x.

4 Photon diffractive dissociation

Photon dissociation, $ep \rightarrow eXp$, is the diffractive equivalent of inclusive deep inelastic scattering from the proton, with the structure of the exchanged trajectory being probed in this case, rather than that of the proton.

In addition to the variables introduced earlier, two more are relevant here:

1. The fraction of the proton's momentum carried by the exchanged trajectory, $x_{I\!P} \simeq (Q^2 + M_X^2 + |t|)/W^2 \simeq 1 - x_L$, where x_L is the fraction of the incoming proton momentum carried by the scattered proton. The region of high x_L, i.e. low $x_{I\!P}$, say $x_{I\!P} < 0.01$, corresponds to the diffractive peak and the exchanged trajectory is mostly a pomeron. At larger $x_{I\!P}$ values, reggeon exchange may become important [18].

2. The fraction of the momentum of the exchanged trajectory carried by the quark struck by the virtual photon, $\beta = x/x_{I\!P}$. This is the Bjorken variable for the exchanged trajectory.

4.1 Experimental signatures of photon diffractive dissociation

Roughly speaking, two techniques have been used so far at HERA [19,20]:

1. A scattered proton with momentum very close (to within a few per cent) to the incoming proton beam momentum has been required. This has

been done [20] at ZEUS by means of a leading proton spectrometer which detects protons scattered at angles so small that they remain inside the beam pipe. This technique selects a clean diffractive sample and allows the direct measurement of t, at the price of a small acceptance.

2. A rapidity gap in the hadronic final state has been demanded. This technique comes in different varieties of which the "$\eta_{\max}$ method" is the most straightforward; the "$\ln M_X^2$ method" is a more refined variation on the same theme. Details are given in [19,20]. The samples collected using this signature may be affected by a larger contamination from proton-dissociative and from non-diffractive events.

4.2 Photon diffractive dissociation at $Q^2 \approx 0$

This process has been studied in great detail by H1 and ZEUS as a function of M_X and t [19,20]. All evidence so far points to the conclusion that at small virtualities the photon behaves like an ordinary hadron which interacts softly with the proton. This conclusion is independent of the value of M_X, up to M_X of the order of several tens of GeVs.

4.3 Photon diffractive dissociation at finite non-zero Q^2

The following issues need to be addressed in this regime:

1. Under which assumptions can a structure function of the pomeron be defined, in analogy to what is done for the nucleon ?

2. If so, what is the partonic content of the pomeron ?

3. Is there any sign of a transition to a regime where pQCD becomes valid as seen (perhaps) in the vector meson case ?

4.4 The pomeron structure function

The cross section for diffractive photon dissociation can be written as follows:

$$\frac{d^4\sigma^D}{dQ^2 d\beta dx_{I\!P} dt} = \frac{2\pi\alpha^2}{\beta Q^4} \left[1 + (1-y)^2\right] F_2^{D(4)}(Q^2, \beta, x_{I\!P}, t), \tag{8}$$

which defines the diffractive structure function $F_2^{D(4)}$ in analogy to the inclusive structure function of the proton $F_2(Q^2, x)$; y is the fraction of the incoming electron energy transferred to the photon in the proton rest frame.

Following Ingelman and Schlein [21] one can introduce the notion of a pomeron structure function. A pomeron structure function can be defined however only under the assumption that

$$F_2^{D(4)}(Q^2, \beta, x_{I\!P}, t) = f_{I\!P}(x_{I\!P}, t) \cdot F_2^{I\!P}(Q^2, \beta), \qquad (9)$$

where $f_{I\!P}(x_{I\!P}, t)$ is the flux of pomerons emitted by the proton and $F_2^{I\!P}(Q^2, \beta)$ is the pomeron structure function. This ansatz is known as factorisation of the pomeron trajectory. In order for $F_2^{I\!P}(Q^2, \beta)$ to be introduced, one has therefore to verify experimentally that $F_2^{D(4)}$ has the same $x_{I\!P}$ and t dependence in different β and Q^2 bins (or equivalently M_X and Q^2 bins). Regge theory predicts the pomeron flux to be proportional to $(1/x_{I\!P})^a$, with $a = 2\alpha_{I\!P} - 1$.

Although the t dependence of the cross section has been studied [20], often an integration over t is performed, yielding the structure function $F_2^{D(3)}$, which is the quantity the HERA experiments have so far measured.

One more remark is in order. It is equivalent to study $F_2^{D(3)}(Q^2, \beta, x_{I\!P})$ (as both H1 and ZEUS do) or $d\sigma^D/dM_X$ vs. M_X^2, Q^2 and W (as ZEUS does).

4.5 A comment on the status of the field

The results are presented in detail in [19,20]. Here we limit ourselves to a few comments.

1. Figure 4 shows the H1 and ZEUS results for $\alpha_{I\!P}$ averaged over t as a function of Q^2 and M_X. The results of the two experiments are consistent. In both cases $\alpha_{I\!P}$ is not far from the soft pomeron value; in the figure the Donnachie and Lanshoff prediction is shown, but other fits give different (in fact higher) values of $\alpha_{I\!P}$. For the time being it is therefore difficult to argue about the setting in of perturbative effects.

2. If $\alpha_{I\!P}$ depends on M_X and Q^2 as the ZEUS data may indicate, then the pomeron trajectory factorisation hypothesis does not hold and a pomeron structure function cannot be introduced.

3. It is nevertheless tempting to determine a pomeron structure function. The first studies [19] indicate that the pomeron is a gluon dominated object, a conclusion supported by investigations of the hadronic final state in photon diffractive dissociation [19,22].

5 Conclusion

The study of diffraction in ep interactions may be a way of shedding light on the nature of the pomeron and investigating the transition between the vector meson dominance and the perturbative regimes.

There are many lines of attack. We have discussed vector meson production and photon diffractive dissociation. As presented in the contributions to

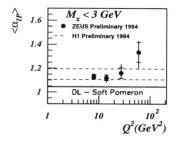 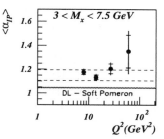

Figure 4: The value of $\alpha_{I\!P}$ averaged over t as a function of Q^2 and M_X. The dashed lines indicate the upper and lower limit of the H1 result [19]. The line labelled "DL – Soft Pomeron" corresponds to the prediction of ref. [4].

this session, jet production, charm production and in general the study of the hadronic final state are also providing a wealth of information which is slowly building into a consistent picture.

Acknowledgments

I would like to thank F.C. Erné and his team for the excellent organisation of this conference. I would also like to express my gratitude to my ZEUS and H1 colleagues for many discussions.

Finally I am very grateful to G. Barbagli, S. Bhadra, J. Crittenden, J. Dainton, E. Gallo, R. Nania and K. Piotrzkowski for their comments on the manuscript.

References

1. For a review see e.g.
   G. Alberi and G. Goggi, Phys. Rep. **74** (1981) 1;
   K. Goulianos, Phys. Rep. **101** (1983) 169;
   N.N. Zotov and A.V. Zarev, Sov. Phys. Uspekhi **51** (1988) 119;
   G. Giacomelli, Int. J. Mod. Phys. A, vol. 5, no. 2 (1990), 223.
2. N. Cartiglia, "Diffraction at HERA", in Proceedings of SLAC Summer School 1996, preprint hep-ph/9703245.
3. T. Regge, Nuovo Cimento **14** (1959) 951;
   T. Regge, Nuovo Cimento **18** (1960) 947;
   see also e.g. P.D.B. Collins, "Regge Theory and High Energy Physics"

300

(Cambridge University Press, Cambridge 1977);
P.D.B. Collins and A.D. Martin, "Hadron Interactions" (Hilger, Bristol 1984).

4. A. Donnachie and P.V. Landshoff, Phys. Lett. **B 185** (1987) 403;
   A. Donnachie and P.V. Landshoff, Nucl. Phys. **B311** (1989) 509;
   P.V. Landshoff, Nucl. Phys. B (Proc.Suppl.) **18C** (1990) 211.
5. J.R. Cudell et al., preprint hep-ph 9601336 (1996).
6. R.J.M. Covolan, J. Montanha and K. Goulianos, Phys. Lett. **B389** (1996) 176.
7. J.J. Sakurai, Phys. Rev. Lett. **22** (1969) 981.
8. M.G. Ryskin, Z. Phys. **C 57** (1993) 89.
9. S.J. Brodsky et al., Phys. Rev. **D50** (1994) 3134.
10. J. Nemchik, N.N. Nikolaev and B.G. Zakharov, Phys. Lett. **B 341** (1994) 228.
11. J. Koehne, these Proceedings.
12. J.A. Crittenden, these Proceedings.
13. M. Kolstein, these Proceedings.
14. J.A. Crittenden, DESY Report 97-068 (1997), to appear as Nr. 140 in Springer Tracts in Modern Physics.
15. ZEUS Collab., M. Derrick et al., Z.Phys. **C69** (1995) 39.
16. NMC Collab., M. Arneodo et al., Nucl. Phys. **B429** (1994) 503.
17. E665 Collab., M.R. Adams et al., Z. Phys. **C72** (1997) 237.
18. See e.g. R.D. Field and G.C. Fox, Nucl. Phys. **B80** (1974) 367;
    N. N. Nikolaev, W. Schaefer and B. G. Zakharov, preprint hep-ph/9607479;
    K. Golec-Biernat, J. Kwiecinski and A. Szczurek, preprint hep-ph/9701254.
19. T. Ebert, these Proceedings.
20. K. Piotrzkowski, these Proceedings.
21. G. Ingelman and P. Schlein, Phys. Lett. **152B** (1985) 256.
22. J. Puga, these Proceedings.

ELASTIC AND DISSOCIATIVE PRODUCTION OF VECTOR MESONS AT SMALL AND LARGER Q^2 AT H1

J.H. KÖHNE

Max-PLanck-Institut für Physik, Werner-Heisenberg-Institut, Föhringer Ring 6, D-80805 München, Germany

The H1 experiment at the ep-collider HERA at DESY in Hamburg has investigated the diffractive production of vector mesons at negligible photon virtualities, $Q^2 \approx 0$ and at higher Q^2 where the scattered lepton is detected in the apparatus. The main characteristics of soft diffractive reactions are observed for the photoproduction of $\rho(770)$ whilst the heavier $J/\Psi(3097)$ deviates from this picture but meets the expectations of QCD-models which assign the vector meson's interaction with the proton to the intrinsic gluon content of the proton. At higher Q^2 the virtual photon proton cross sections are analysed in terms of the photon proton c.m.s. energy, $W_{\gamma p}$, Q^2, the proton momentum transfer squared, t and the vector meson's helicity. The production of the higher mass excitations ρ' and Ψ' has been observed. Studies of diffractive proton dissociation in the vector meson production reveal no significant deviations from the elastic case except for the slope of the fall-off with $|t|$.

1 Introduction

The diffractive process in vector meson production is sketched in figure 1. The process is regarded as a two step reaction. The lepton emits a photon which turns into a virtual hadronic state which undergoes a peripheral interaction with the proton. In the final state only the vector meson decay products and the scattered beam particles are detectable. The interaction can either be regarded as due to the exchange of a soft pomeron Regge-trajectory between a VDM-photon [a] and the proton [1] or due to the exchange of a pair of QCD-gluons (hard pomeron) between a virtual quark-antiquark pair and the constituents of the proton [2,3]. In the latter picture the cross section depends on the gluon density inside the proton.

1.1 H1 Detector

The vector meson analyses are based upon the charged particle reconstruction within the central tracking system consisting of two coaxial cylindrical drift chambers interleaved by proportional chambers. Lepton identification is possible using the surrounding liquid argon (LAr) calorimeter and the muon system housed in the iron return yoke of the solenoid magnet. The scattered

---

[a] Vector Meson Dominance Model

positron is detected in the rear lead scintillator calorimeter. The proton escapes in the beam pipe. In case the proton dissociates and forms a state Y with $m_Y > 1.6$ GeV the decay products become visible either in the forward part of the LAr-calorimeter, the forward muon system or in a set of scintillators mounted 24 m downstream on the proton beamline.

1.2 Kinematics

The kinematic variables of deep inelastic scattering are calculated from the decay products of the vector meson and - if available - from the scattered lepton. The four momenta k, k', q and P denote the in- and outgoing lepton, the virtual photon and the proton respectively. The preferred reconstruction method for $Q^2 = -q^2 = -(k - k')^2$ and $y = P \cdot q / P \cdot k$ is the double angle method [4]. The photon proton c.m.s. energy is calculated from $W_{\gamma p}^2 \approx ys$, s being the c.m. energy in the ep-sytem. The momentum transfer at the proton vertex is calculated from the vector sum of transverse momenta of the meson and the scattered lepton, $|t| \approx (\vec{p}_{\perp e} + \vec{p}_{\perp v})^2$. Following the two-step-view of the process the experimental results are given as virtual photon proton cross sections obtained from the electroproduction cross sections by unfolding the Weizsäcker-Williams photon flux approximation [5].

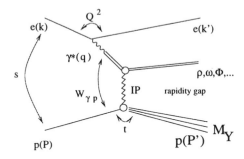

Figure 1: Diffractive production of vector mesons at HERA.

2 Results in Photoproduction

At $Q^2 < 4$ GeV^2 the scattered electron escapes detection in the backward calorimeter. Events of this type are regarded as photoproduction events. They have $< Q^2 >= 0.001 - 0.035$ GeV^2 decreasing with $W_{\gamma p}$. Due to the polar

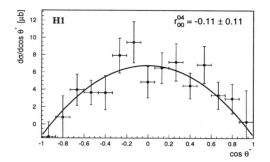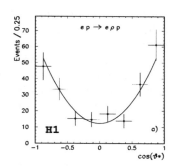

Figure 2: Decay angle distribution in the ρ^0-meson's rest frame: a) in photoproduction (left) and b) at high Q^2.

angle acceptance of the central tracking system the data cover a range of 30 GeV $< W_{\gamma p} <$ 150 GeV.

The result of the ρ^0 measurements in photoproduction [6] is a remarkable success of the VDM-photon plus Regge model. After extrapolating by more than one order of magnitude from the low energy measurements to HERA, the cross section continues a slow logarithmic rise typical for the pomeron trajectory with an universal intercept near unity. The sharp peak in forward direction of the cross section with an exponential fall-off with $|t|$ appears steeper than at low energy, however the precision of this rather early H1-measurement is limited, so that no final conclusions can be drawn. Assuming the polarisation of the vector meson reflects the polarisation of the original photon [b] one observes a predominantly transverse photon spectrum at low Q^2 as expected from a smooth transition to a real photon beam with no longitudinal degree of freedom for the photon helicity. The helicity of the vector meson is measured from the polar decay angle distribution $\cos \theta^*$ as given in figure 2 a).

While the photoproduction of $\rho^0(770)$ with a mass well below the typical hadronisation scale of 1 GeV is convincingly described by VDM plus soft pomeron exchange the heavy J/Ψ deviates strikingly from the expectations of this picture [7]. The cross section rises like $W_{\gamma p}^\delta$ with $\delta = 0.90 \pm 0.06$ [14] which has to be compared to $\delta = 0.32$ expected from soft pomeron exchange (neglecting any shrinkage). The QCD-models can accommodate such a steep rise. In figure 3 the measured cross sections [8] at different values of $W_{\gamma p}$ are

---

[b]This assumption is abbreviated SCHC (s-channel helicity conservation).

translated into a phenomenological gluon density $xg(x)$ as defined by Ryskin[2] at different values of $x \propto 1/W_{\gamma p}^2$. In addition, some of the most popular gluon density parametrisations are shown. Due to an overall normalisation uncertainty of 30% one should rather compare the shape of the spectra. It is a crucial question of consistency between the QCD-models whether the gluon densities obtained from the scaling violations in the F_2 measurements agree with this direct determination.

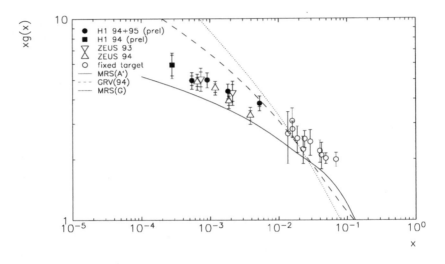

Figure 3: Gluon density $xg(x)$ obtained from J/Ψ-photoproduction as function of x.

The production of Ψ' decaying into $\pi^+\pi^- J/\Psi$ has also been observed in photoproduction[9]. The production ratio of Ψ' to J/Ψ is 0.16 ± 0.06 which is considerably higher when compared to the production of excited ρ' over the light ground state ρ[10].

3 Results at High Q^2

Going from photoproduction to events with high Q^2 introduces another energy scale into the consideration, in addition to $W_{\gamma p}$ and the vector meson mass. The data cover the range 6 GeV$^2 < Q^2 < 50$ GeV^2. An important question is whether the production mechanism of vector mesons still is peripheral. The answer can be seen from the $|t|$-spectra in figure 4. The cross section is forward peaked and shows an exponential fall-off with $|t|$. The slope is smaller than in photoproduction which is plausible from the expectation of the optical model relating the slope parameter b to the transverse sizes of the scattering objects. The higher the Q^2 the smaller the size of the probing hadronic component of the photon and thus the flatter the $|t|$-distribution. Note that the flattening of the $|t|$-distribution is much less evident for the J/Ψ than for the ρ, consistent with the assumption that the mass of the J/Ψ already sets the hard scale.

A $\rho'(1600)$ state decaying into four pions via an intermediate ρ state has been observed at high Q^2. The cross section is of comparable size as the one of the ground state ($R_{\rho'/\rho} = 0.36 \pm 0.13$) in contrast to the situation in photoproduction [10]. This can be related to the larger tranverse size of the probing quark antiquark pair at low Q^2 which overlaps with an extended vector meson wavefunction with one or more radial nodes diminishing the convolution integral in the calculation of the photon coupling. At high Q^2 only the innermost part of the wave function contributes.

The differential virtual photon proton cross section as a function of Q^2 follows a steeply falling power law. The observation is parametrised following a Q^{-2n}-ansatz. For the J/Ψ $(Q^2 + m^2)^{-n}$ is used. The results for ρ, ϕ and J/Ψ are $n = 2.5 \pm 0.5$ [4], $n = 2.0 \pm 0.6$ [11] and $n = 1.9 \pm 0.3$ [4].

The non-negligible photon virtuality allows for longitudinal polarisation of the vector mesons and indeed the major fraction[c] of $r_{00}^{04} = 0.73 \pm 0.5$ [11] of the ρ^0 mesons are longitudinally polarised. The change in helicity composition is seen in figure 2 b). The $W_{\gamma p}$-dependance of the J/Ψ-cross section is similar to the photoproduction case. How do the ρ and ϕ behave? The hard scale in Q^2 leads to the expectation of a steeper rise. H1 data[11] in combination with an old measurement of the NMC collaboration [12] seem to support this. However a recent $\sigma_{\gamma^* p \to \rho p}$-measurement of the E665-experiment [13] at an intermediate $W_{\gamma p}$ and high Q^2 allows an interpretation of the measurements in terms of soft pomeron exchange. So the question has to remain open for the time being.

4 Results on Proton Dissociation

As shown by detailed simulations the H1 detector allows the tagging of a proton excitation with mass above 1.6 GeV with well controlled systematics. Results have been obtained for J/Ψ-photoproduction [14] and for ρ^0 [11] at high Q^2. The cross sections with and without proton dissociation are of comparable size. The cross section rise with $W_{\gamma p}$ does not change drastically. The $W_{\gamma p}^\delta$-fit arrives at $\delta = 1.2 \pm 0.2$ for the J/Ψ. The vector meson polarisation seems not

---

[c] r_{00}^{04} denotes a bilinear combination of ρ production helicity amplitudes which corresponds to the probabilty of finding a longitudinally polarised vector meson from an unpolarised photon beam.

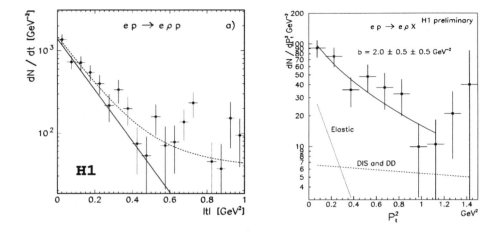

Figure 4: Spectra of squared transverse ρ^0-momenta in the high Q^2 samples: elastic (a) and with proton dissociation (b).

to be affected by what happens to the proton. The results show no significant difference i.e. the J/Ψ are transversely polarised while the ρ at high Q^2 are predominantly longitudinally polarised as was the case without proton dissociation. The only significant impact of the break-up of the proton is on the shape of the forward peak. The t-distribution is shown in figure 4. Exponential fits in restricted p_T^2 ranges arrive at $b = 1.6 \pm 0.3$ GeV^{-2} for the J/Ψ and $b = 2.1 \pm 0.7$ GeV^{-2} for the ρ which have to be compared to the results for elastic production[4] $b = 4.0 \pm 0.3$ GeV^{-2} for the J/Ψ and $b = 7.0 \pm 0.9$ GeV^{-2} for the ρ. The slopes b are already below a value of about 4 GeV^{-2} corresponding to a diffractive scattering of objects with transverse dimensions well below the radius of the proton.

5   Conclusions

H1 has contributed analyses on diffractive production of light and heavy vector mesons in photoproduction and at high Q^2. The results in photoproduction show a good description of the light meson production by the model of VDM plus pomeron trajectory exchange. This description fails, as with the J/Ψ mass a hard energy scale enters the problem. However its failure in the presence of a high Q^2-scale in case of ρ-production is experimentally not yet settled. The

$|t|$-distributions are all consistent with a diffractive production mechanism. Going from photoproduction to higher photon virtualities leads to a flatter $|t|$-spectrum consistent with a smaller transverse size of the scattering object. The vector meson polarisation is purely transverse in photoproduction and mainly longitudinal at high Q^2. The Q^2 dependence of the production cross section follows a power law with Q^{-2n}, n around 2. Excitations Ψ' and ρ' have been observed. The production ratios in photoproduction seem to be more suppressed for the light ρ as for the heavy J/Ψ. The effect of proton dissociation is small for the general features of the vector meson cross section, with the exception of the $|t|$-distribution which is still peripheral but which much flatter slope than in the elastic case.

Acknowledgments

I thank the organisers of PHOTON 97 for their hospitality and support during the conference in Egmond. I thank very much Frank Gaede and John Dainton for helpful discussions.

References

1. A.Donnachie and P.V.Landshoff, *Phys. Lett.* B **348**, 213 (1995).
   A.Donnachie and P.V.Landshoff, *Phys. Lett.* B **296**, 227 (1992).
2. M.G.Ryskin, *Z. Phys.* C **57**, 89 (1993).
3. S.J.Brodsky et al., *Phys. Rev.* D **50**, 3134 (1994)
4. H1 Collab., *Nucl. Phys.* B **468**, 3 (1996).
5. E.J.Williams, *Proc. Roy. Soc. London* A **139**, 163 (1933)
   C.F.Weizsäcker, *Z. Phys.* **88**, 612 (1934)
6. H1 Collab., *Nucl. Phys.* B **463**, 3 (1996).
7. H1 Collab., *Phys. Lett.* B **338**, 507 (1994).
8. G.Schmidt, PhD thesis, University of Hamburg, Germany, 1996
9. H1 Collab., contrib. paper pa02-086, 28th International Conference on High Energy Physics 25-31 July 1996, Warsaw, Poland
10. H1 Collab., contrib. paper pa01-088, 28th International Conference on High Energy Physics 25-31 July 1996, Warsaw, Poland
11. H1 Collab., DESY-97-082, May 1997
12. NMC Collab.,*Nucl. Phys.* B **429**, 503 (1994)
13. E665 Collab., FERMILAB-PUB-97-103-E, April 1997
14. H1 Collab., *Nucl. Phys.* B **472**, 3 (1996).

RECENT RESULTS FROM INVESTIGATIONS OF DIFFRACTIVE VECTOR MESON PRODUCTION WITH THE ZEUS DETECTOR AT HERA

J.A. CRITTENDEN

Physikalisches Institut, Universität Bonn, Nußallee 12, 53115 Bonn, Germany
on behalf of the ZEUS collaboration

We present results from recent investigations of diffractive vector meson production using the ZEUS detector at HERA. These consist of measurements of ρ^0 production in the region of photon virtuality $0.25 < Q^2 < 0.85$ GeV^2, of ρ^0, ϕ, and J/ψ production for values of the momentum transfer to the proton $0.3 < |t| < 4.0$ GeV^2, and of elastic J/ψ production both in photoproduction and for $Q^2 > 2$ GeV^2.

1 Introduction

The subject of elastic vector meson production at high energies has attracted much attention due to its contributions to the new field of hard diffraction. Such measurements of *exclusive* processes, a rarity at high-energy colliders, represent a new opportunity to test calculations within the framework of perturbative quantum chromodynamics (pQCD).[1] Here we present recent measurements of diffractive vector meson production with the ZEUS experiment in the interactions of 27.5 GeV positrons with 820 GeV protons at HERA. Further details may be found in papers submitted to the recent DIS '97 Workshop [2]. We concentrate on three topics:

- elastic production of ρ^0 mesons in an intermeditate range of photon virtuality Q^2, $0.25 < Q^2 < 0.85$ GeV^2. This analysis is based on measurements recorded using a special-purpose electromagnetic calorimeter with acceptance at positron scattering angles between 17 and 35 mrad, called the beam-pipe calorimeter (BPC),

- photoproduction of ρ^0, ϕ, and J/ψ mesons for high absolute values of the squared momentum transferred to the proton, $|t|$, $0.3 < |t| < 4.0$ GeV^2. Since the final-state proton system (usually dissociated) was not detected, its transverse momentum was approximated by the transverse momentum of the final-state vector meson. The difference is kinematically limited to a value less than Q^2. Detection of the final-state positron in another special-purpose calorimeter 44 m distant from the interaction point ("44-meter tagger"), limited Q^2 to values less than 0.01 GeV^2, ensuring the validity of the approximation at that level,

- production of J/ψ mesons both for untagged photoproduction ($10^{-10} < Q^2 < 4$ GeV^2), and for a sample where the final-state positron was detected in the central calorimeter ($Q^2 > 2$ GeV^2).

Central to these investigations is the question of the validity of pQCD calculations, an issue which has stimulated much interest due in part to the novelty of applying perturbative methods to diffractive processes.[3] It has been suggested that the necessary hard scale may be given by Q^2, t, or the vector-meson mass. Our investigations aim to test these ideas.

2   Elastic Electroduction of ρ^0 Mesons

The exclusive dipion BPC sample recorded in 1995 with an integrated luminosity of 3.8 pb^{-1} includes about 6000 events in the ρ^0 mass region and covers the kinematic range $0.25 < Q^2 < 0.85$ GeV^2, $|t| < 0.6$ GeV^2, $20 < W_{\gamma^* p} < 90$ GeV, where $W_{\gamma^* p}$ is the center-of-mass energy of the virtual-photon-proton system. The invariant mass spectrum in the ρ^0 mass region is shown in Fig. 1, together with the results of a fit to the squared coherent sum of a Breit–Wigner resonance term and a nonresonant background term:

$$\frac{dN}{dM_{\pi\pi}} = \left| A \frac{\sqrt{M_{\pi\pi} M_\rho \Gamma_\rho}}{M_{\pi\pi}^2 - M_\rho^2 + i M_\rho \Gamma_\rho} + B \right|^2 . \tag{1}$$

The dashed line on the mass spectrum indicates the sum of the contributions

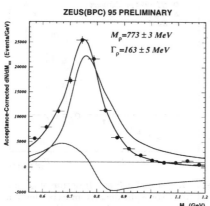

Figure 1: Acceptance-corrected $\pi^+ \pi^-$ invariant mass distribution for elastic ρ^0 production at intermediate Q^2

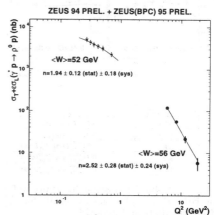

Figure 2: The Q^2 dependence of the ρ^0 elastic cross section

from the Breit–Wigner resonance term (*dotted line*), the nonresonant background term (*dash-dotted line*), and the interference term (*solid line*). The resonant cross section averaged over $W_{\gamma^\bullet p}$ is plotted as a function of Q^2 in Fig. 2 and compared to the measurements [4] at similar $W_{\gamma^\bullet p}$ and high Q^2 in order to investigate the Q^2 dependence. The result of a fit to the dependence $(Q^2 + M_\rho^2)^{-n}$ yields the result $n = 1.94 \pm 0.12(\text{stat}) \pm 0.18(\text{sys})$, consistent with pQCD calculations for longitudinal photons. However, the cross sections measured here are the sum of contributions from longitudinal and transverse photons $\sigma_L + \varepsilon\sigma_T$, where ε is the ratio of the transverse to longitudinal photon flux $(0.97 < \varepsilon < 1.00)$. This ambiguity in the comparison to the calculations will be removed when information on the ratio $R = \sigma_L/\sigma_T$ becomes available.

A first attempt to measure this ratio is exemplified in Figs. 3 and 4. Figure 3 shows the polar angle distribution of the π^+ direction in the ρ^0 rest system with the Z axis defined as the direction opposite to the final-state proton momentum. This distribution depends on the spin-density matrix element r_{00}^{04} (the probability that the ρ^0 is produced with longitudinal polarization [5]):

$$\frac{1}{N}\frac{dN}{d(\cos\theta_h)} = \frac{3}{4}\left[1 - r_{00}^{04} + (3r_{00}^{04} - 1)\cos^2\theta_h\right].\tag{2}$$

The distributions indicate that the BPC data cover a region of transition to increasingly longitudinal polarization at high Q^2. Assuming that the s-channel

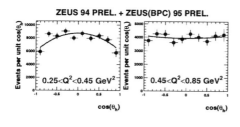

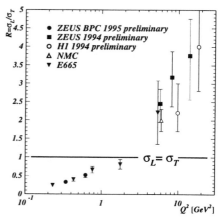

Q^2 (GeV^2)	r_{00}^{04}
0.34	$0.24 \pm 0.02(\text{stat})$
0.62	$0.34 \pm 0.03(\text{stat})$
5.8	$0.71^{+0.03}_{-0.04}(\text{stat})^{+0.01}_{-0.01}(\text{sys})$
8.2	$0.76^{+0.04}_{-0.04}(\text{stat})^{+0.00}_{-0.02}(\text{sys})$
14	$0.79^{+0.04}_{-0.05}(\text{stat})^{+0.02}_{-0.01}(\text{sys})$

Figure 3: Polar decay angle distributions for the BPC ρ^0 samples and fit results for r_{00}^{04} at intermediate and high Q^2

Figure 4: Values for R as a function of Q^2 derived from the spin-density matrix element r_{00}^{04} under the assumption of SCHC

helicity conservation (SCHC) observed at low energy holds at HERA energies, the ratio R is related to this matrix element as $R = r_{00}^{04}/\varepsilon(1 - r_{00}^{04})$. Figure 4 shows the corresponding R values, comparing them to the ZEUS results [4] at high Q^2, those from H1,[6] and those from fixed target muoproduction.[7] The need for this assumption will remain until full helicity analyses are available.

3 Elastic ρ^0, ϕ, and J/ψ Photoproduction at High $|t|$

The ZEUS collaboration has presented [8] a sample of about 80000 untagged elastic photoproduced ρ^0 meson events based on 2.2 pb^{-1} recorded in 1994, covering the kinematic range $10^{-10} < Q^2 < 4$ GeV^2, $\langle Q^2 \rangle \simeq 10^{-2}$GeV^2, $|t| < 0.5$ GeV^2, and $50 < W_{\gamma^* p} < 100$ GeV. The statistical accuracy of this sample allowed the determination of the relative contributions from resonant and nonresonant dipion production as a function of t (eq. 1). The new analysis of about 30000 events from an integrated luminosity of 2.1 pb^{-1} recorded with the 44-m tagger in 1995 ($10^{-9} < Q^2 < 0.01$ GeV^2, $\langle Q^2 \rangle \simeq 10^{-3}$GeV^2, $|t| < 4.0$ GeV^2, and $85 < W_{\gamma^* p} < 105$ GeV) allows the extension of this study to higher $|t|$, as shown in Fig. 5. At values of $|t|$ exceeding 1 GeV^2 the

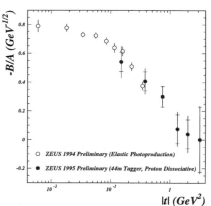

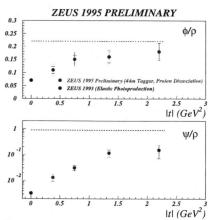

Figure 5: Ratio of dipion mass spectrum fit parameters, B/A, as a function of t (eq. 1)

Figure 6: Ratios of ϕ and J/ψ production to ρ^0 production as a function of t

measurements are consistent with no nonresonant background contribution. The smooth transition and the fact that the high $|t|$ data are dominated by proton dissociative processes indicate that the pion pair production proceeds independently of the proton dissociation.

Clean ϕ and J/ψ signals have also been observed in the 44-m tagger sample, allowing the investigation of production ratios relative to the ρ^0 as a function of $|t|$, shown in Fig. 6. At high $|t|$ the ratios approach values derived from simple quark-counting rules and flavor-independent production which result in the expectation for the ratios: $\rho^0 : \phi : J/\psi = 9 : 2 : 8$.

4   Photo- and Electroproduction of J/ψ Mesons

Photoproduction of J/ψ mesons for $10^{-10} < Q^2 < 4 \text{ GeV}^2$, $\langle Q^2 \rangle \simeq 10^{-1} \text{GeV}^2$, and $40 < W_{\gamma^\bullet p} < 140$ GeV has been investigated [9] via their leptonic decays. An integrated luminosity of 2.70 pb^{-1} (1.87 pb^{-1}) from 1994 was analyzed for the e^+e^- ($\mu^+\mu^-$) decay mode, yielding 460 ± 25 (266 ± 17) events. A fit to the dependence $W_{\gamma^\bullet p}^\delta$ yields the result $\delta = 0.92 \pm 0.14(\text{stat}) \pm 0.10(\text{sys})$, inconsistent with the exchange of a soft Pomeron alone ($\delta \simeq 0.22$).[10] Figure 7 shows the extraction of the $|t|$ dependence in J/ψ photoproduction: **(a)** the dependence of the J/ψ photoproduction cross section on the squared transverse momentum of the J/ψ, p_T^2, **(b)** the factor, F, required to relate the p_T^2 dependence to the $|t|$ dependence, derived from simulations, **(c)** the $|t|$-dependence of the J/ψ elastic photoproduction cross section. The fit to the function $e^{-b|t|}$ yields $b =$

ZEUS 1994

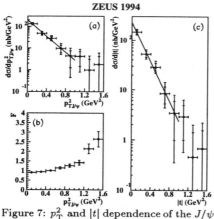

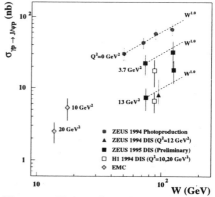

Figure 7: p_T^2 and $|t|$ dependence of the J/ψ elastic photoproduction cross section.

Figure 8: Energy dependence of the J/ψ electroproduction cross section

$4.6 \pm 0.4 \,(\text{stat})^{+0.4}_{-0.6} \,(\text{sys}) \text{ GeV}^{-2}$, indicating that the interaction radius is much smaller than that found [11] for the ρ^0 ($b = 9.8 \pm 0.8 \,(\text{stat}) \pm 1.1 \,(\text{sys}) \text{ GeV}^{-2}$).

An analysis of 6 pb^{-1} recorded in 1995 has allowed a measurement of the $W_{\gamma^\bullet p}$ dependence of the J/ψ electroproduction cross section for $2 < Q^2 < 40 \text{ GeV}^2$ and $50 < W_{\gamma^\bullet p} < 150$ GeV, shown in Fig. 8. A fit to the dilepton mass signal region yields a signal of 101 ± 13 events (e^+e^- and $\mu^+\mu^-$ combined).

The t-slope is found to be $b = 4.5 \pm 0.8\,(\text{stat}) \pm 1.0\,(\text{sys})$ GeV^{-2}, consistent with the photoproduction result.

5 Summary

Analyses of the Q^2 dependence of elastic ρ^0 electroproduction, of ρ^0 photoproduction at high values of the momentum transferred to the target proton, and of the energy dependence in J/ψ photoproduction lend credibility to the idea that the variables Q^2, t, and M_V each can be used to define a transition region between soft and hard diffraction. The ZEUS experiment is sensitive to the transition region in *each* of these variables, allowing detailed, multi-parameter, studies of the transition from nonperturbative to perturbative QCD. The studies are statistics-limited and their precision is expected to improve dramatically when the more recent data sets have been analyzed.

References

1. For a review of HERA results, see J.A.Crittenden, DESY Report 97-068 (1997), to appear as Nr. 140 in *Springer Tracts in Modern Physics*
2. Talks by L. Adamczyk, L. Bellagamba, and T. Monteiro at the 5th International Workshop on Deep Inelastic Scattering and QCD, April, 1997
3. M.G. Ryskin, Z. Phys. **C 57** (1993) 89; M.G. Ryskin *et al.*, Preprint HEP–PH/95-11-228 (1995); S.J. Brodsky *et al.*, Phys. Rev. **D 50** (1994) 3134; L. Frankfurt *et al.*, Phys. Rev. **D 54** (1996) 3194; A. Martin *et al.*, Preprint HEP–PH/96-09-448 (1996); J. Nemchik *et al.*, Phys. Lett. **374** (1996) 199; D.Yu. Ivanov, Phys. Rev. **D 53** (1996) 3564; I.F. Ginzburg and D.Yu. Ivanov, Phys. Rev. **D 54** (1996) 5523; J.R. Forshaw *et al.*, Z. Phys. **C 68** (1995) 137
4. The ZEUS Collaboration, PA02–028, XXVIII International Conference on High Energy Physics, Warsaw, Poland, July 25–31, 1996
5. K. Schilling and G. Wolf, Nucl. Phys. **B 61** (1973) 381
6. The H1 Collaboration, PA03–048, XXVIII International Conference on High Energy Physics, Warsaw, Poland, July 25–31, 1996
7. The NMC Collaboration, Nucl. Phys. **B 429** (1994) 503; The E665 Collaboration, Z. Phys. **C 72** (1997) 237
8. The ZEUS Collaboration, PA02–050, XXVIII International Conference on High Energy Physics, Warsaw, Poland, July 25–31, 1996
9. The ZEUS Collaboration, DESY Report 97-060 (1997)
10. M. Arneodo, these Proceedings
11. The ZEUS Collaboration, Z. Phys. **C 73** (1997) 253

DIFFRACTIVE ELECTROPRODUCTION OF ρ^0 MESONS AT 27.5 GEV.

MACHIEL KOLSTEIN (On behalf of the HERMES collaboration.)
Nationaal Instituut voor Kernfysica en Hoge-Energiefysica (NIKHEF)
PO Box 41882, NL-1009 DB Amsterdam, The Netherlands.

Electroproduction of ρ^0 mesons has been studied at an incident positron beam of 27.5 GeV. ¿From data taken on Hydrogen (^{1}H) and Deuterium (^{2}H) and ^{3}He targets the nuclear transparency has been determined. The measurement of the polar decay angular distribution confirms the results of previous measurements. The evaluation of the cross section and target asymmetry for ρ^0 production is in progress.

1 Introduction

Diffractive ρ^0 production has been studied at HERMES, a deep inelastic positron scattering experiment at DESY. By comparing the ρ^0 production rate on ^{3}He to that on ^{1,2}H, nuclear transparencies were determined. Also measured were the angular distributions of the decay products of the ρ^0 meson, the $\pi^+\pi^-$ pair, which provide information about the validity of s-channel helicity conservation and the various helicity-transfer amplitudes describing vector-meson electroproduction [1]. In this paper the preliminary results of the 1995 data on ^{3}He are presented. An overview of diffractive ρ^0 production can be found in reference [2].

2 The HERMES Experiment

The HERMES experiment at DESY uses the 27.5 GeV polarised positron beam at HERA. The polarised positrons scatter from a polarised internal gas target, which in 1995 was ^{3}He. Also a limited amount of unpolarised ^{1}H and ^{2}H data were collected.

The HERMES spectrometer comprises a dipole magnet together with microstrip gas counters, proportional chambers and drift chambers for track reconstruction. Scattered positrons and forward going hadrons within an angular acceptance of 40 to 220 mrad are reconstructed. A lead glass calorimeter, two rows of hodoscope scintillators and a transition radiation detector provide positron-hadron separation. Additionally, a gas Čerenkov detector provides pion identification above a threshold of 6 GeV. Two small calorimeters monitor the luminosity by measuring the coincidence yield of Bhabha scattering from the target.

3   Data Analysis

Only those events are selected in which both the scattered positron and two hadrons with opposite charge are detected in the spectrometer.

Exclusive ρ^0 events are selected by comparing the invariant mass of the incoming and outgoing nucleon, i.e. by requiring the missing mass to be close to zero. We distinguish *coherent* scattering from the entire nucleus from *incoherent* scattering from individual nucleons by requiring $-t'$, the transverse momentum squared of the ρ^0 meson with respect to the virtual photon, to be smaller or larger than 0.05 GeV^2, respectively. Further cuts on $-t'$ and the energy transfer ν are used to remove background. The contribution of ϕ production is removed by requiring that M_{KK},

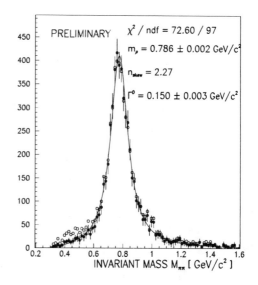

Figure 1: Mass spectrum. The open circles correspond to the data before acceptance correction, the closed circles correspond to the data after acceptance correction.

the invariant mass evaluated under the assumption that both hadrons are kaons, is larger than m_ϕ. After applying these cuts, about 10,000 ρ^0 mesons are obtained.

After subtracting background and applying an acceptance correction, the invariant mass spectrum is evaluated under the assumption that the two detected hadrons are pions. The spectrum is shown in figure 1 together with the results of a fit, described by a skewed relativistic Breit-Wigner resonance [3] with a Ross-Stodolsky skewing factor [4]:

$$\frac{d\sigma}{dM_{\pi\pi}} = \frac{M_{\pi\pi} m_\rho \Gamma_\rho}{(M_{\pi\pi}^2 - m_\rho^2)^2 + m_\rho^2 \Gamma_\rho^2} \left(\frac{m_\rho}{M_{\pi\pi}}\right)^{n_{\text{skew}}} ; \quad \Gamma_\rho = \Gamma_0 \left(\frac{\sqrt{M_{\pi\pi}^2 - 4m_\pi^2}}{\sqrt{m_\rho^2 - 4m_\pi^2}}\right)^3 \frac{m_\rho}{M_{\pi\pi}}.$$

The free parameters in the fit are the position (m_ρ), the width (Γ_0) and the skewing parameter (n_{skew}) of the ρ^0-mass peak. The fitted values, which are shown in figure 1, compare fairly well to the values from the Particle Data

Book[5], i.e. $m_\rho = 768.5 \pm 0.6$ MeV and $\Gamma_0 = 150.7 \pm 1.2$ MeV. The fitted value of m_ρ is somewhat larger, which is likely due to an unseparated contribution from the $\omega(782)$ meson.

4   Nuclear Transparency

The nuclear transparency is defined as the ratio of the cross section for incoherent scattering from a nuclear target, normalised by A, and the cross section for a hydrogen target: $T_A \equiv \frac{\sigma_A}{A \cdot \sigma_H}$. The nuclear transparency can be less than unity due to initial and final state interactions (ISI and FSI) of the vector meson inside the nucleus. The probability for ISI and FSI effects increases with atomic number.

The Color Transparency ansatz[6] leads to a rise of nuclear transparency with increasing Q^2 and

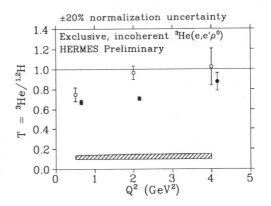

Figure 2: Nuclear Transparency for ^{3}He.

ν. On the other hand, reduction in the ISI for small coherence length[7] would result in a rise of nuclear transparency with increasing Q^2 and with *decreasing* ν. Hence, one would like to measure the nuclear transparency for different Q^2 and ν bins to distinguish between these two effects.

Since only a limited amount of ^{1}H and ^{2}H data were taken in 1995, the data for these two targets are combined, assuming that the nuclear transparency for ^{2}H is close to unity:

$$T_{^3He} = \frac{N_{^3He}}{N_{^1H} + N_{^2H}} \cdot \frac{L_{^1H} + 2\,L_{^2H}}{3\,L_{^3He}}$$

with N_A the number of events and L_A the time integrated luminosity on a particular gas type.

In figure 2 the preliminary measurement of the nuclear transparency for ^{3}He are shown for the **HERMES** 1995 data (open circles). These data are compared to a prediction (filled circles) based on interpolating the fit $T_A = A^{\alpha(Q^2)-1}$ from the E665 ^{1,2}H, C, Ca, Pb ρ^0 production data[8] to A=3. The preliminary HERMES data are closer to unity than the E665-based prediction.

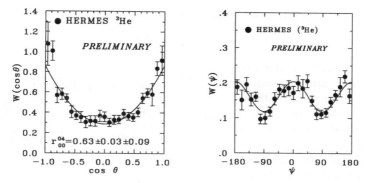

Figure 3: Angular distributions of $\cos(\theta)$ and Ψ as obtained from the HERMES 1995 data on ^{3}He.

5 Angular Distributions

One can express the cross section for exclusive diffractive ρ^0 production in terms of the polarisation states of the ρ^0 meson, the incident beam, the virtual photon and the target. For a longitudinally polarised lepton beam, the production cross section can be expressed in terms of the polar decay angles (θ, ϕ) of the ρ^0 meson in the ρ^0 center of mass frame and the angle between the production plane and the lepton scattering plane Φ in the $\gamma^* p$ center of mass frame (See reference [1]). There is an additional dependence on the target polarisation; in this analysis, however, a sum over both spin states is performed. Under the assumption of s-channel helicity conservation (SCHC) [1], the cross section can be written as a function of only two angles: θ and $\Psi \equiv \phi - \Phi$. After integrating over all angles except for the one that is considered, one obtains the following expressions for the θ and Ψ distributions:

$$W(\cos(\theta)) = \frac{3}{4}[1 - r_{00}^{04} + (3r_{00}^{04} - 1)\cos^2(\theta)], \tag{1}$$

$$W(\Psi) = \frac{1}{2\pi}[1 + 2\epsilon r_{1-1}^1 \cos 2\psi]. \tag{2}$$

The density matrix element r_{00}^{04} represents the longitudinal polarisation of the ρ^0 meson. Within the framework of SCHC, r_{1-1}^1 is the linear polarisation of the ρ^0 meson. Assuming SCHC and using $R = \sigma_L/\sigma_T$ and $\epsilon = \Gamma_L/\Gamma_T$ one obtains:

$$R = \frac{1}{\epsilon} \frac{r_{00}^{04}}{1 - r_{00}^{04}}.$$

318

Assuming - in addition - natural parity exchange in the t-channel, one obtains:

$$r^1_{1-1} = \frac{1}{2}(1 - r^{04}_{00}).$$

In order to evaluate the various angular distributions, a multidimensional acceptance correction was carried out. Subsequentially, all events are projected onto a particular angular coordinate. Figure 3 shows the resulting $\cos(\theta)$ and Ψ distributions. ¿From the $\cos(\theta)$ distribution, a value for r^{04}_{00} was derived: $r^{04}_{00} = 0.63 \pm 0.03 \pm 0.09$, which is averaged over a Q^2 range from 1 to 12 $(GeV/c)^2$. In figure 4 the value of r^{04}_{00} is compared to the

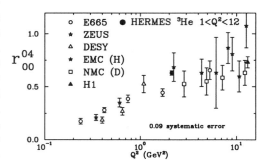

Figure 4: HERMES measurement of r^{04}_{00} as a function of Q^2 compared with data from DESY [9], EMC [10], NMC [11], ZEUS [12] [13], H1 [14] and E665 [15]

results of other experiments. The HERMES measurement is consistent with existing data. Determination of r^{04}_{00} and r^1_{1-1} as a function of Q^2 is in progress.

6   Conclusions and Outlook

A clean sample of diffractive exclusive ρ^0 events has been extracted from the HERMES 1995 data on ^{3}He. A measurement of the nuclear transparency on ^{3}He has been obtained. Combining 1995 and 1996 data (on ^{1}H) may enable a measurement of the nuclear transparency with sufficient accuracy to distinguish between effects due to the coherence length variation and possible effects due to color transparency.

Angular distributions can be measured at HERMES with high statistical accuracy which will enable a test of SCHC in our kinematic range. A preliminary result for the matrix element r^{04}_{00} is shown to be consistent with existing data. The analysis of the target spin dependence of ρ production is in progress. This will enable the extraction of helicity transfer amplitudes which depend on beam and target polarisation.

Acknowledgments

The author acknowledges important contributions of T.G. O'Neill (*Argonne National Lab*) and J.E. Belz (*TRIUMF*).

References

1. K. Schilling and G. Wolf, *Nucl. Phys. B*, **61**, 381 (1973)
2. T.H. Bauer, R.D. Spital, D.R. Yennie, F.M. Pipkin, *Reviews of Modern Physics*, **50**, 261 (1978)
3. J.D. Jackson, *Il Nuovo Cimento*, **34**, 1644 (1964)
4. M. Ross, L. Stodolsky, *Phys. Rev.*, **149**, 1172 (1966)
5. Review of Particle Properties, *Phys. Rev. D*, **54**, 1 (1996)
6. S.J. Brodsky, A.H. Mueller, *Phys. Lett. B*, **206**, 685 (1988)
7. B.Z. Kopeliovich, J. Nemchik, N.N. Nikolaev, B.G. Zakharov, *Phys. Lett. B*, **324**, 469 (1994)
8. M.R. Adams et al. (E665 collaboration), *Phys. Rev. Lett.*, **74**, 1525 (1995)
9. P. Joos et al., *Nucl. Phys. B*, **113**, 53 (1976)
10. J.J. Aubert et al. (EMC), *Phys. Lett. B*,, **161**, 203 (1985)
11. M. Arneodo et al. (NMC), *Nucl. Phys. B*, **429**, 503 (1994)
12. M. Derrick et al. (ZEUS), *Phys. Lett. B*, **356**, 601 (1995)
13. O. Lukina (ZEUS), Ref. pa 02-053, Contribution to the XXVIII Conference on High Energy Physics, Warsaw, 1996
14. S. Aïd et al. (H1), *Nucl. Phys. B*, **468**, 3 (1996)
15. M.R. Adams et al. (E665 collaboration), *Z. Phys. C*, **74**, 237 (1997)

RESULTS ON HARD DIFFRACTION FROM H1

T.R. EBERT

(for the H1 Collaboration)

Oliver Lodge Laboratory, University of Liverpool, Liverpool, U.K.

A measurement of the diffractive structure function $F_2^{D(3)}(\beta, Q^2, x_{I\!P})$ from the H1 experiment is presented. The $x_{I\!P}$ dependence of $F_2^{D(3)}$ is found to vary with β, demonstrating that the factorisation of a universal diffractive flux from the cross-section is not possible. The data are consistent with there being a contribution from both pomeron and meson exchange. The structure function of the exchange ($\tilde{F}_2^D(\beta, Q^2)$) shows scaling violations with Q^2, and a QCD fit leads to the conclusion that the momentum is carried largely by gluons. The properties of the hadronic final state in diffractive events are studied. Measurements of energy flow and charged particle, charm and jet production are presented. They are all consistent with the structure of the pomeron being dominated by gluons.

1 Introduction

Deep inelastic scattering events containing a large interval of rapidity without any hadronic activity (a "rapidity gap")[1,2] are interpreted as being dominantly diffractive in nature[3]. The hadronic final state of any event can be decomposed into two systems X and Y separated by the largest gap in rapidity and in the case of diffraction, the masses of both systems are small compared to the $\gamma^* p$ centre of mass energy (W).

In addition to the standard deep-inelastic variables Q^2, y and W^2, two variables are introduced:

$$\beta \simeq \frac{Q^2}{Q^2 + M_X^2} \qquad x_{I\!P} \simeq \frac{Q^2 + M_X^2}{Q^2 + W^2} \qquad (1)$$

They have a simple interpretation in terms of an exchanged object (e.g. a pomeron); $x_{I\!P}$ is the fraction of the proton's momentum carried by the exchanged object and β is the fraction of the momentum of the exchanged object carried by the struck quark. The 4–momentum transfer squared at the proton vertex is t.

2 The Diffractive Structure Function

The analysis is based on $\sim 2\,\mathrm{pb}^{-1}$ data taken by the H1 experiment in 1994, and covers the kinematic range $2.5 < Q^2 < 65\,\mathrm{GeV}^2$, $0.01 < \beta < 0.9$ and $10^{-4} < x_{I\!P} < 0.05$. Experimentally, diffractive events with a system Y of low mass are selected on the basis of having no activity in a series of forward detectors in H1 [4], with sensitivity to the rapidity range $3.4 < \eta < 7.5$. The selection ensures that the system X is well contained in the detector and the system Y, which is not measured, has a mass $M_Y < 1.6\,\mathrm{GeV}$. The requirement $x_{I\!P} < 0.05$ means that Y carries more that 95% of the incident proton's momentum. The selection restricts t, which is not measured, to the range $|t| < 1\,\mathrm{GeV}^2$. The contribution to the event sample from events with proton dissociation is estimated to be $\sim 5\%$.

H1 Preliminary 1994

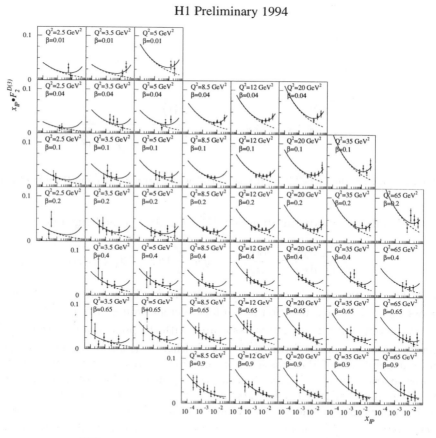

Figure 1: $x_{I\!P} \cdot F_2^{D(3)}(\beta, Q^2, x_{I\!P})$ as a function of $x_{I\!P}$ in bins of β and Q^2. A fit to the data (see text for details) including a pomeron and meson component (solid line) and the pomeron component to this (dashed line) are shown.

H1 Preliminary 1994

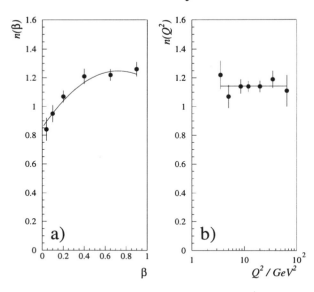

Figure 2: n from the fit $F_2^{D(3)} = A(\beta, Q^2) \cdot x_{I\!\!P}^{-n}$ where (a) $n = n(\beta)$ and (b) $n = n(Q^2)$.

The diffractive structure function $F_2^{D(3)}(\beta, Q^2, x_{I\!\!P})$ is defined as [5]:

$$\frac{\mathrm{d}^3 \, \sigma_{ep \to e'XY}^D}{\mathrm{d}\beta \, \mathrm{d}Q^2 \, \mathrm{d}x_{I\!\!P}} = \frac{4\pi\alpha^2}{\beta Q^4}(1 - y + \frac{y^2}{2})F_2^{D(3)}(\beta, Q^2, x_{I\!\!P}) \qquad (2)$$

with the integral over the measured t range having been performed. Figure 1 shows $x_{I\!\!P} \cdot F_2^{D(3)}$ as a function of $x_{I\!\!P}$ for different values of β and Q^2.

A universal flux of pomerons associated with the proton implies that $F_2^{D(3)}$ can be factorised in the form $F_2^{D(3)} \propto x_{I\!\!P}^{-n}$ where n is $2\alpha(t) - 1$ averaged over the t dependence of the cross-section and $\alpha(t) = \alpha(0) + \alpha't$ is the effective pomeron trajectory [6]. Figure 2 shows the resulting values of n from such a fit to the data, allowing n to vary with either β or Q^2. Whilst there is no evidence for a dependence on Q^2, n increases with increasing β. Therefore the factorisation of $F_2^{D(3)}$ into terms depending only on β and Q^2, with the $x_{I\!\!P}$ dependence describing a universal flux of pomerons is not valid.

The most probable explanation for this is a contribution from meson exchange (e.g. $f_2^0(1270)$). Figure 1 shows a phenomenological fit to $F_2^{D(3)}$ with a pomeron and a meson component:

$$F_2^{D(3)} = A^{I\!\!P}(\beta, Q^2) \cdot x_{I\!\!P}^{-n_{I\!\!P}} + C_M \cdot F_2^M(\beta, Q^2) \cdot x_{I\!\!P}^{-n_M} \tag{3}$$

where $A^{I\!\!P}$ is proportional to the pomeron structure function. The GRV parameterisation of the pion structure function [7] is used for F_2^M and $A^{I\!\!P}$, $n_{I\!\!P}$, C_M and n_M are fitted simultaneously. This procedure gives an excellent fit to the data ($\chi^2/ndf = 165/156$) yielding $n_{I\!\!P} = 1.29 \pm 0.03(\text{stat}) \pm 0.07(\text{syst})$ and $n_M = 0.3 \pm 0.3(\text{stat}) \pm 0.6(\text{syst})$. The influence of a possible interference between the two components is included in the systematic error [9].

The integration over t is corrected for assuming a peripheral t dependence (e^{bt}) with $b_M = 5$ and $b_{I\!\!P} = 6$ and linear trajectories ($\alpha(t) = \alpha(0) + \alpha't$) with $\alpha'_M = 1$ and $\alpha'_{I\!\!P} = 0.3$. This yields $\alpha(0)_M = 0.6 \pm 0.1(\text{stat}) \pm 0.3(\text{syst})$ and $\alpha(0)_{I\!\!P} = 1.18 \pm 0.02(\text{stat}) \pm 0.04(\text{syst})$.

3 The Partonic Structure of Diffractive Exchange

The structure function $\tilde{F}_2^D$:

$$\tilde{F}_2^D(\beta, Q^2) = \int_{x_{I\!\!P}=0.0003}^{x_{I\!\!P}=0.05} F_2^{D(3)}(\beta, Q^2, x_{I\!\!P}) dx_{I\!\!P} \tag{4}$$

which is proportional to the average deep inelastic structure of the exchange, is shown in figure 3. At fixed Q^2, $\tilde{F}_2^D$ is consistent with being independent of β but scaling violations are clearly seen in the Q^2 dependence at fixed β. The conclusions are unaffected by the possible presence of meson exchange [9].

A QCD analysis of $\tilde{F}_2^D$ was performed. The $u + d + s$ quark distributions and the gluon distribution are parameterised at a scale $Q_0^2 = 2.5\,\text{GeV}^2$ with the form $x \cdot f(x) = Ax^B(1 - x)^C$ and evolved to higher Q^2 using DGLAP evolution. Charm is introduced via boson-gluon fusion [10], and no momentum sum-rule is applied [11].

Two possible solutions are considered; only quarks or both quarks and gluons are present at the starting scale. The resulting fits are shown in figure 4. The data requires a significant gluon density at the starting scale.

The parton densities obtained from the QCD fit with both quarks and gluons at the starting scale are shown in figure 5. Close to the starting scale, a "leading" gluon behaviour is seen, in which the exchange is dominated by gluons with fractional momentum $x_{g/I\!\!P} > 0.9$. Also shown is the integrated momentum fraction carried by quarks and gluons as a function of Q^2. Throughout the Q^2 range, gluons carry in excess of 80% of the momentum of the exchange.

324

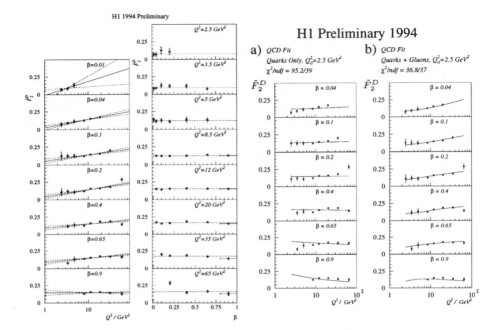

Figure 3: $\tilde{F}_2^D$ as a function of Q^2 for different values of β (left) and as a function of β for different values of Q^2 (right).

Figure 4: QCD fit to $\tilde{F}_2^D$ assuming (a) only quarks (b) both quarks and gluons at the starting scale of $Q_0^2 = 2.5\,\text{GeV}^2$

4   The Hadronic Final State in Diffractive Events

The picture of diffractive deep inelastic scattering described above has consequences for the hadronic final state. If the pomeron is a quark dominated object, the leading order process is $eq \to eq$ with the exchanged photon coupling directly to a quark from the pomeron. The struck quark and pomeron remnant have small transverse momentum with respect to the $\gamma^* I\!\!P$ axis in the $\gamma^* I\!\!P$ centre-of-mass frame. However, for a gluon dominated pomeron, the leading order process is boson-gluon fusion, and the $q\bar{q}$ pair from the hard sub-process can have significant transverse momentum with respect to this axis.

For a gluon dominated pomeron, therefore, more energy flow in the central region of the $\gamma^* I\!\!P$ system and increased high p_T particle production is expected. The thrust distribution will show a two jet configuration, and more di-jet events will be observed. The cross-section for charm production is also

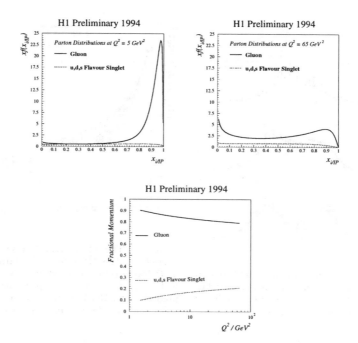

Figure 5: Parton densities from the fit to $\tilde{F}_2^D$ at (a) $Q^2 = 5\,\mathrm{GeV}^2$ and (b) $Q^2 = 65\,\mathrm{GeV}^2$ allowing both quarks and gluons at $Q_0^2 = 2.5\,\mathrm{GeV}^2$. The fraction of the total momentum carried by quarks and gluons as a function of Q^2 is shown in (c).

higher, as the boson-gluon fusion process is dominant.

The Monte Carlo generator RAPGAP [12] was used for comparison with the data. In this model, the pomeron has a partonic structure and the two sets of parton densities obtained from the QCD fit to $\tilde{F}_2^D$ under the assumption that the pomeron contains only quarks (the RG-Q model) or a mixture of quarks and gluons (the RG-QG model) at $Q^2 = 2.5\,\mathrm{GeV}^2$ were used. Two different models of QCD radiation were used for the RG-QG model – leading log parton showers (MEPS) and the colour dipole model (CDM). The RG-Q model uses the colour dipole model.

4.1 Energy Flow and Charged Particle Production

Details of the measurements can be found elsewhere [13]. Results are presented in the kinematic range $7.5 < Q^2 < 100\,\mathrm{GeV}^2$, $0.05 < y < 0.6$ and $x_{I\!P} < 0.025$.

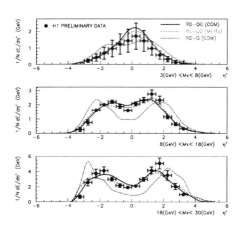

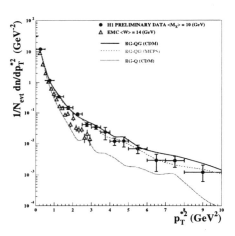

Figure 7: The p_T^{*2} distribution of charged particles. The H1 diffractive data in the $\gamma^* I\!\!P$ frame (black points) are compared to EMC μp data in the $\gamma^* p$ frame (white points). The RG-Q (dotted line) and RG-QG (solid and dashed lines) are also shown.

Figure 6: Energy flow in the $\gamma^* I\!\!P$ frame in ranges of M_X. The H1 data is compared to the RG-Q (dotted line) and RG-QG (solid and dashed lines) models.

Figure 6 shows the energy flow as a function of pseudorapidity in the $\gamma^* I\!\!P$ frame, in bins of M_X. The data is compared to the RG-Q and RG-QG models. Whilst the RG-Q model significantly underestimates the energy flow at $\eta^* \approx 0$, the models which include the "leading gluon" parameterisation for the pomeron are able to describe the data.

The track p_T^{*2} distribution relative to the $\gamma^* I\!\!P$ axis is shown in figure 7. The H1 diffractive data ($< M_X >= 10 \, \text{GeV}$) in the $\gamma^* I\!\!P$ frame is compared to EMC deep–inelastic μp data ($<W>= 14 \, \text{GeV}$) [14] in the $\gamma^* p$ frame. There is an excess of high p_T^{*2} particles in the diffractive data over the EMC data. This presumably arises from the large contribution from boson gluon fusion in the diffractive events, as the EMC data is in a kinematic region where the proton structure is dominated by quarks. This is confirmed by the comparison with the models; whilst the RG-Q model lies below the data, the two RG-QG models are in good agreement with the measured data points.

The Feynman-x (x_F) distribution is shown in figure 8, with the H1 data again compared to EMC data. The EMC data is asymmetric about $x_F = 0$, which is consequence of the fact that unlike the struck parton, the proton remnant is an extended object. In contrast, for the H1 diffractive data the distribution is symmetric, implying a similarity between the struck parton and

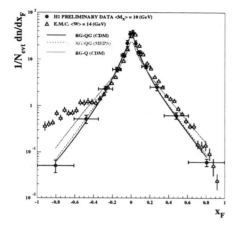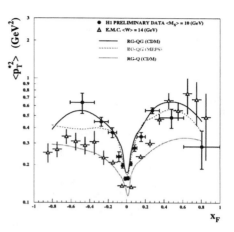

Figure 8: The x_F distribution showing H1 diffractive data in the $\gamma^* I\!\!P$ frame (black points) and EMC μp data in the $\gamma^* p$ frame (white points). The RG-Q (dotted line) and RG-QG (solid and dashed lines) are also shown.

Figure 9: Seagull plot for H1 diffractive data in the $\gamma^* I\!\!P$ frame (black points) and EMC μp data in the $\gamma^* p$ frame (white points). The RG-Q (dotted line) and RG-QG (solid and dashed lines) are also shown.

the pomeron remnant. The data is again described by the RG-QG models.

Figure 9 shows the $< p_T^{*2} >$ as a function of x_F. The EMC data are asymmetric, with the $< p_T^{*2} >$ in the remnant hemisphere suppressed with respect to that in the struck parton hemisphere owing to the extended nature of the proton remnant [15]. In contrast, the H1 diffractive data are symmetric about $x_F = 0$, suggesting that the pomeron remnant is a compact object like the struck parton. The $< p_T^{*2} >$ at $x_F = 0$ is higher for the H1 data than the EMC data, indicating that more of the diffractive events involve a high p_T process. Again whilst the RG-Q model fails to describe the data, the RG-QG model gives a good description of the measured values.

4.2 Observation of Charm

$D^{*\pm}$ mesons are reconstructed via the decay $D^{*\pm} \to D^0 \pi_{slow}^{\pm} \to (K^{\mp}\pi^{\pm})\pi_{slow}^{\pm}$ [13]. The distribution of the mass difference between the $D^{*\pm}$ and D^0 candidates is shown in figure 10.

The cross-section for $D^{*\pm}$ production in the system X is measured to be:

$$\sigma(ep \to eD^*XY) = 380^{+150}_{-120}(\text{stat})^{+140}_{-110}(\text{syst}) \text{ pb}$$

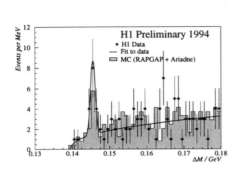

Figure 10: $\Delta M = M(K\pi\pi_{slow}) - M(K\pi)$ for D^* candidates. H1 data are compared to the RG-QG model.

Figure 11: $<T>$ versus $1/M_x$ for H1 diffractive data (black points) and a selection of e^+e^- data (white points).

in the kinematic range $10 < Q^2 < 100\,\mathrm{GeV^2}$, $0.06 < y < 0.6$, $x_{I\!P} < 0.05$, $M_Y < 1.6\,\mathrm{GeV}$, $|\eta(D^*)| < 1.25$ and $p_T(D^*) > 1.0\,\mathrm{GeV}$. The RG-Q model predicts a cross-section of $\sim 10\,\mathrm{pb^{-1}}$ and the RG-QG model predicts a cross-section of $\sim 200\,\mathrm{pb^{-1}}$. The measured cross-section is inconsistent at the 2σ level with the prediction based on a quark dominated pomeron.

4.3 Thrust

In the centre of mass of a system of N particles, thrust is defined as:

$$T = \frac{1}{\sum_{i=1}^{N} |\vec{p_i}|} \times \max\left\{ \Sigma_{i=1}^{N} |\vec{p_i} \cdot \vec{n}| \right\} \qquad (5)$$

and its value varies between 0.5 (isotropic event of infinite multiplicity) and 1.0 (two particles).

The $<T>$ for diffractive events is shown in figure 11 as a function of $1/M_X$. Details of this measurement can be found elsewhere[16]. The H1 diffractive data are compared to measurements from e^+e^- experiments. The results show that the diffractive events are basically two-jet like in nature, with the jets becoming more collimated with increasing M_X. More than $\sim 30\%$ of events have a thrust

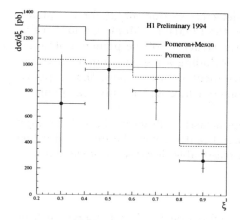

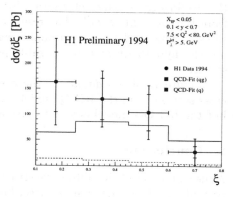

Figure 12: Differential di-jet cross-section in diffractive photoproduction. The data is compared to POMPYT with $I\!P$ (dashed line) and with meson and $I\!P$ (solid line) exchange, with $I\!P$ parton densities obtained from the fit to $F_2^{D(3)}$.

Figure 13: Differential di-jet cross-section for $7.5 < Q^2 < 80\,\mathrm{GeV}^2$. The solid line shows the prediction from the RG-QG model and the dashed line the prediction from the RG-Q model.

jet $p_T^2 > 3\,\mathrm{GeV}^2$. The $<T>$ is lower in the diffractive data than the e^+e^- measurements, indicating a higher parton multiplicity in the diffractive events.

4.4 High p_T Jets

Di-jet production has been studied in both diffractive photoproduction and diffractive deep-inelastic scattering.

The photoproduction analysis covers the kinematic range $10^{-8} < Q^2 < 0.01\,\mathrm{GeV}^2$ and $0.25 < y < 0.7$ and the deep inelastic data considers events with $7.5 < Q^2 < 100\,\mathrm{GeV}^2$ and $0.1 < y < 0.7$. In both cases, $x_{I\!P} < 0.05$. A cone algorithm is used to reconstruct jets in the $\gamma^* I\!P$ centre of mass frame, and at least two jets with $p_T > 5\,\mathrm{GeV}$ with respect to the photon direction are required.

The di-jet cross-section is presented as a function of ξ, which is a hadron level estimator of the momentum fraction of the exchanged object which enters the hard subprocess. ξ is reconstructed from the jets:

$$\xi_{\gamma p} = \frac{(E + P_z)_{jets}}{(E + P_z)_X}; \qquad \xi_{\gamma^* p} = \frac{Q^2 + M_{jj}^2}{Q^2 + M_X^2} \qquad (6)$$

Figure 12 shows the differential di-jet cross-section $d\sigma/d\xi$ for the photo-production data and the prediction from the POMPYT Monte Carlo [17], using the leading gluon parameterisation for the structure of the pomeron obtained from the QCD fit to $\tilde{F}_2^D$. The result of including a meson component is also shown. The model is in reasonable agreement with the data, thus supporting the hypothesis of a factorisable pomeron flux and a universal pomeron structure.

Figure 13 shows $d\sigma/d\xi$ for the deep-inelastic diffractive data. The di-jet cross-section from the RG-Q model is significantly below the measured values but the RG-QG model is able to give a reasonable description of the data.

5   Conclusions

A measurement of the diffractive structure function $F_2^{D(3)}(\beta, Q^2, x_{I\!\!P})$ has been presented. The data can be described by a superposition of pomeron and meson exchange. The structure function of the exchange ($\tilde{F}_2^D$) shows scaling violations with Q^2, and a QCD fit leads to the conclusion that the momentum of the exchange is carried largely by gluons.

Features of the hadronic final state are well reproduced by a model based on a flux of pomerons with parton densities obtained from the QCD fit to the inclusive measurement $\tilde{F}_2^D$. There is increased energy flow and high p_T^* particle, charm and jet production over the expectations from a model in which the pomeron structure is quark dominated.

Acknowledgements

I would like to thank the members of the H1 diffractive group for informative discussions on this material.

References

1. ZEUS Collaboration, Phys. Lett. **B315** (1993) 481.
2. H1 Collaboration, Nucl. Phys. **B429** (1994) 477.
3. H1 Collaboration, Phys. Lett. **B348** (1995) 681.
4. H1 Collaboration, Nucl. Instr. and Meth. **A386** (1997) 310 and **A386** (1997) 348.
5. G. Ingelman and P. Schlein, Phys. Lett. **B152** (1985) 256.
6. See for example P. Collins, "An Introduction to Regge Theory and High Energy Physics", Cambridge University Press, (1997)
7. M. Gluck, E. Reya, A. Vogt, Z. Phys. **C53** (1992) 651.

8. NMC Collaboration, Phys. Lett. **B364** (1995) 107.
   BCDMS Collaboration, Phys. Lett. **B223** (1989) 485.
9. H1 Collaboration, "A Measurement and QCD Analysis of the Diffractive Structure Function $F_2^{D(3)}$", Proc. of ICHEP '96, Warsaw, July 1996.
10. H1 Collaboration, Nucl. Phys. **B470** (1996) 3.
11. L. Trentadue and G. Veneziano, Phys. Lett. **B323** (1994) 201.
12. H. Jung, Comp. Phys. Comm. **86** (1995) 147
13. C. Cormack, Thesis (University of Liverpool) in litt.
14. EMC Collaboration, Z. Phys. **C35** (1987) 417.
15. EMC Collaboration, Phys. Lett. **B149** (1984) 415.
16. H1 Collaboration, "Thrust Jet Analysis of Deep–Inelastic Large Rapidity Gap Events at HERA", Proc. of ICHEP '96, Warsaw, July 1996.
17. P. Bruni and G. Ingelman, Proc. Europhysics Conf. on HEP, Marseilles 1993, 595.

INCLUSIVE DIFFRACTION IN PHOTOPRODUCTION AND DIS AT HERA

K. PIOTRZKOWSKI

(On behalf of the ZEUS Collaboration)

DESY F1, Notkestrasse 85,

D-22603 Hamburg, Germany

piotrzkowski@desy.de

Properties of diffractive photon dissociation in photoproduction and at large Q^2 at HERA were studied. The diffractive structure function has been determined in two different ways using the large Q^2 data.

1 Introduction

HERA (**H**adron-**E**lektron-**R**ing-**A**nlage) is unique storage ring for the study of high energy photon–proton interactions. If an incident electron is scattered under small angle, the virtuality of the exchanged photon, Q^2, is very small. Therefore, such events can be interpreted as quasi-real photoproduction. On the other hand, if the electron is scattered under large angles, then Q^2 is large and one is in the deep inelastic scattering (DIS) regime. In both cases, diffractive phenomena which are characterized by an exponential suppression of the squared four-momentum (t) transferred between photon and proton can be studied.

In this contribution, we report measurements of photon diffractive dissociation, $ep \rightarrow eXp$. In such interactions the incident proton remains intact and loses only a small fraction of its initial momentum, whereas the almost real (or highly virtual) photon dissociates into a hadronic system X. Since the invariant mass, M_X, of this system is much smaller then the photon–proton center of mass energy, W, a large gap in rapidity between the scattered proton and the particles from the decay of system X should be observed.

In the framework of Regge theory and assuming that the photon behaves like an hadron, there are very specific predictions for the cross section for photon diffractive dissociation in the high energy and high M_X limit[1]:

$$\frac{d^2\sigma}{dt\,dM_X^2} = G_{I\!P I\!P I\!P}\, W^{2(2\alpha_{I\!P}(0)-2)} \left(\frac{1}{M_X{}^2}\right)^{\alpha_{I\!P}(0)} \exp\left(b_0 + 2\alpha_{I\!P}{}' \ln\frac{W^2}{M_X^2}\right) t,$$

$$(1)$$

where b_0 is the slope of the t distribution for $W^2 = M_X^2$, $\alpha_{I\!P}(0)$ and $\alpha_{I\!P}{}'$ are respectively the intercept and slope of the pomeron trajectory and $G_{I\!P I\!P I\!P}$ is the triple pomeron coupling. The pomeron trajectory (or just the pomeron, $I\!P$) is introduced in Regge theory primarily to account for the slow rise of the total and elastic cross sections in hadron–hadron collisions at high energies (see also [2]).

Ingelman and Schlein proposed that the pomeron is a particle with a well defined structure [3]. This hypothesis can be verified at HERA by using highly virtual photons as probes of the pomeron structure in diffractive DIS.

The results presented below are based on data collected using the ZEUS detector during 1994. In that period HERA operated with 27.5 GeV positrons and 820 GeV protons.

2 Inclusive diffraction in photoproduction

The process under consideration is $\gamma p \rightarrow XN$, where X is the diffractively dissociated photon system of mass M_X and N is either a proton or a nucleonic system with mass $M_N < 2$ GeV. A detailed discussion of the following results is presented in Ref. [4].

Photoproduction events were identified by detecting the scattered positron in a small forward calorimeter. This ensured that the virtuality of the exchanged photon was below 0.02 GeV^2 with median $\langle Q^2 \rangle = 6 \times 10^{-4}$ GeV^2. The energy range of the positrons corresponded to $176 < W < 225$ GeV.

Diffractive interactions were selected by requiring a rapidity-gap in the event, i.e. no activity in the ZEUS detector in the pseudo-rapidity[a] range $4.3 < \eta < 5.8$. The mass spectrum of the dissociated photon system was obtained after subtracting the remaining non-diffractive contributions using Monte Carlo simulations.

The shape of the M_X distribution was fitted with Eq. 1 integrated over t. In the interval $8 < M_X < 24$ GeV, where the triple pomeron contribution is expected to dominate, a fit yielded an effective pomeron intercept of $\alpha_{I\!P} = 1.12 \pm 0.04(stat) \pm 0.08(syst)$. This value is in good agreement with the results obtained at the Tevatron [5].

The measured cross section for photon dissociation at low masses, $3 < M_X < 8$ GeV, is significantly higher than that expected from the extrapolation of the triple pomeron formula describing the region $8 < M_X < 24$ GeV. Assuming that this discrepancy is due to a pomeron-pomeron-reggeon ($I\!PI\!PI\!R$) term, its contribution to the diffractive cross section in the interval $3 < M_X < 24$ GeV, taking $\alpha_{I\!P}(0) = 1.08$ and $\alpha_{I\!R}(0) = 0.45$, was estimated to be $f_{\boldsymbol{PPR}} = 26 \pm 3(stat) \pm 12(syst)\%$. The size of the $I\!PI\!PI\!R$ contribution is

---

[a]The pseudo-rapidity η is defined as $\eta = -\ln\tan(\theta/2)$, where θ is the polar angle in the laboratory frame, measured with respect to the proton direction.

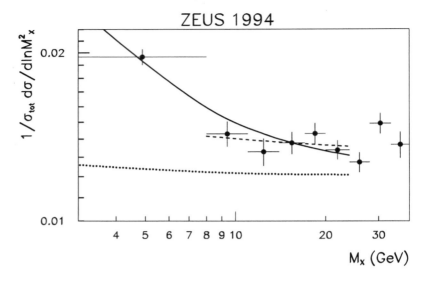

Figure 1: The M_X spectrum in diffractive photoproduction events. The fit to a pure triple pomeron contribution is shown with dashed line. The solid line indicates the result of the fit with the sum of $I\!PI\!PI\!P$ and $I\!PI\!PI\!R$ contributions. The triple pomeron contribution to the combined fit is shown as a dotted line.

similar to that obtained from global fits to diffractive dissociation pp data at low energies [6].

The cross section attributed to the diffractive process $\gamma p \rightarrow XN$ in the interval $3 < M_X < 24$ GeV relative to total photoproduction cross section was measured to be $\sigma_D^{partial}/\sigma_{tot} = 6.2 \pm 0.2(stat) \pm 1.4(syst)\%$. After extrapolating this result to the mass interval of $m_\phi^2 < M_X^2 < 0.05W^2$ and correcting for the small contribution of proton dissociation, the cross section for single diffractive photon dissociation, $\gamma p \rightarrow Xp$, relative to the total photoproduction cross section was found to be $\sigma_{SD}/\sigma_{tot} = 13.3 \pm 0.5(stat) \pm 3.6(syst)\%$. This value is consistent with those obtained from other measurements at HERA [7,8] and at the Tevatron [5].

The t distribution in diffractive photoproduction, $\gamma p \rightarrow Xp$, was directly measured in the Q^2 and W range given above and for masses of the dissociated photon system $4 < M_X < 32$ GeV. It was determined in the range $0.073 < |t| < 0.40$ GeV^2 by measuring the scattered proton in the ZEUS Leading Proton Spectrometer (LPS) [9]. Diffractive events were selected by requiring that the fraction of the beam longitudinal momentum carried by the scattered proton, $x_L = p_z'/p_z$, be in the range $0.97 < x_L < 1.02$.

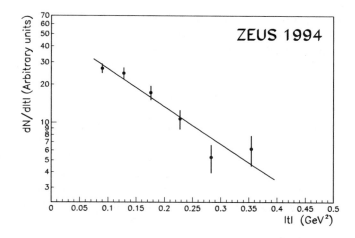

Figure 2: Preliminary differential distribution $dN/d|t|$ for photon diffractive dissociation, $\gamma p \to Xp$, for $176 < W < 225$ GeV, $0.073 < |t| < 0.40$ GeV^{-2}, $4 < M_X < 32$ GeV. The line is the result of the fit described in the text.

The measured t distribution is shown in Fig. 2. A fit assuming that the t distribution has the form $dN/d|t| = A \exp(-b|t|)$ yielded the slope parameter $b = 7.3 \pm 0.9(stat) \pm 1.0(syst)$ GeV^{-2}, close to values measured in fixed target experiments at lower energies [10].

3 Inclusive diffraction in DIS

In analogy to the structure function $F_2(x, Q^2)$ in DIS, one can introduce the notion of the diffractive structure function, F_2^D (see also [2]) for inclusive diffraction, $\gamma^* p \to Xp$. If the pomeron is a particle and diffraction is dominated by pomeron exchange, than F_2^D should factorize into the pomeron flux $f_{I\!\!P}(x_{I\!\!P}, t)$ and the pomeron structure function $F_2^{I\!\!P}(\beta, Q^2)$, where $x_{I\!\!P} \approx 1 - x_L$ and $\beta = x/x_{I\!\!P} \approx \frac{Q^2}{Q^2 + M_X^2}$. In other words, the F_2^D dependence on $x_{I\!\!P}$ and t should not change with Q^2, β or M_X. Regge phenomenology predicts $f_{I\!\!P} \sim (1/x_{I\!\!P})^{2\alpha_{I\!\!P} - 1}$.

Diffractive events in DIS are selected in ZEUS using two different methods. The first approach defines diffractive events as those that form the excess over the exponential fall-off in the measured $\ln M_X^2$ distribution [11]. The second

336

method requires a proton with $x_L > 0.97$ detected in the LPS.

Using the first method, the diffractive cross section $d\sigma_{diff}/dM_X$ was determined as a function of W in the range $60 < W < 200$ GeV for several bins of M_X and Q^2, see Fig. 3. Parametrizing the W dependence, according to Eq. 1, by the form $d\sigma_{diff}/dM_X \propto (W^2)^{(2\overline{\alpha_P}-2)}$ yields values for the pomeron trajectory $\overline{\alpha_P}$, averaged over t, that lie above the prediction from fits to hadron–hadron data [13], $\overline{\alpha_P} \approx 1.05$, see Fig. 4.

With the LPS method, F_2^D (integrated over t and averaged over Q^2 between 5 and 20 GeV^2) was determined in the kinematic range $4 \times 10^{-4} < x_P < 0.03$, $0.015 < \beta < 0.5$. A fit of the form $(1/x_P)^a$ to F_2^D, where the exponent was kept fixed for all values of β, yields $a = 1.04 \pm 0.09$ (stat.)$^{+0.14}_{-0.13}$(syst.). This result corresponds to lower $\overline{\alpha_P}$ compared to the first method. However, at higher values of x_P ($x_P \gtrsim 0.01$), the measurement could be affected by additional contributions from the reggeon trajectories [12], which has a smaller intercept then the pomeron trajectory.

The differential cross section $d\sigma_{diff}/dt$ was measured using the LPS in the same Q^2 and β region, and for $50 < W < 270$ GeV and $0.073 < |t| < 0.4$ GeV^2. The cross section is exponentially falling with $|t|$, with a slope $b = 7.1 \pm 1.1(stat)^{+0.7}_{-1.0}(syst)$ GeV^{-2}.

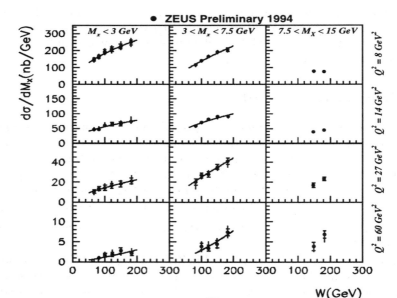

Figure 3: The differential cross sections $d\sigma^{diff}\,(\gamma^*p \to XN)/dM_X$ measured in three M_X and four Q^2 bins. The curves are the results from the fits, see text.

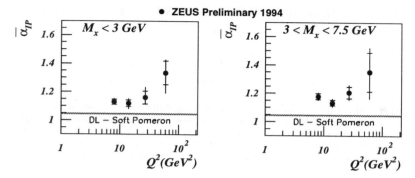

Figure 4: Values of measured $\overline{\alpha_{I\!P}}$ (average over t) as a function of Q^2 for two M_X ranges. The bands labelled "DL–soft pomeron" indicate predictions from Ref.[13].

4 Conclusions

We found that diffractive photon dissociation in photoproduction at HERA can be well described by Regge phenomenology based on fits to the hadron–hadron data. On the other hand, in inclusive diffraction at large Q^2 some deviations might be present from the expectations based on the 'soft' pomeron trajectory. However, more data is needed to resolve the issue of the pomeron nature in this regime.

References

1. A.H.Mueller, *Phys. Rev.* D **2**, 2963 (1970).
2. M.Arneodo, these Proceedings.
3. G.Ingelman and P.Schlein, *Phys. Lett.* B **152**, 256 (1985).
4. ZEUS Coll., J.Breitweg et al., *DESY 97–061* (1997).
5. CDF Coll., F. Abe et al., *Phys. Rev.* D **50**, 5535 (1994).
6. R.D. Field and G.C. Fox, *Nucl. Phys.* B **80**, 367 (1974).
7. H1 Coll., S. Aid et al., *Z. Phys.* C **69**, 27 (1995).
8. ZEUS Coll., M. Derrick et al., *Z. Phys.* C **63**, 391 (1994).
9. ZEUS Coll., M. Derrick et al., *Z. Phys.* C **73**, 253 (1997).
10. T.J. Chapin et al., *Phys. Rev.* D **31**, 17 (1985).
11. ZEUS Coll., M. Derrick et al., *Z. Phys.* C **70**, 391 (1996).
12. ZEUS Coll., M. Derrick et al., ICHEP96, pa02–026.
13. A.Donnachie and P.V.Landshoff, *Phys. Lett.* B **296**, 227 (1992).

JETS AND CHARM IN DIFFRACTIVE EVENTS AT HERA

JUAN PUGA

On behalf of the ZEUS Collaboration

Universidad Autónoma de Madrid, Cantoblanco, Madrid E-28049, Spain

Measurements of differential dijet cross sections in diffractive photoproduction and of $D^{*\pm}$ production in diffractive deep inelastic scattering (DIS) are presented. The diffractive cross sections measurements together with the results of the diffractive structure function in DIS are analized within a framework in which the partons densities of the pomeron are evolved according to the DGLAP equations.

1 Hard Diffraction at HERA

Electron-proton collisions at HERA have shown evidence for hard processes in diffractive reactions. Both in DIS ($Q^2 > 10$ GeV^2, where Q^2 is the virtuality of the exchanged photon) and in photoproduction ($Q^2 \approx 0$), events characterized by a large rapidity gap (LRG) towards the proton direction have been observed and interpreted as resulting from diffractive scattering[1,2]. The measurement of the diffractive structure function in DIS,[3] combined with the measured jet cross sections in diffractive photoproduction gave the first experimental evidence for the gluon content of the pomeron [4]. Based on data collected by the ZEUS detector during 1994, when HERA operated with positrons of $E_e = 27.5$ GeV and protons of $E_p = 820$ GeV, new measurements of diffractive hard processes have been performed and are presented here: a) the dijet cross sections in diffractive photoproduction, and b) the cross section for $D^{*\pm}$ production in diffractive DIS with $Q^2 > 10$ GeV^2.

Single diffractive processes in ep collisions are characterized by a final state consisting of a hadronic system X, the scattered positron and the scattered proton, $e(k) + p(P) \rightarrow e'(k') + p'(P') + X$. The kinematics of this process are described in terms of four variables: $Q^2 = -(k - k')^2$, the Bjorken variable $x = Q^2/(2P \cdot q)$, the fraction of the momentum of the initial proton carried by the scattered proton ($x_f = P' \cdot q/(P \cdot q)$), and the square of the momentum transfer between the initial and final state proton ($t = (P - P')^2$). In the analyses presented here, the outgoing proton was not observed, and an integral over t was performed. Another useful variables are $x_{I\!P} \equiv 1 - x_f$ and $\beta \equiv x/x_{I\!P}$, which are interpreted in factorisable models[5,6,7][a] as the fraction of the incident proton's momentum carried by the pomeron and as the momentum fraction

---

[a]In these models the emission of the pomeron is assumed to be independent of the hard scattering process.

of the struck parton within the pomeron, respectively. Diffractive processes give rise to a LRG between the hadronic system X and the scattered proton. The same signature is expected for double dissociation where the scattered proton is replaced by a low-mass baryonic system. Events with a LRG were identified with the variable η_{max}, which is defined as the pseudorapidity [b] ($\eta = -\ln(\tan\frac{\theta}{2})$) of the most forward calorimeter deposit with energy greater than 400 MeV.

2 The Diffractive Structure Function

In analogy with $F_2(x, Q^2)$, the diffractive structure function $F_2^{D(3)}(\beta, Q^2, x_{I\!P})$ was extracted [3] in the kinematic range of $0.08 < y \equiv Q^2/(4xE_eE_p) < 0.5$, $8 < Q^2 < 100$ GeV^2, $6.3 \cdot 10^{-4} < x_{I\!P} < 10^{-2}$ and $0.1 < \beta < 0.8$. The data were found to be consistent with factorisation, i.e. $F_2^{D(3)}(\beta, Q^2, x_{I\!P}) = f(\beta, Q^2) \cdot (1/x_{I\!P})^a$, at the present level of precision. $F_2^{D(3)}$ was integrated over the measured range of $x_{I\!P}$ to study its β and Q^2 dependence.

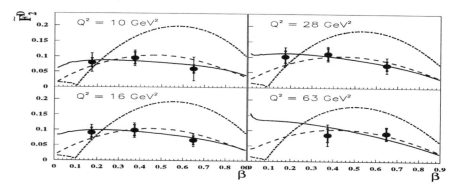

Figure 1: The measured $\tilde{F}_2^D(\beta, Q^2)$ compared with the fits from the combined QCD analysis.

The resulting values of the integrated [c] $F_2^{D(3)}$ ($\tilde{F}_2^D(\beta, Q^2)$), shown in figure 1, are approximately independent of Q^2 for fixed β, consistent with a flat β dependence for fixed Q^2. The observed Q^2 dependence is consistent with the hypothesis that the underlying mechanism for diffractive DIS is the scattering of a virtual photon with charged partons (quarks) within the pomeron.

---

[b] The ZEUS coordinate system is defined as right-handed with the Z axis pointing in the proton beam direction, hereafter referred to as forward, and the X axis horizontal, pointing towards the centre of HERA.

[c] The data in figure 1 were subtracted for an estimated 15%±10% contribution from double dissociation.

3 Diffractive Dijet Photoproduction and Global QCD Analysis

Diffractive photoproduction of dijets at HERA, $e(k) + p(P) \rightarrow e(k') + X(= jet + jet + X_r) + p'(P')$, provides a process which at leading order (LO) QCD is sensitive both to the quark and gluon densities in the pomeron at $\mu^2 \sim (E_T^{jet})^2$. At LO two processes are responsible for jet production. In the *direct* processes, the full energy of the photon participates in the interaction with a parton in the pomeron and the fraction of the photon momentum (x_γ) participating in the hard process is equal to one. In the *resolved* processes, the photon behaves as a source of partons which can scatter off those in the pomeron. The unscattered constituents of the photon then give rise to a hadronic system, known as the photon remnant, going approximately in the direction of the original photon.

A cone algorithm in η-ϕ space with a radius of 1 unit was used to reconstruct jets according to the Snowmass convention. Measurements have been performed of the differential dijet cross sections as a function of the transverse energy (pseudorapidity) of each jet, E_T^{jet} (η^{jet}), and of $x_\gamma^{obs} = (E_T^{jet_1} e^{-\eta^{jet_1}} + E_T^{jet_2} e^{-\eta^{jet_2}})/E_\gamma$, in events with the most forward-going hadron of the hadronic system at $\eta_{max}^{had} < 1.8$. They are given in the kinematic region $0.2 < y < 0.85$ and $Q^2 < 4$ GeV^2 with a median $Q^2 \approx 10^{-3}$ GeV^2 for dijet events satisfying $-1.5 < \eta^{jet} < 1$ and $E_T^{jet} > 6$ GeV. The measured cross sections are shown in figure 2. The contaminations from non-diffractive processes and double dissociation have been subtracted from the data. The inner error bars represent the statistical errors and the total error bars the statistical and systematic uncertainties −not associated with the energy scale of the jets which is indicated by the shaded band− added in quadrature. The comparison of the dijet cross section as a function of x_γ^{obs} (figure 2a) with the predictions of the POMPYT [8] generator gives evidence for the presence of a resolved-photon component in diffractive hard photoproduction.

Following the proposal by Collins et al [9], a combined QCD analysis of the ZEUS measurements of $\tilde{F}_2^D(\beta, Q^2)$ and of the dijet cross sections in diffractive photoproduction has been performed. The fits to the DIS data are made with full next-to-leading (NLO) QCD calculations. On the other hand, the fits to the photoproduction data make use only of LO calculations (based on POMPYT) and include both direct and resolved photon contributions. The pomeron flux factor of Donnachie and Landshoff [7] has been used in both cases. Each of the fits is represented by a parametrization of the initial distributions at $Q_0^2 = 4$ GeV^2 for the u ($= \bar{u} = d = \bar{d}$) quark and for the gluon in the pomeron ($f_{i/\mathbb{P}}(\beta, \mu^2)$, with $i = q, g$). The other quark distributions are assumed to be zero at the initial scale. The parton distributions are evolved in Q^2 according to the DGLAP equations at NLO QCD with the number of flavours set equal to 3 and using the program from the CTEQ group.

The results of three different fits are compared to the ZEUS data in figures 1 and 2(b,c): a) $\beta f_{u/\mathbb{P}}(\beta, Q_0^2) = a_1\beta(1-\beta)+c_1(1-\beta)^2$, $\beta f_{g/\mathbb{P}}(\beta, Q_0^2) = 0$ (dot-dashed line), b) $\beta f_{u/\mathbb{P}}(\beta, Q_0^2) = a_2\beta(1 - \beta)$, $\beta f_{g/\mathbb{P}}(\beta, Q_0^2) = b_2\beta(1 - \beta)$ (solid line), and c) $\beta f_{u/\mathbb{P}}(\beta, Q_0^2) = a_3\beta(1-\beta)$, $\beta f_{g/\mathbb{P}}(\beta, Q_0^2) = b_3\beta^8(1-\beta)^{0.3}$ (dashed line), where a_i, b_i and c_i are the free parameters of the fits. The model in which the pomeron is assumed to be made exclusively of quarks at the initial scale is not able to describe simultaneously the measured diffractive structure function and the dijet cross sections in diffractive photoproduction. However, the models which include a substantial hard momentum component of gluons at Q_0^2 describe the shape and normalization of both sets of measurements.

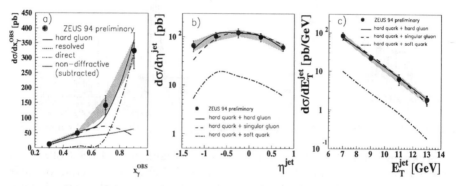

Figure 2: The measured dijet cross sections in diffractive photoproduction compared with the fits from the combined QCD analysis (see text).

4 $D^{*\pm}$ Production in Diffractive Deep Inelastic Scattering

Diffractive production of $D^{*\pm}$ in DIS at HERA, $e(k) + p(P) \rightarrow e(k') + X(= D^{*\pm}+X_r)+p'(P')$, provides yet another process which at LO QCD is sensitive to the gluon (e.g. via $\gamma g \rightarrow c\bar{c}$) density in the pomeron at $\mu^2 \sim Q^2$. The large gluon component in the pomeron as extracted from the global QCD analysis described in the previous section would lead to a significant diffractive contribution to open charm production in DIS. D^* mesons are reconstructed from their decay products through the decay mode $D^{*+} \rightarrow D^0\pi_s^+ \rightarrow (K^-\pi^+)\pi_s^+$ (plus the charge conjugated one). The small mass difference $M(D^*) - M(D^0) = 145.42 \pm 0.05$ MeV [11] yields a prominent signal just above the threshold of the $M(K\pi\pi_s) - M(K\pi)$ distribution, where the phase space contribution is highly suppressed. Measurements of the cross sections for $D^{*\pm}$ production have been performed in the restricted kinematic region $10 < Q^2 < 80$ GeV^2, $0.04 < y <$

342

0.7, $p_T^{D^*} > 1$ GeV and $-1.5 < \eta^{D^*} < 1.5$. The η_{max} distribution for the sample, shown in figure 3a, exhibits a plateau towards low-η_{max} values suggestive of a contribution from a diffractive process mediated by pomeron exchange. The mass difference distribution for the diffractive candidates ($\eta_{max} < 2$) is shown in figure 3b. The measured ep cross sections are $\sigma_{all}(D^{*\pm}) = 3.9 \pm 0.4$(stat.) nb and $\sigma_{\eta_{max}<2}(D^{*\pm}) = 875 \pm 248$(stat.)$^{+395}_{-199}$(syst.) pb (including the contribution from double dissociation). It is observed that approximately $20 \pm 10\%$ of the $D^{*\pm}$ produced in DIS above 10 GeV^2 are diffractively produced.

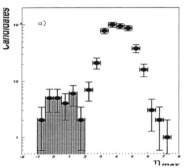 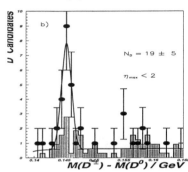

Figure 3: The distribution of η_{max} (left) and ΔM ($\eta_{max} < 2$) (right) for D^* candidates

Acknowledgements: It is a pleasure to thank the ZEUS Collab., in particular Jo Cole, Claudia Glasman, Jason McFall and Juan Terrón for their contributions and advise in the preparation of the material reported here. Specials thanks to the PHOTON'97 team for organizing a nice conference.

References

1. H1 Collaboration, Ahmed, T., et al., *Nucl. Phys.* **B429**, 477 (1994).
2. ZEUS Collaboration, Derrick, M., et al., *Phys. Lett.* **B315**, 481 (1993).
3. ZEUS Collaboration, Derrick, M., et al., *Zeit. Phys* **C68**, 569 (1995).
4. ZEUS Collaboration, Derrick, M., et al., *Phys. Lett.* **B356**, 129 (1995).
5. Ingelman, G., and Schlein, P., *Phys. Lett.* **B152**, 256 (1985).
6. Berger, E.L., et al., *Nucl. Phys.* **B286**, 704 (1987).
7. Donnachie, A., and Landshoff, P.V., *Nucl. Phys.* **B303**, 634 (1988).
8. Bruni, P., and Ingelman, G., Proc. of the International Europhysics Conference, edited by J. Carr and M. Perrotet, Marseille, France, July 1993 (Ed. Frontieres, Gif-sur-Yvette, 1994) p. 595.
9. Collins, J.C., et al., *Phys. Rev.* **D51**, 3182 (1995).
10. Ingelman, G., and Jansen-Prytz, K., *Zeit. Phys.* **C58**, 285 (1993).
11. Barnett, R.M., et al., Particle Data Group, *Phys. Rev.* **D54**, 1 (1996).

PROBING HARD COLOR-SINGLET EXCHANGE AT DØ

B. MAY

Northwestern University, Evanston, IL 60208, USA

We present latest preliminary results on hard color-singlet exchange in proton-antiproton collisions. The fraction of dijet events produced via color-singlet exchange is measured as a function of jet transverse energy, dijet pseudorapidity separation, and proton-antiproton center-of-mass energy. These results are qualitatively consistent with a color-singlet fraction that increases with increasing quark-initiated processes.

Dijet production via hard color-singlet exchange has been observed at both the Tevatron[1,2,3] and HERA[4]. The measured rate, roughly 1% in proton-antiproton collisions[1,2,3] and 10% in positron-proton collisions[4], is too large to be produced by electroweak boson exchange thus indicating a strongly-interacting process[3,4].

Measuring the fraction of color-singlet exchange in dijet events as a function of dijet transverse energy (E_T), dijet pseudorapidity separation ($\Delta\eta$), and proton-antiproton center-of-mass energy ($\sqrt{s}$) probes the color-singlet dynamics and its coupling to quarks and gluons. Decreasing $\sqrt{s}$ or increasing the dijet E_T or $\Delta\eta$ (i.e. increasing Bjorken x) increases the fraction of initial quark processes. Therefore, if the color singlet couples more strongly to quarks than a single gluon couples to quarks, the color-singlet fraction is expected to rise with increasing fraction of initial quark processes. The behavior of the color-singlet fraction as a function of E_T, $\Delta\eta$, and $\sqrt{s}$ is expected to deviate from this simple behavior if the dynamics of color-singlet exchange is significantly different from that of simple gluon exchange. In this paper we present the new measurements by the DØ collaboration of the color-singlet fraction as a function of dijet E_T, $\Delta\eta$, and $\sqrt{s}$.

Although standard QCD (NLO calculations and parton shower Monte Carlos) cannot account for the existence of hard color-singlet exchange, higher-order QCD processes may explain this phenomenon[5,6,7,8,9]. The exchange of two perturbative gluons in a color-singlet state was originally proposed by Bjorken as a simple mechanism to produce rapidity gaps between jets with a predicted fraction on the order of 1-5% depending on the initial partons[5]. Since the two-gluon singlet couples more strongly to gluons by a 9/4 color factor compared to single gluon exchange, the observed fraction is expected to decrease with increasing initial quark processes.

This simple two-gluon picture has been expanded to include certain dynamical effects using a leading-log BFKL approximation to two-gluon exchange[7]. These effects lead to a rapidly decreasing fraction with increasing dijet E_T and a rising fraction at large dijet $\Delta\eta$.

Soft color rearrangement[9] is an alternative QCD-motivated explanation for rapidity gap production. In this model, color exchange can be canceled by the exchange of nonperturbative soft gluons, leading to an effective colorless exchange. Since initial quarks have fewer possible color combinations than initial gluons, this model predicts a color-singlet fraction that increases with increasing initial quark processes, in contrast to the two-gluon model. In addition, assuming that initial gluon processes are highly suppressed, the soft color model is estimated to give a color-singlet fraction of $(1/9)^2 \sim 1\%$.

An alternative to the QCD-based models, the exchange of a hard U(1) gauge boson that couples only to baryon number (quarks), has been proposed to explain the observed rapidity gap phenomena[10]. With an appropriate choice of the mass and coupling constant, a color-singlet fraction of 1% can be obtained. Since the boson couples only to quarks, the color-singlet fraction is predicted to increase with increasing initial quark content. Dynamics of the gauge boson predict a fraction that increases with dijet E_T more rapidly than from parton distribution functions alone.

The color-singlet fraction calculated from models for the exchange of a hard color singlet (i.e. a two-gluon singlet or U(1) boson) includes the probability that a rapidity gap is not contaminated by particles from spectator interactions ($\sim 10\%$)[5,11,12]. This probability is expected to be independent of the flavor of the initiating partons in the hard scattering and to have a weak dependence on the proton-antiproton center-of-mass energy ($\sqrt{s}$)[11,12].

Data from two center-of-mass proton-antiproton energies of $\sqrt{s} = 1800$ GeV and $\sqrt{s} = 630$ GeV are used in this analysis. Three opposite-side dijet triggers with different dijet E_T thresholds were taken at 1800 GeV, and one low-E_T data sample was taken at 630 GeV (see Table 1). At the trigger level all events were required to have two jets with $|\eta| > 1.6$ and $\Delta\eta > 4$ (1800 GeV) or 3.2 (630 GeV). Offline, events are required to have $|\eta| > 1.9$ and a vertex within 50 cm of the center of the detector. Events with more than one proton-antiproton interaction were rejected using vertex and timing information. Corrections are applied to account for multiple interaction events remaining in the sample (as a function of instantaneous luminosity) and the small fraction ($\sim 10\%$) of single vertex events incorrectly removed from the sample.

The offline jet E_T and η cuts have been optimized for each measurement. For the comparison of the 630 and 1800 GeV samples the offline E_T threshold is the same as the trigger threshold (12 GeV) since any inefficiencies cancel in the ratio of the two measurements. For the 1800 GeV samples used in the

Table 1: Triggers and data samples showing trigger and offline E_T cuts and number of events after all offline cuts.

Measurement	Sample Name	Dijet E_T Threshold Trigger	Offline	N_{Events} $|\eta| > 1.9$ (1.7)
$E_T, \Delta\eta$	low E_T	12	15	6.2K
dependence	medium E_T	18	25	33K
at 1800 GeV	high E_T	25	30	73K (104K)
$\sqrt{s}$	630	12	12	8.5K
dependence	1800	12	12	11.6K

dijet E_T and $\Delta\eta$ measurements, the offline E_T thresholds are higher than the trigger thresholds in order to make the measurement in the largely efficient region of each trigger. The high E_T sample used for the $\Delta\eta$ measurement has a less restrictive cut of $|\eta| > 1.7$ in order to increase statistics in the sample.

The multiplicity distribution of final-state particles in the pseudorapidity region between the dijets has been shown to be a useful way to observe and measure color-singlet exchange[1,2,3]. We utilize the electromagnetic calorimeter and central drift chamber as a measure of particle multiplicity (denoted n_{cal} and n_{trk}, respectively) and use a negative binomial distribution (NBD) to parametrize the color-exchange background and extract the color-singlet signal (see[3] for details). In order to reduce the sensitivity to multiple interaction contamination, we fit only the low multiplicity region of the data. The color-singlet fraction (f_s) is defined as the number of events above the color-exchange background parametrization divided by the number of events in the sample. For the high E_T sample we obtain $f_s = (0.85 \pm 0.06(\text{stat}) \pm 0.07(\text{syst}))\%$. The systematic error is dominated by the uncertainty in the background subtraction.

Figure 1 shows the multiplicity distribution (n_{cal}) between the jets for the low E_T 630 and 1800 GeV samples. Using a NBD to parametrize the color exchange multiplicity distribution for each sample, we obtain $f_s = (0.6 \pm 0.1(\text{stat}))\%$ at 1800 GeV and $f_s = (1.6 \pm 0.2(\text{stat}))\%$ at 630 GeV. The ratio of the two measurements is $2.6 \pm 0.6(\text{stat})$. Systematic errors have not yet been finalized, but uncertainties in the fitting and jet energy scale do not significantly affect this result.

In order to measure the color-singlet fraction as a function of E_T and $\Delta\eta$ the data samples must be divided into several subsamples leading to large uncertainties in the color-exchange background subtraction. We thus use a method of determining the E_T and $\Delta\eta$ dependence which is largely independent of the background. We calculate the fraction for each bin of E_T or $\Delta\eta$ using the (0,0) multiplicity bin ($n_{cal} = n_{trk} = 0$), where the color-exchange

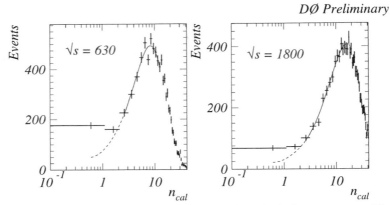

Figure 1: The calorimeter multiplicity (n_{cal}, the number of calorimeter towers with $E_T >$ 200 MeV) between the dijets for the 630 and 1800 GeV samples, plotted on a logarithmic x scale to emphasize low multiplicity bins.

background is negligible ($\sim 5\%$). For each sample the overall measured (0,0) fraction is normalized to the overall color-singlet fraction previously obtained for that sample using the NBD fit method. This approach allows a more accurate determination of the shape of the color-singlet fraction as a function of E_T and $\Delta\eta$.

Figure 2(a) shows the color-singlet fraction at 1800 GeV binned as a function of the second leading jet E_T and plotted at the average dijet E_T for that bin. Figure 2(b) shows the color-singlet fraction at 1800 GeV as a function of dijet $\Delta\eta$ for the high E_T sample.

The measured color-singlet fraction in Fig. 2(a-b) shows a slight rise as a function of dijet E_T and $\Delta\eta$, and the ratio of the fraction at 630 and 1800 GeV is greater than one. Qualitatively, these results are consistent with a color-singlet fraction that rises with increasing initial quark content and thus appear to be inconsistent with current two-gluon models. Directly comparing to existing models, however, requires understanding higher-order dynamical effects in the data that may not be properly taken into account by the current models.

In conclusion, we have presented new information on the fraction of dijet events produced via color-singlet exchange. These results are qualitatively consistent with a color-singlet fraction that increases with increasing quark content. These results will be used to put constraints on color-singlet coupling and dynamics and thus differentiate between current theoretical models.

We thank the staffs at Fermilab and the collaborating institutions for their

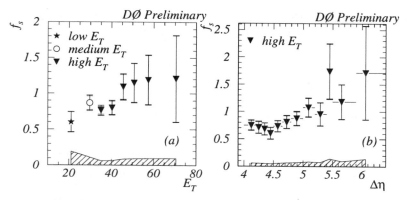

Figure 2: The color-singlet fraction: (a) as a function of the second leading jet E_T plotted at the average dijet E_T for that bin; (b) as a function of $\Delta\eta$ between the leading dijets. Statistical (inner error bars) and statistical plus systematic errors (outer error bars) are shown. The error band at the bottom shows the normalization uncertainty in each sample.

contributions to the success of this work, and acknowledge support from the funding agencies in the U.S., France, Russia, Brazil, India, Colombia, Mexico, Korea and Argentina.

1. S. Abachi *et al.* (DØ Collaboration), Phys. Rev. Lett. 72, 2332 (1994).

2. F. Abe *et al.* (CDF Collaboration), Phys. Rev. Lett. **74**, 855 (1995).

3. S. Abachi *et al.* (DØ Collaboration), Phys. Rev. Lett. **76**, 734 (1996).

4. M. Derrick *et al.* (ZEUS Collaboration), Phys. Lett. B **369**, 55 (1996); M. Derrick *et al.* (ZEUS Collaboration), Phys. Lett. **B315**, 481 (1993).

5. J. D. Bjorken, Phys. Rev. D**47**, 101 (1992).

6. H. Chehime *et al.*, Phys. Lett. B **286**, 397 (1992).

7. V. Del Duca and W. K. Tang, *Proceedings of the 5th Blois Workshop on Elastic and Diffractive Scattering* (1993), ed. H.M. Fried, K. Kang, and C.-I. Tan, (World Scientific 1994).

8. H. Chehime and D. Zeppenfeld, MAD/PH-814 (1994).

9. O. J. P. Eboli, E. M. Gregores, F. Halzen, MAD/PH-96-965 (1997).

10. C. D. Carone, H. Murayama, Phys. Rev. Lett. 74, 3122 (1995); C. D. Carone, H. Murayama, Phys. Rev. D**52**, 484 (1995).

11. R. S. Fletcher and T. Stelzer, Phys. Rev. D**48**, 5162 (1993).

12. E. Gotsman, E.M. Levin and U. Maor, Phys. Lett. B **309**, 199 (1993).

13. B. May (for the DØ Collaboration), *Proceedings of the 8th Meeting, Division of Particles and Fields* (1994), ed. S. Seidel (World Scientific, 1995).

THE GOLD FLASHLIGHT: COHERENT PHOTONS (AND POMERONS) AT RHIC

SPENCER KLEIN and EVAN SCANNAPIECO

Lawrence Berkeley National Laboratory, Berkeley, CA, 94720, USA

The Relativistic Heavy Ion Collider (RHIC) will be the first heavy ion accelerator energetic enough to produce hadronic final states via coherent $\gamma\gamma$, γP, and PP interactions. Because the photon flux scales as Z^2, up to an energy of about $\gamma \hbar c/R \approx 3$ GeV/c, the $\gamma\gamma$ interaction rates are large. RHIC γP interactions test how Pomerons couple to nuclei and measure how different vector mesons, including the J/ψ, interact with nuclear matter. PP collisions can probe Pomeron couplings. Because these collisions can involve identical initial states, for identical final states, the $\gamma\gamma$, γP, and PP channels may interfere, producing new effects. We review the physics of these interactions and discuss how these signals can be detected experimentally, in the context of the STAR detector. Signals can be separated from backgrounds by using isolation cuts (rapidity gaps) and $p_\perp$. We present Monte Carlo studies of different backgrounds, showing that representative signals can be extracted with good rates and signal to noise ratios.

1 Physics Processes

The Relativistic Heavy Ion Collider[1] (RHIC) will be energetic enough to produce massive final states via $\gamma\gamma$, γP, and PP interactions that coherently couple to the nuclei as a whole. As the number of virtual photons associated with each nuclei goes as Z^2 up to a photon energy of approximately $\gamma \hbar c/R \approx 3$ GeV/c, the $\gamma\gamma$ rate at intermediate energies will be comparable to those of the next generation e^+e^- colliders. RHIC will also produce a high number of coherent photon-Pomeron interactions (γP) and two-Pomeron interactions.

1.1 $\gamma\gamma$ Interactions

The luminosity of $\gamma\gamma$ collisions at heavy ion colliders has been discussed by several authors[2,3,4]. To avoid events where hadronic particle production overshadows the $\gamma\gamma$ interaction, events where the nuclei physically collide (with impact parameter $b < 2R_A$, R_A being the nuclear radius) are excluded from calculations of the usable luminosity. This reduces the luminosity by about 50%, depending on the energy.

The usable $\gamma\gamma$ luminosity for gold, copper and iodine collisions at RHIC design luminosity is given in the left panel of Fig. 1. The lighter nuclei benefit from the higher AA luminosity, slightly higher beam energy, and smaller nuclear radius, which more than compensates for the reduced Z. Comparison

348

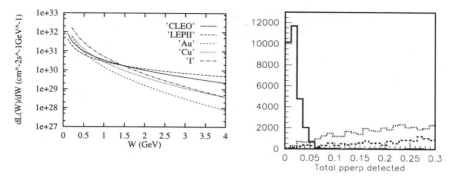

Figure 1: Left: Comparison of $\gamma\gamma$ luminosities at RHIC, for gold, iodine and copper beams, with those of CESR(CLEO) and LEP II. Right: Comparison of $p_\perp$ between $\gamma\gamma$ and background passing our cuts. The solid curve is for $\rho^0\rho^0$ production near threshold. The short dashes are beam-gas and the long dashes are peripheral nuclear backgrounds.

curves for CLEO at CESR and LEP2 are also shown.

Due to the nuclear form factor, the photons are almost real, with a Q^2 cutoff given by the nuclear size, about $(30 \text{ MeV/c})^2$ for gold. Because of this cutoff, the perpendicular momentum of the photons is small, $p_\perp < \hbar c/R$; this is important for separating coherent from incoherent interactions. This is illustrated in the right panel of Fig 1.

1.2 γP Interactions

γP interactions on proton targets have been studied extensively at HERA. RHIC can study these interactions in a nuclear environment. For the reaction $\gamma P \rightarrow V$, where V is a vector meson, RHIC will reach higher center of mass energies and luminosities than the NMC[6] and E-665[7] studies, producing 100,000's of exclusive ρ and ϕ mesons per year, along with large numbers of excited states. RHIC will also produce significant numbers of J/ψ. In the Vector Dominance Model, these rates measure the interaction between the vector meson and the nucleus.[5] Measurements of how vector meson production scales with A can probe meson absorption by nuclear matter. Because meson scattering has a similar form factor to the photon coupling, this reaction has similar kinematics to $\gamma\gamma$ processes.

1.3 PP Interactions and Interference Measurements

Unobscured PP interactions can only occur in the impact parameter range $2R_A + 2R_P > b > 2R_A$, where R_P is the range of the Pomeron. A measurement of the PP cross section can thus measure the range of the Pomeron. The difficulty in this measurement is separating $\gamma\gamma$ and PP interactions; the two reactions have very similar kinematics and a statistical separation is required. However the relative rates will change as A varies; for protons, PP interactions will dominate, while $\gamma\gamma$ should dominate for Au. The $\gamma\gamma$ luminosity can be measured from $\gamma\gamma \rightarrow e^+e^-$ and the PP luminosity found by subtraction. It may also be possible to use impact parameter dependent signals of nuclear breakup to better distinguish γ and P emission[4].

The similarity between $\gamma\gamma$, γP and PP events allows for the possibility of interference between the two channels. One example is dilepton production from $\gamma\gamma \rightarrow e^+e^-$ and $\gamma P \rightarrow V \rightarrow e^+e^-$; the two channels can interfere, and a measurement of the phase of the interference is sensitive to the real part of the Pomeron and the interaction of the vector meson with the nuclear potential[8].

2   Experimental Feasibility

For any of these measurements to be feasible, it must be possible to separate these coherent interactions from incoherent backgrounds at both the trigger and analysis levels[9]. The major backgrounds that we have identified are grazing nuclear collisions, photo-nuclear interactions, beam gas interactions, debris from upstream beam breakup, and cosmic ray muons; the latter two only affect triggering.

Two useful factors for separating these signals from backgrounds are rapidity gaps and perpendicular momentum. We have concentrated on final states that can be completely reconstructed. We then require that the detector contain nothing except the final state in question. For central events, this naturally reduces to requiring rapidity gaps. Because of the coherence, the $p_\perp$ scale is $\sqrt{2}\hbar c/R$, about 45 MeV/c for gold, much smaller than the typical hadronic momentum scale of 300 MeV/c.

2.1   STAR

The Solenoidal Tracker at RHIC (STAR) is a general purpose large acceptance detector[10]. A time projection chamber tracks charged particles with pseudorapidity $-2 < \eta < 2$. A silicon vertex tracker measures impact parameter over $-1 < \eta < 1$. A time of flight (TOF) system and dE/dx in the TPC help with particle identification. Two forward TPCs are sensitive to charged particles with $2.5 < |\eta| < 4$, and an electromagnetic calorimeter detects photons in the range $-1 < \eta < 2$.

STAR has a multi-level trigger which is well suited to studying peripheral collisions. Scintillators and wire chamber readouts surrounding the TPC measure the charged multiplicity for $-2 < \eta < 2$ on each beam crossing. Events are selected based on multiplicity and topology. At higher trigger levels, the calorimeter can contribute to the trigger and TPC tracking information can be used to select events based on the location of the event vertex and total $p_\perp$.

2.2 Signal and Background Simulation

We have performed Monte Carlo calculations of the $\gamma\gamma$ signals and backgrounds from grazing nuclear and beam gas interactions.[1] Other backgrounds have been estimated by scaling and other methods.

We calculated tables of $\gamma\gamma$ luminosity as a function of invariant mass and rapidity, and then generated simulated events based on these tables. Transverse momentum spectra were included using a Gaussian form factor with a characteristic width of $1/R$. Cuts were applied to simulate the detector acceptance and planned analysis procedure.

Grazing nuclear collisions and beam gas events were simulated using both the FRITIOF and Venus nuclear Monte Carlos. These events were subject to the same cuts. Photo-nuclear collision rates were estimated by scaling from the beam gas rates, making use of the similar kinematics; a more detailed estimate is in progress.

To determine the feasibility of studying $\gamma\gamma$ interactions with STAR, we have considered 3 sample analyses: $\gamma\gamma \rightarrow f_2(1270) \rightarrow \pi^+\pi^-$, $\gamma\gamma \rightarrow \rho^0\rho^0 \rightarrow \pi^+\pi^-\pi^+\pi^-$ and $\gamma\gamma \rightarrow \eta_c \rightarrow K^{*0}K^-\pi^+$. These reactions were chosen to be representative of a wide range of reactions that produce two or four charged particles in the STAR TPC. To separate these events from backgrounds, we have applied cuts to the charged and neutral multiplicity visible in STAR, required that $p_\perp < 100$ MeV, and required an appropriate invariant mass cut. The predicted rates and backgrounds for these analyses are given in Table 1. Although the FRITIOF and Venus predictions are very different, this analysis shows that $f_2(1270) \rightarrow \pi^+\pi^-$ and $\gamma\gamma \rightarrow \rho^0\rho^0 \rightarrow \pi^+\pi^-\pi^+\pi^-$ reactions should be clearly separable from backgrounds, while more challenging measurements such $\Gamma(\gamma\gamma)$ for the 2960 MeV $J^{PC} = 0^{-+}$ $c\bar{c}$ resonance $\eta_c \rightarrow K^{*0}K^-\pi^+$ may be possible with appropriate particle identification by TOF and dE/dx.

We have also considered the problem of triggering on these events. In addition to the grazing nuclear collisions, beam gas events and photonuclear interactions, at the trigger level there are backgrounds from beam nuclei interactions upstream of the detector and cosmic ray muons. Monte Carlo studies have shown that, using the multi-level trigger in STAR, it is possible to devise trigger algorithms with good acceptance for coherent interactions and good

Table 1: Rates and backgrounds for $\gamma\gamma$ events for gold on gold collisions at RHIC for 3 sample analyses. The $\rho^0\rho^0$ events were near threshold, with invariant masses between 1.5 and 1.6 GeV/c^2. The last line assumes particle identification by dE/dx and TOF.

Channel	Efficiency	Detected Events/Yr	FRITIOF Background	Venus Background
$f_2(1270) \to \pi^+\pi^-$	85%	9.2×10^5	53,000	100,000
$\rho^0\rho^0 \to \pi^+\pi^-\pi^+\pi^-$	38%	1.6×10^4	3,500	1,400
$\eta_c \to K^{*0}K^-\pi^+$	57%	70	210	510
η_c (w/ PID)	57%	70	8	20

background rejection. The trigger algorithms are based on requiring two or four tracks in the central TPC, with nothing else visible in the detector.

Acknowledgements

We would like to thank our colleagues in the STAR collaboration for their advice and support. This work was supported by the U.S. DOE under contract DE-AC-03-76SF00098. E.S. was partially supported by an NSF Fellowship.

References

1. *Conceptual Design of the Relativistic Heavy Ion Collider*, BNL-52195, May 1989, Brookhaven National Laboratory.
2. Cahn, R. N. and Jackson, J. D., Phys. Rev. **D42**, 3690 (1990).
3. Baur, G. and Ferreira Filho, F., Nucl. Phys. **A518**, 786 (1990).
4. Hencken, K., Trautmann, D., and Baur G., Z. Phys. **C68**, 473 (1995).
5. Brodsky, S., Kinoshita, T., and Terazawa, H., Phys. Rev. **D4**, 1532 (1971).
6. J. Ashman *et al.*, Z. Phys. **C39**, 169 (1988).
7. H. Schellman, in *Proc. 29th Rencontres de Moriond: QCD and High Energy Hadronic Interactions*, Meribel les Allues, France, 1994.
8. Leith, D. in *Electromagnetic Interactions of Hadrons VI*, ed. A. Donnachie and G. Shaw (Plenum Press, New York,1978)
9. S. Klein, in *Photon 95*, ed. D. J. Miller, S. L. Cartwright and V. Khoze (World Scientific, Singapore, 1996)
10. STAR Collaboration, *STAR Conceptual Design Report*, LBL-PUB-5347, June, 1992.
11. S. Klein and E. Scannapieco, STAR Note 243, Feb. 1995, available at http://www.rsgi01.rhic.bnl.gov/star/starlib/doc/www/sno/ice/sn0243.html

MULTIPARTICLE PRODUCTION IN HIGH-MASS DIFFRACTION DISSOCIATION AND THE INTERPLAY OF PHOTONS AND POMERONS

F.W. BOPP

Universität Siegen, Fachbereich Physik, D–57068 Siegen, Germany

R. ENGEL

DESY, D–22603 Hamburg, Germany

J. RANFT

INFN - Laboratori Nationali del Gran Sasso, I–67010 Assergi AQ, Italy

A. ROSTOVTSEV

Institute of Theoretical and Experimental Physics Moscow, Russia

presented by R. Engel

Multiple interaction models satisfying s-channel unitarity predict that, in contrast to inelastic processes, factorization is violated in diffractive processes. The size of this effect can be characterized in terms of the rapidity gap survival probability. The possibility of its measurement at HERA is pointed out. Furthermore a method to measure photon diffraction dissociation at LEP2 and planned linear colliders is discussed and cross section predictions are given

1 Unitarity, pomerons, and factorization

Assuming that high virtual masses are damped due to the dynamics of the the strong interaction, hadronic interactions can be described by Gribov's Reggeon field theory (RFT)[1,2]. The total amplitude can be written as the sum of n-pomeron exchange amplitudes $A^{(n)}(s, t)$. Unitarity implies that at high energies graphs with n-pomeron exchange become important. However, it should be emphasized that only the one-pomeron exchange graph satisfies factorization as assumed, for example, in parton model calculations of hadronic jet production.

Why do we expect factorization in inclusive processes? For example, let's consider the simplest "factorization-breaking" contribution, the two-pomeron graph. To discuss particle production, we apply the optical theorem together with the AGK cutting rules[3]. Three different cut configurations are giving the dominant contributions: the diffractive cut with the weight 1 (Fig. 1 a)), the one-pomeron cut with the weight -4 (Fig. 1 b)), and the two-pomeron cut with the weight 2 (Fig. 1 c)). Assuming that a two-pomeron cut gives two times

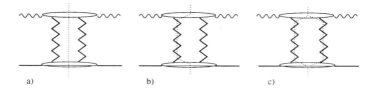

Figure 1: *Breakdown of the total discontinuity of the two-pomeron exchange graph according to the AGK cutting rules: a) the diffractive cut describing low-mass diffraction, b) the one-pomeron cut, and c) the two-pomeron cut.*

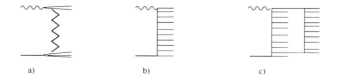

Figure 2: *Inelastic final states resulting from a) the diffractive cut describing low-mass diffraction, b) the one-pomeron cut, and c) the two-pomeron cut.*

the particle yield compared to the one-pomeron cut (in central pseudorapidity region, see Fig. 2), the inclusive inelastic charged particle cross section reads

$$\frac{d\sigma_{\rm ch}}{d\eta}\bigg|_{\eta\approx 0} \sim 0 \times (+1)\frac{dN_1}{d\eta} + 1 \times (-4)\frac{dN_1}{d\eta} + 2 \times (+2)\frac{dN_1}{d\eta} = 0 \qquad (1)$$

where the particle density in pseudorapidity of produced by a one-pomeron cut is denoted by $dN_1/d\eta$. Note that the cross section contribution of the two-pomeron graph vanishes. Analogously, the factorization violating contributions due to multi-pomeron exchange graphs cancel out in all orders. This means that only the one-pomeron graph determines the inclusive particle cross section in the central region (AGK cancellation). It can be shown that the same cancellation effects old true also in the case of inclusive jet production.

In high-mass diffraction dissociation we have to consider only final state configurations with sufficiently large rapidity gaps. It is important to notice that all the configurations with more than one cut pomeron (multiple-interaction contributions, see Fig. 2 c)) are not considered for the diffractive cross section since in this case the rapidity gap of the diffractive process is filled by particles belonging to additional pomeron cuts. However, as shown above, these configurations are needed to cancel other negative terms implied by unitarity. Consequently, factorization is violated in diffraction dissociation since the cross section contributions of the higher-order multi-pomeron graphs do not vanish. For example, within the triple-pomeron approximation the diffractive cross section would grow with the energy like $\sigma_{\mathrm{diff}} \sim (s_{\gamma^* p})^{2\Delta}$. The measured flat energy dependence is explained due to unitarity corrections: additional interactions produce particles filling the rapidity gap of the diffractive interaction. This can be effectively parametrized introducing a energy- and process-dependent *rapidity gap survival probability* $\langle|S|^2\rangle$ [4].

2   A possible measurement of $\langle|S|^2\rangle$

In the following we will discuss some consequences for particle production in high-mass photon dissociation at HERA. In comparison to hadron-hadron interactions, there are two important new effects to note: **(i)** the photon has a dual nature and can interact as a gauge boson (pointlike) or a hadron (resolved), and **(ii)** the photon has an additional degree of freedom, the photon virtuality. Both (i) and (ii) give a handle to suppress the relative size of the uni-

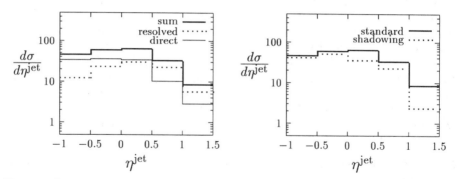

Figure 3: Differential single-inclusive jet cross section $E_\perp > 6$ GeV: a) breakdown in direct and resolved processes for $\langle|S_{\mathrm{res}}|^2\rangle =1$, b) cross sections for $\langle|S_{\mathrm{res}}|^2\rangle =1$ (standard) and $\langle|S_{\mathrm{res}}|^2\rangle =0.5$ (shadowing)

tarity corrections (e.g. the relative size of the multi-pomeron graphs compared to the one-pomeron exchange) [5].

Using these effects, the rapidity gap survival probability can be determined experimentally as follows
(i) measurement of the diffractive structure function F_3^D in deep-inelastic photon-proton scattering
(ii) extraction of parton densities of the pomeron (gluon densities are determined from scaling violation effects *without* using photoproduction data)
(iii) application of these parton densities to the calculation of single-inclusive particle cross sections or jet cross sections in high-mass diffraction dissociation of real photons. Comparison with measurements

In $\gamma^\star p$ scattering with not too small Q^2, multiple pomeron exchange contributions are suppressed at least by a factor $1/Q^2$ compared to the leading amplitude. Hence in diffractive DIS unitarity corrections are small and the measurement (i) provides the "true" parton density of the pomeron. However, in photoproduction unitarity effects (e.g. multiple-pomeron exchange contributions) are important. Furthermore the rapidity gap survival probability in hard diffraction differs significantly between direct and resolved photon interactions. In direct photon interactions, there is no hadronic remnant to allow for multiple interactions (e.g. two-pomeron exchange). Rapidity gap events with a resolved hard photon interaction are suppressed by a factor of about $2 \ldots 3$ compared to events with direct hard photon interactions. Having the possibility to distinguish in experiment between diffractive direct and resolved photoproduction in (iii) offers a unique means to check the predictions of multiple-interaction models and the concept of the rapidity gap survival probability. For example, we consider single-inclusive jet production applying the cut $\eta_{\max} < 1.5$ to select diffractive events in a simple "back–white" model where all resolved processes are treated as purely hadronic ones. The calculations were done using PHOJET [6,7]. In Fig. 3 a) the cross section is shown for direct and resolved events separately assuming $\langle |S_{\mathrm{res}}|^2 \rangle = 1$ for all processes. In Fig 3 b) the total jet cross section is shown for the case of $\langle |S_{\mathrm{res}}|^2 \rangle = 1$ and $\langle |S_{\mathrm{res}}|^2 \rangle = 0.5$. It should be emphasized that both curves differ in shape. Similar results are obtained in case of the transverse energy distribution of jets where resolved processes contribute mainly to the low-$E_\perp$ part.

3 On the determination of the diffractive cross section in $\gamma\gamma$ collisions

The diffractive contribution to the total $\gamma\gamma$ cross section is difficult to measure since the LEP detectors have only a very small acceptance for such events. On the other hand, the knowledge of the diffractive cross section is very important for many theoretical calculations as well as background estimations.

In analogy to the $\eta_{\max}$ cut applied by the HERA collaborations to identify diffractive events, a similar quantity can be defined for the case of $\gamma\gamma$ interactions [8]. Here one has to deal with the variation of the rapidity of the $\gamma\gamma$ system in the lab. frame. A possible way to define $\eta_{\max}$ in this case is to use a forward em. detector as a trigger for hadronic activity. In events with forward hadronic activity, $\eta_{\max}$ is then given by the pseudorapidity of the most-forward scattered particle seen in the central detector (for example, with a coverage of $|\eta| < 3$). This is illustrated in Fig. 4 a). The differential $\eta_{\max}$ cross section is shown in Fig. 4 b). Selecting events with a visible energy $W_{\mathrm{vis}} > 10$ GeV leads

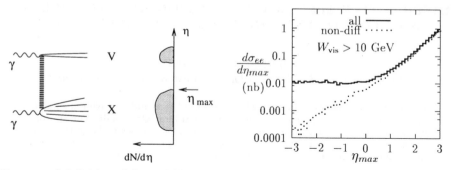

Figure 4: a) definition of the variable η_{max} in $\gamma\gamma$ collisions. b) ee cross section for all and for non-diffractive $\gamma\gamma$ at LEP2.

to an almost flat cross section for negative values of η_{max} clearly showing the diffractive contribution to the total $\gamma\gamma$ cross section. Of course, the method presented here can also applied to $\gamma\gamma$ collisions at linear colliders.

Acknowledgments

We acknowledge valuable discussions with S. Roesler. One of the authors (R.E.) was supported in parts by the Deutsche Forschungsgemeinschaft under contract No. Schi 422/1-2.

References

1. V. N. Gribov: Sov. Phys. JETP 26 (1968) 414
2. M. Baker and K. A. Ter-Martirosyan: Phys. Rep. 28C (1976) 1
3. V. A. Abramovski, V. N. Gribov and O. V. Kancheli: Sov. J. Nucl. Phys. 18 (1974) 308
4. J. D. Bjorken: Phys. Rev. D47 (1993) 101
5. F. W. Bopp, R. Engel and A. Rostovtsev: Hadron production in photon collisions at high energies, (hep-ph/9612344) to appear in Proceedings of the XXVI International Symposium on Multiparticle Dynamics, Faro, Portugal, 1996
6. R. Engel: Z. Phys. C66 (1995) 203
7. R. Engel and J. Ranft: Phys. Rev. D54 (1996) 4244
8. R. Engel and A. Rostovtsev: How to measure diffraction in two-photon collisions at LEP, Univ. Siegen preprint SI 96-12, (hep-ph/9611205), 1996

DIFFRACTIVE ELECTROPRODUCTION AT INTERMEDIATE AND LOW Q^2 AND THE PHOTON WAVE FUNCTION

THIERRY GOUSSET

NIKHEF, P.O. Box 41882, 1009 DB Amsterdam, The Netherlands

A photon light cone wave function which links the "hadronic" behavior at small Q^2 to the "perturbative" quark-antiquark behavior at large Q^2 is built. The approach relies on a phenomenological description of the $q\bar{q}$ dynamics at large transverse distance and the link is obtained from duality arguments. The resulting wave function is used to compute the total real and virtual photon-proton cross section.

1 Introduction

One of the challenging aspect of electroproduction off nucleons at high-energy is the understanding of the transition from real photons to virtual photons in the GeV^2 region. In the high-energy fixed Q^2 kinematical domain, i.e., at small $x_{\rm B}$, the physics can be traced back to the understanding of the photon structure in the center of mass frame of the photon-proton collision. The viewpoint is interesting because in this regime photon-hadron and hadron-hadron interactions are similar: they are diffractive scatterings. In the Regge approach, this similarity is understood as being due to the universality of the Pomeron. Implicitly, this assertion assumes that the photon has developed an internal structure due to its coupling to strongly interacting quark fields and that this structure gives, at small $x_{\rm B}$, the main contribution to its interaction, as compared to the direct contribution from its "bare component".[1] It is thus clear that a great deal of insight can be gained from a common understanding of photon-hadron and hadron-hadron collisions.

In QCD, Pomeron exchange can be understood as soft multi-gluon exchange. An approach to this nonperturbative sector of the theory is provided by the model of the stochastic vacuum of Dosch and Simonov.[2] The application of the model of the stochastic vacuum to diffractive scatterings of hadrons has been carried out.[3] Recently[4], the same approach was used to describe diffractive leptoproduction of vector mesons in the range $Q^2 = 2\text{--}10$ GeV^2, thus starting to implement the above mentioned comparison. The extension of the phenomenology to $Q^2 \to 0$ is clearly interesting.

The interaction amplitude for the exclusive vector meson photoproduction off a proton can be be written as[4]

$$\mathcal{M}(\gamma^* + p \to V + p) = is \int \frac{dz\, r dr}{2} \psi_V^* \psi_\gamma(z, r)\, J_p^{(0)}(z, r, t). \tag{1}$$

ψ_V and ψ_γ are, respectively, the vector meson and virtual photon $q\bar{q}$ light cone wave functions. If the final vector meson wave function is replaced by the virtual photon wave function and the momentum transfer is sent to 0, one gets the forward Compton amplitude which is $is\,\sigma_{\gamma^*p}^{tot}$. The quantity $J_p^{(0)}(z,r,t)$ represents the Pomeron exchange amplitude for scattering of a $q\bar{q}$ dipole of size r off the proton target, where an average over the dipole orientations has been carried out. The light cone fraction carried by the quark in the photon is denoted by z. The Mandelstam variables for the process are $s = W^2$ and t. The photon is characterized by its virtuality Q^2 and polarization λ.

The quantity $J_p^{(0)}$ has been derived in the model of the stochastic vacuum [4] following the method of Ref. [3]. In these references, the few parameters which fix the magnitude and shape of $J_p^{(0)}$ have been adjusted to fit the phenomenology of proton-proton elastic cross section. Using the same parametrization, let us focus below on the photon structure. [5]

2 Photon wave function at low Q^2

One can compute the $q\bar{q}$ light cone wave function of the photon in perturbation theory. The large transverse distance behavior is exponentially damped, $\psi_\gamma \propto \exp(-\varepsilon r)$, with an extension parameter $\varepsilon = [z(1-z)Q^2 + m_f^2]^{1/2}$, m_f being the current quark mass. The perturbative expression is sensible if large transverse distances are effectively suppressed. For light quarks and small values of ε, the confining gluonic forces and/or the spontaneous chiral symmetry breaking will intervene and limit the transverse extent of the photon wave function. The possibility we want to examine here is the kind of chiral transition that light quarks experience with decreasing resolution, the outcome being the development of an effective mass at low virtualities. This physical aspect has been described long ago by Politzer. [6]

At a quantitative level, the transition can be studied using duality arguments. For this purpose, let us consider the three point function

$$G^{\mu\nu}(q,r) = \int d^4x\, e^{iqx} \langle 0|T\left[J^\mu(x)\bar{\psi}(r/2)\gamma^\nu\psi(-r/2)\right]|0\rangle,$$

where $J^\mu = \bar{\psi}\gamma^\mu\psi$. It is related to the polarization function $G^{\mu\nu}(q,r=0) = (q^\mu q^\nu - g^{\mu\nu}q^2)\,\Pi(q^2)$. The polarization function itself is only determined up to a subtraction constant, but its derivatives $\Pi^{(n)}$ can be written for $n \geq 1$ by dispersion relations. Due to asymptotic freedom, the polarization function has a very good phenomenological representation in the $Q^2 = -q^2 \geq 0$ region consisting of the ground state vector meson pole, with mass m_V and residue

F_V, and perturbative $q\bar{q}$ continuum calculated with a current quark mass:

$$\Pi_{\rm ph}^{(n)}(Q^2) = \frac{n!\, F_V^2}{(Q^2 + m_V^2)^{n+1}} + \frac{n!}{\pi} \int_{s_t}^{\infty} ds \frac{{\rm Im}\,\Pi(s, m_f)}{(s + Q^2)^{n+1}}.$$

The photon wave function plays the role of the three point function which we want to approximate. We take as approximate wave function the perturbative $q\bar{q}$ wave function but replace the current mass m_f by an effective mass $m_{\rm eff}(Q^2)$. Here some improvement is still possible [5], since Q^2 appears in the extension parameter ε in combination with the light cone momentum fraction through the term $z(1-z)$. Leaving this possibility aside, one can derive an analytical expression for the derivatives of the approximate polarization function, $\Pi_{\rm a}^{(n)}$, as functions of Q^2 and $m_{\rm eff}$.

The next step is to determine the effective mass in such a way that the approximate two point function, $\Pi_{\rm a}^{(n)}$, coincides with the model two point function, $\Pi_{\rm ph}^{(n)}$. The procedure has been checked [5] in the nonrelativistic framework of a two-dimensional harmonic oscillator model which provides an interesting testing ground for the physics involved in the transverse plane. The identification $\Pi_{\rm a}^{(n)}(Q^2, m_{\rm eff}) = \Pi_{\rm ph}^{(n)}(Q^2)$ gives the effective quark mass as a function of Q^2 from the purely hadronic parameters m_V and F_V appearing in $\Pi_{\rm ph}^{(n)}$. The result depends slightly on the number, n, of differentiation assumed. For $m_f = 0$, the effective mass starts at $Q^2 = 0$ at 220 MeV for $n = 2$ and 245 MeV for $n = 3$, which are typical constituent quark mass values. The effective mass drops to 0 at $Q_0^2 \approx 1.5\text{--}2\, m_\rho^2$. A simple linear parametrization of the result is

$$\begin{aligned}
m_{\rm eff}(Q^2) &= 0.22\,(1 - Q^2/Q_0^2), \text{ in GeV, for } Q^2 \leq Q_0^2 = 1.05 \text{ GeV}^2, \\
m_{\rm eff}(Q^2) &= 0, \text{ for } Q^2 \geq Q_0^2.
\end{aligned} \tag{2}$$

A more refined procedure would be to make a smooth connection between the small Q^2 behavior obtained with the present method and the behavior obtained around 1 GeV^2 using Operator Product Expansion. [6] We shall not dwell on this possibility here.

The construction adopted here shares similarities with a description of the proton structure function via dispersion relation [7]. The latter representation incorporates a vector meson component which dominates at low Q^2 and an asymptotic part which accounts for the large Q^2 region. This second part which can be extracted from structure function analysis at large Q^2 naturally fulfills perturbative QCD evolution which is experimentally observed at large virtualities. Such perturbative corrections are not implemented in our approach and one may anticipate some deviations at large Q^2 between our results and those including evolution effects.

3 Photon-proton total cross section

Let us now use our photon wave function to compute the total photon-proton cross section, starting at $Q^2 = 0$. From the imaginary part of the amplitude, Eq. (1), replacing $\psi_V^* \to \psi_\gamma^*$, putting $t = 0$ and dividing by s, we form

$$\sigma_\lambda^{\text{tot}} = \int \frac{dz r \, dr}{2} |\psi_{\gamma(\lambda)}(z, r)|^2 \, J_p^{(0)}(z, r, t = 0).$$

In the following we consider data at a center of mass energy $W = 20$ GeV. We choose this value because it is the one where the model parameters are adjusted to fit the corresponding proton-proton elastic scattering data.[3,4] At this center of mass energy, the photon-proton total cross section is 118 μb. The Pomeron part of the Donnachie-Landshoff fit[8] gives $\sigma_{\text{Pom}} = 110$ μb, the remaining part being attributed to other Regge trajectories. The model of the stochastic vacuum accounts for the Pomeron part of the cross section. The charm quark contribution is measured independently and is rather small, 1 μb. In the present study, we focus on u, d and s which give the bulk of the cross section. According to Donnachie and Landshoff[8], the strange quark contribution to the total cross section is 8.3 μb.

Our results for the light, u and d, and strange quark contributions are:

$$\sigma_{u+d} = 84 \ \mu\text{b},$$
$$\sigma_s = 9.4 \ \mu\text{b}.$$

Since the photoproduction cross section depends crucially on the value of the constituent quark mass, the reproduction of the cross section within 10–20% is encouraging with respect to the fact that, as explained in Sec. 2, we have determined the effective quark mass, $m_{\text{eff}}(Q^2 = 0) = 0.22$ GeV, without quantitatively extracting anything from electroproduction phenomenology. For the strange quark, the comparison with the extracted cross section is correct within 10%. This result is obtained using the effective strange mass, $m_{s\,\text{eff}}(Q^2 = 0) = 0.31$ GeV, derived if one applies the method described in Sec. 2 to the $s\bar{s}$ channel. As an indication, let us note that the cross section one would derive with a current strange quark mass of 150 MeV is much too large: 31 μb.

We now consider virtual photon, $Q^2 \neq 0$, scattering off a proton. We form the structure function

$$F_2(Q^2) = \frac{Q^2}{\pi e^2}(\sigma_T + \sigma_L)$$

Since light and strange quarks contribute in a different way, we calculate their contributions separately. Special attentions will be paid to the Q^2 dependence

362

of the structure function at fixed $W = 20$ GeV, which corresponds to the energy where we determined our input dipole-proton cross section. In Fig. 1, we show the theoretical results for $F_2^{u+d}(x_B = Q^2/W^2, Q^2)$ and $F_2^s(x_B = Q^2/W^2, Q^2)$ at a fixed energy $W = 20$ GeV. At this energy and in the Q^2 range considered, the Reggeon contribution to F_2 is less than 5%.[8] We compare our results with data from both E665 [9] and NMC [10]. At intermediate Q^2 the description is good. At large Q^2 the prediction exceeds data by 10–20%. We have already mentionned some possible deviations in this region. Other sources of corrections with increasing Q^2, which at fixed energy corresponds to increasing x_B, are threshold suppressions. [8,5]

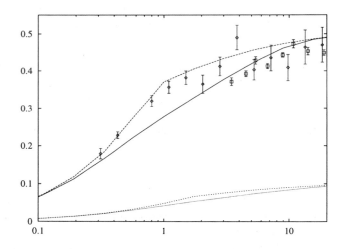

Figure 1: Theoretical calculation of F_2 as a function of Q^2. The long-dash curve is the $u + d$ contribution with the effective quark mass given in Eq. (2). The solid curve is with a z dependent effective quark mass [5]. An analogous treatment [5] for the strange quark leads to contributions shown as a dashed curve and a dotted curve, respectively. One has to add light and strange quark contributions before comparing with data.

Acknowledgments

The study described here was done in collaboration with H.G. Dosch and H.J. Pirner. This work is part of a training Project of the European Community under Contract No. ERBFMBICT950411.

References

1. T.H. Bauer, F.M. Pipkin, R.D. Spital, and D.R. Yennie, *Rev. Mod. Phys.* **50**, 261 (1978).
2. For a review see H.G. Dosch, *Prog. Part. Nucl. Phys.* **33**, 121 (1994).
3. H.G. Dosch, E. Ferreira and A. Krämer, *Phys. Rev.* D **50**, 1992 (1994).
4. H.G. Dosch, T. Gousset, G. Kulzinger and H.J. Pirner, *Phys. Rev.* D **55**, 2602 (1997).
5. H.G. Dosch, T. Gousset and H.J. Pirner, work in progress.
6. H.D. Politzer, *Nucl. Phys.* B **117**, 397 (1976) and *Phys. Lett.* B **116**, 171 (1982).
7. B. Badelek and J. Kwieciński, *Phys. Lett.* B **295**, 263 (1992).
8. A. Donnachie and P.V. Landshoff, *Z. Phys.* C **61**, 139 (1994).
9. E665 collab., M.R. Adams *et al*, *Phys. Rev.* D **54**, 3006 (1996).
10. NMC, M. Arneodo *et al.*, *Phys. Lett.* B **364**, 107 (1995).

Session E

Future Directions

PROGRESS IN PHOTON COLLIDERS

VALERY TELNOV

Institute of Nuclear Physics, 630090, Novosibirsk, Russia

Last two years were very important in history of a photon colliders. This option is included now in conceptual design reports of the NLC, JLC and TESLA/SBLC projects. All the designs foresee two interaction regions: one for e^+e^- and the second for $\gamma\gamma$, γe and e^-e^- collisions. This paper is focused on three aspects: 1) arguments for photon colliders; 2) parameters of current projects; 3) ultimate luminosities and energies, new ideas. Recent studies have shown that the main collision effect - coherent pair creation - is suppressed at photon colliders with the energy ($2E < 2$ TeV) due to the beam repulsion, and one can achieve, in principle, the $\gamma\gamma$ luminosity exceeding 10^{35} cm^{-2}s^{-1} . The required electron beams with very small emittances can be obtained, for example, using a laser cooling of electron beams. This new method requires a laser with a power by one order of magnitude higher than that required for the "conversion" of electrons to photons. Such lasers are not available today, but hopefully they will appear by the time when linear colliders will be built. High energy $\gamma\gamma$, γe colliders with the luminosity comparable to that in e^+e^- collisions are beyond the competition in study of many phenomena of particle physics.

1 Introduction

Let me remind briefly the basic scheme of a photon collider [1, 2], see fig.1. Two electron beams after the final focus system are traveling toward the interaction point (IP). At a distance of about 0.1–1 cm upstream from the IP, at the conversion point (C), the laser beam is focused and Compton backscattered by electrons, resulting in the high energy beam of photons. With reasonable laser parameters one can "convert" most of electrons into high energy photons. The photon beam follows the original electron direction of motion with a small angular spread of order $1/\gamma$, arriving at the IP in a tight focus, where it collides with the similar opposing high energy photon beam or with an electron beam. The photon spot size at the IP may be almost equal to that of electrons at IP and therefore, the luminosity of $\gamma\gamma$, γe collisions will be of the same order of magnitude as the "geometric" luminosity of basic ee beams. The detailed description of photon colliders properties can be found in refs [2–5] and in the Berkeley Workshop Proceedings [6].

Now, this option is included into the Conceptual Design Reports of the NLC [7], TESLA–SBLC [8] and JLC [9]. All these linear collider projects foresee the second interaction region for $\gamma\gamma$,γe collisions. This is quite a success but for final decisions it is necessary to have very clear justification that photon colliders are realistic and can substantially add to a discovery potential of linear colliders. Below are some arguments for photon colliders.

1. Some phenomena can be studied at photon colliders better than anywhere, for example, the measurement of $\gamma\gamma \to$ Higgs width, which is sensitive to all heavy charged particles; study of the vertex $\gamma\gamma WW$.

2. Cross sections for the pair production of charged scalar, leptons and top in $\gamma\gamma$ collisions are larger than those in e^+e^- collisions by a factor of 5; for WW production this factor is even larger: 10–20.

3. In γe collisions charged supersymmetric particles with masses higher than in e^+e^- collisions can be produced (heavy charged particle plus light neutral).

4. The luminosity of photon colliders (in the high energy part of luminosity spectrum) with electron beam parameters considered in the present designs will be about 10^{33} cm^{-2}s^{-1} or by a factor 5 smaller than $L_{e^+e^-}$. But the absence of collisions effects at $0.1 - 1$ TeV photon colliders allows to reach $L_{\gamma\gamma}$ up to 10^{35} cm^{-2}s^{-1} using electron beams with very low emittances. High luminosity photon colliders can provide two orders high production rate of WW pair and other charged particles (see item 2).

5. Obtaining of the ultimately high luminosities requires the development of new techniques, such as the laser cooling of electron beams [12]. However, linear colliders will appear (may be) only in one decade and will work next two decades. The upgrading of the luminosity requires the injection part modification only; it may be a separate injector for a photon collider, merging of many low emittance RF-photoguns (with or without laser cooling) is one of possible variants.

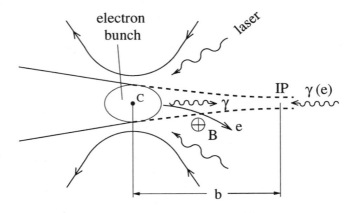

Figure 1: Scheme of $\gamma\gamma$; γe collider.

6. Linear colliders are very expensive facilities and their potential should be used in the best way. Two detectors (one for e^+e^- and the other for $\gamma\gamma$ and γe) can give much more results than the simple doubling of statistics in e^+e^- collisions with one detector .

7. Development of X-ray FEL lasers based on linear colliders (which are now under way) will favour the work on FEL required for photon colliders.

2 Physics potential, requirements to $\gamma\gamma$ luminosity

The physics in $\gamma\gamma$, γe colliders is very rich. The total number of papers devoted to the physics at photon colliders approaches to one thousand. Some examples are given in the introduction. Recent review of physics at photon colliders can be found in TESLA/SBLC Conceptual Design Report [8] and in the talk of G. Jikia at this workshop.

The resonance production of Higgs in $\gamma\gamma$ collisions and measurement of its $\gamma\gamma$ width is a task of primary importance.

Cross sections of the charged particle production in $\gamma\gamma$ collisions are higher than those in e^+e^- collisions. At $E \gg Mc^2$ the ratio of cross sections are the following ($R_{XX} = \sigma_{\gamma\gamma \to X^+X^-}/\sigma_{e^+e^- \to X^+X^-}$): $R_{H^+H^-} \sim 4.5$; $R_{t\bar{t}} \sim 4$; $R_{W^+W^-}(|cos\vartheta| < 0.8) \sim 15$; $R_{\mu^+\mu^-}(|cos\vartheta| < 0.8) \sim 8.5$.

To have the same statistics in $\gamma\gamma$ collisions the luminosity may be smaller than that in e^+e^- collisions at least by a factor of 5. Note that result in $\gamma\gamma$ and e^+e^- collisions are complimentary even for the same final states because diagrams are different (for example, the vertex $\gamma\gamma WW$ can be studied only in $\gamma\gamma$ collisions).

A reasonable scaling for the required $\gamma\gamma$ luminosity (in the high energy peak of the luminosity distribution) at $\gamma\gamma$ collider is

$$L_{\gamma\gamma} \sim 3 \times 10^{33} S(\text{TeV}^2), \text{ cm}^{-2}\text{s}^{-1}. \tag{1}$$

With such a luminosity one can detect 3.5×10^3 H^+H^-; 2×10^4 $\mu^+\mu^-$ ($|cos\vartheta| < 0.8$); 2×10^4 $t\bar{t}$; 2×10^5 W^+W^- ($|cos\vartheta| < 0.8$); 2×10^6 $S(\text{TeV}^2)$ W^+W^- for the time $t = 10^7$ c . Somewhat larger luminosity ($\sim 10^{33}$) is required for the search and study of the "intermediate" ($M_H \sim 100 - 200$ GeV) Higgs boson.

With an electron beam considered in current projects [7, 8] with 2E~500 GeV one can obtain $L_{\gamma\gamma} \sim 10^{33}$ cm^{-2}s^{-1} at $z = W_{\gamma\gamma}/2E > 0.7$ (see next section). It is determined only by the "geometric" e^-e^- luminosity. Using beams with smaller emittances one can get higher luminosity. Analyses of principle restrictions on luminosity of photon colliders have shown [13] (see sect.4) that at $2E \leq 5$ TeV one can obtain (in principle) $L_{\gamma\gamma} \geq 10^{35}$ cm^{-2}s^{-1}.

3   Current projects

Recently, two groups NLC [7] and TESLA/SBLC [8] (and soon JLC) have published Conceptual Design Reports of their linear collider projects containing comprehensive appendixes devoted to $\gamma\gamma$, γe options. Below is a short review of these designs.

3.1   Collision schemes

Two collision scheme were considered. scheme A ("without deflection"). There is no magnetic deflection of spent electrons and all particles after the conversion region travel to the IP. The conversion point may be situated very close to the IP; scheme B ("with deflection") After the conversion region, particles pass through a region with a transverse magnetic field ($B \sim 0.5$–1 T) where electrons are swept aside. Thereby one can achieve more or less pure $\gamma\gamma$ or γe collisions.

In both schemes, the removal of the disrupted spent beam is done by using the crab crossing scheme with the crossing angle about 30 mrad. The maximum disruption angle does not exceed 10 mrad and outgoing beams travel outside the final quads located at a distance about 2 m from the IP.

3.2   Conversion region. Requirements to lasers. Optics at the IP.

The conversion region is situated at the distance $b \sim 1.5\gamma\sigma_y = 0.5$–$1.5$ cm from the IP. An optimum laser wave length for the collider with $2E = 500$ GeV is about 1 μm (for $x = 4E_0\omega_0/m^2c^4 = 4.8$) and grows proportionally to the beam energy. The required flash energy for obtaining the conversion coefficient $k \sim 0.65$ is about 1–4 J for an electron bunch length $\sigma_z = 0.1$–0.5 mm, laser peak power is about 0.5–0.7 TW, average power is about 20 kW.

Obtaining such parameters is possible with either solid state lasers or free electron lasers. For $\lambda > 1$ μm ($E_0 > 250$–300 GeV) FEL is the only option seen now. The possible layout of optics near the IP is shown in fig 2.

3.3   Luminosity

In current projects, the $\gamma\gamma$ luminosity is determined by the "geometric" ee–luminosity. Due to the absence of beamstrahlung, beams in $\gamma\gamma$ collisions can have much smaller horizontal beam size than that in e^+e^- collisions, therefore the beta functions were taken as small as possible (some restrictions are posed by the Oide effect connected with chromatic aberrations due to synchrotron radiation in the final quads).

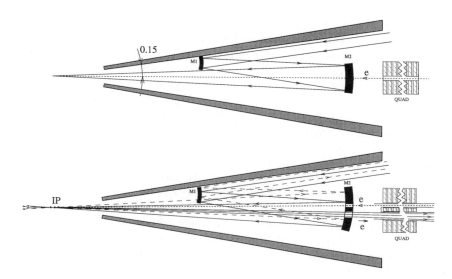

Figure 2: Layout of laser optics near the IP; upper - side view, down - top view, dashed lines – exit path of light coming from the left through one of the CP points (right to the IP), the distance between the IP and quads is about 2 m

Typical $\gamma\gamma$ luminosity distribution is broad with its peak at maximum invariant masses at $z = W_{\gamma\gamma}/2E_0 \sim 0.8$ (for x=4.8). The region $z > 0.65$ is the most valuable part of luminosity due to high energy and high degree of polarization. The luminosity in this part is about 10% of the geometric ee luminosity.

The results of simulations for different projects are the following. For the "nominal" beam parameters (the same as in e^+e^- collisions) and the optimum final focus system the luminosity $L_{\gamma\gamma}(z > 0.65) \sim (0.8/1.2/0.7) \times 10^{33}$ cm^{-2}s^{-1} for NLC/TESLA/SBLC. The peak luminosity is also an important characteristic, it is approximately equal to $dL_{\gamma\gamma}/dz \sim 7L_{\gamma\gamma}(z > 0.65)/z_{max}$. These numbers are close for the schemes with and without magnetic deflection.

In the scheme without deflection, γe collisions can be studied simultaneously with $\gamma\gamma$ collisions. In this case the γe luminosity is even higher than $L_{\gamma\gamma}$ by a factor of 1.5 (this is valid only for considered beam parameters; for very small beam sizes $L_{\gamma e} \ll L_{\gamma\gamma}$ due to beam–beam repulsion). The magnetic deflection allows to obtain almost clean γe collisions with FWHM~7%.

There are several possibilities for increasing luminosity.

1) Reduction of the horizontal emittance by optimizing the damping rings. For example, at the TESLA, the decrease in ϵ_{nx} by a factor 3.5 leads to an

increase in $L_{\gamma\gamma}$ up to 3×10^{33} cm^{-2}s^{-1}.

2) One can use the low emittance RF-photoguns instead of damping rings. Unfortunately, even with best photoguns the luminosity will be somewhat lower than that with damping rings. However, there is one possible solution. The normalized emittance in photoguns is approximately proportional to the number of particles in the electron bunch. It seems possible to merge (using some difference in energies) many ($N_g \sim 5 - 10$) low current beams with low emittances to one high current beam with the same transverse emittance. This gives the gain in luminosity more than by a factor N_g in comparison with one photogun ("more" because the lower emittance allows smaller beta functions due to the Oide effect). Joining beams from five photoguns with experimentally achieved parameters leads at TESLA/SBLC to $L_{\gamma\gamma} = (3\text{--}4)\times10^{33}$ cm^{-2}s^{-1}.

For a considerable step in luminosity the beams with much lower emittances are required that needs the development of new approaches such as a *laser cooling* [12] (sect.4.2). Potentially this method allows to attain the geometric luminosity by two orders higher than those achievable by the methods discussed above. One example [8] of the luminosity distributions for the "super" TESLA with round beams and emittances by a factor 50 lower than that achieved with RF–photoguns is shown in fig 3. Beam parameters and resulting luminosities are given below.

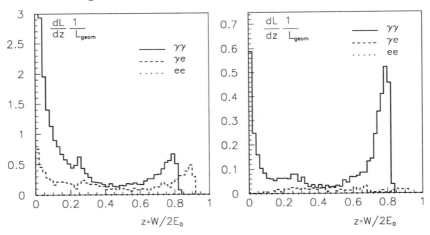

Figure 3: Luminosity spectra for the "super" TESLA parameters (see the text). Left – without the deflection; right – $\gamma\gamma$ collisions with the magnetic deflection ($B = 0.5$ T)

Electron beam parameters of the "super" TESLA
$N = 3.63 \times 10^{10}$, $\sigma_z = 0.5$ mm, $2E = 500$ GeV, $f = 5.65$ kHz,

$$\epsilon_{nx} = \epsilon_{ny} = 0.2 \times 10^{-6} \text{ m rad}, \ \beta_x = \beta_y = 0.5 \text{ mm}, \ \sigma_x = \sigma_y = 14 \text{ nm},$$
$$L_{geom} = 2 \times 10^{35} \text{ cm}^{-2} \text{ c}^{-1}$$

Luminosities without deflection: $b = \gamma \sigma_y = 0.7$ cm,

$$L_{\gamma\gamma} = 1.15 \times 10^{35}, \ L_{\gamma\gamma}(z > 0.65) = 1.5 \times 10^{34} \text{ cm}^{-2} \text{ c}^{-1},$$
$$L_{\gamma e} = 3.6 \times 10^{34}, \ L_{\gamma e}(z > 0.65) = 1.2 \times 10^{34} \text{ cm}^{-2} \text{ c}^{-1},$$

Luminosities with magnetic deflection: $b = 1.5$ cm, $B = 0.5$ T,

$$L_{\gamma\gamma} = 2 \times 10^{34}, \ L_{\gamma\gamma}(z > 0.65) = 1 \times 10^{34} \text{ cm}^{-2} \text{ c}^{-1},$$
$$L_{\gamma e} = 2.5 \times 10^{33}, \ L_{\gamma e}(z > 0.65) = 6 \times 10^{32} \text{ cm}^{-2} \text{ c}^{-1},$$

Results are impressive: $L_{\gamma\gamma}(z > 0.65) = (1\text{--}1.5) \times 10^{34}$ cm^{-2}s^{-1} (2–3 times higher than those in e^+e^- collisions). It is not the limit (see sect.4.3)

4 New ideas

4.1 Laser cooling

Recently [12], a new method was considered — laser cooling of electron beams — which allows, in principle, to reach $L_{\gamma\gamma} \geq 10^{35}$ cm^{-2}s^{-1}.

The idea of laser cooling of electron beams is very simple. During a collision with optical laser photons (in the case of strong field it is more appropriate to consider the interaction of an electron with an electromagnetic wave) the transverse distribution of electrons (σ_i) remains almost the same. Also, the angular spread (σ_i') is almost constant, because for photon energies (a few eV) much lower than the electron beam energy (several GeV) the scattered photons follow the initial electron trajectory with a small additional spread. So, the emittance $\epsilon_i = \sigma_i \sigma_i'$ remains almost unchanged. At the same time, the electron energy decreases from E_0 down to E. This means that the transverse normalized emittances have decreased: $\epsilon_n = \gamma\epsilon = \epsilon_{n0}(E/E_0)$. One can reaccelerate the electron beam up to the initial energy and repeat the procedure. Then after N stages of cooling $\epsilon_n/\epsilon_{n0} = (E/E_0)^N$ (if ϵ_n is far from its limit).

Some possible sets of parameters for the laser cooling are: $E_0 = 4.5$ GeV, $l_e = 0.2$ mm, $\lambda = 0.5$ μm, flash energy $A \sim 10$ J. The final electron bunch will have an energy of 0.45 GeV with an energy spread $\sigma_E/E \sim 13\%$, the normalized emittances $\epsilon_{nx}, \epsilon_{ny}$ are reduced by a factor 10. A two stage system with the same parameters gives 100 times reduction of emittances. The limit on the final emittance is $\epsilon_{nx} \sim \epsilon_{ny} \sim 2 \times 10^{-9}$ m rad at $\beta_i = 1$ mm. For comparison, in the TESLA (NLC) project the damping rings have $\epsilon_{nx} = 14(3) \times 10^{-6}$ m rad, $\epsilon_{ny} = 25(3) \times 10^{-8}$ m rad.

This method requires a laser system even more powerful than that for $e \to \gamma$ conversion. However, all the requirements are reasonable taking into account fast progress of laser technique and time plans of linear colliders. A multiple use of the laser bunch can reduce considerably an average laser power.

4.2 Stretching of laser focus depth

The laser and electron beams interact with each other most efficiently when laser and electron beams have the same duration and the depth of laser focus (Rayleigh length) is somewhat shorter than the beam length. It turns out that in many cases, the density of laser photons is so high that instead of the Compton scattering an electron interacts simultaneously with many photons (synchrotron radiation). This is not desirable since in the regime of strong field ($eB\lambda > mc^2$) the spectrum of scattered photons after conversion region is not so peaked as in the Compton scattering case. In the method of laser cooling the strong field leads to higher values of minimum emittance and higher polarization loss. Of course, one can take laser bunch longer to keep collision probability constant and the density of photons below the critical value. However, in this case, the laser flash energy should be larger than that under optimum conditions given in the beginning of this paragraph. Due to this nonlinear QED effect the laser flash energy required for photon colliders should grow proportionally to the collider energy [4, 5].

Recently [12], it was found how to avoid this problem. In the suggested scheme the focus depth is stretched without changing the radius of this area. In this case, the collision probability remains the same but the maximum value of the field is smaller. The solution is based on use of chirped laser pulses and chromaticity of the focusing system [a]. In this scheme, the laser target consists of many laser focal points (continuously) and light comes to each point exactly at the moment when the electron bunch is there. One can consider that a short electron bunch collides on its way sequentially with many short light pulses of length $l_\gamma \sim l_e$ and focused with $2Z_R \sim l_e$.

The required flash energy in the scheme with a stretched laser focus is determined only by diffraction and at the optimum wave length ($x=4.8$) does not depend on the collider energy. The stretching of laser focus enables a substantial decrease in flash energy in the method of laser cooling, to achieve minimum emittances and to conserve polarization of electron beams.

4.3 Ultimate luminosity and energy of photon colliders

The only collision effect restricting $\gamma\gamma$ luminosity at photon colliders is the coherent pair creation which leads to the conversion of a high energy photon

---

[a]In a chirped pulse the wave length is linearly depends on longitudinal position. Such pulses are obtained and used now in all short-pulse lasers.

into e^+e^- pair in the field of opposing electron beam[10, 4, 5]. There are three ways to avoid this effect: a) to use flat beams; b) to deflect the electron beam after conversion at a sufficiently large distance from the IP; c) under certain conditions (low beam energy, long bunches) the beam field at the IP is below the critical one due to the repulsion of electron beams[11]. The problem of ultimate luminosities for different beam parameters and energies was analyzed recently in ref.[13] analytically and by simulation. Resume is the following.

The maximum luminosity is attained when the conversion point is situated as close as possible to the IP: $b = 3\sigma_z + 0.04E[\text{TeV}]$ cm (here the second term is equal to the minimum length of the conversion region). In this case, the vertical radius of the photon beam at the IP is also minimum: $a_\gamma \sim b/\gamma$ (assuming that the vertical size of the electron beam is even smaller). An optimum horizontal beam size (σ_x) depends on the beam energy, number of particles in a bunch and bunch length. The dependence of the $\gamma\gamma$ luminosity on σ_x for various energies and number of particles in a bunch is shown in fig.4. The bunch length is fixed to be equal to 0.2 mm. The collision rate is calculated from the total beam power which is equal to $15E[\text{TeV}]$ MW (close to that in current projects). In the fig.4 we see that at low energies and small number of particles the luminosity curves follows their natural behaviour $L \propto 1/\sigma_x$ while at high energy and large number of particles in a bunch the curves make zigzag which is explained by $\gamma \to e^+e^-$ conversion in the field of the opposing beam.

What is remarkable in these results? First of all, the maximum attainable luminosities are huge. At low energies there are no coherent pair creation even for a very small σ_x when the field in the beam is much higher than the critical field $B_{cr} = \alpha e/\gamma r_e^2$. This is explained by the fact that beams during the collision are repulsing each other so that the field on the beam axis (which affects on high energy photons) is below the critical field. It means that the $\gamma\gamma$ luminosity is simply proportional to the geometric electron-electron luminosity (approximately $L_{\gamma\gamma}(x > 0.65) \sim 0.1 L_{ee}$) for $\sigma_x, \sigma_y > b/\gamma \sim 3\sigma_z/\gamma + 0.2$ nm. For the energies $2E < 2$ TeV which are in reach of next generation of linear colliders the luminosity limit is much higher than it is required by our scaling low given by Eq.1.

4.4 Backgrounds

One of important problems at high luminosities is a background due to relatively large total cross section $\sigma_{\gamma\gamma \to hadrons} \sim 5 \times 10^{-31}$ cm^2.

The average number of hadron events/per bunch crossing is about one at $L_{\gamma\gamma}(z > 0.65) = 2 \times 10^{34}$ cm^{-2}s^{-1} at the typical collision rate 10 kHz. However, in the scheme without deflection the total $\gamma\gamma$ luminosity is larger than the "useful" $L_{\gamma\gamma}(z > 0.65)$ by a factor 5–10. This low energy collisions increase background by a factor 2–3 [8].

Let us assume the photon collider luminosity to be $L_{\gamma\gamma}(z > 0.65) \sim 10^{35}$ cm^{-2}s^{-1} (top of our dreams), this leads to about 15 (effectively) high energy $\gamma\gamma \rightarrow hadron$ events per bunch crossing. Approximately the same number (~ 30) of events/collision is expected in detectors at the LHC . However, there is an important difference between pp and $\gamma\gamma$ colliders: in the case of an interesting event (high P_t jets or leptons) the total energy of final products at photon colliders is equal to E_{cm}, while at proton colliders it is only about $(1/6)E_{cm}$. In comparison with the pp collider the ratio of the signal to background at

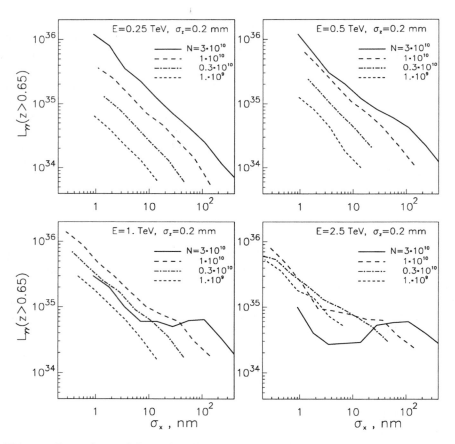

Figure 4: Dependence of the $\gamma\gamma$ luminosity on the horizontal beam size for $\sigma_z = 0.2$ mm, see comments in the text.

photon colliders is better by a factor of 6 at the same number of hadronic events per crossing. Note, however, that at NLC and JLC the time between collisions is only about 1.5 ns and background from a few neighbouring events will overlap. At more realistic top $\gamma\gamma$ luminosities about $L_{\gamma\gamma}(z > 0.65) \sim 10^{34}$ cm^{-2}s^{-1} even with this fact the background conditions will be acceptable. These arguments and detailed simulation [8] show that the problem of hadronic background is not dramatic for photon colliders.

Acknowledgments

I would like to thank the organizers of "Photon 97" for the nice Workshop which was one of important steps towards photon colliders.

References

1. I.Ginzburg, G.Kotkin, V.Serbo, V.Telnov, *Pizma ZhETF*, **34** (1981) 514; *JETP Lett.* **34** (1982) 491.

2. I.Ginzburg, G.Kotkin, V.Serbo, V.Telnov, *Nucl. Instr. & Meth.* **205** (1983) 47.

3. I.Ginzburg, G.Kotkin, S.Panfil, V.Serbo, V.Telnov, *Nucl. Instr. & Meth.* **219** (1984) 5.

4. V.Telnov, *Nucl. Instr. &Meth.A* **294** (1990) 72.

5. V.Telnov, *Nucl. Instr. &Meth.A* **355** (1995) 3.

6. *Proc.of Workshop on $\gamma\gamma$ Colliders*, Berkeley CA, USA, 1994, *Nucl. Instr. &Meth. A* **355** (1995) 1–194.

7. *Zeroth-Order Design Report for the Next Linear Collider* LBNL-PUB-5424, SLAC Report 474, May 1996.

8. *Conceptual Design of a 500 GeV Electron Positron Linear Collider with Integrated X-Ray Laser Facility* DESY 79-048, ECFA-97-182

9. JLC, to be published soon

10. P.Chen,V.Telnov,*Phys.Rev.Letters*, **63** (1989)1796.

11. V.Telnov, *Proc.of Workshop "Photon 95"*, Sheffield, UK, April 1995, p.369.

12. V.Telnov, *Proc.of ITP Workshop "New modes of particle acceleration techniques and sources"* Santa Barbara, USA, August 1996, NSF-ITP-96-142, SLAC-PUB 7337, Budker INP 96-78, *Phys.Rev.Lett.*, **78**(1997)4757, e-print: hep-ex/9610008.

13. V.Telnov, *Proc.of ITP Workshop "Future High energy colliders"* Santa Barbara, USA, October 21-25, 1996, Budker INP 97-47, e-print: physics/9706003.

PHYSICS AT THE PHOTON LINEAR COLLIDER

G. JIKIA[a]

Albert–Ludwigs–Universität Freiburg, Fakultät für Physik
Hermann–Herder Str.3, D-79104 Freiburg, Germany
and
Institute for High Energy Physics, Protvino
Moscow Region 142284, Russian Federation

The physics prospects of the high energy Photon Linear Collider are reviewed, emphasizing its potential to study the symmetry breaking sector, including Higgs searches and precision anomalous W couplings measurements.

1 Introduction

Using the process of Compton backscattering of laser beams off electron beams from the linear collider one can obtain $\gamma\gamma$ and γe colliding beams with an energy and luminosity comparable to that in e^+e^- collisions[1]. The expected physics at the Photon Linear Collider (PLC) is very rich and complementary to that in e^+e^- collisions. Since there exist several excellent extensive reviews on the subject[2-7] only the issues concerning the electroweak physics based on recent progress that have been achieved since Photon'95 Conference in Sheffield will be summarized here.

2 Higgs boson physics

Discovery and study of Higgs boson(s) will be of primary importance at future pp and linear e^+e^- and $\gamma\gamma$ colliders. The survey of the Higgs physics opportunities of PLC is simultaneously a very good example showing how the complete phenomenological portrait is obtained only by combining the complementary information available from these distinct types of machines.

2.1 Measurements of the Higgs boson couplings

The most fundamental properties of the Higgs boson are its mass, its total width and its partial widths. Ideally, one would wish to determine, *in a model-independent way,* all of the tree-level and one-loop couplings of the h_{SM}, its spin, parity, and CP nature, and its total width. The total Higgs width, while certainly important in its own right, becomes doubly so since it is required

---

[a]Alexander von Humboldt Fellow; e-mail: jikia@phyv4.physik.uni-freiburg.de

in order to compute many important partial widths, which provide the most direct means of verifying that the observed Higgs boson is or is not the h_{SM}. While branching ratios, being the ratio of a partial width to the total width can not be unambiguously interpreted, any deviations of partial widths from SM predictions can be directly compared to predictions of alternative models such as the MSSM, the NMSSM, or the general two Higgs doublet model (2HDM).

Higgs Total Widths

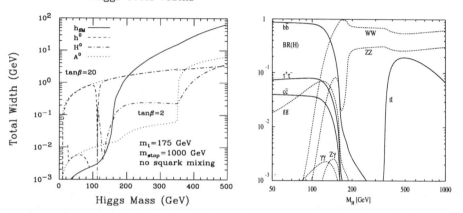

Figure 1: Total width versus mass of the SM and MSSM Higgs bosons for $m_t = 175\,\mathrm{GeV}$ [11] and the main branching ratios $BR(H)$ of the Standard Model Higgs decay channels [12].

The predicted width, $\Gamma_{h_{\mathrm{SM}}}^{\mathrm{tot}}$, and branching ratios are plotted in Fig. 1 as a function of $m_{h_{\mathrm{SM}}}$. For $m_{h_{\mathrm{SM}}} \lesssim 2M_W$, $\Gamma_{h_{\mathrm{SM}}}^{\mathrm{tot}}$ is too small to be reconstructed in the final state and only indirect determination of $\Gamma_{h_{\mathrm{SM}}}^{\mathrm{tot}}$ is possible at NLC and LHC using a multiple step process,[b] the best process depends upon the Higgs mass. In this respect $\gamma\gamma$ collider mode offers a unique possibility [8-10] to produce the Higgs boson as an s-channel resonance decaying, for instance, into $b\bar{b}$:

$$\gamma\gamma \rightarrow h^0 \rightarrow b\bar{b} \tag{1}$$

and thereby measuring the rate for the Higgs boson production in $\gamma\gamma$ mode of the linear collider we can determine the value of the Higgs two-photon width itself. Assuming that 300-500 GeV linear collider will first start operating in e^+e^- mode, the mass of the h^0 will already be known from the Bjorken reaction $e^+e^- \rightarrow Z^* \rightarrow Zh$, and the beam energy could be tuned so that the $\gamma\gamma$ luminosity spectrum peaks at m_h. The Higgs two-photon decay width is

---

[b]The other alternative is to employ FMC $\mu^+\mu^-$ collisions at $\sqrt{s} \sim m_{h_{\mathrm{SM}}}$ and directly measure $\Gamma_{h_{\mathrm{SM}}}^{\mathrm{tot}}$ by scanning [11].

of special interest by itself since it appears at the one-loop level. Thus, any heavy charged particles which obtain their masses from electroweak symmetry breaking can contribute in the loop. Moreover, for $m_{h_{\rm SM}} \lesssim 130\,{\rm GeV}$ (*i.e.* in the MSSM m_{h^0} range), *the only known procedure for determining the total Higgs width* $\Gamma^{\rm tot}_{h_{\rm SM}}$ is that based on the measurement of $\Gamma(h_{\rm SM} \to \gamma\gamma)$ in the reaction (1) as described in Ref. [11].

The following procedure could be used. First one should measure the cross section of the single Higgs production at PLC

$$\sigma(\gamma\gamma \to h^0 \to X) = \tau \frac{dL_{\gamma\gamma}}{d\tau} \frac{8\pi^2}{m_h^3} \Gamma(h^0 \to \gamma\gamma) \cdot BR(h^0 \to X)(1 + \lambda_1\lambda_2) \quad (2)$$

and determine $\Gamma(h_{\rm SM} \to \gamma\gamma)BR(h_{\rm SM} \to b\bar{b})$. Here the effective photon-photon luminosity $L_{\gamma\gamma}$ is introduced. Then one can compute the two-photon width as a ratio

$$\Gamma(h \to \gamma\gamma) = \frac{[\Gamma(h \to \gamma\gamma)BR(h \to b\bar{b})]}{BR(h \to b\bar{b})}. \quad (3)$$

The branching ratio $BR(h^0 \to b\bar{b})$ will also already be known from e^+e^- annihilation. Indeed, measuring $\sigma(e^+e^- \to ZH)$ (in the missing mass mode) and $\sigma(e^+e^- \to ZH)BR(h \to b\bar{b})$ in e^+e^- mode of the linear collider we can compute $BR(h^0 \to b\bar{b}) = [\sigma(e^+e^- \to ZH)BR(h \to b\bar{b})]/\sigma(e^+e^- \to ZH)$, the error in the branching ratio is estimated at $\pm(5 \div 10)\%$ [11]. Finally, one can compute the total Higgs boson width $\Gamma^{tot}_h = \Gamma(h \to \gamma\gamma)/BR(h \to \gamma\gamma)$, using the $BR(h_{\rm SM} \to \gamma\gamma)$ determination(s) at NLC and LHC [11]

$$
\begin{aligned}
BR(h \to \gamma\gamma) &= BR(h \to b\bar{b})\frac{[\sigma(e^+e^- \to Zh)BR(h \to \gamma\gamma)]}{[\sigma(e^+e^- \to Zh)BR(h \to b\bar{b})]} \quad (4) \\
&= BR(h \to b\bar{b})\frac{[\sigma(pp \to Wh)BR(h \to \gamma\gamma)]}{[\sigma(tt \to Wh)BR(h \to b\bar{b})]}
\end{aligned}
$$

and compute *in a model-independent way* partial Higgs decay widths that are directly related to fundamental couplings

$$\Gamma(h \to b\bar{b}) = \Gamma^{tot}_h BR(h \to b\bar{b}), \quad \Gamma(h \to gg) = \Gamma^{tot}_h BR(h \to gg) \ldots \quad (5)$$

The observable cross section for the $\gamma\gamma$ Higgs signal in the gluon fusion reaction at the LHC can depend quite strongly on the masses and couplings of the superpartners and Higgs bosons, particularly if they are not too heavy, and it varies from a few fb to more than 100 fb over the parameter space of the MSSM, even in the scenario that supersymmetry is not discovered at LEP2 [14]. Having measured $BR(h \to gg) \cdot \Gamma(h \to \gamma\gamma)$ (with an error of order $\pm 22\%$ at

$m_{h_{SM}} = 120$ GeV [15]) and combining this number with the value of the Higgs total and two-photon decay width, measured in $\gamma\gamma$ and e^+e^- experiments one can calculate the two-gluon Higgs branching ratio and partial width.

The main background to the h^0 production is the continuum production of $b\bar{b}$ and $c\bar{c}$ pairs. In this respect, the availability of high degree of photon beams circular polarization is crucial, since for the equal photon helicities ($\pm\pm$) that produce spin-zero resonant states, the $\gamma\gamma \rightarrow q\bar{q}$ QED Born cross section is suppressed by the factor m_q^2/s [10]. Another potentially dangerous backgrounds originate from the resolved-photon processes [16,17,19] in which a gluon from the photon structure function produces $b\bar{b}$, $c\bar{c}$ pairs, and from the continuum production of $b\bar{b}$ pairs accompanied by the radiation of additional gluon [18,20], calculated taking into account large QCD $\mathcal{O}(\alpha_s)$ radiative corrections [17], which are not suppressed even for the equal photon helicities. Virtual one-loop QCD corrections for $J_z = 0$ were found to be especially large due to the double logarithmic enhancement factor, so that the corrections are comparable or even larger than the Born contribution for the two-jet final topologies [17]. For small values of the cutoff y_{cut}, separating two and three-jet events, two-jet cross section, calculated to order α_s, becomes even negative in the central region. Recently leading QCD corrections for $J_z = 0$ have been calculated at the two-loop level [21]. The non-Sudakov form factor in the double logarithmic approximation, including the two-loop contribution [21], is given by

$$\frac{\sigma_{2-loop}}{\sigma_{Born}} = 1 - 2\frac{\alpha_s}{\pi}\log^2(\frac{s}{m_b^2}) + \frac{121}{108}\left(\frac{\alpha_s}{\pi}\right)^2\log^4(\frac{s}{m_b^2}). \tag{6}$$

The account of two-loop contribution makes cross section to be positive and the authors of Ref. [21] argue that the higher order contributions are not so anomalously large. Anyway, these detailed studies [11,17-21] have shown that the Higgs signal can still be observed well above the background with the statistical error of the Higgs cross section at the $10 \div 30\%$ level in the wide range of Higgs mass $60 \div 150$ GeV. The net error on $\Gamma(h_{\text{SM}} \rightarrow \gamma\gamma)BR(h_{\text{SM}} \rightarrow b\bar{b})$ for $L = 50$ fb^{-1} is illustrated in Fig. 2 [11]. Thus, the error in the $m_{h_{\text{SM}}} \lesssim 120$ GeV mass region will be in the 8%-10% range, rising to 15% by $m_{h_{\text{SM}}} = 140$ GeV and peaking at 30% at $m_{h_{\text{SM}}} = 170$ GeV, as illustrated in Fig. 2.

For the Higgs bosons heavier that $2M_Z$ the Higgs signal in $\gamma\gamma$ collisions can be observed in ZZ decay mode [9,13] if one of the Z's is required to decay to l^+l^- to suppress the huge tree-level $\gamma\gamma \rightarrow W^+W^-$ continuum background. However, even though there is no tree-level ZZ continuum background, such a background due to the reaction $\gamma\gamma \rightarrow ZZ$ does arise at the one-loop level in the electroweak theory [22] which makes the Higgs observation in the ZZ mode impossible for $m_h \gtrsim (350 \div 400)$ GeV. It was found that for $185 < m_h <$

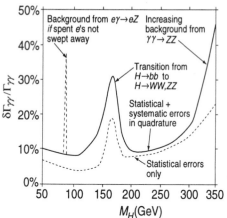

Figure 2: Accuracy (including systematic as well as statistical errors) with which $\Gamma(h_{\mathrm{SM}} \rightarrow \gamma\gamma)BR(h_{\mathrm{SM}} \rightarrow b\bar{b}$ or$WW, ZZ)$ can be measured at the PLC collider with integrated luminosity of $L = 50$ fb^{-1} [11].

300 GeV the ZZ mode will provide a 10-20% determination of the quantity $\Gamma(h \rightarrow \gamma\gamma) \cdot BR(h \rightarrow ZZ)$ (see Fig. 2).

The accuracies of the various measurements involved are a crucial issue. The errors for $\Gamma^{\mathrm{tot}}_{h_{\mathrm{SM}}}$ are tabulated[c] in Table 1 [11].

2.2 Measurements of the Higgs boson CP-properties

The ability to control the polarizations of back-scattered photons provides a powerful means for exploring the CP properties of any single neutral Higgs boson that can be produced with reasonable rate at the Photon Linear Collider [23]. A CP-even Higgs boson h^0 couples to the combination $\vec{\varepsilon_1} \cdot \vec{\varepsilon_2} = -1/2(1+\lambda_1\lambda_2)$, while a CP-odd Higgs boson A^0 couples to $\vec{\varepsilon_1} \times \vec{\varepsilon_2} \cdot \vec{k_\gamma} = \omega_\gamma/2i\lambda_1(1 + \lambda_1\lambda_2)$, where $\vec{\varepsilon_i}$ and λ_i are photon polarization vectors and helicities. The first of these structures couples to linearly polarized photons with the maximal strength if the polarizations are parallel, the letter if the polarizations are perpendicular. Moreover, if the Higgs boson is a mixture of CP-even and CP-odd states, as can occur $e.g.$ in a general 2HDM with CP-violating neutral sector, the interference of these two terms gives rise to a CP-violating asymmetries [23]. Two CP-violating ratios could contribute to linear order with respect to CP-

---

[c]For $m_{h_{\mathrm{SM}}} \gtrsim 130\,\mathrm{GeV}$ one can compute $\Gamma^{\mathrm{tot}}_{h_{\mathrm{SM}}} = \Gamma(h_{\mathrm{SM}} \rightarrow WW^\star)/BR(h_{\mathrm{SM}} \rightarrow WW^\star)$ using LHC data. Combined error for $\Gamma^{\mathrm{tot}}_{h_{\mathrm{SM}}}$ is quted in the Table 1 for this mass range.

Table 1: The errors for $\Gamma(h_{SM} \to \gamma\gamma)$ as determined using luminosity of $L = 50$ fb^{-1} accumulated in $\gamma\gamma$ collisions at $\sqrt{s}_{e^+e^-} \sim m_{h_{SM}}/0.8^{11}$. Approximate errors for Higgs total width, branching ratios, and couplings-squared are given for $L = 200$ fb^{-1} at $\sqrt{s} = 500$ GeV NLC. For $BR(h_{SM} \to \gamma\gamma)$ the NLC and LHC results are combibed.

Quantity	Errors			
$\mathbf{m_{h_{SM}}}$**(GeV)**	80	100	110	120
$(\gamma\gamma h_{SM})^2/(b\bar{b}h_{SM})^2$	$\pm42\%$	$\pm27\%$	$\pm24\%$	$\pm22\%$
$BR(h_{SM} \to b\bar{b})$	$\pm5\%$			
$BR(h_{SM} \to \gamma\gamma)$	$\pm15\%$	$\pm14\%$	$\pm13\%$	$\pm13\%$
$(\gamma\gamma h_{SM})^2$	$\sim \pm12\%$			
$\Gamma^{tot}_{h_{SM}}$	$\pm19\%$	$\pm18\%$	$\pm18\%$	$\pm18\%$
$(b\bar{b}h_{SM})^2$	$\pm20\%$	$\pm19\%$	$\pm18\%$	$\pm18\%$
$\mathbf{m_{h_{SM}}}$**(GeV)**	130	140	150	170
$(\gamma\gamma h_{SM})^2/(b\bar{b}h_{SM})^2$	$\pm23\%$	$\pm26\%$	$\pm35\%$	$-$
$BR(h_{SM} \to b\bar{b})$	$\pm6\%$		$\pm9\%$	$\sim 20\%?$
$BR(h_{SM} \to \gamma\gamma)$	$\pm13\%$	$\pm18\%?$	$\pm35\%$	$-$
$(\gamma\gamma h_{SM})^2$	$\pm15\%$	$\pm17\%$	$\pm31\%$	$-$
$\Gamma^{tot}_{h_{SM}}$	$\pm13\%$	$\pm9\%$	$\pm10\%$	$\pm11\%$
$(b\bar{b}h_{SM})^2$	$\pm14\%$	$\pm11\%$	$\pm13\%$	$\pm23\%$
$\mathbf{m_{h_{SM}}}$**(GeV)**	180	190	200	300
$(ZZh_{SM})^2$	$\pm4\% - \pm5\%$		$\pm6\%$	$\pm9\%$
$(\gamma\gamma h_{SM})^2$	$\pm13\%$	$\pm12\%$	$\pm12\%$	$\pm22\%$
$\Gamma^{tot}_{h_{SM}}$	$\pm13\%$	$\pm14\%$	$\pm15\%$	$\pm28\%$

violating couplings:

$$\mathcal{A}_1 = \frac{|\mathcal{M}_{++}|^2 - |\mathcal{M}_{--}|^2}{|\mathcal{M}_{++}|^2 + |\mathcal{M}_{--}|^2}, \quad \mathcal{A}_2 = \frac{2Im(\mathcal{M}_{--}^* \mathcal{M}_{++})}{|\mathcal{M}_{++}|^2 + |\mathcal{M}_{--}|^2}. \tag{7}$$

Since the event rate for Higgs boson production in $\gamma\gamma$ collisions is given by

$$
\begin{aligned}
dN &= dL_{\gamma\gamma} d\Gamma \frac{1}{4}(|\mathcal{M}_{++}|^2 + |\mathcal{M}_{--}|^2) \\
&\times [(1 + \langle \xi_2\tilde{\xi}_2 \rangle) + (\langle \xi_2 \rangle + \langle \tilde{\xi}_2 \rangle)\mathcal{A}_1 + (\langle \xi_3\tilde{\xi}_1 \rangle + \langle \xi_1\tilde{\xi}_3 \rangle)\mathcal{A}_2],
\end{aligned} \tag{8}
$$

where ξ_i, $\tilde{\xi}_i$ are the Stokes polarization parameters, two CP-violating asymmetries could be observed

$$A_{circ} = \frac{N_{++} - N_{--}}{N_{++} + N_{--}} = \frac{\langle \xi_2 \rangle + \langle \tilde{\xi}_2 \rangle}{1 + \langle \xi_2\tilde{\xi}_2 \rangle}\mathcal{A}_1, \tag{9}$$

where $N_{\pm\pm}$ correspond to the event rates for positive (negative) initial photon helicities. Experimentally the measurement of the asymmetry is achieved by simultaneously flipping the helicities of both of the initiating laser beams. Since the A_{circ} is proportional to the imaginary part of the SM contribution to the $\gamma\gamma \rightarrow h^0$ amplitude, which is very small below $2M_W$ threshold, this asymmetry can be useful only for $m_h \gtrsim 2M_Z$. The asymmetry to be observed with linearly polarized photons is given by

$$A_{lin} = \frac{N(\chi = \frac{\pi}{4}) - N(\chi = -\frac{\pi}{4})}{N(\chi = \frac{\pi}{4}) + N(\chi = -\frac{\pi}{4})} = \frac{\langle \xi_3 \tilde{\xi}_1 \rangle + \langle \xi_1 \tilde{\xi}_3 \rangle}{1 + \langle \xi_2 \tilde{\xi}_2 \rangle} A_2, \tag{10}$$

χ is the angle between the linear polarization vectors of the photons. The attainable degree of linear polarization l_γ at PLC depends on the value of $z_m = (\sqrt{s_{\gamma\gamma}})_{max}/2E_b$ which can be changed in the case of free electron laser [1]. For $z_m = 0.82$ the degree of linear polarization is $l_\gamma \sim 0.33$ only, but $l_\gamma \gtrsim 0.8$ at $z_m \lesssim 0.5$. One finds [23] that the asymmetries are typically larger than 10% and are observable for a large range of 2HDM parameter space if CP violation is present in the Higgs potential.

2.3 The discovery of the heavy states in extended Higgs models.

The PLC potential to discover Higgs bosons is especially attractive in the search for heavy Higgs states in the extended models such as MSSM [9,24]. The most important limitation of a e^+e^- collider in detecting the MSSM Higgs bosons is the fact that they are produced only in pairs, $H^0 A^0$ or $H^+ H^-$ and the parameter range for which the production process, $Z^* \rightarrow H^0 A^0$ has adequate event rate is limited by the machine energy to $m_{A^0} \sim m_{H^0} \leq \sqrt{s_{ee}}/2 - 20$ GeV ($m_{H^0} \sim m_{A^0}$ for large m_{A^0}) [24]. At $\sqrt{s_{ee}} = 500$ GeV, this means $m_{A^0} \leq 230$ GeV. As $e^+e^- \rightarrow H^+ H^-$ is also limited to $m_{H^\pm} \sim m_{A^0} \leq (220 \div 230)$ GeV, it could happen that only a rather SM-like h^0 is detected in e^+e^- mode of the linear collider, and none of the other Higgs bosons are observed. On the other hand, H^0 and A^0 can be singly produced as s-channel resonances in the $\gamma\gamma$ mode and PLC might allow the discovery of the H^0 and/or A^0 up to higher masses [9,24]. Particularly interesting decay channels at moderate $\tan\beta$ and below $t\bar{t}$ threshold are $H^0 \rightarrow h^0 h^0$ (leading to a final state containing four b quarks) and $A^0 \rightarrow Z h^0$. These channels are virtually background free unless $m_h^0 \sim m_W$, in which case the large $\gamma\gamma \rightarrow W^+ W^-$ continuum background would have to be eliminated by b-tagging. Discovery of the A^0 or H^0 up to about $0.8\sqrt{s_{ee}}$ would be possible. For large $\tan\beta$, the detection of the A^0 or H^0 in the $b\bar{b}$ channel should be possible for masses $\leq 0.8\sqrt{s_{ee}}$ [9,24], provided that effective luminosities as high as 200 fb^{-1} can be accumulated.

3 Gauge boson physics

Without the discovery of a Higgs boson at LEP2, LHC or linear collider, the best alternative to study the symmetry breaking sector lies in the study of the self-couplings of the W. The PLC will be the dominant source of the W^+W^- pairs at future linear colliders due to the reaction $\gamma\gamma \rightarrow W^+W^-$ with the large cross section, that fast reaches at high energies its asymptotic value $\sigma_W = 8\pi\alpha^2/M_W^2 \approx 81$ pb, which is at least an order of magnitude larger than the cross section of W^+W^- production in e^+e^- collisions. With the rate of about 1–3 million of W pairs per year PLC can be really considered as a W factory and an ideal place to conduct precision tests on the anomalous triple [3, 25, 26] and quartic [3] couplings of the W bosons.

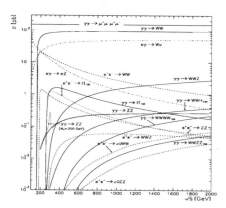

Figure 3: The cross sections of some processes in $\gamma\gamma$, γe and e^+e^- collisions.

The cross sections of main processes with the W and Z production at PLC within SM are shown in Fig. 3 [27]. When the energy increases, the cross sections of a number of higher–order processes become large enough.

In spite of enormous WW event rates, prospects to improve the precision of the measurement of the W mass at LEP2 seem to be quite limited. The reason is that the best estimated error on M_W of $30 \div 40$ MeV [28] is extracted from the direct reconstruction of invariant mass of the W decay products by a kinematical fit using the constraints of energy and momentum conservation. Since the energy of colliding photons is not so precisely fixed this method would not be effective at the PLC.

At $\sqrt{s} = 500$ GeV the benefits of the reaction $\gamma\gamma \rightarrow W^+W^-$ are clearly visible [26] in Fig. 4, since when combined with the bounds from $e^+e^- \rightarrow W^+W^-$ the parameter space shrinks considerably. Since only one combination of triple anomalous couplings (corresponding to W anomalous magnetic moment) contributes to the reaction $\gamma\gamma \rightarrow W^+W^-$ the allowed region is constrained to be between two planes, while $e^+e^- \rightarrow W^+W^-$ being sensitive to several anomalous couplings constrains the parameter space outside the ellipsoid.

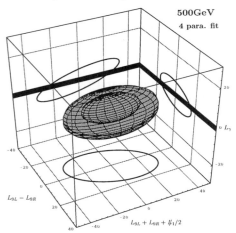

Figure 4: The tri-dimensional bounds in the case of 4 different anomalous couplings for a fit at $\sqrt{s} = 500$ GeV [26]. The ellipsoid represents the e^+e^- constraints, while $\gamma\gamma$ bounds are shown as two band projections on the planes.

With the natural order of magnitude on anomalous couplings [29], one needs to know the SM cross sections with a precision better than 1% to extract these small numbers. The predictions for W pair production, including full electroweak radiative corrections in the SM are known with very little theoretical uncertainty at least for energies below 1 TeV [30,31].

Although the cross section of WW production is much larger in $\gamma\gamma$ collisions, this fact itself is not to be considered as an obvious advantage of PLC. The reason is that although the anomalous contribution to the amplitude of longitudinal $W_L W_L$ pair production is enhanced by a factor of s/M_W^2 both in $\gamma\gamma$ for $J_z = 0$ and e^+e^- collisions, the SM amplitude of $W_L W_L$ production at PLC is suppressed as M_W^2/s, so that the contribution of the interference term to the total cross section is decreasing as $1/s$ at PLC [26]. On the contrary, in e^+e^- collisions the anomalous contribution is enhanced, corresponding to non-decreasing cross section of $W_L W_L$ production. Recently the authors of Ref. [26] have demonstrated that enhanced coupling could still be exploited in the $\gamma\gamma$ mode. Their clever idea is to reconstruct the non diagonal elements of the WW polarization density matrix by analyzing the distributions of the decay products of the W's, thereby achieving the improvement over simple counting rate method of more that an order of magnitude at $\sqrt{s} = 2$ TeV. However, although the benefits from $\gamma\gamma$ mode are evident at $\sqrt{s} = 500$ GeV, at energies above 1 TeV combining results from e^+e^- and $\gamma\gamma$ modes does not considerably reduce the bounds obtained from $e^+e^- \to W^+W^-$ alone [26]. This is especially true for fits with one anomalous coupling. Qualitatively these results can be understood considering the ratio $S/\sqrt{B}$ as a measure of statistical significance of the anomalous coupling signal S with respect to the SM background B. Since the total SM cross section is decreasing as $1/s$ in e^+e^- collisions and is constant $\gamma\gamma$ collisions, while the enhanced anomalous cross section behaves like a constant we get $S(e^+e^- \to W^+W^-)/\sqrt{B(e^+e^- \to W^+W^-)} \propto \sqrt{s}$, while $S(\gamma\gamma \to W^+W^-)/\sqrt{B(\gamma\gamma \to W^+W^-)} \propto 1$. If we take into account that anomalous couplings affect mostly the cross section in the central region, where the SM cross section behaves like $\sigma(\gamma\gamma \to W^+W^-) \sim 8\pi\alpha^2/p_T^2$, we get $S(\gamma\gamma \to W^+W^-)/\sqrt{B(\gamma\gamma \to W^+W^-)} \propto p_T$, *i.e.* the same improvement at higher energy as for e^+e^- collisions only for large values of $p_T \sim s$ cut, with which the cross section of WW production in $\gamma\gamma$ collisions is not enhanced with respect to production in e^+e^- collisions any more.

The process of W production with the highest cross section in γe collisions, $\gamma e \to W\nu$, with the asymptotic cross section of $\sigma_{\gamma e} \to W\nu = \sigma_W/8\sin^2\Theta_W \approx 43$ pb, is very sensitive to the admixture of right–handed currents in W coupling with fermions and could be used to constrain the anomalous magnetic moment of W [25]. Another example of the asymmetry, that could be used for the measurement of the W-boson anomalous magnetic and quadrupole moments has been proposed recently [32] and is given by the so called polarization asymmetry $A^{+-} = (\sigma_{++} - \sigma_{+-})/(\sigma_{++} + \sigma_{+-})$, where $\sigma_{\lambda_\gamma\lambda_e}$ is the polarized cross section of the reaction $\gamma e \to W\nu$. Using a quantum loop expansion it was shown that must be a center of mass energy where the polarization asymmetry possesses a zero. The position of the zero may be determined with sufficient precision to constrain the anomalous couplings of the W to better than the 1% level at 500 GeV [32]. At higher energies the same problems as those discussed for W pair production in $\gamma\gamma$ collisions appear.

At higher energy the effective W luminosity becomes substantial enough to allow for the study of $W^+W^- \to W^+W^-$, ZZ scattering in the reactions $\gamma\gamma \to WWWW$, $WWZZ$, when each incoming photon turns into a virtual WW pair, followed by the scattering of one W from each such pair to form WW or ZZ [2,3,33,34]. The result is that a signal of SM Higgs boson with m_h up to 700 GeV (1 TeV) could be probed in these processes at 1.5 TeV (2 TeV) PLC, assuming integrated luminosity of 200 fb^{-1} (300 fb^{-1}). However even larger luminosity is needed in order to extract the signal of enhanced $W_L W_L$ production in models of electroweak symmetry breaking without Higgs boson [33,34]. The main problem is again large background from transverse $W_T W_T W_T W_T$, $W_T W_T Z_T Z_T$ production.

4 Conclusions

Photon Linear Collider based on e^+e^- collider with $\sqrt{s} = 500$ GeV

– provides unique opportunities to measure $\Gamma(h^0 \rightarrow \gamma\gamma)$ up to $m_h \lesssim$ 350 GeV, making possible with the use of NLC and LHC measurements to measure $\Gamma_{tot}(h^0)$ and Higgs boson partial widths;

– substantially extends NLC reach in discovering heavy Higgs states H^0, A^0 in extended Higgs models such as MSSM;

– can provide much more stringent complementary bounds on W anomalous couplings.

One can fully exploit PLC potential at higher energies $\sqrt{s_{\gamma\gamma}} \sim 1 \div 2$ TeV if luminosity much higher than in e^+e^- collisions is achievable [1]

Acknowledgments

I am grateful to the organizers of the Workshop for financial support and warm hospitality. This work was supported by the Alexander von Humboldt Foundation.

References

1. V.I. Telnov, these proceedings.
2. S.Brodsky, *Proc.of Workshop on Physics and Exper.with Linear e^+e^- Colliders*, Waikoloa, Hawaii, World Scientific, 1993, p.295.
3. M. Baillargeon, G. Belanger, and F. Boudjema, Proc. of the *"Two-Photon Physics from DAΦNE to LEP200 and Beyond"*, 1994.
4. S.Brodsky, P.Zerwas, *Nucl.Instr.&Meth.* **A355**(1995)19.
5. M.Chanowitz, *Nucl.Instr.&Meth.* **A355**(1995)42.
6. I.Ginzburg, *Proc.of Workshop 'Photon 95'*, Sheffield, UK, 1995 and these proceedings.
7. G. Belanger, *Proc.of Workshop 'Photon 95'*, Sheffield, UK, 1995.
8. T. Barklow, *Proc. of the 1990 DPF Summer Study on High-Energy Physics: "Research Directions for the Decade"*, Snowmass, CO, 1990, p. 440.
9. J.F. Gunion and H.E. Haber, *Phys. Rev.* **D48** (1993) 5109.
10. D.Borden,D.Bauer,D.Caldwell, *SLAC-PUB*-5715, *UCSD-HEP*-92-01.

11. J.F. Gunion, L. Poggioli, R. Van Kooten, C. Kao, P. Rowson, *Proc. of the 1996 DPF/DPB Summer Study on "New Directions in High Energy Physics"*, 1996, Snowmass, Colorado, UCD-97-5, 1997, hep-ph/9703330.

12. A. Djouadi, J. Kalinowski, M. Spira, preprint DESY-97-079, hep-ph/9704448.

13. D.L. Borden, D.A. Bauer, D.O. Caldwell, Phys. Rev. **D48** (1993) 4018.

14. G.L. Kane, G.D. Kribs, S.P. Martin and J.D. Wells, *Phys. Rev.* **D53** (1996) 213.

15. A. Bartl et al., Report LBL-39413, *Proc. of 1996 DPF/DPB Summer Study on New Directions for High-Energy Physics)*, Snowmass, CO, 1996.

16. O.J.P. Éboli, M.C. Gonzalez-Garcia, F. Halzen, and D. Zeppenfeld, *Phys. Rev.* **D48** (1993) 1430.

17. G. Jikia, A. Tkabladze, *Nucl. Instr. & Meth.* **A355** (1995) 81; *Phys. Rev.* **D54** (1996) 2030;

18. D. L. Borden, V. A. Khoze, W. J. Stirling, and J. Ohnemus, *Phys. Rev.* **D50** (1994) 4499; V. Khoze, in *Proc.of Workshop 'Photon 95'*, Sheffield, UK, 1995, p. 392.

19. M. Baillargeon, G. Belanger and F. Boudjema, *Phys. Rev.* **D51** (1995) 4712.

20. T. Ohgaki and T. Takahashi, preprint HUPD-9705, AJC-HEP-30, hep-ph/9703301, these proceedings.

21. V.S. Fadin, V.A. Khoze and A.D. Martin, preprint DTP/97/14, hep-ph/9703402.

22. G. Jikia, Phys.Lett. **B298** (1993) 224; *Nucl. Phys.* **B405** (1993) 24; M.S. Berger *Phys. Rev.* **D48** (1993) 5121; D.A. Dicus and C. Kao, *Phys. Rev.* **D49** (1994) 1265.

23. B. Grzadkowski and J.F. Gunion, *Phys. Lett.* **B294**, 261 (1992); J.F. Gunion and J. Kelly, *Phys. Lett.* **B333** (1994) 110; M. Krämer, J. Kün, M.I. Stong and P.M. Zerwas, *Z. Phys.* **C64** (1994) 21; G.J. Gounaris and G.P. Tsirigoti, preprint THES-TP 97/03, hep-ph/9703446.

24. J.F. Gunion, A. Stange, S. Willenbrock, Report UCD-95-28, 1995, hep-ph/9602238.

25. S.Y.Choi, F.Shrempp, Phys.Lett. **B272** (1991) 149; E.Yehudai, Phys. Rev. **D44** (1991) 3434.

26. M. Baillargeon, G. Bélanger and F. Boudjema, preprint ENSLAPP-A-639/97, hep-ph/9701372.

27. M. Baillargeon et al., *DESY 96-123D* (1996) 229.

28. Z. Kunszt and W.J. Stirling, Workshop on LEP2 Physics, hep-ph/9602352.

29. F. Boudjema, in Physics and Experiments with Linear e^+e^- Colliders, Morioka, Japan, 1995.
30. A. Denner, S. Dittmaier, and R. Schuster, *Nucl. Phys.* **B452** (1995) 80; Report BI-TP 96/03, WUE-ITP-96-001, hep-ph/9601355.
31. G. Jikia, Proc. of the Workshop Physics and Experiments with Linear e^+e^- Colliders, Morioka, Japan, 1995; *Nucl. Phys.* **B494** (1997) 19.
32. S.J. Brodsky and I. Schmidt, *Phys. Lett.* **B351** (1995) 344; S.J. Brodsky, T.G. Rizzo and I. Schmidt, *Phys. Rev.* **D52** (1995) 4929.
33. G. Jikia, *Nucl. Instr. & Meth.* **A355** (1995) 84; *Nucl. Phys.* **B437** (1995) 520.
34. K. Cheung, *Phys. Lett.* **B323** (1994) 85; *Phys. Rev.* **D50** (1994) 4290.

SOME NEW POSSIBILITIES FOR PHOTON COLLIDERS

ILYA F. GINZBURG[a]

Institute of Mathematics, 630090, Novosibirsk, Russia.

Three different themes are joined here with following results:

1. A Photon collider is the best place for discovery of Higgs with mass ≤ 200 GeV and for its detail study.

2. $Z\gamma$ interactions could be studied well at an $e\gamma$ collider with polarized electrons (mainly, following).

3. In the conversion $e \to \gamma$ one can use very high density of laser photons (as compared with earlier estimates).

1 Higgs boson at photon collider

In the SM, Higgs fields can belong several isotopic doublets, triplets etc. So, the main problems for the physics of Higgs boson look as follows:

1. To discover something and to measure its mass.

2. To test spin.

3. To test parity.

4. To measure couplings with particles — to test Higgs mechanism of mass origin.

5. To measure total width Γ_{tot}.

6. To measure two photon width $\Gamma_{\gamma\gamma}$ – the counter for particles in SM with $M > M_H$.

Most of these properties will be obtained by the combination of results from different colliders.[1] Nevertheless, the results from a single collider are preferable since the influence of systematical inaccuracies can be reduced much more strong. In table 1 we compare the potential of different colliders for the enumerated problems.

Below we consider the minimal variant of SM — Higgs boson is an isotopic doublet.

If Higgs boson mass $M_H > 2M_Z$, it can be discovered at LHC, photon colliders or e^+e^- linear colliders via the sizable decay mode $H \to ZZ$ with

---

[a]E-mail: ginzburg@math.nsc.ru

problem	Tevatron–LHC	e^+e^- linear collider	Photon collider	$\mu^+\mu^-$ collider
Discovery	+	+	$M_H \leq 400\text{GeV}$	$M_H > 400\text{GeV}$
Mass	+	+	+	The best
Spin	Poor	Poor	+	+
Parity	—	—	The best^b	+
Γ_{tot}	Poor	Poor	At $M_H > 200$ GeV	The best
$\Gamma_{\gamma\gamma}$	Poor	—	The best	—

Table 1:

small background. If $M_H < 145$ GeV, Higgs boson can be discovered at e^+e^- linear colliders or photon colliders via the dominant decay mode $H \to b\bar{b}$ and at LHC – via the decay mode $H \to \gamma\gamma$.

The mass range $M_H = 140 - 190$ GeV is most difficult one for the Higgs discovery. Here the decay mode $H \to W^+W^-$ with real or virtual W's ($W^* \to q\bar{q}, e\bar{\nu}, ...$) is dominant, branching ratios of other decay modes are small, and their using for Higgs boson discovery is very difficult. The use of $H \to W^+W^-$ decay at e^+e^- collider is also difficult due to a strong nonresonant W^+W^- background.

The Higgs boson with $M_H = 140 - 190$ GeV can be discovered at the photon collider in the $\gamma\gamma \to W^+W^-$ reaction[3]:

As it was noted earlier[4], photon collider provides new opportunity for the discussed mass interval. Indeed, Higgs boson production cross section averaged over wide enough range of M_{WW} is $< \sigma_{\gamma\gamma \to H} > = 4\pi^2\Gamma_{\gamma\gamma}/M_H^3 \approx 1$ pb in the considered mass range (it depends on M_H weakly) and down to $M_H = 145$ GeV the W^+W^- decay mode remains dominant. On the other hand, the QED background decreases fast with decrease in M_{WW}.

The motivation of paper was large interference of $\gamma\gamma \to H \to WW$ and nonresonant QED amplitudes at $M_{WW} \approx 200$ GeV[5]. The results of similar calculations (without interference effects and with nonrealistic forms of photon spectra) were reported in ref.[6].

The basic equation is ($\mathcal{M}^0$ is the QED amplitude, $\mathcal{M}^H$ is the Higgs amplitude):

$$d\sigma \propto |\mathcal{M}|^2 \equiv |\mathcal{M}^0|^2 + 2Re(\mathcal{M}^{0*}\mathcal{M}^H) + |\mathcal{M}^H|^2. \tag{1}$$

At 170 GeV $< M_H < 250$ GeV this equation gives two–peak curve with peaks obliged by interference item. Below the nominal threshold $M_{WW} = 2M_W$ this process takes place also — due to final width of W boson. The final

4–fermion state is described as W^*W^* state (usually WW^*) with off shell W–bosons W^* having masses M_i.

Close to the threshold, the $\gamma\gamma \to W^+W^-$ cross section can be approximated as:

$$\sigma \propto |\mathcal{M}|^2_{s=4M_W^2}\ \beta \Rightarrow |\mathcal{M}|^2_{s=4M_W^2}\ \tilde{\beta};\quad \beta = \frac{1}{s}\sqrt{(s-s_1-s_2)^2-4s_1s_2}\ ; \quad (2)$$

$$\tilde{\beta} = \int ds_1 ds_2\ \varrho(s_1)\ \varrho(s_2)\ \beta(s,s_1,s_2)\ \theta(s_1)\ \theta(s_2)\ \theta(\sqrt{s}-\sqrt{s_1}-\sqrt{s_2}). \quad (3)$$

The first of these equations relates to the stable W's, the second one takes into account effect of finite width. Here β is the relative velocity of W bosons in the c.m.s. ($M_i = M_W$) and $\varrho(M)$ is the Breit–Wigner spectral density for W boson.

The obtained cross section is shown in Fig. 1 for the initial state with mean helicity of photons $< \lambda_i > = 1$ (total helicity — 0) and for production angles $20° < \theta < 160°$.

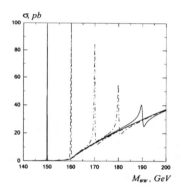

Fig.1. The $\gamma\gamma \Rightarrow WW$ cross sections for different M_H.

After averaging over initial photon energy distribution, the Higgs boson signal decreases and seems hardly observable (this very fact was pointed out in recent ref. [7]). To avoid this difficulty, the observation of W bosons in the final state with fixing of M_{WW} is mandatory (perhaps, via quark jets). To account a finite resolution in M_{WW}, we consider a "smeared" cross section:

$$\frac{d\sigma}{dM_{WW}^{meas}} = \int \frac{dM_{WW}}{\sqrt{2\pi}\ d} \exp\left[-\frac{(M_{WW}^{meas}-M_{WW})^2}{2d^2}\right]\frac{d\sigma}{dM_{WW}}. \quad (4)$$

We do not make any convolution with initial photon spectra. It is because of the fact that the real form of these effective spectra strongly depends on the details of the conversion design. We have in mind "monochromatic" variant of the photon collider with the effective width of the $\gamma\gamma$ energy distribution $\sim 15\%$. The results for $d = 5$ GeV are shown in Figs. 2, 3 and in table 2. The table represents also the effect of "realistic" polarization of initial photon beams. (Here $< \lambda >$ is mean photon helicity.)

So, the effect is about 1 pb in the discussed energy interval. Therefore, the luminosity integral about 1 fb⁻¹ is sufficient to see this Higgs, define its mass, spin and parity.

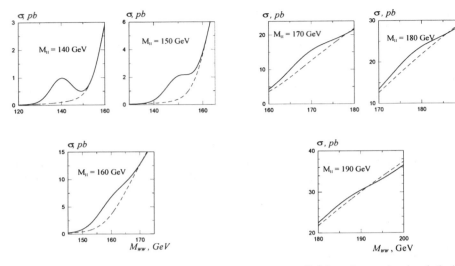

Fig.2. Smeared cross sections below the threshold.
Dashed lines - nonresonant background.

Fig.3. Smeared cross sections above the threshold.
Dashed lines - nonresonant background.

The similar calculation for ZZ production below nominal threshold gives Higgs contribution $< \sigma > \sim$ 50 fb almost without nonresonant background. Therefore, with the luminosity integral $\sim$ 10 fb^{-1} one can also observe a Higgs boson in ZZ decay mode in the discussed region of M_H.

2 The study of $Z\gamma$ interactions in γe collisions [8]

The study of anomalous interactions of gauge bosons (anomalies) is the key for seeing the world beyond SM. The observed deviation from SM predictions will be signature of some anomaly and the separation of the anomaly responsible for this effect will be the next problem. Unfortunately, these anomalies exhibit itself in the observed processes in complex combinations so that it is difficult often to separate their effects.

The γe and $\gamma\gamma$ colliders provide opportunity to see γWW anomalies without admixture of ZWW in the processes $\gamma e \rightarrow W\nu$ and $\gamma\gamma \rightarrow W^+W^-$. The possibility to separate effects of $Z\gamma$ interactions seems very important in this respect.

The $Z^*\gamma X$ interaction with high enough rate can be studied via the process $e\gamma \rightarrow eX$ ($X = t\bar{t}$, W^+W^-, H, ...). This interaction will be observed here simultaneously with $\gamma\gamma X$ interaction. The last gives usually main contribu-

M_H, GeV	M_{WW}, GeV	$< \lambda >$	σ^{bkgd}, pb	σ^{tot}, pb	$\dfrac{\sigma^{tot} - \sigma^{bkgd}}{\sigma^{bkgd}}$
140	140	1.0	0.11	0.98	8.0
		0.9	0.17	0.96	4.6
150	150	1.0	0.42	2.10	4.0
		0.9	0.60	2.13	2.6
160	159.7	1.0	3.65	6.81	87%
		0.9	4.86	7.74	59%
170	169.3	1.0	12.6	15.5	23%
		0.9	16.0	18.5	16%
180	178.5	1.0	21.8	23.7	8.7%
		0.9	25.3	27.0	6.7%
190	185	1.0	26.0	27.0	3.8%
	200		37.3	36.5	-2.1%
	185	0.9	29.9	30.8	3.0%
	200		40.2	39.4	-2.0%

Table 2:

tion.

We consider collisions with (longitudinally) polarized electrons. Let σ^L and σ^R are the cross sections for light–hand polarized and right–hand polarized electron. Taking into account only the diagrams with photon and Z boson exchanges (other diagrams contribute negligibly) one can connect these cross sections with contributions of vector current M_V and axial current M_A. The M_A is obliged to interaction of incident photon with Z^* (J^Z), in the good approximation $M_V \propto J^\gamma$:

$$M_V = \frac{1}{Q^2}J^\gamma + \frac{1/4 - \sin^2\theta_W}{Q^2 + M_Z^2}J_V^Z; \quad M_A = \frac{1}{Q^2 + M_Z^2}J_A^Z. \tag{5}$$

With these notations

$$\sigma_{L,R} \propto |M_V \pm M_A|^2; \tag{6}$$

These cross sections differs markedly at $Q^2 > (2 \div 3) \cdot 10^3$ Gev^2, when Z boson denominator is comparable with photon denominator. So, we can consider only the data with recording of scattered electron with such transferred momenta. The reliable accuracy in the extraction of Z contribution is possible here.

Most useful for analysis are quantities

$$\sigma^L - \sigma^R \propto Re(M_V^* M_A), \quad \sigma^L + \sigma^R \equiv 2\sigma_{nonpol} \propto (|M_V|^2 + |M_A|^2). \tag{7}$$

This program was realized (partially) for the reaction $\gamma e \to eWW$ [9] where $\sigma_L - \sigma_R \approx 3$ pb at $Q^2 > 2500$ GeV^2 for $\sqrt{s} \approx 2$ TeV (with $\sigma_{tot} \approx 22$ pb) and for reaction $\gamma e \to eH$ [10]. In particular, it was shown in [10] that in SM for $Q^2 > 10^4$ GeV^2 V and A contributions compensate each other almost entirely in σ_R. It shows high sensitivity of these experiments to $Z\gamma H$ anomalies.

3 The nonlinear QED effects in spectra of photons for photon colliders [11]

To obtain high energy photons for photon collider one should use the Compton backscattering of laser photons on the electrons (or positrons) of linear collider. To have high conversion coefficient and good quality of spectra of collided photons, it is necessary to focus laser light on the conversion region at some distance from collision point [12].

The conversion coefficient $e \to \gamma$ is calculated earlier provided the intensity of laser light to be not extremely high. The detail studies with taking into account expected parameters of various linear colliders show some advantages of higher intensity for construction of laser.

But, the effects of strong electromagnetic field in the conversion region change spectra. The variation of mean field strength within conversion region results in smearing of final spectra, so it seems that to have high quality of spectra the upper value of intensity should be limited from above strongly [13]. We show that real limitation is not so strong.

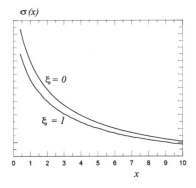

Figure 4: ξ^2/ξ_{max}^2 from t/t_{tot}.

There are two ideas in the basis of this statement:

- The main part of high energy photons is produced in the area of highest density of photons. Area with small density contribute weakly in the final spectra — see Fig. 4 (the curves here correspond different relations between the beam parameters).

- In the intensive field shift of upper bound of spectrum is accompanied by increasing of threshold energy for the e^+e^- pair production. So, to work with such field one can use laser photon with higher energy without large pair production.

The standard notations for the discussed problems are: E, ω_0 or ω are the energies of initial electron, laser photon γ_0 or produced photon; P_c and λ_e are the mean helicities of the laser photons and initial electrons, λ_γ – helicity of produced photon, λ is wave length of laser light, $\lambda_e \equiv \hbar/mc$ is the Compton wave length of electron. Besides,

$$x = \frac{4E\omega_0}{m^2c^4}; \quad y = \frac{\omega}{E}.$$

The basic for the description of these phenomena is *the nonlinearity parameter* ξ^2. It is defined via the mean (in time) value of the laser electromagnetic wave field strength squared F^2 or the volume density of laser photons n_γ:

$$\xi^2 = \left(\frac{eF\hbar}{m_e\omega_0 c}\right)^2 \equiv \frac{2\alpha}{\pi} V n_\gamma \quad (V = \pi\lambda_e^2\lambda). \tag{8}$$

Two treatments of this parameter are useful.

- The quantity $\xi^2 m_e^2 c^2$ is mean value of the electron transverse momentum squared in the field of laser light. It means that in the all equations we should change

$$m^2 \rightarrow m_*^2 \equiv m^2(1+\xi^2) \Rightarrow x \rightarrow x_* = \frac{x}{1+\xi^2}. \tag{9}$$

- The ξ^2 is the number of laser photons in the cylinder with the circle of Compton radius in the base and light wave length in the height, multiplied on $2\alpha/\pi$ (8). Therefore, the relative probability of the simultaneous collisions of several (n) laser photons with electron or earlier produced high energy photon is $\propto \xi^{2(n-1)}$.

$$n\gamma_0 + e \rightarrow e + \gamma; \quad n\gamma_0 + \gamma \rightarrow e^+e^-. \tag{10}$$

It is natural to treat such processes as those related by n–th harmonic.

In reality we deal with sums over harmonics — nonlinear Compton effect and nonlinear e^+e^- pair production.

We used equations for the probabilities of these processes from the papers.[14] (The experiments in this field were reported recently.[15]

The way of length dz within laser target with photon density n_γ corresponds to *the reduced optical thickness* of this laser target dt. So, the probability of some process in small region of strong EM field is proportional to dt:

$$dt = \pi r_e^2 n_\gamma dz; \quad dw \equiv W dt \quad (r_e = \alpha/m_e). \tag{11}$$

We denote quantity W as *reduced probability of process*. In the weak field the cross section of corresponding process in collision with one laser photon is $\sigma = W\pi r_e^2$. So, one can define effective cross section of non-linear Compton effect as $\sigma(\xi) \equiv W(\xi)\pi r_e^2$. Our calculations shows slow dependence of this quantity on ξ^2, this "cross section" decreases by $\sim 10\%$ with variation of ξ from 0 to 1 (see Fig. 5).

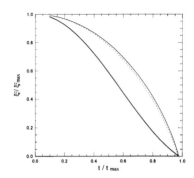

Figure 5: $\sigma(x)$ for $\xi = 0$ and $\xi = 1$.

The quality of photon spectrum is better (it is most sharp in the high energy) if quantity x is higher (and for $2\lambda_e P_c = -1$). However, even for low density of laser photons at $x > 4.8$ new process is switched on in the conversion region – e^+e^- pair production in collision of high energy photon with laser one. This process gives both background and losses of photons with highest energy, so $x \approx 5$ is considered usually as an upper value of x for the effective conversion.

In fact, even at low density of laser photons and $x < 4.8$ some fraction of e^+e^- pairs is produced, and one should remove both electrons and positrons from the collision region to reduce background. With the growth of density of laser photons the bounds for both processes considered are shifted, and new picture takes place.

At $\xi \neq 0$ the threshold for the e^+e^- pair production in the 1–st harmonics is shifted to $4\omega\omega_0 = 4(m_ec^2)^2(1+\xi^2) \Rightarrow x = 4.8(1+\xi^2)$. Therefore for the higher values of ξ one can use the laser photons with higher energy keeping in mind above limitation. Having in mind that more than one half of produced photons is produced from the region $\xi^2 > 0.6\xi_{max}^2$, we consider phenomena at $x = 4.8(1 + 0.6\xi_{max}^2$, that corresponds to $x = 7.68$ for $\xi = 1$.

For the first glance, the quality of spectrum become worse with the growth of ξ even with this growth of x: However, the real interest is related to the spectral distribution of luminosity, corresponding to the "monochromatic" variant of photon collider. For $x = 4.8$ it considers usually such distance b between conversion point and collision point that

$$b^2/(\gamma a_e)^2 = 0.4$$

(a_e is the electron bunch radius in the collision point without conversion.)

Fig. 6 shows this luminosity distribution for $\xi = 1$, $x = 7.68$ in comparison with that usually considered for $\xi = 0$, $x = 4.8$; solid lines are luminosities for total photon helicity 0 and dashed lines – for total photon helicity 2. It is

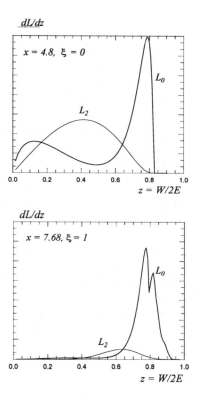

Figure 6: Luminosity spectrum for $\rho^2 = 0.4$ and a) $x = 4.8$, $\xi = 0$; b) $x = 7.68$, $\xi = 1$.

seen that with the growth of ξ the spectrum become slightly more wide, but it shifts to the higher energies. Besides, the degree of polarization is much better for the case $\xi = 1$.

So, high density of photons in conversion region, giving $\xi_{max}^2 \approx 1$, with corresponding increasing of laser photon energy can be considered in the R&D for the photon collider.

Acknowledgements

This work is supported by grants of INTAS–93–1180ext and RFBR 96-02-19114.

References

1. J.F. Gunion, L. Poggiolli and R. van Kooten, *hep-ph/9703330* (1997).
2. G.L. Kotkin, V.G. Serbo, *hep-ph* /96-11345, *report at this conference*.
3. I.F. Ginzburg, I.P. Ivanov, *hep-ph/9704220*.
4. I.F. Ginzburg, *"PHOTON'95"*, *Sheffield, World Sc. Singapore* (1995) 399–416.
5. D.A. Morris, T.N. Truong, D. Zappala, *Phys. Lett.* **B323** (1994) 421.
6. J.F. Gunion, H.E. Haber, *Phys. Rev.* **D48** (1993) 5109.
7. E.E.Boos, T.Ohl, *hep-ph/9705374.*
8. I.F. Ginzburg, V.A. Ilyin, *in preparation.*
9. I.F. Ginzburg, V.A. Ilyin, A. Pukhov, V.G. Serbo, *in preparation.*
10. Gabriele, V.A. Ilyin, B. Mele, *hep-ph/9702414*, I.F. Ginzburg, I.P. Ivanov, *in preparation.*
11. I.F. Ginzburg, G.L. Kotkin, V.G. Serbo, *in preparation.*
12. I.F. Ginzburg, G.L. Kotkin, V.G. Serbo and V.I. Telnov, *Sov. ZhETF Pis'ma* **34** (1981) 514; *NIMR* **205** (1983) 47; I.F. Ginzburg, G.L. Kotkin, S.L. Panfil, V.G. Serbo and V.I. Telnov, *NIMR* **219** (1983) 5.
13. V.I. Telnov, *NIMR* **A294**(1990) 72.
14. V.I. Ritus, A.I. Nikishov, *Trudy FIAN* **111** (1979).
15. Bula et al. *Phys. Rev. Lett.* **76** (1996) 3116.

A POSSIBILITY TO CONTROL THE POLARIZATION OF HIGH-ENERGY PHOTONS BY MEANS OF A LASER BEAM

G.L. KOTKIN, V.G. SERBO

Novosibirsk State University, 630090, Novosibirsk, Russia

E-mail: serbo@math.nsc.ru

The elastic light-light scattering below the threshold of the e^+e^- pair production leads to a variation in polarization of hard γ-quanta traversing (without loss) a region where the laser light is focused. This effect can be used to control the γ-quantum polarization. Equations are obtained which determine the variation of Stokes parameters of γ-quanta in this case, and their solutions are given. It is pointed out that this effect can be observed in the experiment of the type of E-144 at SLAC. It should be taken into account and, perhaps, it can be used in experiments at future $\gamma\gamma$ colliders.

1 Introduction

It is well known that a region with an electric and magnetic fields can be regarded as anisotropic medium (see, for example, [1] §129-130 and [2]). A possibility to consider a bunch of laser photons as a "crystal" is pointed out in Ref. [3], but the concrete calculations of this possibility are not given.

In the present paper we study in detail properties of such a "crystal" considering head-on collision of hard γ-quanta with the bunch of polarized laser photons. For the energy of γ-quanta below the threshold of the e^+e^- pair production $\hbar\omega < \hbar\omega_{\rm th} = m_e^2 c^4/(\hbar\omega_L)$ (here $\hbar\omega_L$ is the laser photon energy) the main interaction is the elastic light-light scattering $\gamma\gamma_L \to \gamma\gamma_L$. Cross section of this process is very small $\lesssim \alpha^2 r_e^2$ (here r_e is the electron classical radius). Therefore, the laser bunch is practically transparent for such γ-quanta. On the other hand, the variation in polarization for the γ-quantum traversing the bunch is determined by the interference of the incoming wave and the wave scattered at zero angle. As a result, in this case the essential variation in the γ-quantum polarization can occur practically without loss in intensity of γ-quanta. This effect can be interesting for the following reasons:

(i) It can be used to control the polarization of hard γ-quanta without loss in their intensity.

(ii) The experimental observation of variation in the γ-quantum polarization will be indirect observation the process of the elastic light-light scattering. The conditions close to those necessary for observation of such effect is realized now at SLAC in E-144 experiment [4].

(iii) The discussed problem is also actual in connection with projects of

$\gamma\gamma$ colliders which under development now (see Refs. [5],[6],[7]).

2   Equations for Stokes parameters of the γ-quantum

Let us consider the head-on collision of γ-quanta with the bunch of laser photons. We choose the z axis along the momenta of γ-quanta. The polarization state of γ-quantum is described by Stokes parameters $\xi_{1,2,3}$. In the helicity basis (λ, $\lambda' = \pm 1$) the density matrix of γ-quantum has the form (see, for example, Ref. [1] §8):

$$\rho^{\gamma}_{\lambda\lambda'} = \frac{1}{2} \begin{pmatrix} 1 + \xi_2 & -\xi_3 + i\xi_1 \\ -\xi_3 - i\xi_1 & 1 - \xi_2 \end{pmatrix} . \tag{1}$$

For the laser photon such a matrix $\rho^{L}_{\lambda\lambda'}$ is described by the following parameters: the degree of the circular polarization P_c, the degree of the linear polarization P_l and the direction of the linear polarization (let us choose the x axis along this direction). We will also use a compact expression describing the polarization of both photons $\rho_{\Lambda\Lambda'} = \rho^{\gamma}_{\lambda_1\lambda'_1} \rho^{L}_{\lambda_2\lambda'_2}$.

As is well known the variations in intensity and polarization of the wave passing through a medium are due to interference it with the wave scattered at zero angle. Let the incoming wave has the form $A_\Lambda e^{ikz}$. Here the amplitude A_Λ describes the polarization state of the γ-quantum and the laser photon, the wave vector $k = \omega/c$ (the frequency of laser photon $\omega_L \ll \omega$). When the wave passes through a "target" layer of a thickness dz it is appeared the forward scattered wave

$$f_{\Lambda\Lambda'} A_{\Lambda'} 2n_L \, dz \int \frac{e^{ikr}}{r} \, dx \, dy = \frac{2\pi i}{k} f_{\Lambda\Lambda'} A_{\Lambda'} 2n_L \, dz \, e^{ikz} = dA_\Lambda e^{ikz} , \tag{2}$$

where $f_{\Lambda\Lambda'}$ is the forward amplitude for the process of elastic scattering light by light and n_L is the concentration of the laser photons. The factor 2 in front of n_L is due to relative motion of the γ-quanta and the "target".

The matrix $\rho_{\Lambda\Lambda'}$ is expressed trough the product of A_Λ as follows: $\rho_{\Lambda\Lambda'} = \langle A_\Lambda A^*_{\Lambda'} \rangle / N$, $N = \langle A_\Lambda A^*_\Lambda \rangle$, where $\langle ... \rangle$ denotes a statistical averaging. The quantity N is proportional to the γ-quantum intensity J. When the wave passes through the layer of a thickness dz its relative variation in intensity is equal to

$$\frac{dJ}{J} = \frac{dN}{N} = \frac{2}{N} \operatorname{Re} \langle dA_\Lambda A^*_\Lambda \rangle = -\frac{4\pi}{k} \operatorname{Im} (f_{\Lambda\Lambda'} \rho_{\Lambda'\Lambda}) 2n_L \, dz = -\sigma_{\gamma\gamma} 2n_L dz , \tag{3}$$

where $\sigma_{\gamma\gamma}$ is the total cross section for the light-light scattering. Analogously,

$$d\rho_{\Lambda\Lambda'} = d\frac{\langle A_\Lambda A^*_{\Lambda'}\rangle}{N} = \frac{2\pi i}{k}\left(f_{\Lambda\Lambda''}\rho_{\Lambda''\Lambda'} - f^*_{\Lambda'\Lambda''}\rho_{\Lambda\Lambda''}\right)2n_L dz - \rho_{\Lambda\Lambda'}\frac{dN}{N}. \quad (4)$$

Among the five independent helicity amplitude $f_{\Lambda\Lambda'} \equiv f_{\lambda_1\lambda_2\lambda'_1\lambda'_2}$ only three ones are not equal zero for the forward scattering, namely f_{++++}, f_{+-+-}, f_{++--}. We will use further the following real dimensionless quantities R and I proportional correspondingly to the real and imaginary parts of the scattering amplitudes:

$$\frac{4\pi}{k}\frac{1}{2}\mathrm{Im}(f_{++++} + f_{+-+-}) = \pi r_e^2\, I_{np}\,, \quad (5)$$

$$\frac{4\pi}{k}\frac{1}{2}(f_{++++} - f_{+-+-}) = \pi r_e^2\,(R_c+iI_c)\,, \quad \frac{4\pi}{k}\frac{1}{2}f_{++--} = \pi r_e^2\,(R_l+iI_l)\,. \quad (6)$$

As a result, we obtain the expression for the cross section $\sigma_{\gamma\gamma} = \pi r_e^2\,(I_{np} + \xi_2 P_c\, I_c + \xi_3 P_l\, I_l)$ and equations for Stokes parameters. To write down these equations it is convenient to introduce the quantity $dt = 2\pi r_e^2\,n_L dz$ which we will call the reduced optical thickness of the layer dz. Then

$$d\xi_1/dt = (-R_c\xi_3 + I_c\xi_1\xi_2)\,P_c + (R_l\xi_2 + I_l\xi_1\xi_3)\,P_l\,,$$

$$d\xi_2/dt = -I_c(1 - \xi_2^2)\,P_c + (-R_l\xi_1 + I_l\xi_2\xi_3)\,P_l\,, \quad (7)$$

$$d\xi_3/dt = (R_c\xi_1 + I_c\xi_2\xi_3)\,P_c - I_l\,(1 - \xi_3^2)\,P_l\,.$$

The forward scattering amplitudes (and, therefore, quantities R and I) depend on the single variable $r = \omega/\omega_{\mathrm{th}}$. Using for amplitudes $f_{\lambda_1\lambda_2\lambda'_1\lambda'_2}$ formulas from Refs. [8] and [1] §127 we obtain

$$I_{np} = 0 \quad \text{at} \quad r < 1\,;$$

$$I_{np} = u\left[2(1 + u - 0.5u^2)\cosh^{-1}\sqrt{r} - (1 + u)\sqrt{1 - u}\,\right] \quad \text{at} \quad r > 1\,,$$

$$R_c+iI_c = (2/\pi)u(-3B_- + T_-)\,, \quad R_l+iI_l = (1/\pi)u\left(1 + uB_- + 0.5u^2 T_+\right)\,, \quad (8)$$

where $u = 1/r$ and

$$B_- = \begin{cases} \sqrt{u-1}\sin^{-1}\sqrt{r} - \sqrt{u+1}\sinh^{-1}\sqrt{r} & \text{at } r < 1 \\ \sqrt{1-u}\cosh^{-1}\sqrt{r} - \sqrt{u+1}\sinh^{-1}\sqrt{r} - i(\pi/2)\sqrt{1-u} & \text{at } r > 1, \end{cases}$$

$$T_\pm = \begin{cases} -(\sin^{-1}\sqrt{r})^2 \pm (\sinh^{-1}\sqrt{r})^2 & \text{at } r < 1 \\ -(\pi^2/4) + (\cosh^{-1}\sqrt{r})^2 \pm (\sinh^{-1}\sqrt{r})^2 - i\pi\cosh^{-1}\sqrt{r} & \text{at } r > 1. \end{cases}$$

Note that extremums of R_c and R_l are at the threshold of the pair production: $R_c = 0.315$, $R_l = -0.348$ at $r = 1$.

3 A laser bunch as a transparent anisotropic medium

A laser bunch becomes transparent for γ-quanta with the energy $\omega < \omega_{\text{th}}$. If the laser photons are linearly polarized ($P_l \neq 0$, $P_c = 0$), the solution of Eqs. (7) has the form

$$\xi_1 = \xi_1^0 \cos \varphi_l + \xi_2^0 \sin \varphi_l \,, \quad \xi_2 = -\xi_1^0 \sin \varphi_l + \xi_2^0 \cos \varphi_l \,, \quad \xi_3 = \xi_3^0 \,, \qquad (9)$$

where the phase $\varphi_l = P_l R_l t$ and ξ_i^0 are the initial Stokes parameters. It is seen from this solution that in this case the laser bunch is an anisotropic medium with different refraction indices n_x and n_y along the x and y axes: $n_x - n_y = \frac{c}{\omega} 2\pi r_e^2 n_L P_l R_l$. Such a medium transforms the circular polarization of γ-quanta into the linear one and vice versa.

If the laser photons are circularly polarized ($P_c \neq 0$, $P_l = 0$), the solution of Eqs. (7) has another form

$$\xi_1 = \xi_1^0 \cos \varphi - \xi_3^0 \sin \varphi \,, \quad \xi_2 = \xi_2^0 \,, \quad \xi_3 = \xi_1^0 \sin \varphi + \xi_3^0 \cos \varphi \,, \qquad (10)$$

where the phase $\varphi = P_c R_c t$. From this solution it is seen that in this case the laser bunch is an gyrotropic medium.

Above the threshold of the $e^+ e^-$ pair production ($\omega > \omega_{\text{th}}$) the variation in the γ-quantum polarization is accompanied by a reduction in their intensity in accordance with Eq. (3).

4 Discussion.

1. Let us illustrate the magnitude of the discussed effects using as an example the parameters of the laser bunch given in Ref. [7] (they are close to the parameters which are realized in the experiment E-144 at SLAC [4]): $\hbar\omega_L = 1.18$ eV, the energy of the laser flash is 1 J, the laser bunch length is 1.8 ps, and the peak intensity is about 10^{18} W/cm^2. The reduced optical thickness for this flash is equal to $t = 1.4$. In this case the phases $\varphi_l = P_l R_l t$ and $\varphi = PRt$ which determine the magnitude of the effect can reach values $\approx 0.3t \sim 1$. According to Eqs. (9) and (10) it means that the variation in the γ-quantum polarization may be very large.

2. With the growth of the intensity of laser flash it is necessary to take into account the effects of intense electromagnetic fields (see Ref. [9] and literature therein) which we neglect in the present paper.

3. In the scheme of the $e \to \gamma$ conversion adopted for the $\gamma\gamma$ colliders, γ-quanta are produced inside the laser bunch. When such γ-quanta travel further in the laser bunch they can essentially vary their polarization. It should be noted, however, that for the optimal conversion the laser photons and the hardiest γ-quanta are circularly polarized [5],[7]. These γ-quanta conserve their polarization on the rest way through the bunch. But the γ-quanta with a lower energy have a fraction of the linear polarization, and the rotation of the direction of this linear polarization should be, generally speaking, taken into account.

4. The linear polarization of γ-quanta is needed for a number of interesting experiments. For example, in Ref. [10] it is stressed that the best way to determine the CP value of the neutral Higgs boson with the intermediate mass is to use $\gamma\gamma$ collisions with the parallel or perpendicular linear polarizations. However, the $\gamma\gamma$ luminosity for such polarization is considerable less then the luminosity for the circular one. Using the additional laser bunches to transform the circular polarization into the linear one may lead to the luminosity of the $\gamma\gamma$ collision with the linear polarizations close to that for the optimal conditions.

Acknowledgements

We are very grateful to I. Ginzburg, V. Maisheev, A. Melissinos, V. Mikhalev and A. Onuchin for useful discussions. This work is supported in part by the Russian Fund of Fundamental Researches (code No. 96–02–19079).

V.G. Serbo is very thankful to Organizing Committee for financial support and warm hospitality.

References

1. V.B. Beresteskii, E.M. Lifshitz, L.P. Pitaevskii, *Quantum Electrodynamics* (Pergamon, Oxford, 1982).
2. R. Cameron *et al.*, *Phys. Rev. D* **D47**, 3707 (1993).
3. V.A. Maisheev *et al.*, it Sov. J. ZhETF **101**, 1376 (1992).
4. C. Bula *et al.*, *Phys. Rev. Lett.* **76**, 3116 (1996).
5. I.F. Ginzburg *et al.*, *Pis'ma ZhETF* **34**, *514 (1981)*; *Nucl. Instrum. Methods* **205**, 47 (1983).
6. *Nucl. Instrum. Methods* **A355**, 1-194 (1995).
7. *Zeroth-Order Design Report for the Next Linear Collider*, Report No. SLAC-474, (May, 1996) v.2, 971-1042.
8. B. De Tollis, *Nuovo Chim.* **32**, 754 (1964) and **35**, 1182 (1965).
9. V.N. Baier *et al.*, *JETP* **69**, 1893 (1975).
10. M. Krämer *et al.*, *Z. Phys.* **C64**, 21 (1994).

MEASURING THE TWO-PHOTON DECAY WIDTH
OF INTERMEDIATE-MASS HIGGS AT A
PHOTON-PHOTON COLLIDER

T. OHGAKI and T. TAKAHASHI[a]
Department of Physics, Hiroshima University,
1-3-1 Kagamiyama, Higashi-Hiroshima, 739, Japan

I. WATANABE
Akita Keizai Hoka University Junior College
46-1 Morisawa, Sakura, Shimokitate, Akita, 010 Japan

Feasibility of a measurement of the partial decay width of the intermediate-mass Higgs boson into two photons at a photon-photon collider is studied by a simulation. It is found that the two-photon decay width can be measured with the statistical error of 7-8 % with the integrated luminosity of 10 fb^{-1}.

1 Introduction

It is well known that the measurement of two photon decay width of the Higgs boson provides us an important informatiom beyond the Standard model and photon-photon colliders are good places to play around [1]. Two photons couple to the Higgs boson through loop diagrams of massive charged particles, and contribution of any massive charged particles are not decoupled as long as their mass are originated by the Higgs mechanism. Therefore deviation of the measured two-photon width from the standard model (SM) prediction indicates additional contributions from unknown particles, and thus it is a signature of the new physics beyond SM which cannot be provided directly in the ordinary collider experiments. For example, the minimal extension of the standard model (MSSM) predicts the ratio of the two-photon decay widths $\Gamma(h^0 \rightarrow \gamma\gamma, \text{MSSM})/\Gamma(H \rightarrow \gamma\gamma, \text{SM})$ as much as 1.2 for the lightest Higgs boson around the mass of 120 GeV [2].

Since Higgs signals come from the total angular momentum $J = 0$ of two photon system while quark pairs are produced by $J_z = 0$ state, it is possible to enhance Higgs signals and suppress the $\gamma\gamma \rightarrow q\bar{q}$ background events. Recently, several authors reported that the effect of QCD corrections to $\gamma\gamma \rightarrow q\bar{q}$ is large and could be a serious source of background for a measurement of the intermediate-mass Higgs boson [1,3]. According to their studies, three-jet events from $J_z = 0$ state can mimic two-jet events and helicity suppression

---

[a]e-mail:tohrut@kekux1.kek.jp

by controlling the polarization of photon beams does not work due to gluon emission. In our study, the contribution of the QCD corrections to the cross section of the process $\gamma\gamma \to q\bar{q}$ is taken into account according to a paper by Jikia and Tkabladze[3] and the shapes of three-jet events are taken into account through a parton shower treatment of $q\bar{q}$ evolution[4].

In this work we fixed the mass of the Higgs boson at 120 GeV and estimated the feasibility in a realistic condition as;

- Calculating luminosity distribution of a photon-photon by a Monte Carlo simulation program CAIN[6].

- Generation of event according to the luminosity distribution.

- Detector simulation[7].

- QCD radiative correction

The detail of the work can be found elsewhere[5].

2 Photon-Photon Collision

In order to study the Higgs boson of 120 GeV, we prepared a set of parameter for a photon-photon collider based on e^+e^- of $\sqrt{s_{e+e-}}$=150 GeV. The energy of the laser photon is 4.18 eV which result in the maximum photon energy of 60 GeV. The combination of the polarization of the laser P_L and the electron P_e is chosen to be $P_L P_e = -1.0$ to make the photon spectrum peaked at its maximum energy. In order to enhance Higgs production and to suppress background events from quark pairs, helicity combination of two high-energy photons is chosen to make $J_z = 0$ state at the highest energy. A simulation program, CAIN, is used to estimate luminosity of the photon-photon collision and the calculated luminosity distribution is shown in fig. 1.

3 Event Generation and Detector Simulation

For the intermediate-mass Higgs, the cross section of $\gamma\gamma \to H \to b\bar{b}$ is described by a Breit-Wigner approximation,

$$\sigma_{\gamma\gamma \to H \to b\bar{b}} = 8\pi \frac{\Gamma(H \to \gamma\gamma)\Gamma(H \to b\bar{b})}{(s_{\gamma\gamma} - M_H^2)^2 + M_H^2\Gamma_H^2}(1 + \lambda_1\lambda_2), \qquad (1)$$

where $\sqrt{s_{\gamma\gamma}}$ is the $\gamma\gamma$ collision energy, $\Gamma(H \to \gamma\gamma)$, $\Gamma(H \to b\bar{b})$ and Γ_H are decay width of two photons, b quark pair and total width of the Higgs boson. λ_1 and λ_2 are initial photon helicities.

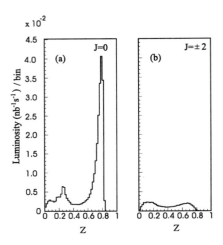

Figure 1: Luminosity distribution of the photon-photon collider of $\sqrt{s}_{e+e-}=150$ GeV at $P_L P_e = -1.0$. The bin size is 0.02. (a) Polarized luminosity distribution with the $J_z = 0$. (b) Polarized luminosity distribution with the $J_z = \pm 2$.

The effective production cross-section, obtained with convolution of luminosity distribution, and decay amplitude are calculated using BASES [9]. The decay branching ratios $Br(H \rightarrow b\bar{b})$, $Br(H \rightarrow c\bar{c})$, and $Br(H \rightarrow gg)$ are taken to be 64 %, 2.7 %, and 8.3 % which are calculated by HDECAY program [8]. Using the results from BASES, 4-momenta of $b\bar{b}$ pair from Higgs decay are generated by SPRING [9]. Subsequent hadronization of quark pairs is simulated by JETSET 7.3 [4] with the parton shower QCD correction.

The $\gamma\gamma \rightarrow q\bar{q}$ background events are generated in a similar way as in Higgs production, except that the production amplitude is calculated by a helicity amplitude calculation program HELAS [10]. As mentioned before, the shapes of three-jet events are taken into account through a parton shower treatment of $q\bar{q}$ evolution by JETSET7.3 and the total cross section calculated with the QCD corrections is applied to estimate $q\bar{q}$ background.

Signal and background events generated are fed into the detector simulator to estimate efficiency and background contamination. As a detector for a linear collider, the JLC detector is adapted [7]. The b-quark tagging by the vertex detector is crucial in this simulation. A CCD detector is assumed in the current JLC-I design and its impact parameter resolution is,

$$\sigma_d^2 = 11.4^2 + (28.8/p)^2/\sin^3\theta \ (\mu m^2), \qquad (2)$$

where p is the momentum of the charged particle in GeV/c, θ is the scattering

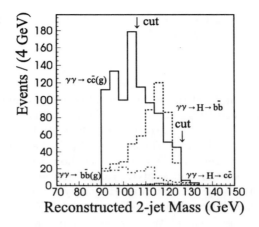

Figure 2: Mass distribution of two-jets with applying b-tagging requirements. An integrated luminosity of 10 fb^{-1} and standard model branching fractions for the Higgs boson are assumed. The effects of the QCD corrections to $\gamma\gamma \to q\bar{q}$ as background process are assumed.

angle.

4   Event Analysis

The analysis requires reconstruction of two-jet final states from the Higgs boson decay. The two jet events are chosen with JADE clustering algorithm [11] with y_{cut}=0.02. $|\cos\theta_{jet}| < 0.7$, where θ_{jet} is the scattering angle of the jet, is applied to make sure that events are well contained in the detector volume and to increase the ratio of signal events to backgrounds. A $b(\bar{b})$ jet is selected by requiring five or more tracks in each jet which has the normalized impact parameter $d/\sigma_d > 2.5$ and $d < 1.0$ mm in each jet, where d is the impact parameter. The tagging efficiency of $b\bar{b}$ events are found to be 0.65.

5   Results

The two jets mass distribution is plotted in fig. 2. In order to enhance signal, two-jet mass regions of 106 GeV $< M_{jj} < 126$ GeV are selected.

Assuming $10 fb^{-1}$ of total integrated luminosity, the number of estimated signal and background is 380(signal)/459(background) with the QCD corrections. The Most of the background is from $\gamma\gamma \to c\bar{c}(g)$. ¿From this number, statistical errors $\sqrt{N}_{obs}/(N_{obs} - N_{bg})$ of the two-photon decay width of the SM Higgs boson at $M_H=120$ GeV 7.6 %.

6 Summary

We studied the feasibility of the measurement of the two-photon decay width of an Intermediate-mass Higgs at a photon-photon collider by the Monte Carlo simulation. Our study took into account, a realistic luminosity distribution by CAIN, detector effect and the QCD correction for the background process. For QCD correction, we count on JETSET parton shower for event shape. Comparing with parton shower and analytic calculation at $y_{cut}=0.08$, the parton shower makes more two jets event than the analytic calculation. Since there is a difficulty to calculation differential cross section for lower y_{cut}, it is not possible to apply analytic calculation for event shape, however, comparison at the $y_{cut}=0.08$ shows that our estimation provided a conservative result in this sense. In any case, an improvement in this point are expected.

Acknowledgements: We greatly appreciate Prof. I. Endo for useful discussions and encouragement. We would like to thank Profs. G. Jikia, T. Takeshita, T. Tauchi, A. Tkabladze, A. Miyamoto, and K. Yokoya for useful discussions.

References

1. See, for example, G. Jikia in this workshop.
2. D.L. Borden, D.A. Bauer, and D.O. Caldwell, Phys. Rev. D **48**, 4018 (1993).
3. G. Jikia and A. Tkabladze, Phys. Rev. D **54**, 2030 (1996).
4. T. Sjöstrand, Comput. Phys. Commun. **82**, 74 (1994).
5. T. Ohgaki, T. Takahashi and I. Watanabe, HUPD-9705, to be published in Phys. Rev. D56 Vol. 3(1997)
6. P. Chen, T. Ohgaki, A. Spitkovsky, T. Takahashi, and K. Yokoya, SLAC-PUB-7426, HUPD-9707 (1997)
7. JLC-I, KEK Report 92-16, December (1992).
8. M. Spira, in Proc. of 5th Int. Workshop on New Computing Techniques in Physics Research:(AIHENP 96), Lausanne, Switzerland, Sep. 2-6,1996.
9. S. Kawabata, Comput. Phys. Commun. **41**, 127 (1986); **88**, 309 (1995).
10. H. Murayama, I. Watanabe, and K. Hagiwara, KEK Report 91-11, January (1992).
11. JADE Collaboration, W. Bartel et al., Z. Phys. C **26**, 93 (1984).

PRODUCTION OF HIGGS BOSONS IN $\gamma\gamma$ AND γp COLLISIONS AT PRESENT AND FUTURE COLLIDERS

MARIA KRAWCZYK

Institute of Theoretical Physics, University of Warsaw,
ul. Hoza 69, 00-681 Warsaw, Poland

Abstract

The Higgs boson production in $\gamma\gamma$ collision at future colliders may offer very importrant source of information on the two Higgs doublet extension of the Standard Model (MSSM and 2HDM). In the general 2HDM a very light neutral Higgs scalar or pseudoscalar (with mass below 40-50 GeV) is still allowed by present data. The $\gamma\gamma$ option at the Next Linear colliders may provide an unique opportunity to study the resonant production of such a light Higgs particle[1,2].

A search for the light Higgs particle in the framework of MSSM and 2HDM may also be performed at *ep* collider HERA. In the γp scattering a crucial role play the γg fusion and processes with the resolved photon (in particular the gg fusion)[3,1,4].

References

1. M. Krawczyk, Talk at ICHEP'96, Warsaw 1996 (hep-ph 9612460), in Proc. eds. Z. Ajduk and A. K. Wroblewski, World Sciencific 1997, p. 1460.
2. D. Choudhury, M.Krawczyk, MPI-PTh/06-46, IFT 96/13 (hep-ph/9607271) and in Proc. of the Workshop-Annecy,Grann Sasso,Hamburg 1995, ed. P. M. Zerwas, DESY 96-123D p. 521; Phys. Rev. **D 55** (1997) 2774.
3. A. C. Bawa and M. Krawczyk, Phys. Lett. **B357** (1995) 637.
4. M. Krawczyk, Workshop "Future Physics of HERA", Hamburg 1995/6, in Proc. p.244 (hep-ph 9609477)

Related Topics

PHOTONS FROM THE UNIVERSE
NEW FRONTIERS IN ASTRONOMY

HINRICH MEYER

University of Wuppertal, Gaußstraße 20,
42097 Wuppertal, Germany

This century has seen a dramatic increase in observational possibilities of the physics of the universe. Several of the very recent new developments with emphasis on the particle physics aspect and in particular $\gamma\gamma$ interactions are briefly discussed in this talk.

1 The universal photon background

At any point between galaxies in the universe one encounters a field of photons ranging in energy from the long wave end of the radiospectrum at $10^{-12}eV$ to at least $10^{11}eV$ and possibly $10^{20}eV$ which is the upper end of the cosmic ray spectrum observed at earth. To a large extend astronomy is based on the observation of local deviations from this universal background and was based over millenia on photons in a very narrow energy interval at about $1eV$ accessible for detection by the human eye. Since the 1940th the radio range was explored and after 1960 the X-ray, the MeV and GeV range and the infrared and extreme ultraviolet mostly using instruments launched by rockets and operating outside the earth atmosphere. The photon energy range to be explored with these new experimental possibilities expanded by many orders of magnitude and entirely new processes in the universe became available as tools of astronomy. As one result of the observations it now becomes possible to construct the universal photon flux for all wavelengths up to about 100 GeV photon energy. To achieve this one has to eliminate the local foreground flux of photons with the galaxy obviously as the most prominent local enhancement visible over the whole energy spectrum. In the infrared region only upper limits are available, due to the brilliance of our very local environment in this energy range. The universal photon background was given about 10 years ago by Ressell and Turner [1]. Since then, new information became available, at almost all wavelengths and an attempt has been made to update the compilation in [2]. This is shown in figure 1 as photon flux in units of $cm^{-2}s^{-1}sr^{-1}$ and figure 2 as energy flux per unit decade in eV. The highest flux originates from rather early in the universe at a black body temperature of presently $\approx 2.7°K$. It is a pure Planck spectrum exact to a very high degree, with dipole distortion due to the motion of the solar system and remaining nonuniformities at the 10^{-5}

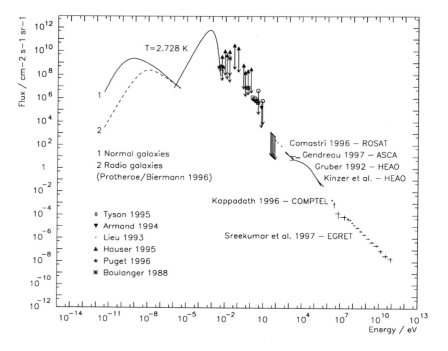

Figure 1: Flux of the diffuse extragalactic background radiation.

level indicating seeds of structure formation in an expanding universe [3].

In the radio range the source of photons is synchrotron radiation of relativistic electrons in ambient magnetic fields mostly from normal radio galaxies with a sizeable contribution from a small subclass of galaxies with a highly active nucleus (AGN) [4]. The AGNs are also contributing a dominant part of the x-ray region [5] as well as in the MeV - GeV range, which has only very recently been revealed from observations using the Compton Gamma Ray Observatory (CGRO) [6]. Beyond 100 GeV the photon background is not yet known; shown here is a theoretical estimate [7] based on a universal flux of cosmic rays at energies $> 10^{19} eV$ that interact and cascade in the universal photon background. This cascade starts with single pion photoproduction of protons on photons from the $2.7° K$ field [8] and develops with short cascade length until all photons have energies $\ll 100\,TeV$ where the interaction length becomes very large again [9]. The energy range between 100 GeV and 100 TeV is at present the frontier region of astronomy with photons (TeV - astronomy).

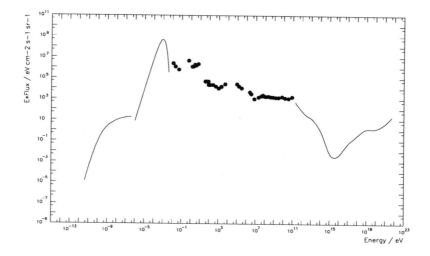

Figure 2: The energy flux of the intergalactic universal photon background. The line above 100 GeV indicates a model calculation only, since no measurements are available yet in this energy range.

For energies > 100 TeV the density of the photon background does not allow to look beyond our own galaxy (see figure 3). Here neutrinos may step in and at energies $> 10^{19} eV$ even protons depending on the structure and strength of magnetic fields in and beyond our local cluster. It thus appears that the energy range >100 GeV is a true domain of high energy physics in the universe where processes usually studied in the laboratory at particle accelerators are used to reveal the nature of extreme objects and environments in space, with the very early universe at temperatures >100 GeV as the most prominent and singular spot in spacetime.

2   The process $\gamma\gamma \to e^+e^-$ in the universe

Soon after the discovery of the positron the cross–section for the fundamental process photon + photon → electron + positron was calculated [10]. For an incoming photon of energy E colliding with a target photon of energy ε at an angle Θ the threshold energy E_{th} is given by

$$E_{th} = \frac{2 \cdot m_e^2}{\varepsilon(1 - \cos\Theta)}$$

and in units relevant for TeV astronomy:

$$E_{th} \simeq \frac{1}{2}\left[\frac{1\,TeV}{\varepsilon}\right]eV \tag{1}$$

The total cross–section for the process is given as [11]

$$\sigma_{\gamma\gamma} = \frac{3}{16}\sigma_0(1 - \beta^2)\left[(3 - \beta^4)\ln\frac{1 + \beta}{1 - \beta} - 2\beta(2 - \beta^2)\right] \tag{2}$$

with

$$\beta \equiv \left(\frac{1 - 2m_e^2}{E\varepsilon(1 - \cos\Theta)}\right)^{\frac{1}{2}}$$

and

$$\sigma_0 = 6.65 \cdot 10^{-25}\,cm^2$$

the Thompson cross section.

The cross section rises rapidly after threshold with a peak value of about 200 mbarn at about $2 \cdot E_{th}$ and then it falls off approximately as $1/E$. This behavior of the cross section folded with the $2.7°K$ Planck spectrum then results in the deep absorption trough at about 2 PeV shown in figure 3 taken from [12]. At about 1 eV light from stars dominates and absorbs most strongly at about 1 TeV while the far infrared part of the $2.7°K$ photons should cut off all photons at about 150 TeV. The transparency in the window (1 - 150) TeV is very uncertain, as the universal photon flux in the range from $6 \cdot 10^{-3}$ eV to $6 \cdot 10^{-1}$ eV is not measured yet and can be estimated only from rather involved models of dust- and star formation throughout the lifetime of the universe. Several such calculations have become available recently and can be used to calculate a Gamma Ray Horizon see figure 3 and [13]. It is obvious that considerable uncertainty is present on how deep into space high energy photon sources can be revealed. Interesting structures in the universe are

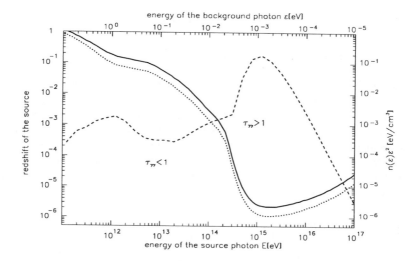

Figure 3: The γ-ray horizon for photons of energy $> 10^{11}\ eV$ (solid line). It is based on a photon background density as shown by the dashed line (and right hand scale). The region of optical and infrared photons is described here by a model calculation[12]

nearby galaxies at say 1 Mpc that could not be seen above 100 TeV while below 100 TeV the local cluster and beyond is probably accessible, although the uncertainty on how far one will be able to see is presently very much open. One of the very challenging tasks of TeV astronomy is the exploration of the γ-ray horizon and various ideas on possible sources at the horizon have been published recently [14].

3   The pair–compton cascade

As can be seen from figure 3 the absorption of >100 TeV photons by the ubiquitous $2.7^\circ K$ photon background has a characteristic length of ~ 10 kpc, which is short compared to intergalactic distances. The resulting pair electrons have a similarity short compton scattering length and therefore an intergalactic pair–compton cascade develops as long as there are photons left in the cascade with energy $\gg 100$ TeV. The e^+e^- pairs 'see' intergalactic magnetic fields, or stronger fields near galaxies which results in measurable delay phenomena of bursts [15], the creation of so called pair halos near the source [16] or changes in the power law spectra due to pile up of cascade photons [17]. This will serve as great tools to explore intergalactic magnetic fields at values $< 10^{-11}G$ that are hardly accessible by other experimental means.

4 Active galactic nuclei (AGN)

Galaxies with an active nucleus have been known for long time and have been the subject of countless investigations. A particularly interesting feature is the high variability of the emission from the nucleus. In the radio and the optical sizeable polarization has been detected, which points to synchrotron radiation at the source. At radio frequencies thanks to interferometry between antenna far apart even up to intercontinental distances spatial resolutions at better than 1/1000 of an arcsec can be obtained. These observations resolved the AGN emission into a succession of 'blobs' seemingly moving with superluminal velocity (v>c) across the sky. If the train of 'radioblobs' is to consists of relativistic plasma (emitting the radio photons) with Lorentzfactors $\gg 1$ moving towards us at small angle $< 10°$ in a jet like fashion, consideration of Lorentz transformation gives for the transverse velocity (β) of the blob with

$$\beta = \frac{\beta_j \sin \Theta}{1 - \beta_j \cos \Theta} \simeq \frac{2}{\Theta} \quad (for \Theta \ll 1 \ and \ \beta_j \rightarrow 1) \tag{3}$$

with β_j the velocity of the blob and Θ the viewing angle. This explains the apparent superluminal motions observed in many jets at AGN. As a further consequence the observed luminosity L_{obs} of the source is considerably enhanced over the restframe luminosity L according to

$$L_{obs} = D_j^3 L \tag{4}$$

with

$$D_j = \frac{1}{\gamma_j (1 - \beta_j \cos \Theta)} \quad and \quad \gamma_j = \left(\frac{1}{(1 - \beta_j^2)} \right)^{\frac{1}{2}}$$

The AGN should in fact not only have a jet pointing to the observer but a balancing jet receding in the opposite direction. The same relativistic transformation effect responsible for the high brilliance of the jet towards us renders the receding jets hardly observable. At larger inclination angle however both jets become visible. Small changes in the viewing angle for the jet moving towards us may be responsible for the large and somewhat stochastic nature of the intensity variations as it may result from moving the plasma at relativistic velocity along helical path. There is indeed evidence for this from radio observations[18].

It is assumed that the jets originate from a central black hole of mass 10^8-10^{11} solar masses. The black hole accretes matter from a flat disk spinning at relativistic speed at it's inner edge not far from the horizon of the black hole. This setup may be surrounded by a huge dust torus connecting up with stars and interstellar matter of the host galaxy. Different viewing angles then produce a large variety of observational phenomena for the AGN's.

The energy flux versus wavelength for AGN is rather flat within 1-2 orders of magnitude from the radio range over more than 20 orders of magnitude into the GeV range. It renders AGN as prominent contributors to the universal photon flux in the universe at almost all energies (see figure 1). The most notable exception is of course the $2.7° K$ microwave background that originates from the big bang.

5 AGN at GeV-Energies

Launched in spring 1991 the $\underline{C}ompton$ $\underline{G}amma$ $\underline{R}ay$ $\underline{O}bservatory$ (CGRO) has provided the first all sky survey in the high energy (up to 100 GeV) gamma ray range using the EGRET instrument. As a result many new sources have been discovered and in addition the diffuse gamma emission from the galaxy and from extragalactic space have been determined rather accurately[19]. Among the sources the identification of 65 AGN at the $>(4\text{-}5)$ σ level stands out as a great discovery. Several of these AGN have - when flaring - the highest energy flux in the GeV region, they all show dramatic variability in flux and the spectra are rather flat with power law index on average about 2. They constitute a fraction $>10\%$ of all known flat spectrum AGN, out to a distance of z=2.5[20]. The contrast in amplitude is large about an order of magnitude, seemingly larger then at the other wavelengths. Since EGRET provided only rather moderate sensitivity it is not unreasonable to assume that mostly the peaks of the emission have been seen and future missions with higher sensitivity and also better exposure (e.g. GLAST) may detect all flat spectrum AGN's. These sources also may provide a sample of candidates for "Beacons at the Gamma Ray Horizons[14]" if the energy spectra could be followed to higher energies. The more distant one's should hit the horizon at ten's of GeV (see figure 3). It is therefore of great importance to increase the sensitivity of GeV-TeV gamma ray instruments to finally detect the absorption feature in the energy spectra due to the universal photon background in the universe.

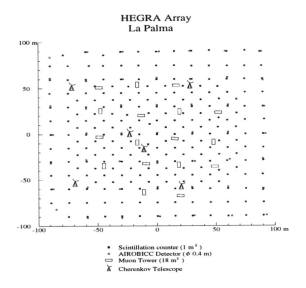

Figure 4: Layout of the HEGRA experiment.

6 The new frontier - TeV energies

At TeV energies the flux of photons is low, the strongest steady source in the sky is the CRAB nebula which gives only $0.4 \cdot 10^{-11}$ photons/cm^2sec at 1 TeV. Large collection areas are required, of the order few·$10^4 m^2$ certainly impossible for space based experiments at present. One therefore is confined to experiments on earth's surface. The key feature of the presently most successful technique makes use of the air as a Cherenkov medium, with changing index of refraction and nicely transparent to the Cherenkov photons. The air is about 23 r.l. thick thus confining the electromagnetic shower generated by the incoming TeV photon. For stability of observational conditions clear air is needed preferentially at an elevation of order 2500 m and above the cloud level. The Observatorio del Roque de los Muchachos (ORM) on La Palma is such a location and has been chosen by the HEGRA collaboration for the deployment of an extended airshower array for TeV observations (see figure 4). Details of the installations and properties of the detectors can be found in [21]. Of particular importance are the Air Cherenkov telescopes with large detection area of about 30.000 m^2, good separation power of photon- versus hadron showers and $\sim 1/10°$ angular resolution. Like optical telescopes good observations are possible only in clear nights and low moon light. The field of view of the telescopes is about 4° and at any given setting essentially only one source can be observed. Several telescopes combined (presently 4 of the 6 installed at ORM on La Palma) give improved gamma hadron separation and also angular resolution at the expense of some fraction of the detection area. The first source definitely detected in the TeV-range has been the CRAB nebula[22], the remnant of the AD 1054 supernova that also houses the 33 msec CRAB pulsar. As a mechanism for the generation of TeV photons in the nebula it is assumed that electrons are accelerated to very high energies of order 10^8 GeV. The electrons produce synchrotron radiation in an ambient magnetic field of the order tens of μT. The synchrotron photon spectrum reaches up to a few GeV and is detected by EGRET[23]. Compton upscattering of the synchrotron photons by the primary electrons is taken responsible for the very high photons up to tens of TeV[24]. There must however exist in the CRAB nebula an efficient mechanism to accelerate the electrons to energies $\gg TeV$ with shock wave acceleration usually assumed as such a mechanism. More sources of similar structure are to be expected in the galaxy and indeed TeV photons from SN 1006 and from 1706-44 as similar supernova remnants have been observed using the Air Cherenkov technique at a site in Australia[25].

In a follow up observation of EGRET sources the Whipple collaboration discovered TeV photons from one of the closest extragalactic sources in the EGRET sample the Markarian galaxy Mkn 421 at a redshift of z=0.031 ($\sim$ 300 Mill.ly.)[26]. This observation was confirmed by HEGRA[27]. In addition a similar galaxy, Mkn 501 at z=0.034 was detected as a rather weak source and again confirmed by HEGRA[28]. Both galaxies have an active nucleus and belong to a subclass of AGN's, the so called Bl Lac objects named after the first galaxy of this type at a distance of z=0.069. The active nucleus of Bl Lac's is at the center of an elliptical galaxy that has only narrow emission lines of width < 5Å. In May 1996 the Whipple telescope was lucky enough to detect two very big and extremely rapid flares from Mkn 421 (missed by HEGRA because of daylight at La Palma)[29]. Most of the time both Mkn 421 and 501 are near the detection limit of the telescopes however not inconsistent with the typical behavior of the flat spectrum AGN's, that seem to change continuously their emission intensity e.g. in the radio or optical region. When Mkn 501 became observable again this spring it was seen in a state of rapid flaring (see figure 5) much brighter than 1996 and frequently much more intense than the 'standard candle' CRAB, indeed up to 10 times the CRAB flux was observed making Mkn 501 the most intense TeV gamma ray source in the sky.

424

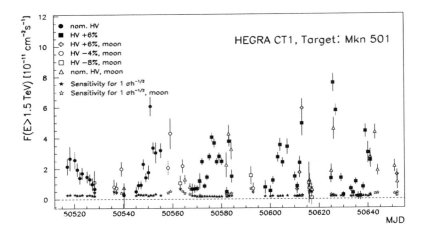

Figure 5: The "lightcurve" of Mkn 501 from March to July 1997 at E > 1.5 TeV. The data are preliminary. They have been obtained using the first Cherenkov telescope CT1 of the HEGRA–collaboration.

Furthermore the energy spectrum was observed to extend well beyond 10 TeV with a seemingly unabsorbed power law with spectral index ~2.5 similar to the CRAB [30]. As an immediate consequence, given the distance of Mkn 501, it became clear that the universal infrared background must be very much lower than the upper limits obtained so far and likely very close to the lower end of recent theoretical estimates [12,13]. This opens up the possibility to really detect the universal infrared background through observation of the absorption in the spectra at some tens of TeV. The position of Mkn 501 can now be found with TeV photons at the level of 0.01°, better than arcmin, which is considered as a sort of entrance ticket to real astronomy. Mkn 501 is observed to continue flaring at a high level and is meanwhile being detected by several instruments using the Air Cherenkov technique [31].

7 Terra Incognita at >100 TeV

As shown in chapter 2 photons with energy >100 TeV get readily absorbed in the 2.7°K microwave background and as a result the horizon out to which one can see into the universe comes down to galactic distances. Only a faint halo of isotropic 'skyshine' is expected to remain from photons created at >100 TeV [9]. However we get knowledge of phenomena of energy at least six orders of magnitude higher since airshowers up to 10^{20}eV total energy (with a few events beyond) have been observed. At very high energies $> 10^{19}$eV when charged particles (say protons) would become stiff enough to keep direction in intergalactic magnetic fields they may reveal sources in our local universe out to about 50 Mpc, since on longer distances protons would be absorbed through photon pion production in the 2.7°K photon background [8]. This possibility of 'proton astronomy' may soon be explored, when the two 'Auger' arrays of size several thousand km^2 become operational. As a further possibility we should be aware that proton acceleration to very high energies $\gg$100 TeV in e.g. AGN should not only produce π° via photo pion production that may have – as one of the possibilities – been observed with 10 TeV photons from Mkn 421 and Mkn 501. It implies charged pion production as well and therefore we obtain from π, μ decay a muon- and electron neutrino flux of TeV energies. If detected it surely tells of a similar photon flux, while the reverse is not necessarily true since photons could have primary electrons as the only source. Therefore it is of great importance to detect >100 TeV neutrinos from distant sources to cover the highest energy window inaccessible to photon detection. A rather promising project (AMANDA) to detect the very high energy neutrinos is under construction using the ice of Antarctica at the south pole station [32]. Last antarctic summer several strings of photomultipliers ~400 m long have been successfully lowered to a depth beyond 1500 m of ice. This setup should safely detect neutrinos originating from cosmic ray interactions in earth atmosphere and it may come close to detect (with some luck) extragalactic neutrinos. This would open up yet another new window into the universe with entirely new information on the most violent processes in the universe.

8 Bursts of γ–rays

An enigmatic astrophysical phenomenon, the so called γ–ray bursts were serendipitously discovered in the early 70th in the course of verification of the nuclear test ban treaty. Short bursts of γ–rays in the keV-MeV range were observed ranging in time from msec to min. Nothing else was seen at the γ–burst position that could reveal the nature of phenomenon. A big surprise came with the CGRO which had with BATSE a dedicated all sky monitor for γ–ray bursts on board. It detected bursts at a rate of about one a day, more than 1500 by now. The distribution on the sky was found to be completely isotropic (at the < 2% level; see figure 6) while the intensity distribution is inhomogeneous, less frequent at low flux. The simplest hypothesis places them at cosmological

426

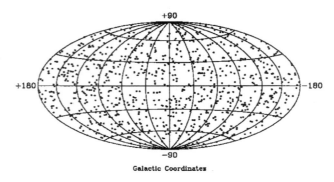

921 BATSE Gamma–Ray Bursts

Galactic Coordinates

Figure 6: Angular distribution of 921 GRBs in galactic coordinates.

distances corresponding to a redshift z∼1 which implies an energy budget of
∼ 10^{48} erg/sec at the source. Recently a new attempt was made to find
counterparts with the deployment in space of the "Beppo-Sax" X–ray satellite.
It allows for arcmin localization of γ–ray bursts in the lower X–ray band within
hours. A burst on 28/Feb./97 was the first case where a fading counterpart
was observed in the X–ray range by Beppo-Sax as well as in the optical band
using the William Herschel 4.2 meter telescope at ORM on La Palma[33]. Very
recently on 8/May/97 again an optical counterpart was detected at first getting
brighter and than fading again. This burst for the first time gave a lower limit
on the distance of z≥0.835 observing absorption lines features in the spectrum
using the KEK telescope on Mauna Kea, Hawaii. More such observations might
finally reveal an underlying mechanism, the present observations being fully
consistent with a nonisotropic relativistically expanding plasma as the source
of γ–ray bursts [34]. This resembles similarity with radio blobs in AGN jets
however many more accurate pointings and counterpart detections are needed
to find a clue.

9 Closing remark

This century has seen a dramatic extension of knowledge about the universe in particular exploring observational possibilities in e.g. the radioband, the X–ray range and very recently up to the TeV photons. Entirely new information should come from very high energy neutrino observation. A further leap into new territory is sure to come once gravitational waves will have been detected. Exiting times at new frontiers in astronomy are ahead of us.

References

1. Ressell, M.T. and Turner, M.S.; *Comments Astrophys.* 1990, Vol. 14, 323.
2. Hohl, H. and Meyer, H.O.; to be published.
3. Fixsen, D.J. et al.; *ApJ* 473, 576, 1996.
4. Protheroe, R.J. and Biermann, P.L.; *Astroparticle Physics* 6, 45, 1996.
5. Setti, G.; *Proceedings of the 17th Texas Symposium 1994*, ed. H. Boehringer.
6. Sreekumar, P. et al.; to be published
   G. Kanbach private communication.
7. Lee, S.; *FERMILAB-Pub-96/066-A*, 1996.
8. Greisen, K.; *Phys. Rev. Lett.* 16, 748, 1966.
   Zatsepin, G.T. and Kuzmin, V.A.; *JETP Lett.* 4, 78, 1966.
9. Wdowczyk, J. et al.; *J. Phys.* A5, 1419, 1972.
   Halzen, F. et al. *Phys. Rev.* D 41, 342, 1990.
10. See Jauch, Rohrlich, *The Theory of Electrons and Photons.*
11. Gould, R.J. and Schréder, G.; *Phys. Rev.* 155, 1408, 1967.
12. Funk, B.; Thesis, unpublished.
    Funk, B. et al.; submitted.
13. Stecker, F.W. et al.; *ApJ* 390, L 49, 1992.
    Berezinsky, V. et al.; *Phys. Lett. B*, to be published.
    Stanev, T. and Franceschini, A.; submitted, *astro-ph/9708162.*
14. Mannheim, K. et al; *Astron. and Astrophys.* 315, 77, 1996.
15. Plaga, R.; *Nature* 374, 430, 1995.
16. Aharonian, F. et al.; *ApJ* 423, L5, 1994.
17. Protheroe, R.J. and Stanev, T.; *MNRAS* 264, 191, 1993.
18. Krichbaum, T.P. et al.; *Proc. Heidelberg Workshop on Gamma–Ray Emitting AGN* Kirk, J.G. ed., MPIH–V37–1996.
19. Strong, A.W. and Mattox, J.R.; *Astron. Astrophys. Lett.* 308, 21, 1996.
20. Hartmann, R.C. et al.; *ApJS*, 1997 submitted.

21. Rhode, W., HEGRA coll.;*Nucl. Phys. B (Proc. Suppl.)* 48, 491, 1996.
22. Weekes, T.C. et al.; *ApJ* 342, 379, 1989.
23. Ramanamurthy, P.V., et al.; *ApJ* 447, L 109, 1995.
24. Gould, R.J.; *Phys. Rev. Lett.* 15, 577, 1965.
    De Jager, O.C. and Harding, A.K.; *ApJ* 396, 161, 1992.
25. Kifune T. et al.; *ApJ* 439, L 91, 1995;
    Yoshikoshi, T. et al.; preprint *astro-ph* 9707203 and contribution to *25th Int. C.R.C., Durban, South Africa.*
26. Punch, M et al.; *Nature* 358, 477, 1992;
27. Petry, D. et al.; *Astron. Astrophys.* 311, L 13, 1996.
28. Quinn, J. et al.; *ApJ* 456, L 83, 1996.
    Bradbury, S.M. et al.; *Astron. Astrophys.* 320, L 5, 1997.
29. Gaidos, J.A. et al.; *Nature* 383, 319, 1996.
30. Aharonian, F. et al.; *Astron. Astrophys.*, accepted.
31. CAT coll., HEGRA coll. and Whipple coll.; contribution to 25th *Int. C.R.C., Durban, South Africa.*
32. AMANDA coll.; *Science* 267, 1174, 1995.
33. Groof, P.J.; *IAU* 6584, March 1997 and *Nature*, in print.
34. Mészáros, P.; *Proceedings of the 17th Texas Symposium 1994*, ed. H. Boehringer.

Summary Talks

AN EXPERIMENTER'S HIGHLIGHTS

D.J. MILLER

University College London, Gower Street, London WC1E 6BT, England

This selection concentrates more on $\gamma\gamma$ results, with some reference to the related HERA photoproduction data. Progress has been made on a wide range of topics, from F_2^γ to the "stickiness" of glueball candidates, but many channels still need better statistics and/or a real photon target before they can match the comparable ep studies.

1 Introduction

The HERA photoproduction data are the main experimental component in Forshaw's "Theorist's Highlights" [1], so this talk gives more stress to photon-photon collisions, with some mention of related HERA results. There are five sections; F_2^γ hadronic; Other Photon Structure Functions; Inclusive Processes; Exclusive Processes; and Dreams - possible future developments. Many important contributions have had to be left out for lack of time and space.

2 F_2^γ, hadronic

New results on $F_2^\gamma(x, Q^2)$ from singly tagged events have been presented by three LEP experiments, DELPHI [2], ALEPH [3] and OPAL [4,5].

Figure 1 is the Feynman graph for a $\gamma\gamma$ scattering event at an e^+e^- collider. For singly tagged events one of the scattered electrons is detected, giving a good measurement of $Q^2 = 2E_b E_{tag}(1 - cos\theta_{tag})$ for the probing photon. The other lepton is required not to be seen, which keeps the value of P^2 for the target photon close to zero. The invariant mass of the hadronic system is $W_{\gamma\gamma}$, which is underestimated because some of the hadronic energy is poorly measured

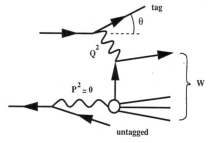

Figure 1: Variables in electron-photon DIS.

in the forward regions of the detectors [6,7]. This means that the value of $x = Q^2/(Q^2 + W_{\gamma\gamma}^2)$ is overestimated. The experiments use unfolding packages [8,9] to correct for this. (Things are much easier at HERA for the measurement of the proton structure function. There the target proton has a unique

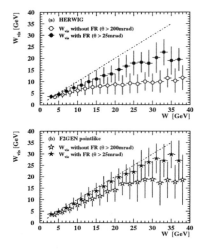

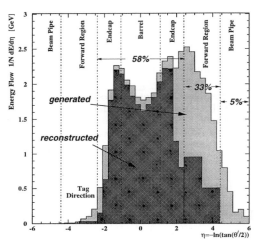

Figure 2: $W - W_{\mathrm{vis}}$ correlation for various Monte Carlo models with and without the included simulation of the OPAL forward region (FR) between $25 < \theta < 200$ mrad.

Figure 3: Hadronic energy flow per event as a function of pseudorapidity based on the HER-WIG generator, before and after detector simulation. The tag is always at negative η and is not shown.

high momentum instead of the soft distribution of virtual target gammas radiated from the electron beams at LEP, the ep event rate at large values of W is much higher than in $e\gamma$, and x is well determined.)

OPAL[5] has new $F_2^{\gamma}(x, Q^2)$ data for two bins with average Q^2 values of 1.86 and 3.76 GeV^2, the first measurements in this low Q^2 region since TASSO[10] and TPC/2γ[11]. Electrons were tagged in the OPAL Silicon-Tungsten luminometer at angles down to 27 mrad from the beam, with the LEP e^+e^- energy close to the peak of the Z^0. Since LEP has now moved on past the WW threshold these may be the last measurements in this Q^2 range for a long time.

The unfolded F_2^{γ} distributions at low Q^2 show the following characteristics:

- There is no sudden change of the shape of $F_2^{\gamma}(x)$ when Q^2 drops below 5 GeV^2 (compare shape in ref[5] with ref[3] and ref[4]). This is in contrast with the previous measurement from $TPC/2\gamma$.

- The absolute value of F_2^{γ} (ref[5] Fig. 2) is higher than either the GRV[12,13] or the SaS-1D[14] predictions. The GRV-HO curve comes closest.

- A rise at $x < 0.01$, as seen in the proton structure at HERA [15,16], is allowed but not established, largely because –

- The systematic errors after unfolding are much larger than the statistical errors (true for all LEP F_2^γ measurements, see discussion in next few paragraphs).

The values of F_2^γ in the medium to large Q^2 range $(5 < Q^2 < 120 \text{ GeV}^2)$ from the three LEP experiments [2,3,4] are in good agreement (see Figure 3 in [4]). All of them are consistent with the expected $\ln Q^2$ rise from QCD [12]. The DELPHI error bars are less than those from ALEPH and OPAL, for comparable statistics, because DELPHI has a different approach to calculating the systematic errors from unfolding; what Lauber [6] calls "the problem".

The problem was posed – in exaggerated form, we now know – by Forshaw (reporting an exercise of Seymour, corroborated by Lönnblad) at Photon'95 [17]. Events from the HERWIG [18] Monte Carlo program were passed through a simple detector simulation which modelled the way the experimental analyses had previously been done by suppressing all hadron reconstruction in the endcap regions $(\theta < 200mr)$. In this HERWIG exercise, for generated values of $W_{\gamma\gamma} > 15$ GeV almost all correlation was lost between the visible reconstructed value W_{vis} and the generated value – see the open circles in Figure 2 [19].

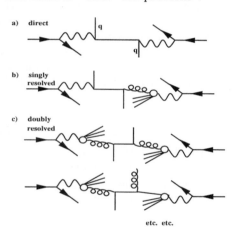

Figure 4: Feynman graphs of direct and resolved processes.

Studies with PYTHIA [20] and ARIADNE [21] showed a similar effect. If this were representative of what is really happening in experiments it must mean that, for large $W_{\gamma\gamma}$ and hence for small x, unfolding results would be unreliable – as experimenters already feared [22]. An immediate partial remedy was clear to the experimenters; use the sampled hadron energy from the forward electromagnetic calorimeters. Figure 3 shows that approximately one third of this energy is actually measured by OPAL. ALEPH and DELPHI are similar. The result is shown as the solid circles in Figure 2(a). Some correlation is already restored.

But study of the data has led all three LEP experiments to doubt the completeness of the modelling in HERWIG and PYTHIA. The measured hadronic energy flows in OPAL and ALEPH, as reported here [3,4], show less energy in the partially sampled forward region than predicted by these two Monte Carlo models, and more energy goes into parts of the well-measured central region. In OPAL the shape of the observed energy flow is closer to that from the simple F2GEN [23] model where the outgoing hadronic system is generated as the pointlike production of a quark-antiquark pair, though this must be an incomplete model of the QCD process. Figure 2(b) shows how much better the correlation is between W_{vis} and the true value for events generated with this pointlike F2GEN model, both with and without the sampled hadronic energy from the forward region. The distribution of hadronic transverse energy $E_{\text{t,out}}$, perpendicular to the beam-tag plane, is also very different between data and HERWIG or PYTHIA, especially at low x [6]. And Rooke [24] has shown that the number of events with 2 high transverse energy jets is much lower in HERWIG and PYTHIA than in the data. In both of these cases the pointlike F2GEN sample lies on the other side of the data points from HER-WIG and PYTHIA. Butterworth (private communication) has speculated that HERWIG and PYTHIA may be underestimating the contribution from one or more hard-parton processes; photon-gluon fusion, for instance (Figure 4(b)).

The way the game is now being played is shown in Figure 5 as a flowchart. Lauber [6] described an exercise with Seymour and Lönnblad which is represented by the nearly vertical dotted arrow from item F to item B on the flowchart, using the energy flow and $E_{\text{t,out}}$ histograms from experiment, item F, to tune the parameters of the parton shower generators, item B, in HER-WIG and PYTHIA. Tyapkin [2] reported a similar exercise with the DELPHI generator TWOGAM which has an

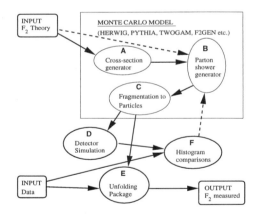

Figure 5: F_2^γ measurement flow chart.

explicit singly resolved photon component [25], including photon-gluon fusion. The nearly horizontal dotted arrow, from INPUT to item B on the flowchart, represents a feature of both HERWIG and PYTHIA which use the input set of theoretical parton density functions in their parton shower generators as well as in the cross section generator. The large systematic errors on the OPAL and

ALEPH unfoldings come from assuming a set of Monte Carlo models which cover the whole range of variations in the histogrammed quantities. The DELPHI errors are smaller because they only use the tuned TWOGAM Monte Carlo for unfolding.

There is a serious dilemma here. If we tune the generators perfectly, to match all of the observed histograms, then it will not matter what input parametrisation of $F_2^\gamma(x, Q^2)$ we have used; the unfolding package, item E, will automatically give us back the input $F_2^\gamma(x, Q^2)$ as our measured output. What is needed is a set of Monte Carlo models whose parameters are all tied down, either by QCD theory or by fits to other data – hadronic scattering, HERA photoproduction, etc. We must use them to unfold $F_2^\gamma(x, Q^2)$ from the visible x distribution, but we must also check that they give good energy flows, jet numbers and $E_{t,out}$ distributions. If they do not there must be something missing from them which will have to be added in a well motivated way, or we have to look for better models. It is intriguing that the PHOJET Monte Carlo model [26] fits some features of the untagged $\gamma\gamma$ data as well as PYTHIA does [27]. A version of PHOJET with off-shell photons is eagerly awaited, as are re-engineered versions of HERWIG and PYTHIA.

The last three or four years of LEP running will double or triple the statistics available for photon structure function analysis. If the Monte Carlo tools can be refined to match there is every prospect of clear answers to two questions; can we measure Λ_{QCD} from the high Q^2 evolution, and is there a rise of $F_2^\gamma(x, Q^2)$ at low x? Of course, we would also like to measure the gluon density in the photon – but that is only accessible directly through inclusive processes, see below.

3   Other Photon Structure Functions

There is no reason to expect surprises from measurements of the QED structure functions of the photon. A large part of our motive for studying them is to use them as a testbed for the techniques used to extract the hadronic structure functions. The longitudinal hadronic structure function F_L^γ is particularly interesting because it should have different QCD scaling [28] behaviour from F_2^γ. But it had been shown before LEP started up [29] that F_L^γ would be hard to measure there because of poor statistics for events with the highest sensitivity to F_L^γ, events with low tagged electron energies. The difficulties are now known to be even greater due to background from fake-tags by off-momentum electrons in the beam halo (e.g. [25]). More recently Field and others [30,31] have pointed out that there are other structure functions which are akin to F_L^γ, but which can be measured from the main sample of tagged data.

ALEPH [32] and OPAL [33] both reported results from singly tagged $\gamma\gamma \rightarrow$ $\mu^+\mu^-$ samples. The new structure functions govern the distribution of the azimuthal angle χ between plane of the outgoing muons and the plane of the beam and the tagged electron in the $\gamma\gamma$ C. of M. Both saw significant values for $F_B^{\gamma,QED}$, in agreement with the QED prediction. ALEPH also presented the first measurement of $F_A^{\gamma,QED}$. $F_B^{\gamma,QED}$ multiplies the $cos2\chi$ term in the angular distribution and $F_A^{\gamma,QED}$ multiplies the $cos\chi$ term. Since the two experiments used different sign conventions for the definition of χ it may well be that OPAL "folded away" their sensitivity to $F_A^{\gamma,QED}$. Successful measurement of $F_B^{\gamma,QED}$ is particularly encouraging because its hadronic form has the same parton content as F_L^{γ}, in the limit of massless quarks, though it comes from a different set of helicity amplitudes.

The task now is to try and use the outgoing jets in hadronic events in the same way as the outgoing muons to define a χ angle. There will be problems. Whereas the tagged $\mu^+\mu^-$ events have a constrained fit which gives a precisely defined final state $\gamma\gamma$ energy, the hadronic events are very poorly defined because of the incomplete sampling of hadron energies in the forward regions. And only a sub-set of hadronic events has a clear two-jet axis. Telnov suggested that the statistics may be increased by including untagged events in which the electron recoil plane is implicitly defined by the overall transverse momentum of the hadronic system, but it is not clear that this will work. New ideas are still needed. If we are lucky Photon '99 may see the first analyses for the hadronic F_B^{γ} and its evolution with Q^2.

4   Inclusive processes

H1 continues to tease the $\gamma\gamma$ community by trying to extract photon structure from jets in photoproduction. The latest study [34] uses an appropriate set of cuts to get a differential cross section which they say should be equal to the pointlike anomalous contribution to the photon interaction $\alpha^{-1}x_\gamma(q+\frac{9}{4}g)$. When this is plotted against the p_T^2 of the jets it has a logarithmic rise, as would be expected from the scale-breaking nature of the photon-quark coupling. In fact, the rise seems to be significantly steeper than either the GRV prediction or the observed logarithmic rise in $F_2^{\gamma}(Q^2)$[4]. This may be a hint that the gluon contribution is doing something unexpected or – more likely I fear at this stage – that the H1 analysis could contain systematic effects which have not yet been understood. It is noticeable that H1 did not present an update at Photon '97 of the Photon '95 analysis [35] that claimed to measure the gluonic structure of the photon, presumably because of systematic difficulties in separating the primary signal from underlying multiple parton interactions, as described at

Photon '95 by ZEUS [36].

Progress has been made in inclusive $\gamma\gamma$ analysis, thanks to two important factors: a) LEP has moved away from the Z^0 peak; b) the HERA experiments have developed analysis techniques which can be applied to $\gamma\gamma$ as well as to γp. Even though the integrated LEP luminosity above the Z^0 is still only 10s of pb^{-1} compared with over 100pb^{-1} on peak, the rate for collecting untagged $\gamma\gamma \rightarrow hadrons$ is much greater than for tagged events – and the Z^0 background can be kept well below 10% of the sample with reasonable cuts.

DELPHI [25] presented a preliminary empirical survey of how the properties of events evolve with $\sqrt{s_{e+e^-}}$. The observed cross section, after selection cuts, rises at about 10 pb/GeV from $\sqrt{s_{e+e^-}} \simeq 132$ GeV to $\sqrt{s_{e+e^-}} \simeq 172$ GeV, and it extrapolates back plausibly to just below the points at $\sqrt{s_{e+e^-}} \simeq 91$ GeV, under the background from the Z^0. The same TWOGAM Monte Carlo model that they use for unfolding F_2^γ [2] gives predicted distributions of final state quantities, including $W_{\gamma\gamma}$, energy flow as a function of psuedorapidity, transverse momentum of jets and number of jets. Most of them agree well; this home-made model seems to have a good combination of hard and soft components. But they draw attention to one disagreement between data and Monte Carlo at $\sqrt{s_{e+e^-}} \simeq 172$ GeV, where the energy flow in the forward region drops below the prediction in a way which is very reminiscent of the effect seen in the OPAL tagged data [4,5,6].

OPAL's inclusive analysis [27] goes further than DELPHI, and may be a prototype that other experiments could follow ($\gamma\gamma \rightarrow hadrons$ has long had as many different analysis techniques as experiments [37], which meant that no experiment could check another's results). OPAL uses a development of the x_γ variable from HERA as an estimator of the fraction of the target photon's momentum carried by the hard parton which produces identified jets with high E_T.

$$x_\gamma^\pm = \frac{\sum_{jets} E_j \pm p_{z,j}}{\sum_{hadrons} E_i \pm p_{z,i}},$$

where $p_{z,i}$ is the momentum of a hadron projected along the LEP beam direction. The $\pm$ ambiguity arises because the initial state is intrinsically symmetric, unlike the situation at HERA, and either photon might be the target. Three main categories of events with high E_T jets are expected: direct, singly resolved and doubly resolved (Figure 4) [38]. Using the PYTHIA Monte Carlo, OPAL shows that the direct sample should be very cleanly separated from the resolved samples by requiring both x_γ^+ and x_γ^- to be greater than 0.8. They confirm this separation in the experimental data for two jet events with $E_T > 3$ GeV by computing an effective parton scattering angle θ^* in the dijet C. of M. and showing that the direct ($x_\gamma^\pm > 0.8$) sample has the expected rather flat distribution, while the resolved samples (x_γ^+ or x_γ^- less than 0.8) are much more forward-backward peaked, as predicted on a parton level by lowest order QCD (and as seen in a very similar analysis of photoproduction by ZEUS, quoted in Aurenche's introduction to the inclusive session [39]).

Given the evidence, at least in the two jet sample, for approximate jet-parton duality, OPAL has compared the E_T distribution of jets with the parton level NLO matrix element predictions of Kleinwort and Kramer [40]. The effects of measurement errors are removed by unfolding. The match between theory and experiment is good for $E_T > 5$ GeV and is consistent with the predicted domination by the direct matrix element for $E_T > 8$ GeV. Aurenche also showed how well these NLO curves matched $\gamma\gamma$ data from AMY and TOPAZ, as well as photoproduction from H1 and ZEUS.

Comparison of the OPAL inclusive two-jet cross sections with Monte Carlo predictions is tantalising. For direct events ($x_\gamma^\pm > 0.8$) the PYTHIA and PHO-JETS predictions agree with one another and with the data, regardless of the set of PDFs used. But for x_γ^+ or x_γ^- less than 0.8, i.e. for the resolved samples, there are some disagreements between the two programs with the same PDFs, and large disagreements between different PDFs in the same program. The LAC1 [41] PDFs, for instance, give much too high a cross section with both programs, surely because of too much gluon. Better statistics and further analysis may lead to an independent measurement of the gluon content of the photon.

The total cross section $\sigma_{\gamma\gamma}$ has been one of the worst measured quantities in particle physics [42] (but see "Dreams" below). It remains so for $W_{\gamma\gamma} < 5$ GeV, but L3 has presented first measurements from LEP [43] with $5 < W_{\gamma\gamma} < 70$ GeV which are much more coherent than anything at lower energies. They show a significant rise over this range, consistent with the logarithmic rise seen in hadron-hadron and γp cross sections. The problem with this measurement is an intensified version of the problem discussed above for F_2^γ, how to correct for the lost hadronic energy in the forward region. In the tagged events used for the structure function some transverse momentum is required in the hadronic system to balance the tagged electron. But the bulk of the events in the total cross section have no tag, and at high $W_{\gamma\gamma}$ there must be a large fraction of diffractive events in which the hadrons hardly have enough transverse momentum to enter the forward luminosity detectors. Most of these events give no trigger and the only way of allowing for them is to use a Monte Carlo program to correct for their loss. Rather surprisingly the PHOJETS and PYTHIA Monte Carlo models give very similar distributions for the W_{visible} distribution, including the barrel region and the forward detectors, so the total cross section values do not change much when unfolded with either PYTHIA or PHOJETS. But a plot was shown [43] of cluster energies in the forward luminosity detectors alone in which there was a marked divergence at high energies between, on the one hand, the data and the PHOJETS prediction, which both levelled off and agreed with one another, and on the other hand, the PYTHIA prediction which fell away much more sharply. This is all we know about the region where many events must be totally unseen, so it is hard to be completely confident in the measurement until one or more of DELPHI, ALEPH and OPAL have done a similar analysis, hopefully with a larger selection of Monte Carlo models.

Charm production in $\gamma\gamma$ remains intractable. The new L3 result for the inclusive charm cross section [44] agrees with the QCD model [45], but it is only based on 43 events at LEP1 in 80pb^{-1} and 29 events at LEP2 in 20pb^{-1}, both tagged with muons from charm decay. It is frustrating to know that there are thousands of unresolved charm events there, boosted forward by the $\gamma\gamma$ kinematics so that they cannot be identified in the microvertex detectors. A few more tagging channels can be added, however, and the eventual LEP2 luminosity should give a factor of $\simeq \times 20$, so a worthwhile test of the theory should come by Photon '01.

A potentially important $\gamma^*\gamma^*$ study has been suggested by Hautmann and others [46,47] who make predictions from the high energy limit of QCD (using the BFKL pomeron) which give a significant doubly-tagged rate for $e^+e^- \rightarrow e^+e^- hadrons$ (approximately 1 event per pb^{-1} at LEP2 with $Q^2 \simeq 10$ GeV^2). There was some surprise that the effect has not yet been noticed in LEP1 data, if it is there. A few dozen doubly tagged events have been seen. They are routinely rejected from the singly tagged samples of thousands of events which are used for structure function studies. There may just be enough of them, after inefficiencies have been allowed for, to accommodate the new prediction. As ever, a Monte Carlo study of the hadronic acceptance will be needed to find out if a significant part of the signal is being lost. This will surely be settled by Photon '99. Come to Freiburg to see if BFKL survives!

5 Exclusive processes

There is no shortage of data, but there is a serious shortage of people to work on it. Cleo II now has over 3fb^{-1} of integrated luminosity, and we can expect even more from the specialised beauty factory experiments, Belle in Japan and BaBar at Stanford. For higher mass $\gamma\gamma$ systems LEP is accumulating worthwhile samples. And there is no shortage of problems to be solved, both from QCD [48] and in resonance physics where predictions proliferate for glueballs, hybrids, molecules, 4-quark states and recurrences. I concentrate on two beautiful results from Cleo II, supplemented by L3, and mention a first survey from H1.

Cleo II has sufficient integrated luminosity to do a precision study on tagged samples of $\gamma^*\gamma \to \pi^0, \eta$ and η' [49]. They have recalibrated the inner edge of their tagging detector so that they can use incompletely contained electron showers to go down to a lower limit of $Q^2 = 1.5$ GeV^2, joining on well for the π^0 with lower Q^2 data from CELLO. There is a clear difference between the Q^2 behaviour of η' and the behaviour of π^0 and η. Both π^0 and η form factors appear to obey the perturbative QCD prediction of Brodsky and Lepage [48]:

$$\lim_{Q^2 \to \infty} |Q^2 \cdot F_{\gamma^*\gamma m}(Q^2)| = 2f_m,$$

where m is the particular pseudoscalar meson, and they have consistent values ($\Lambda_{\pi^0} \simeq 776 \pm 20$ MeV, $\Lambda_\eta \simeq 774 \pm 30$ MeV) for the π^0 and η mass parameters in the monopole formula:

$$F(Q^2) = F(0)\frac{1}{1 + Q^2/\Lambda_m^2}.$$

But the η' form factor rises to approximately twice the pQCD prediction at $Q^2 \simeq 15$ GeV^2, and it has a higher monopole mass ($\Lambda_{\eta'} \simeq 859 \pm 25$ MeV; L3 is consistent [50] but with bigger errors). Brodsky and Ruskov – in their talks [48,51] and over breakfast this morning – agree that these results mean that the π^0 and η are behaving as if their wavefunctions are already close to asymptotic whereas the η' is a much more complicated mixed object.

Cleo II's other beautiful result was totally negative [52] but very clear. This was a search for $\gamma\gamma$ production of the glueball candidate $f_J(2220)$ and its decay to $K_s K_s$. Cleo II sees many other resonances in this analysis, so there is no question about their sensitivity, but they do not see even a hint of the $f_J(2220)$. They therefore put the highest ever lower limit (> 82 at 95% confidence) on the "stickiness" [53] of a meson, the normalised ratio of its $\gamma\gamma$ width to its radiative branching ratio from J/ψ. Both BES and Mk II have clear signals for J/ψ decays to the $f_J(2220)$. This object must now be one of the strongest of all glueball candidates. Two other experiments, L3 [50] and ARGUS [54] reported $\gamma\gamma$ resonance studies. The L3 results are promising and should soon have a physics impact. They demonstrate a good acceptance and resolution for many states with masses from 1200 to 1750 GeV/c^2 and the statistics will triple or quadruple before Photon '01.

There was an encouraging first look at exclusive resonance production at HERA from H1 [55], making particular use of the new SPACAL calorimeter to measure multi photon final states boosted in the backward direction. Clear π^0, ω and η signals were seen, but no η'. There was also a suggestion of an $a_0(980)$ peak. As well as conventional $\gamma\gamma$ or γ-pomeron processes, some of these channels should be sensitive to more exotic exchanges, such as the "odderon". With rising HERA luminosity this could become very interesting.

6 Dreams; possible future developments

A recurrent good dream seems closer to the real world after Romanov's talk[56]. This is the hope for precise measurement of the total cross section $\sigma_{\gamma\gamma}$ in the resonance region by using double tagging at around zero scattering angle in an e^+e^- collider. The KEDR detector at the VEPP-4M collider in Novosibirsk has focusing spectrometers built into it which measure the outgoing electron and positron to very high precision (we saw results from a setting-up experiment on photon splitting using one of the two spectrometers[57]). The collider will run with $\sqrt{s} \simeq 1$ GeV soon, but should then go up to around 12 GeV. The resolution on the mass of the system recoiling against the two tags will be better than 20 MeV/c^2 over a range of masses from $\simeq 0.5$ to 3.5 GeV/c^2, with a tagging efficiency of better than 15%. The main KEDR detector will have good tracking and calorimetry to measure the properties of the hadronic final state, so this experiment could make a substantial contribution to resonance studies. A daydream which some of us indulge in is to imagine the same kind of zero angle tagging system installed in one of the spare LEP straight sections, together with good luminosity monitors and forward tracking, with a simple barrel detector to trigger on hadronic systems. A well designed specialised experiment could push the $\sigma_{\gamma\gamma}$ measurement up to $\sqrt{s} \simeq 70$ GeV or more, could solve the big problem of measuring $W_{\gamma\gamma}$ in the study of F_2^γ, could see the BFKL effects predicted by Hautmann et al. and would be much more sensitive than the present LEP experiments to such diffractive processes as $\gamma\gamma \to \rho\rho, J/\psi\rho$ etc. But I hear there is to be a new user for the LEP tunnel after 2001.

In this morning's talks on the high energy photon linear collider Telnov reported[58] on the steady progress being made in solving the fundamental problems of realising the full potential luminosity of such a machine and Jikia[59], Ginzburg[60], Krawcyk[?] and Takahashi[61] updated some of the feasibility studies on physics, including measuring the couplings of Higgs bosons to $\gamma\gamma$. Because this coupling could be sensitive to the existence of very heavy fermions and bosons – well beyond anything reachable at planned machines – it remains one of the most important of all the numbers to be determined once a Higgs boson is found. Nothing has been said here to undermine the conclusion presented at the LCWS in Morioka[62] that, if a Higgs boson is found with a mass of less than 350 GeV, then a high energy $\gamma\gamma$ collider must be built to study it. Such a machine in $e^-\gamma$ mode will also give the definitive measurement of the high Q^2 evolution of F_2^γ, avoiding the big problem of measuring $W_{\gamma\gamma}$ by using a narrow band beam of real photons as the target [63]. Brodsky says that he believes the study of $e^-\gamma \rightarrow W\nu$ will give the best possible measurement of the γWW couplings. Telnov reminded us that if a high energy linear e^+e^- collider is built there must be provision for a second interaction region with a finite beam crossing angle to be built at a later date for real $\gamma\gamma$ and γe^- physics.

The idea of a lower energy photon linear collider was mentioned in passing. It could be a superb tool for studying resonances in the 1 to 4 GeV/c^2 mass range [64,65]. If it were done as part of an upgrade of the SLC at Stanford it might even reach the $e^-\gamma \rightarrow W\nu$ threshold.

7 Summary and conclusions

In measuring F_γ^2 the LEP experiments agree with one another that the shape and evolution are consistent with QCD. But the problem of modelling the parton shower must be solved before the two important questions can be settled: is the hadronic part of the photon so like the proton that at low x it has the same kind of rising structure function; and can a precise measurement of the QCD scale be made from the evolution at high Q^2? The influence of HERA photoprodcution on untagged $\gamma\gamma$ studies is very important. It will be intriguing to see whether LEP or HERA gets the best eventual measurement of the gluon density in the photon; each has its own systematics and intrinsic background problems. Resonance studies continue to be frustrated by lack of effort; the work is intricate and time consuming, and it can be unrewarding if the results are not clear cut. Here Cleo II used its large statistics to report two convincingly clear results. L3 should be able to follow suit with its excellent neutral particle reconstruction.

The connections between photoproduction and $\gamma\gamma$ physics grow closer. Many of the "dreams" of $e\gamma$ and $\gamma\gamma$ physicists, from the previous section, involve achieving comparable statistics and precision to what HERA can already do in ep or γp. This may only be possible at a linear collider.

Acknowledgements

The organisers of the conference are to be congratulated on the scientific organisation, on their choice of venue and on the care they have taken of us. Completion of the written version of this review has depended heavily upon the kind advice and help of Dr. Jan Lauber.

References

1. J. R. Forshaw. These Proceedings.
2. I. Tyapkin for the DELPHI collaboration. These Proceedings.
3. A. Finch for the ALEPH collaboration. These Proceedings.
4. R. Nisius for the OPAL collaboration. These Proceedings.
5. J. Bechtluft for the OPAL collaboration. These Proceedings. OPAL Collaboration, K. Ackerstaff *et al*, Z.Phys. **C74** (1997)33
6. J. A. Lauber, with L. Lönnblad and M. Seymour. These Proceedings.
7. K. Ackerstaff et al.: Z. Phys. C74 (1997) 33–48, OPAL Collaboration
8. V. Blobel, DESY-84-118, 1984.
9. A. Höcker and V. Kartvelishvili. Nucl. Instr. Meth. **A372** (1996) 469
10. TASSO collaboration, M. Althoff *et al*, Z.Phys. **C31** (1986) 527
11. $TPC/2\gamma$ collaboration, H. Aihara *et al*, Z.Phys. **C34** (1987) 1
12. A. Vogt. These Proceedings
13. M. Glück, E. Reya and A. Vogt, Phys. Rev. **D46** (1992) 1973
    M. Glück, E. Reya and A. Vogt, Phys. Rev. **D45** (1992) 3986
14. G. A. Schuler and T. Sjöstrand, Z. Phys. **C68** (1995) 607.
15. ZEUS Collaboration, M. Derrick *et al.*, Phys. Lett. **B316** (1993) 412.
16. H1 Collaboration, I. Abt *et al.*, Nucl. Phys. **B407** (1993) 515.
17. J. R. Forshaw. Proceedings of Photon '95, Sheffield, England 8-13 April 1995, eds Miller, Cartwright and Khoze; World Scientific, Singapore (1995) 3.
18. G. Marchesini and B. R. Webber, Nucl. Phys. **B310** (1988) 461
    M. H. Seymour, Z. Phys **C56** (1992) 161
19. J. A. Lauber for the OPAL collaboration. Proceedings of ICHEP '96, Warsaw, eds Z. Ajduk and A. K. Wroblewski, World Scientific, Singapore (1996) 725
20. T. Sjöstrand, Comp. Phys. Comm. **82** (1994) 74
    T. Sjöstrand, PYTHIA 5.7 and JETSET 7.4: Physics and Manual, CERN-TH/93-7112
21. L. Lönnblad. Comp. Phys. Comm. **71** (1992) 15.
22. D. J. Miller. Proceedings of Workshop on Two-Photon Physics at LEP and HERA, Lund, Sweden, May 1994; eds G. Jarlskog and L. Jönsson, Lund University (1994) 4
23. A. Buijs, W. G. J. Langeveld, M. H. Lehto and D. J. Miller. Comp. Phys. Comm. **79** (1994) 523
24. A. M. Rooke for the OPAL collaboration. These Proceedings.
25. N. Zimin for the DELPHI collaboration. These Proceedings.

444

26. R. Engel, with F. W. Bopp, J. Ranft and A. Rostovtsev. These Proceedings.
27. R. Bürgin for the OPAL collaboration. These Proceedings.
28. E. Witten, Nucl. Phys.**B120** (1977) 189
29. D. J. Miller. Proceedings of ECFA workshop on Physics at LEP200, Aachen 1986, eds A. Böhm and W. Hoogland; CERN 87-08; ECFA 87/108; 207
30. J. H. Field. Proceedings of Photon '95, Sheffield, England 8-13 April 1995, eds Miller, Cartwright and Khoze; World Scientific, Singapore (1995) 485.
31. P. Aurenche *et al*; $\gamma\gamma$ working group report; in Physics at LEP2, CERN 96-01, 301
32. C. A. Brew for the ALEPH collaboration. These Proceedings.
33. M. Doucet for the OPAL collaboration. These Proceedings.
34. H. Rick for the H1 collaboration. These Proceedings.
35. M. Erdmann for the H1 collaboration. Proceedings of Photon '95, Sheffield, England 8-13 April 1995, eds Miller, Cartwright and Khoze; World Scientific, Singapore (1995) 59.
36. J. M. Butterworth for the ZEUS collaboration. Proceedings of Photon '95, Sheffield, England 8-13 April 1995, eds Miller, Cartwright and Khoze; World Scientific, Singapore (1995) 53
37. D. J. Miller. Proceedings of the Lepton Photon Symposium, Cornell University, August 1993, eds P. Drell and D. Rubin, AIP Conference Proceedings No. 302; 654
38. C. H. Llewellyn-Smith, Phys. Lett. **B79** (1978) 83.
39. P. Aurenche. These Proceedings.
40. T. Kleinwort and G. Kramer. Phys. Letts **B370** (1996) 141
41. H. Abramowicz, K. Charchula and A. Levy, Phys. Lett. **B269** (1991) 458
42. G. Pancheri. These Proceedings.
43. W. van Rossum for the L3 collaboration. These Proceedings.
44. V. P. Andreev for the L3 collaboration. These Proceedings.
45. M. Drees, M. Krämer, J. Zunft and P. M. Zerwas, Phys. Lett. **B306** (1993) 371
46. F. Hautmann with S. Brodsky and D. Soper. These Proceedings and Phys. Rev. Lett. **78** (1997) 803
47. J. Bartels, A. De Roeck and H. Lotter. DESY-96-168, hep-ph/9608401
48. S. Brodsky. These Proceedings
49. V. Savinov for the Cleo II collaboration. These Proceedings.
50. S. Braccini for the L3 collaboration. These proceedings.

51. R. Ruskov with A. V. Radyushkin. These Proceedings.
52. H. Paar for the Cleo II collaboration. These Proceedings.
53. M. S. Chanowitz. proceedings of the VIIIth International Workshop on Photon-Photon Collisions, Shoresh, Israel, April 1988; ed U. Karshon. World Scientific, Singapore (1988) 205
54. G. Medin for the ARGUS collaboration. These Proceedings.
55. S. Tapprogge for the H1 collaboration. These Proceedings.
56. L. Romanov for the KEDR collaboration. These Proceedings.
57. A. Maslennikov for the KEDR collaboration. These Proceedings.
58. V. Telnov. These Proceedings.
59. G. Jikia. These Proceedings
60. I. F. Ginzburg. These Proceedings
61. D. Choudhury, M. Krawcyk, Phys. Rev. D **55** (1997) 2774
62. T. Takahashi. These Proceedings.
63. D. J. Miller. Proceedings of the Workshop on Physics and Experiments with Linear Colliders, Morioka-Appi, Japan, September 1995, eds A. Miyamoto, Y. Fujii, T. Matsui, S. Iwata, World Scientific, Singapore (1996) 322
64. D. J. Miller and A. Vogt. e^+e^- Collisions at TeV Energies; the Physics Potential. ed P.M.Zerwas, DESY 96-123D (1996) 473
65. D. A. Bauer, D. L. Borden, D. J. Miller and J. E. Spencer, SLAC-PUB-5816 (1992)
66. D. J. Miller. Nucl. Instr. Meth. **A355** (1995) 101

PHOTON '97: THEORY SUMMARY

JEFFREY R. FORSHAW

Department of Physics & Astronomy, University of Manchester, Manchester, M13 9PL, UK.

Some recent developments in the physics of photon induced reactions are discussed. My presentation is biased towards HERA physics with David Miller's talk being biased towards the $\gamma\gamma$ topics [1]. Within the context of the data which were presented, I shall concentrate upon the the following topics: diffraction; jets; prompt photons; open charm and charmonium.

1   Diffraction

I'm going to restrict myself to diffractive phenomena in γp interactions (where the photon can be real or virtual). For the present purposes "diffraction" means that there is a rapidity gap in the final state (I'll have more to say on this later). Let's start by recalling some results on total rates [2]. In particular, I want to discuss the W-dependence of total rates (W is the γp invariant mass). A convenient way to parameterize the data on the W-dependence is to extract an effective pomeron intercept, $\alpha_P(0)$. It is to be understood that this value would be the true pomeron intercept if the physics were solely due to exchange of a single Regge pole. Recall that total hadronic cross-sections and exclusive photoproduction of light vector mesons (e.g. $\gamma p \rightarrow V p$ where V is a vector meson and the photon is close to its mass-shell, i.e. $Q^2 \approx 0$) can be described with a single value of $\alpha_P(0) \approx 1.08$ [3]. However, there are processes which do not follow this trend. The dissociation process, $\gamma^* p \rightarrow X p$ (X denotes the dissociation products which are distant in rapidity from the outgoing proton), is characterized by a rather large effective intercept, i.e. $\alpha_P(0) = 1.18 \pm 0.02 \pm 0.04$ [4]. There is also a tendency for the intercept to grow as Q^2 increases [5]. In addition, the growth for $\gamma p \rightarrow J/\psi\, p$ is larger still, $\alpha_P(0) \approx 1.3$ (even for photoproduction, i.e. $Q^2 \approx 0$). The situation for light meson production off virtual photons is less clear [6,7]. There is a suggestion that the W dependence is much steeper than it would be for on-shell photons, and that it steepens as Q^2 rises [7]. However the conclusion relies upon extrapolating from low energy data, where the recent E665 measurement [8] (of a high cross-section value at $W \approx 11$ GeV) confuses the issue. Data from Hermes should help sort this out [9]. It seems that a large photon virtuality or a large quark mass is correlated with a more rapidly rising cross-section (recall also that the deep inelastic total cross-section rises rapidly with increasing W, i.e. at small x). Michele Arneodo asked "just what is the scale which determines how steep the rise is?" [2]. To gain some insight into the physics which determines the answer to this question is the next part of my talk.

1.1 A physical picture of diffraction

Consider shining a coherent beam of partons onto a target at rest and let z_i & b_i be the fraction of the total beam energy carried by parton i and its position in the plane transverse to its direction of travel respectively. We expect that, as the beam energy increases, so too does the probability that the parton passes through the target undeflected (i.e. any momentum transfer it receives is too small to deflect it appreciably). Of course the target itself can be broken up by the momentum transfer (or scattered into some excited state or scattered elastically). This type of event can have a big rapidity gap between the final state partons and the products of the target. It also follows that the eigenstates of this kind of reaction will be states of fixed z_i and b_i. The target simply alters the profile of the incoming beam. The coherent sum over the final state partons will lead to a state which has some overlap with the initial state (elastic scattering) and also will lead to states which have non-zero overlap with other final states. The analogy with optical diffraction is clear (the parton states play the analogous role the the Huygens wavelets) and hence the name. It's now time to turn to diffraction in photon induced reactions.

To describe the hadronic interactions of the photon we need to consider its fluctuation into a $q\bar{q}$ pair and the subsequent interaction with the target (at high beam energy, the pair will typically be produced way upstream of the target). We describe the $q\bar{q}$ fluctuations with the wavefunction, $\psi_\gamma(z, r)$, i.e.

$$|\gamma\rangle = \int dz d^2r \, \psi_\gamma(z, r)|z, r\rangle. \tag{1}$$

The defining statement that the eigenstates of diffraction are states of fixed z and r can be written

$$\hat{T}|z, r\rangle = i\tau(s, b; z, r)|z, r\rangle \tag{2}$$

where $\hat{T}$ is the operator which determines how the $q\bar{q}$ state scatters off the target and the eigenvalue $i\tau(s, b; z, r)$ is the associated amplitude for scattering the partons elastically (I just chose to take out a factor of i since it turns out that the amplitude is dominanted by its imaginary part, i.e. τ is real). The γ–Target invariant mass is denoted $s = W^2$ and b is the impact parameter for the collision.

The **elastic scattering** amplitude,

$$A^{\text{el}}(s, t) = \int d^2b \, e^{iq \cdot b} \langle \gamma|\hat{T}|\gamma\rangle, \tag{3}$$

(we have taken the Fourier transform so as to get the amplitude in terms of the momentum transfer, $-t = q^2 > 0$) can then be written:

$$
\begin{aligned}
\frac{\mathrm{Im}A^{\mathrm{el}}(s, t = 0)}{s} &= \int dz d^2 r \, |\psi_\gamma(z, r)|^2 \sigma(s, r) \\
&= \sigma_{\mathrm{tot}}^{\gamma T}(s),
\end{aligned}
\tag{4}
$$

where $\sigma_{\mathrm{tot}}^{\gamma T}(s)$ is the total γ−Target cross-section and

$$
\int d^2 b \frac{\tau(s, b; z, r)}{s} \equiv \sigma(s, r)
$$

is the total cross-section for scattering the $q\bar{q}$ pair off the target (for convenience we suppress any dependence on z). In writing these last two formulae, we have made use of the optical theorem.

Similarly, we can write the cross-section for **vector meson production**:

$$
\left. \frac{d\sigma}{dt} \right|_{t=0} = \frac{1}{16\pi} \left[\int dz d^2 r \, \psi_V^*(z, r) \psi_\gamma(z, r) \sigma(z, r) \right]^2,
\tag{5}
$$

where ψ_V is the meson wavefunction.

For **photon dissociation** processes, we want to sum incoherently over the cross-sections to scatter into all possible final states, i.e.

$$
\left. \frac{d\sigma}{dt} \right|_{t=0} = \frac{1}{16\pi} \int dz d^2 r \, |\psi_\gamma(z, r)|^2 \sigma(s, r)^2.
\tag{6}
$$

So with nothing more than a bit of quantum mechanics and our definition of diffraction we have arrived at these useful formulae. In particular note that the elastic scattering amplitude and the photon dissociation cross-section only involve the photon wavefunction (calculable in QED) and the universal cross-section, $\sigma(s, r)$. The essential physics of diffraction lives in $\sigma(s, r)$ (e.g. pomeron exchange, gluon ladders,...). In order to proceed further, and gain some insight into the aforementioned W-dependencies, we need to input a bit more physics.

The photon wavefunction is calculated from the vacuum polarization graph and possesses the following properties: (1) an exponential suppression sets in for $r^2 > 1/[Q^2 \bar{z} + m^2]$; (2) $|\psi_\gamma^L|^2 \sim Q^2 \bar{z}^2$; (3) $|\psi_\gamma^T|^2 \sim Q^2 \bar{z}$. The superscripts label the mode of polarization, $\bar{z} \equiv z(1 - z)$ and m is the quark mass. Gousset discussed the large size behaviour of the photon wavefunction [10].

The dipole cross-section, $\sigma(s, r)$, must vanish in proportion to r^2 as $r^2 \to 0$. This is the colour transparency property which follows directly from QCD. For large r we expect $\sigma(s, r)$ to saturate to some typical hadronic size, R^2 (due to confinement). We are now ready to make some qualitative statements about photon induced diffraction phenomena.

We'll start with the diffraction dissociation cross-section, (6), and look seperately at the contributions from large size $q\bar{q}$ pairs (i.e. $r > R$) and small size pairs (i.e. $r < 1/Q$). For the large size pairs the important range of the z integral comes from the end-points, where $\bar{z} < 1/[Q^2 R^2]$ (these are the only regions which don't feel the exponential suppression from the tail of the wavefunction), i.e. the $q\bar{q}$ pair is produced with a highly asymmetric partitioning of the photon energy. No such restriction is present for scattering small size pairs. We can get a feel for what is going on without having to go into too much detail.

For the large size pairs we can write

$$\frac{d\sigma}{dt}\bigg|_{t=0} \sim \frac{1}{Q^2 R^2} \cdot R^2 \cdot Q^2 \left(\frac{1}{Q^2 R^2}\right)^n \cdot R^4. \tag{7}$$

The first factor on the rhs $(1/[Q^2 R^2])$ is from the volume of the z integral, the second (R^2) is from the r integral, the third is the wavefunction factor ($n = 1$ for transverse photons and $n = 2$ for longitudinal photons) and the final factor is $\sigma^2 \sim R^4$. Thus the rate induced by transverse photons is $\sim R^2/Q^2$ whilst that by longitudinal photons is suppressed by an additional factor of Q^2, i.e. $\sim 1/Q^4$. The additional factor of $\bar{z}$ in the longitudinal photon wavefunction makes all the difference by suppressing the z end-point contribution.

For the small size pairs, similar reasoning gives

$$\frac{d\sigma}{dt}\bigg|_{t=0} \sim 1 \cdot \frac{1}{Q^2} \cdot Q^2 \cdot \frac{1}{Q^4} \sim \frac{1}{Q^4}. \tag{8}$$

The z volume gives the factor unity, the r volume is now $\sim 1/Q^2$ and the photon wavefunction simply gives a factor $\sim Q^2$ (regardless of the polarization). The final factor is from $\sigma^2 \sim r^4 \sim 1/Q^4$. The contribution is therefore higher twist.

We have arrived at the interesting conclusion that *there is a leading twist contribution to the diffraction dissociation rate and that it is a result of scattering large size $q\bar{q}$ pairs produced by transversely polarized photons.* The HERA data support this picture, except perhaps for the fact that the qualitative picture I've just presented suggests that $\alpha_P(0) \approx 1.08$ should be observed (since the dominant contribution comes from scattering large size $q\bar{q}$ pairs). The fact that a larger value is seen is interesting and presumably arises because of QCD corrections which build up an anomalous dimension which leads to an enhancement of the short distance contribution.

Now let's turn to vector meson production (5). For "heavy" mesons (e.g. J/ψ), the non-relativistic approximation leads us to assume that $|\psi_V|^2 \sim \delta(z - 1/2)$ (or else the meson could not be bound together). There is no end-point contribution and the quark mass is large therefore the contribution from large size pairs is exponentially suppressed. The rate for producing J/ψ mesons off on-shell photons rises rapidly with increasing W. This is a characteristic of perturbation theory and is in accord with our conclusion that only small size $q\bar{q}$ pairs need be considered.

For light mesons the situation is much more complicated and, not surprisingly, depends critically on the end-point behaviour of the meson wavefunction [11]. For example, if we assume [a] that $\psi_V^* \psi_\gamma^T \sim \bar{z}^{m+1/2}$ and that $\psi_V^* \psi_\gamma^L \sim \bar{z}^{m+1}$ then it follows (following precisely the same reasoning that led to the estimates for the dissociation rate) from (5) that

$$\frac{\sigma_T(r > R)}{\sigma_T(r < 1/Q)} \sim (Q^2 R^2)^{1-2m} \tag{9}$$

and

$$\frac{\sigma_L(r > R)}{\sigma_L(r < 1/Q)} \sim (Q^2 R^2)^{-2m}. \tag{10}$$

Putting $n = 1/2$ (which seems reasonable), means that the production rate off transverse photons is sensitive to all sizes (i.e. both perturbative and non-perturbative configurations) whilst the rate off longitudinal photons is dominated by scattering of small size pairs (perturbative). *Light meson production is thus a potentially very interesting mix of soft and hard physics.* Information which will help untangle what is going on comes in the form of measurements of σ_L/σ_T and the variation of the total rate with Q^2 and W.

1.2 Pomeron parton densities

Regge theory inspires the factorization of the structure function, $F_2^{D(3)}$, extracted from high Q^2 photon dissociation [2,4,5], i.e.

$$F_2^{D(3)}(\beta, Q^2, x_P) = f_P(x_P) F_2^P(\beta, Q^2) + \text{ secondary exchanges.} \tag{11}$$

The data support this picture and are moving into the domain where they can really test the notion of universal pomeron parton distribution functions. At present, a model with DGLAP evolution describes the ZEUS data on diffractive dijet production in photoproduction and on $F_2^{D(3)}$ [12]. Also, H1 results on

---

[a] This really is an educated guess, it is a real challenge to understand the light meson wavefunction.

the hadronic final state (high p_t particle production, energy flows and charm production in DIS dijets in both DIS and photoproduction) are all consistent with the DGLAP approach [4].

The universality of the pomeron parton densities is intimately connected to the notion of the gap survival probability [13]. Comparison between data on direct and resolved processes, and from the Tevatron, will certainly provide essential information in helping unravel the nature of diffraction.

1.3 Squeezing the pomeron

There are some rare diffractive processes whose rates can be calculated purely using perturbative QCD.

Hautmann presented results on the $\gamma^*\gamma^*$ total cross-section [14]. It is extracted (using the optical theorem) from the elastic $\gamma^*\gamma^*$ amplitude at $t = 0$, so is concerned with the physics of diffraction. Since the photons are way off shell, they scatter perturbatively via exchange of "reggeized gluons" between their respective $q\bar{q}$ pairs. There are no hadrons to worry about, so the calculation is very clean and worth looking for at LEP2 and beyond.

An even better [b] way of keeping things perturbative is to look at high-t diffraction. For example, one can look for a pair of high p_t jets which are separated by a big rapidity gap. Presumably one is looking at parton-parton elastic scattering at $-t \approx p_t^2$ and, since there's a gap, without exchange of colour. The fraction of dijet events with a gap to all diject events as a function of increasing gap size has been presented by ZEUS [15] out to gaps of ≈ 4 units and by D0 [16] out to gaps of ≈ 6 units. To really unravel the important physics behind these data requires an understanding of the gap survival probability. A very similar process that can be studied at HERA and which avoids the issue of gap survival is high-t vector meson production (the proton dissociates to produce a forward jet, which, since it need not be seen, means bigger gaps are admitted) [17]. Both H1 and ZEUS are starting to accumulate good data on this process [6,7].

2 Jets: Rates and Shapes

For an introduction to jet photoproduction, I refer to Patrick Aurenche's presentation [18].

The structure of the virtual photon is starting to be examined at HERA, and Rick presented results which showed that the γ^* has a significant "re-

---

[b]There is no need to worry about diffusion effects

solved" component for Q^2 as big as 50 GeV^2 in those events where jets are produced with $E_T^2 > Q^2$ [19].

2.1 Dijets

Data on two or more jets [15,19,20] provides us with further options to test QCD and understand the nature of the "strongly interacting" photon [18]. ZEUS has defined direct enriched and resolved enriched samples by separating events according to a cut at $x_\gamma = 0.75$. The direct enriched sample is very sensitive to the small-x gluon content of the proton: the more backward the dijets, the lower the x values in the proton that are probed. Conversely, the resolved enriched sample is sensitive to the gluon content in the photon. In addition, NLO calculations for the dijet rates are now available for comparison with the data [21,22]. Let's summarize the situation as it stands right now.

For $x_\gamma > 0.75$, the NLO theory does a good job [15]. However there remains quite a large contamination from the large-x part of the photon quark distribution functions. This arises because of the harder form of the photon quark densities. To unravel the effects of the low-x gluons in the proton from the large-x quarks in the photon requires a tighter cut on x_γ. To facilitate a clean comparison between data and theory, the ZEUS collaboration has started to use the k_t-cluster algorithm [23].

For $x_\gamma < 0.75$ the theory falls well below the data for the lowest E_T forward dijets [15]. The effect exhibits a strong dependence upon the E_T cut, which suggests that it cannot be explained by modifying the parton distribution functions of the photon in any sensible way. Presumably, this is the same problem as that which has been encountered for the single jets [24], i.e. H1 and ZEUS both see an excess of single jet events in the forward direction for $E_T < 15$ GeV (see [18]). We really need to understand what is going on before we can extract the gluon density of the photon. Furthermore, these forward jets are fatter than might naively be expected [20].

A likely explanation for this effect could be due to the presence of a large soft underlying event. Multiple parton interactions (MI) simulate (at least part of) this physics [13,25,26]. MI are anticipated on the grounds that forward jets at low E_T are produced as a result of interactions between slow partons in the colliding particles. We know that QCD predicts a proliferation of these slow partons, and as such it may well be that more than one pair of them can interact in each γp interaction. MI can describe the broader nature of the forward jets [20] and also increase the cross-sections for forward jet production, e.g. see [27]. One way of unambiguously identifying MI might be to look at higher (3 or 4) jet rates [20].

Bürgin presented the OPAL results of jets in $\gamma\gamma$ [28]. Separation of events into classes involving direct and/or resolved photons was performed via the $x_\gamma^\pm$ variable and good agreement with the NLO calculations of Kleinwort & Kramer [29] were found. However, the error bars are still too large to allow much discrimination between different parton distribution function parameterizations.

In conclusion, the dijets provide information which complements the single jet measurements. The data are now reaching a high level of precision, and comparison with NLO theory has revealed a number of pressing issues. In particular, we need to understand better the forward jets and use the most appropriate jet algorithm. Once these issues have been addressed, we can expect to gain further insight into the gluon content of both the photon and proton.

2.2 Soft gluons

The ZEUS dijet measurements have been made with a cut on the minimum E_T of the jets and the cut is the same for both jets. This introduces a further theoretical problem. This arises because most of the jets will be produced around the minimum allowable E_T, i.e. the typical difference between the jet transverse momenta, Δp_T, will be small. So, the 3 parton final state (which is present in the NLO calculation) must have one of the partons either collinear with another, or very soft. The collinear configuration is easy to deal with (it is factorized) but the soft parton emission leads to a $\ln \Delta p_T$ contribution. This large logarithm signals that multiple soft parton emission is important. These soft parton effects can be studied by looking explicitly at the Δp_T distribution of the dijets or they can be avoided by making a cut which keeps away from $\Delta p_T \approx 0$ [18].

Similar effects need to be considered in double prompt photon production which is being observed at the Tevatron [30]. D0 cut on the photon transverse energies, i.e. $E_{T1} > 14$ GeV and $E_{T2} > 13$ GeV. The need to sum the soft gluon effects can be seen in that the theory overshoots data for $\Delta p_T < 3$ GeV.

3 Prompt Photon Production

The rates for prompt photon production seen by D0 and CDF suggest a possible excess of events at low $E_T/\sqrt{s}$ [30]. However, Andreas Vogt pointed out that the data are within the theoretical uncertainty.

Gordon presented results on prompt γ plus jet at HERA [31]. The NLO calculation is coded into Monte Carlo. This process is sensitive to the gluon density of the photon (for low x_γ where there are no data yet) and isolation cuts kill off the fragmentation contribution. We saw the good agreement between these NLO calculations and the ZEUS data[32]. At present the data are statistics limited.

4 Open Charm

The photoproduction of charm quarks at large p_T is a process which involves two large scales, $p_T, m_c \gg \Lambda$ and as such, makes life more complicated from the theoretical point of view. Good data, which can be expected in the future (especially if the charm can be tagged using a microvertex detector), will surely shed light on this intriguing area. At present, there are two main routes used in theoretical calculations.

Massive charm: The charm quark mass is considered to provide the hard scale, as such charm only ever appears in the hard subprocess and there is no notion of radiatively generated charm in the sense of parton evolution. This means that terms $\sim \alpha_s \ln(p_T^2/m_c^2)$ are not summed to all orders (in the parton distribution and fragmentation functions). As such, we might expect this approach to become less accurate when $p_T^2 \gg m_c^2$. However, it does provide a systematic way of accounting for charm quark mass effects, which will be important for $m_c \sim p_T$.

Massless charm: In this approach, the charm quark is treated as massless (above threshold), and as such is treated like any other light quark in the parton evolution equations and hard subprocess cross-sections. The $\ln(p_T/m_c)$ terms are now summed to all orders, but charm quark mass effects are ignored. So, this approach should get better as p_T/m_c increases.

Gladilin presented new results from ZEUS [33]. At present the data lie in the intermediate region where $p_T < 10$ GeV, i.e. it is not clear which, if any, of the two approaches should be used. In order to compute the inclusive D^* rate, one needs the appropriate fragmentation function. Either the Peterson [34] form or the $x^a(1-x)^b$ form do a good job, and can be well constrained by e^+e^- data.

Initial comparisons between theory and data suggest that the massive charm calculation is too low, e.g see [33]. However, the full NLO calculations require that the fragmentation function be consistently extracted from the e^+e^- data. When this is done, Cacciari and Greco find that the theoretical predictions are increased significantly relative to what is found using the softer (LO) fragmentation functions [18,35]. This is true for both massless and massive charm calculations and, within theoretical uncertainties, both are now consistent with the present data.

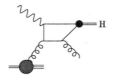

Figure 1: Leading contribution to quarkonium photoproduction.

More data at large p_T and increased statistics at intermediate p_T will certainly help in our study of the interplay of $\ln(p_T^2/m_c^2)$ and m_c^2/p_T^2 effects. In addition, for $p_T \gg m_c$ we have the possibility to study the "intrinsic" charm within the photon (charm in dijets offers good prospects here).

In e^+e^-, Andreev presented new results from L3 [36]. The open charm total cross-section agrees with the NLO calculation of Drees et al. [37]. We can look forward to more statistics which will allow comparison with differential distributions.

5 Charmonium

Originally, inelastic photoproduction of charmonium, e.g. J/ψ, was advertised as an ideal way to extract the gluon density in the proton (since it is driven by photon-gluon fusion into a $Q\bar{Q}$ pair). More recently, NLO calculations have put a dampener on this goal [38]. However, there has been a great deal of recent interest in the non-relativistic QCD (NRQCD) approach to heavy quarkonium production, and the inelastic photoproduction of heavy quarkonia provides the ideal opportunity to test NRQCD.

Bodwin, Braaten and Lepage derived a factorization formula which describes the inclusive production (and decay) of a heavy quarkonium state [39]. In the case of photoproduction, Fig.1 shows the lowest order contribution. The NRQCD factorization formula for the corresponding cross-section reads

$$d\sigma(H + X) = \sum_n d\hat{\sigma}(Q\bar{Q}[n] + X)\langle O_n^H \rangle. \tag{12}$$

X denotes that the process is inclusive, $d\hat{\sigma}(Q\bar{Q}[n] + X)$ is the perturbatively calculable cross-section for $\gamma p \rightarrow Q\bar{Q} + X$ and it can be written as a series expansion in $\alpha_s(m_Q)$. The $Q\bar{Q}$ pair is produced with quantum numbers n. The matrix element, $\langle O_n^H \rangle$, contains the long distance physics associated with the formation of the quarkonium state H from the $Q\bar{Q}$ state – it is essentially the probability that the pointlike $Q\bar{Q}$ pair forms H inclusively. The typical scale associated with this part of the process is $\sim m_Q v$ which is much smaller than m_Q (v is the relative velocity of the $Q\bar{Q}$ pair, and is small for heavy enough quarks). This hierarchy of scales underlies the NRQCD factorization. Note that the $Q\bar{Q}$ state is not restricted to having the same quantum numbers as the meson. Fortunately, there exist "velocity scaling rules" which allow us to identify which states, n, are the most important. More precisely, the "velocity scaling rules" order the operators $\langle O_n^H \rangle$ according to how many powers of v they contain, i.e. relativistic corrections can be computed systematically.

The NRQCD approach therefore provides us with a systematic way of computing inclusive heavy quarkonium production (modulo corrections which are suppressed by powers of $\sim \Lambda/m_Q$). The strategy is first to organise the sum over n into an expansion in v and then to systematically compute $d\hat{\sigma}$ order-by-order in $\alpha_s(m_Q)$. Technically, we do not a priori know where our efforts are best placed, i.e. do we work at lowest order in v and to NLO in α_s or do we attempt to work at higher orders in v, but computing each hard subprocess to lowest order? We need to know v in order to judge better what to do.

One final word before moving on to discuss J/ψ photoproduction. For small p_T, NRQCD factorization is likely to break down, due to contamination from higher twist effects. Also, one expects breakdown of the NRQCD approach in the vicinity of the elastic scattering region, i.e. $z \to 1$ where z is the fraction of the photon energy carried by the quarkonium (see later).

Inelastic photoproduction of J/ψ is something which has already been measured at HERA. Let's see how the theory shapes up. To lowest order in the velocity expansion, $[n] = [1,^3S_1]$. The first entry in the square brackets tells us that the $c\bar{c}$ is in a colour singlet state, whilst the second entry tells us the spin and angular momentum of the state. Not surprisingly, to lowest order in the velocity expansion, the $c\bar{c}$ must be produced with the same quantum numbers as the J/ψ. This is just the colour singlet model (CSM) of old. The lowest order diagram which can contribute is shown in Fig.1 and

$$\langle O^{J/\psi}[1,^3S_1] \rangle \sim |\phi(0)|^2$$

where $\phi(0)$ is the wavefunction at the origin (it can be extracted from the electronic width of the J/ψ). NLO(α_s) corrections have been computed [40] and shown to be large. The NLO corrections enhance the LO calculation and lead to a reduced sensitivity to the gluon density in the proton.

One might well ask as to the significance of the resolved photon contribution. It is important at small enough z [38,41,42]. In addition, for mesons produced at high enough p_T we have an additional scale to consider and terms which are leading in α_s can be suppressed by powers of $\sim m_c^2/p_T^2$. This is true for example of the diagram shown in Fig.1 relative to that shown in Fig.2. The latter fragmentation contribution is higher order in α_s, however there is one less hard quark propagator and so it will dominate for large enough p_T. Fragmentation contributions and resolved photon contributions are not important in computing the total rate for $z > 0.4$ (which is essentially where the data are).

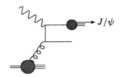

Figure 2: Fragmentation contribution to the production of the J/ψ.

Going to NLO in the velocity expansion means moving away from the CSM. For the first time we encounter colour octet contributions. In particular, the $LO(\alpha_s)$ diagram is again that of Fig.1 [c] now the $c\bar{c}$ can be formed in one of 5 states, i.e. $[n] = [8,^1S_0], [8,^3S_1], [8,^3P_{0,1,2}]$. The price one pays for having to convert this state into the J/ψ is an extra power of v^4 relative to the colour singlet matrix element, i.e.

$$\langle O^{J/\psi}[n]\rangle \sim v^4 \langle O^{J/\psi}[1,^3S_1]\rangle.$$

It turns out that the $v^4 \sim 0.01$ suppression of the long distance matrix elements is partially compensated for by a strong enhancement of the corresponding short distance cross-section. In particular, this is so for the $[8,^1S_0]$ and $[8,^3P_{0,2}]$ states. The colour singlet matrix element can be extracted from data, e.g. the leptonic width of the J/ψ. Likewise, we need to fit these new matrix elements to data (or extract them from lattice calculations). It is therefore clear that a test of the NRQD framework requires data from different sources – the challenge being to find a consistent description. This is a particularly topical issue, since an explanation of the Tevatron excess of direct J/ψ and ψ' production needs, in addition to fragmentation contributions, colour octet contributions [43]. One can use the Tevatron data to fit the relevant matrix elements. The validity of this explanation can be checked on comparing to data which can be obtained from HERA. Unfortunately, the matrix elements which are important at the Tevatron are not so important in J/ψ photoproduction for $z > 0.4$. However, the key matrix element for the Tevatron ($[8,^3S_1]$)

---

[c] There is a lower order contribution in which no gluon is radiated off, however this would give a contribution only at $z = 1$ which lies outside our region of interest.

does play a key role in the region of lower z, where (for large enough p_T) the dominant contribution comes from the fragmentation mechanism via resolved photons [38,42]. Another process which is sensitive to the $[8,^3S_1]$ state is the photoproduction of $J/\psi + \gamma$ (where the photon is produced in the hard subprocess, i.e. not via the radiative decay of a P-wave quarkonium) [44]. So, with the anticipated increase in statistics, we can really expect to test NRQCD at HERA. Going back to the J/ψ, there are some weak constraints on the important matrix elements from the Tevatron data and these have been used in the theoretical calculations of [45]. The HERA data on the z distribution compare very well with the colour singlet calculation [18,33]. The colour octet contribution however, is much too large at large z. Thus the HERA data is not supporting a large colour octet contribution at large z. However, one must be careful in interpreting this as evidence against the NRQCD approach, since the $z \rightarrow 1$ region is sensitive to higher order non-perturbative contributions which lead to the breakdown of the NRQCD expansion [46].

In addition to the processes just discussed, increased statistics will allow measurement of other meson states, e.g. ψ' and Υ, which will certainly further test our understanding of QCD.

6 Outlook

We really need to improve our understanding of the $e\gamma$ final state [1] if we are to reduce the systematic uncertainty which presently dominates the experimental measurements of F_2^γ.

An improved understanding of the soft underlying event and of multiple interactions is needed in order to understand the gap survival probability in diffractive events. It is also needed for a better understanding of forward jets at HERA (which can then be used to extract the gluon density of the photon).

We can look forward to the accumulation of data on prompt photon production, $\gamma^*\gamma^*$ reactions and virtual photon structure, high t diffraction and diffractive meson production at high Q^2. Comparison of diffraction data from deep inelastic scattering with that from photo- (and hadro-) production will play a central role in developing our understanding of diffraction. It would be great to see data on diffraction in $\gamma\gamma$ collisions [13]. Meanwhile, the search for the odderon will continue [47].

Charm production will provide tests of NRQCD and allow us to unravel the subtle issues associated with open charm production.

Acknowledgements

Thanks to the organizers for such an enjoyable conference. I also want specifically to thank David Miller and Lionel Gordon for helping me put the talk together.

References

1. D.J. Miller, these proceedings.
2. M.Arneodo, these proceedings.
3. A.Donnachie and P.V.Landshoff, *Phys. Lett.* B **296**, 227 (1992).
4. T.Ebert, these proceedings.
5. K.Piotrzkowski, these proceedings.
6. J.H.Köhne, these proceedings.
7. J.A.Crittenden, these proceedings.
8. E665 collaboration, M.R.Adams et al., MPI-PHE-97-03, FERMILAB-PUB-97-103-E.
9. M.Kolstein, these proceedings.
10. T.Gousset, these proceedings.
11. S.J.Brodsky, et al., *Phys. Rev.* D **50**, 3134 (1994).
12. J.Puga, these proceedings.
13. R.Engel, these proceedings.
14. F.Hautmann, these proceedings.
15. M.Hayes, these proceedings.
16. B.May, these proceedings.
17. J.R.Forshaw and M.G.Ryskin, *Z. Phys.* C **68**, 137 (1995); J.Bartels, J.R. Forshaw, H.Lotter and M.Wusthoff, *Phys. Lett.* B **375**, 301 (1996).
18. P.Aurenche, these proceedings.
19. H.Rick, these proceedings.
20. E.Strickland, these proceedings.
21. M.Klasen and G.Kramer, *Phys. Lett.* B **366**, 385 (1996); DESY-96-246, hep-ph/9611450.
22. B.W.Harris and J.F.Owens, presented at the *Annual Divisional Meeting of the Division of Particles and Fields of the APS*, Minneapolis, USA (1996), hep-ph/9608378; FSU-HEP-970411, hep-ph/9704324.
23. S.Catani, Yu.L.Dokshitzer, M.H.Seymour and B.R.Webber, *Nucl. Phys.* B **406**, 187 (1993).
24. H1 collaboration, I.Abt et al., *Phys. Lett.* B **314**, 436 (1993); *Phys. Lett.* B **328**, 176 (1994); *Z. Phys.* C **70**, 17 (1996); ZEUS collaboration, M.Derrick, et al., *Phys. Lett.* B **322**, 287 (1994); *Phys. Lett.* B **342**,

417 (1995); contribution pa02-041 to 28th ICHEP, Warsaw (1996).

25. J.Chyla, these proceedings.
26. G.Pancheri, these proceedings.
27. J.M.Butterworth, J.R.Forshaw and M.H.Seymour, *Z. Phys.* C **72**, 637 (1996).
28. R.Burgin, these proceedings.
29. T.Kleinwort and G.Kramer, DESY-96-223, hep-ph/9610489.
30. W.Chen, these proceedings.
31. L.E.Gordon, these proceedings.
32. T.Vaiciulis, these proceedings.
33. L.Gladilin, these proceedings.
34. C.Peterson, D.Schlatter, I.Schmitt and P.M.Zerwas, *Phys. Rev.* D **27**, 105 (1983).
35. M.Cacciari and M.Greco, DESY 97-029, hep-ph/9702389.
36. V.Andreev, these proceedings.
37. M. Drees, M. Kramer, J. Zunft and P.M.Zerwas, *Phys. Lett.* B **306**, 371 (1993).
38. M.Cacciari and M.Krämer, in *Future Physics at HERA*, Proceedings of the Workshop 1995/96, Volume 1, hep-ph/9609500.
39. G.T.Bodwin, E.Braaten and G.P.Lepage, *Phys. Rev.* D **51**, 1125 (1995).
40. M.Krämer, J.Zunft, J.Steegborn and P.Zerwas, *Phys. Lett.* B **348**, 657 (1995); M.Krämer, *Nucl. Phys.* B **459**, 3 (1996).
41. R.Godbole, D.P.Roy and K.Sridhar, *Phys. Lett.* B **373**, 328 (1996).
42. B.A.Kniehl and G.Kramer, DESY 97-036, hep-ph/9703280.
43. E.Braaten and S.Fleming, *Phys. Rev. Lett.* **74**, 3327 (1995); M.Cacciari, M.Greco, M.L.Mangano and A.Petrelli, *Phys. Lett.* B **356**, 560 (1995); P.Cho and A.K.Leibovich, *Phys. Rev.* D **53**, 150 (1996); *Phys. Rev.* D **53**, 6203 (1996).
44. M.Cacciari, M.Greco and M.Krämer, *Phys. Rev.* D **55**, 7126 (1997).
45. M.Cacciari and M.Krämer, *Phys. Rev. Lett.* **76**, 4128 (1996).
46. M.Beneke, I.Z.Rothstein and M.B.Wise, CERN-TH/97-86, hep-ph/9705286.
47. S.Tapprogge, these proceedings.

Papers Submitted
without Presentation

AN APPROACH TO THE INVARIANT MASS RECONSTRUCTION FOR THE SINGLE-TAGGED $\gamma\gamma^*$ EVENTS

V.N.POZDNYAKOV

JINR(Dubna) and Dipartimento di Fisica, Università di Milano and INFN.

A method of the $W_{\gamma\gamma}$ reconstruction for the single-tagged two-photon interactions is proposed. The experimental conditions of a typical setup are simulated and the comparison of the results, obtained with the different methods, is presented.

The study of the reaction $e^+e^- \rightarrow e^+e^- + X$, where X is a system of hadrons produced by the collision of two photons coming from the beam particles, gives an opportunity to measure the photon structure function F_2^γ. If the squared four-momentum Q^2 of one photon is large enough (order of 10 GeV^2), the reaction is viewed as the deep inelastic scattering of the lepton off the quasi-real target photon. The cross section of the process depends mostly on Q^2, the invariant mass of the colliding photons W_{true} and the structure function $F_2^\gamma(Q^2, W_{true})$. The F_2^γ measurement is carried out in so called single-tagged interactions where, together with observed hadron system, the scattered lepton is required to be detected (tagged) in order to determine Q^2.

F_2^γ can not be directly measured due to following reasons:

- an essential part of produced hadrons escapes the setup undetected in and around beam pipe. This results in the events lost. Even in the events, passed the selection criteria, the detected invariant mass W_{rec} is at average of (60-70)% of W_{true} for the LEP1 experimental conditions and the value is predicted to be smaller for LEP2 [1]. This effect of the limited acceptance, making any analysis to be model-dependant, influent on the absolute normalization of measured F_2^γ;

- the energetic and spacial resolutions of the device used for the tagging result in (usually) 10% uncertainty of the measured Q^2.

In order to recover all these effects, a procedure must be applied to transform (unfold) W_{rec} to W_{true}. The input of the procedure is the simulation of events which must reproduce experimental distributions. The quality of result obtained (a number of unfolded data points, correlations between them) depends on how W_{rec} is close to W_{true}.

New approach of the W_{true} reconstruction is proposed. The energy and momentum of the probe photon (E_{probe}, $p_{z,probe}$ and $p_{T,probe}$) are determined by the tagged particle measurement. In order to determine the parameters

464

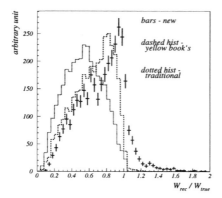 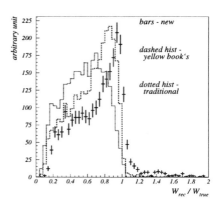

Figure 1: A ratio of W_{rec}/W_{true} for the new (bars), light-cone (dashed hist) and traditional (dotted hist) methods of the W_{rec} calculations corresponding to the LEP1 (left) and LEP2 (right) beam energy.

of the target photon the following suggestion is used. If the detected hadron system has a z component of its momentum $p_{z,hadr}$ in the direction opposite to the tagged particle, the energy of the target photon E_{tar} must be large enough to 'flip' (boost) produced hadrons. This allows to determine a minimum of the target photon energy and to apply this value to the W_{rec} calculation.

$$p_{z,tar}(\simeq E_{tar}) = p_{z,hadr} - p_{z,probe},$$
$$W_{rec}^2 = (E_{probe} + E_{tar})^2 - p_{T,probe}^2 - (p_{z,probe} + p_{z,tar})^2$$

The experimental conditions of a typical setup are simulated and the comparisons of the results, obtained with the different methods, is shown on the figure below. The traditional method is the use of the detected hadrons and photons for the invariant mass calculation. Third method tested is the use of the light-cone components[1].

The cost of the improvement in the ratio above is a decrease of the statistics of the data since the special kinematical case is treated. But it has to be mentioned that the approach proposed allows to avoid of the requirement on the minimum of W_{rec}. This can restore (a part) the statistics and has to be treated for the concrete setup.

In summary, the method is proposed to improve the W_{rec}/W_{true} ratio for the single-tagged $\gamma\gamma^*$ events.

References

1. *Physics at LEP2*, eds. G.Altarelli, T.Sjöstrand and F.Zwirner, CERN yellow report 96-01, vol.2, p.199.

ENERGY FLOWS AND JET PRODUCTION IN TAGGED $e\gamma$ EVENTS AT LEP

A.M. ROOKE for the OPAL collaboration
Department of Physics, UCL, Gower Street, London WC1E 6BT, UK.

1 Introduction

It has been shown [1] that the predictions of the hadronic energy flow in $e\gamma$ DIS processes by the QCD-based Monte Carlo generators, HERWIG and PYTHIA, disagree with the data in the $Q^2 = 6$–30 GeV^2 region.

	0 jet	1 jet	2 jet
Data	30.7%	63.8%	5.4%
HERWIG	34.0%	63.6%	2.4%
PYTHIA	32.8%	65.5%	1.7%

Table 1: Jet rates of HERWIG and PYTHIA compared to the data.

The disagreements are particularly marked in the regions of pseudorapidity well measured by the OPAL detector and hence where jets can be accurately reconstructed.

2 Results And Conclusions

Table 1 shows that the fraction of data events with 2 cone jets (of transverse energy $E_{T,\text{jet}} > 3\text{GeV}$ and pseudorapidity $|\eta_{\text{jet}}| < 2$) exceeds predictions from the HERWIG and PYTHIA samples by over a factor of 2. Fig. 1a) shows the average hadronic energy flow per event as a function of pseudorapidity and b), c) and d) show the contributions to a) from events with 0, 1 or 2 jets. The underestimation by HERWIG and PYTHIA of

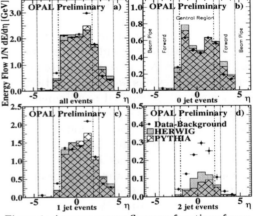

Figure 1: Average energy flow as a function of pseudorapidity $\eta = -\ln\tan\frac{\theta}{2}$ (see text)

events with 2 jets combined with their imperfect modelling of energy flow (particularly in the pseudorapidity region $0.9 < \eta < 1.8$ for events with 1 jet) give rise to the previously reported discrepancies [1] shown in fig. 1a). By selecting events with 2 identified hadron cone jets, we have found a subset of the data in which disagreements with Monte Carlo predictions are greatly enhanced. This result has been used to constrain improvements to the models [2].

References

1. OPAL Collab., K. Ackerstaff *et al*, *Z. Phys.* C **74**, 33 (1997)
2. J.A. Lauber, L. Lönnblad and M.H. Seymour, *these proceedings*

SIMULATIONS OF THE INTERACTION REGION IN A PHOTON-PHOTON COLLIDER

P. CHEN[1],

Stanford Linear Accelerator, Stanford University, Stanford, CA94309, USA

T. OHGAKI, T. TAKAHASHI[a],

Dept. of Physics, Hiroshima university, Higashi-Hiroshima, 739, Japan

A. SPITKOVSKY

Dept. of Physics, Univ. of California Berkeley, Berkeley, CA 94720, USA

K. YOKOYA

High Energy Accelerator Research Organization, Tsukuba, 305, Japan

For the estimation of backgrounds in the detector as well as to calculate realistic luminosity in linear colliders, detail calculation laser-Compton and beam-beam interaction is inevitable. In particular, to estimate the effect in realistic condition, we have to rely on numerical simulation. To meet the necessity of simulation program for interaction and Compton region of $\gamma\gamma$ colliders, the project CAIN has started in 1993. The progress of the project has been reported in previous workshop in Berkeley and Sheffield [1]. Recently, a program meet all of original requirement was written by Yokoya [2]. and is now being debugged. The program can be applied to all 4 type of linear colliders as; e^+e^-, e^-e^-, $e\gamma$ and $\gamma\gamma$ colliders. The processes included are; non-linear Compton and Bethe-Heitler interaction at the the laser-electron interaction region, sweeping magnet between Compton and interaction region including synchrotron radiation and beam-beam interaction at the interaction point including beam disruption, coherent pair creation, incoherent pair creation such as Landau-Lifsitz, Breit-Wheeler and Bethe-Heitler processes.

Since last years, the NLC and the JLC group performed the simulation study of $\gamma\gamma$ colliders. The NLC used CAIN in a part of the calculation and the JLC used CAIN for their entire simulation. Both works were published as part of design study report, i.e., Zeroth-order Design Report for the Next Linear Collider and JLC Design Study.

1. P. Chen, G. Horton-Smith, T. Ohgaki, A.W. Weidemann, K. Yokoya, *Nucl. Instr. Meth.* **A335** (1995) 107.
2. P. Chen, T. Ohgaki, A. Spitkovsky, T. Takahashi, K. Yokoya, *SLAC-PUB-7426, HUDP-9707, to be published in Nucl. Instr. Meth A*

---

[a]e-mail: tohrut@kekux1.kek.jp

List of Participants

V. Andreev   Division PPE, CERN
CH-1211 Geneva 23, Switzerland
valeri.andreev@cern.ch

M. Arneodo   DESY, Notkestrasse 85
D-22603 Hamburg, Germany
arneodo@vxdesy.desy.de

P. Aurenche   LAPP, Boite Postale 110
F-74941 Annecy-le-Vieux Cédex, France
aurenche@lapp.in

J. Bechtluft   III. Physikalisches Institut, RWTH Aachen
Sommerfeldstrasse, D-52076 Aachen, Germany
joerg@physik.rwth-aachen.de

A. Bel'kov   Particle Physics Lab., J.I.N.R.
141980 Dubna, Moscow Region, Russia
belkov@cv.jinr.dubna.su

H. Bienlein   DESY, Notkestrasse 85
D-22603 Hamburg, Germany
bienlein@desy.de

E. Boglione   University of Durham, South Road
Durham DH1 3LE, United Kingdom
elena.boglione@durham.ac.uk

L. Bourhis   LPTHE, Université de Paris XI
Bâtiment 211, F-91405 Orsay Cédex, France
bourhis@qcd.th.u-psud.fr

S. Braccini   Division PPE, CERN
CH-1211 Geneva 23, Switzerland
saverio.braccini@cern.ch

C.A. Brew   Dept. of Physics, University of Sheffield
The Hicks Building, Sheffield S7 7RH, U.K.
c.a.brew@shef.ac.uk

S.J. Brodsky   SLAC, P.O. Box 4349
Stanford, CA 94309, U.S.A.
sjbth@slac.stanford.edu

R. Bürgin   University of Freiburg, Hermann-Herder-Strasse 3
D-79104 Freiburg, Germany
buergin@ruhpb.physik.uni-freiburg.de

P. Bussey   University of Glasgow, Glasgow G12 8QQ
United Kingdom

J. Butterworth	bussey@v6.ph.gla.ac.uk,
	Physics and Astronomy Dept., University College London
	Gower Street, London WC1E 6BT, U.K.
	jmb@hep.ucl.ac.uk
A. Buijs	University Utrecht, Princetonlaan 4
	3584 CB Utrecht, The Netherlands
	a.buijs@fys.ruu.nl
C. Carimalo	Lab. de Physique Corpusculaire, Collège de France
	11, Place Marcelin Berthelot, F-75231 Paris Cédex 05, France
	carimalo@in2p3.fr
W. Chen	State Univ. of N.Y. at Stony Brook, MS 352
	P.O. Box 500, Batavia, IL 60510, U.S.A.
	wchen@fnal.gov
J. Chyla	Institute of Physics, Czech Academy of Sciences
	Na Slovance 2, Prague 8, Czech Republic
	chyla@fzu.cz
E. Clay	Dept. of Physics and Astronomy, University College London
	Gower Street, London WC1E 6BT, U.K.
	ec@hep.ucl.ac.uk
A. Courau	LAL, Université Paris-Sud
	Bâtiment 200, F-91405 Orsay, France
	courau@lal.in2p3.fr
J.A. Crittenden	Physics Institute, University Bonn
	Nussallee 12, D-53115 Bonn, Germany
	crittenden@vxdesy.desy.de
A. Csilling	KFKI - RMKI, P.O. Box 49
	H-1525 Budapest, Hungary
	csilling@rmki.kfki.hu
M. Doucet	Lab. de Physique Nucléaire, Université de Montréal
	C.P. 6128 - Centre Ville, Montréal, Quebec H3C 3J, Canada
	doucet@lps.umontreal.ca
T. Ebert	University of Liverpool, Oxford Street
	P.O. Box 147, Liverpool L69 3BX, U.K.
	trebert@hep.ph.liv.ac.uk
R. Engel	Inst. of Theoretical Physics, Leipzig University
	Augustusplatz 10, D-04109 Leipzig, Germany
	eng@tph200.physik.uni-leipzig.de
J.J. Engelen	NIKHEF, P.O. Box 41882
	1009 DB Amsterdam, The Netherlands
	engelen@nikhef.nl

M. Erdmann   Physikalisches Institut, University Heidelberg
Philosophenweg 12, D-69120 Heidelberg, Germany
erdmann@physi.uni-heidelberg. de

F.C. Erné   NIKHEF, P.O. Box 41882
1009 DB Amsterdam, The Netherlands
z63@nikhef.nl

J. Fayot   LPNHE Paris - VI, 4, Place Jussieu
F-75252 Paris Cédex 05, France
fayot@in2p3.fr

T. Feldmann   Theoretical Physics Dept., University of Wuppertal
D-42097 Wuppertal, Germany
feldmann@theorie.physik.uni-wuppertal.de,

J. Field   Dept. de Phys. Nucl. et Corpusc., University of Geneva
24, quai Ernest Ansermet, CH-1211 Geneva 4, Switzerland
john.field@cern.ch

A.J. Finch   School of Physics and Astronomy, Lancaster University
Lancaster LA1 4YB, U.K.
a.finch@lancaster.ac.uk,

J. Forshaw   Dept. of Physics and Astronomy, University of Manchester
Brunswick Street, Manchester M13 9PL, U.K.
forshaw@a13.ph.man.ac.uk

C. Friberg   Theoretical Physics II, Solvegatan 14A
S-22362 Lund, Sweden
christer@thep.lu.se

C.M. Ginsburg   DESY-ZEUS, Notkestrasse 85
D-22603 Hamburg, Germany
ginsburg@vxdesy.desy.de

I. Ginzburg   Dept. of Theor. Physics, Institute of Mathematics
630090 Novosibirsk, Russia
ginzburg@math.nsc.ru

L. Gladilin   Inst. of Experimental Physics II, University of Hamburg
Luruper Chaussee 149, D-22761 Hamburg, Germany
gladilin@mail.desy.de

N. Goguitidze   DESY, Notkestrasse 85
D-22603 Hamburg, Germany
nellyg@mail.desy.de

L.E. Gordon   High Energy Physics Division, Argonne National Laboratory
Argonne, IL 60439, U.S.A.
gordon@hep.anl.gov

T. Gousset   NIKHEF, P.O. Box 41882

	1009 DB Amsterdam, The Netherlands
	thierryg@nikhef.nl
K. Grzelak	Warsaw University, Hoza 69
	00 681 Warsaw, Poland
	kaste@fuw.edu.pl
R.C.W. van Gulik	Inst. Lorentz for Theor. Physics, P.O. Box 9506
	2300 RA Leiden, The Netherlands
	gulik@lorentz.leidenuniv.nl
G. Gustafson	Dept. of Theoretical Physics, Lund University
	Solvegatan 14A, SE-22362 Lund, Sweden
	gosta@thep.lu.se
F. Hautmann	Inst. of Theoretical Science, University of Oregon
	Eugene, OR 97403, U.S.A.
	hautmann@oregon.uoregon.edu
M. Hayes	H.H. Wills Physics Lab., University of Bristol
	Tyndall Avenue, Bristol, U.K.
	mhayes@zow.desy.de
A. Ichola	Lab. de Physique Corpusculaire, Collège de France
	11, Place Marcelin Berthelot, F-75231 Paris Cédex 05, France
	ichola@ds5500.u-picardie.fr
G. Jikia	University of Freiburg, Hermann-Herder-Strasse 3
	D-79104 Freiburg, Germany
	jikia@phyv4.physik.uni-freiburg.de
U. Karshon	Particle Physics Dept., Weizmann Institute
	Rehovot 76100, Israel
	fhkarsho@rosinante.weizmann.ac.il
B.W. Kennedy	Rutherford Appleton Lab., Chilton, Didcot
	Oxfordshire OX141 0QX, United Kingdom
	b.w.kennedy@rl.ac.uk
S.R. Klein	Lawrence Berkeley Natl. Lab., MS 70A-3307
	1 Cyclotron Road, Berkeley, CA 94720, U.S.A.
	srklein@lbl.gov
J.H. Köhne	DESY - FH1K, Notkestrasse 85
	D-22603 Hamburg, Germany
	kohne@desy.de
M. Kolstein	NIKHEF, P.O. Box 41882
	1009 DB Amsterdam, The Netherlands
	machiel@nikhefk.nikhef.nl
J. Konijn	NIKHEF, P.O. Box 41882
	1009 DB Amsterdam, The Netherlands

j.konijn@nikhef.nl

M. Krawczyk   Inst. of Theoretical Physics, University of Warsaw
                     Hoza 69, 00681 Warsaw, Poland
                     Maria.Krawczyk@fuw.edu.pl

P. Ladron de Guevara Inst. de Investigacion Basica, CIEMAT
                     Avenida Complutense 22, E-28040 Madrid, Spain
                     ladron@ae.ciemat.es

D. Lanske   III. Physalisches Institut A, RWTH
                     Sommerfeldstrasse, D-52056 Aachen, Germany
                     lanske@rwth-aachen.de

J. Lauber   Dept. of Physics and Astronomy, University College London
                     Gower Street, London WC1E 6BT, U.K.
                     jal@hep.ucl.ac.uk

A.L. Maslennikov   Budker Institute of Physics, Lavrentyeva 11
                     630090 Novosibirsk, Russia
                     maslennikov@inp.nsk.su

S. Matsumoto   Dept. of Physics, Chuo University
                     Kasuga, Bunkyo-ku, Tokyo 112, Japan
                     matsumoto@kekvax.kek.ac.jp

B. May   Fermi Lab., MS 357, Northwestern University
                     Batavia, IL 60510, U.S.A.
                     may@fnald0.fnal.gov

E. McKingney   Division PPE, CERN
                     CH-1211 Geneva 23, Switzerland
                     edward.mckingney@cern.ch

G. Medin   Jozef Stefan Institute, Jamova 39, p.p. 3000
                     1001 Ljubljana, Slovenia
                     gordana.medin@ijs.si

H. Meyer   BUGH - Wuppertal, Gaussstrasse 20
                     D-42097 Wuppertal, Germany
                     meyer@wpos7.physik.uni-wuppertal.de,

D. Miller   Dept. of Physics and Astronomy, University College London
                     Gower Street, London WC1E 6BT, U.K.
                     djm@hep.ucl.ac.uk

D. Milstead   University of Liverpool, Ebertallee 40
                     D-22607 Hamburg, Germany
                     milstead@mail.desy.de

F. Murgia   I.N.F.N., Sezione di Cagliari
                     Via Ada Negri 18, I-09127 Cagliari, Italy
                     francesco.murgia@ca.infn.it

R. Nisius   Division PPE, CERN
CH-1211 Geneva 23, Switzerland
Richard.Nisius@cern.ch

J. Olsson   DESY, Notkestrasse 85
D-22603 Hamburg, Germany
jan.olsson@desy.de

S. Ong   CEN Saclay, DAPHNIA/SPhN
F-91191 Gif-sur-Yvette, France
ong@phnx7.saclay.cea.fr

H.P. Paar   UC San Diego, 9500 Gilman Drive
La Jolla, CA 92093, U.S.A.
hpaar@sdphug.ucsd.edu

F. Palumbo   I.N.F.N., P.O. Box 13
I-00044 Frascati (Roma), Italy
palumbof@lnl.infn.it

G. Pancheri   I.N.F.N., Via E. Fermi 40
I-00044 Frascati (Roma), Italy
pancheri@lnf.infn.it

J. Parisi   Lab. de Physique Corpusculaire, Collège de France
11, Place Marcelin Berthelot, F-75231 Paris Cédex 05, France
parisi@in2p3.fr

K. Piotrzkowski   DESY, Notkestrasse 85
D-22603 Hamburg, Germany
piotrzkowski@desy.de

J. Puga   DESY, Notkestrasse 85
D-22603 Hamburg, Germany
puga@zow.desy.de

T. van Rhee   PPE Division, CERN
CH-1211 Geneva 23, Switzerland
rhee@hpl3.cern.ch

H. Rick   FH1K, DESY
Notkestrasse 85, D-22603 Hamburg, Germany
rick@mail.desy.de

S. Riemersma   DESY - Zeuthen, Plantanenallee 6
D-15738 Zeuthen, Germany
riemersm@ifh.de

L. Romanov   Budker Inst. of Nuclear Physics, Lavrentyeva 11
630090 Novosibirsk, Russia
romanov@inp.nsk.su

T. Rooke   Dept. of Physics and Astronomy, University College London

	Gower Street, London WC1E 6BT, U.K.
	amr@hep.ucl.uk
W. van Rossum	University Utrecht, P.O. Box 80.000
	3508 TA Utrecht, The Netherlands
	d59@nikhef.nl
R. Ruskov	Lab. of Theoretical Physics, J.I.N.R.
	141 980 Dubna, Moscow Region, Russia
	ruskovr@thsun1.jinr.dubna.su
A. Savine	DESY, Notkestrasse 85
	D-22603 Hamburg, Germany
	savin@vxdesy.desy.de
V. Savinov	SLAC/CLEO-II Collaboration, Cornell University
	Dryden Road, Ithaca, N.Y. 14850, U.S.A.
	savinov@lns62.lns.cornell.edu
G.A. Schuler	Theory Division, CERN
	CH-1211 Geneva 23, Switzerland
	Gerhard.Schuler@cern.ch
F. Schunck	CPES, University of Sussex
	Falmer, Brighton BN1 9QJ, United Kingdom
	fs@astr.maps.susx.ac.uk
V.G. Serbo	Dept. of Physics, Novosibirsk State University
	630090 Novosibirsk, Russia
	serbo@math.nsc.ru
W. da Silva	LPNHE Paris - VI, 4, Place Jussieu
	F-75252 Paris Cédex, France
	dasilva@in2p3.fr
T. Sjostrand	Dept. of Theoretical Physics, Solvegatan 14A
	S-223 62 Lund, Sweden
	torbjorn@thep.lu.se
S. Söldner-Rembold	Freiburg University, Hermann-Herder-Strasse 3
	D-79104 Freiburg, Germany
	soldner@ruhpb.physik.uni-freiburg.de
E. Strickland	Glasgow University, 30 Buccleuch Street
	Glasgow G3 6PJ, United Kingdom
	e.strickland@physics.gla.ac.uk
G. Susinno	Office 4A-12, Building 32, CERN
	CH-1211 Geneva 23, Switzerland
	gabriele.susinno@cern.ch
M. Sutton	DESY, Notkestrasse 85
	D-22603 Hamburg, Germany

sutt@desy.de

T. Takahashi   Dept. of Physics, Hiroshima University
1-3-1 Kagamiyama, 739 Higashi - Hiroshima, Japan
tohrut@kekux1.kek.jp

S. Tapprogge   High-Energy Physics, University of Heidelberg
Schröderstrasse 90, D-69102 Heidelberg, Germany
tapprogge@ihep.uni-heidelberg.de

T. Telnov   Budker Institute of Physics, Lavrentyeva 11
630090 Novosibirsk, Russia
telnov@inp.nsk.su

H. Tiecke   NIKHEF, P.O. Box 41882
1009 DB Amsterdam, The Netherlands
tiecke@nikhef.nl

I. Tyapkin   Division PPE, CERN
CH-1211 Geneva 23, Switzerland
tyapkin@vxcern.cern.ch

T. Vaiciulis   University of Wisconsin, DESY
Notkestrasse 85, D-22603 Hamburg, Germany
vaiciulis@vxdesy.desy.de

A. Vogt   Inst. Theoretische Physik, University of Würzburg
Am Hubland, D-97074 Würzburg, Germany
avogt@physik.uni-wuerzburg.de

J.H. Vossebeld   NIKHEF-ZEUS Group, DESY
Notkestrasse 85, D-22603 Hamburg, Germany
vossebeld@nikhef.nl

A. Wright   Division PPE, CERN
CH-1211 Geneva 23, Switzerland
awright@afal32.cern.ch

N. Zimine   Division PPE, CERN
CH-1211 Geneva 23, Switzerland
zimin@vxcern.cern.ch